ANNUAL REPORTS ON
NMR SPECTROSCOPY

Volume 4

ANNUAL REPORTS ON
NMR SPECTROSCOPY

Edited by

E. F. MOONEY

Anacon (Instruments) Limited, Bourne End, Buckinghamshire, England

Volume 4

ACADEMIC PRESS

London and New York

1971

CHEMISTRY

ACADEMIC PRESS INC. (LONDON) LTD.
24–28 Oval Road
London, NW1

U.S. Edition published by
ACADEMIC PRESS INC.
111 Fifth Avenue
New York, New York 10003

Library of Congress Catalog Card Number: 68–17678
SBN: 0–12–505 304–5

PRINTED IN GREAT BRITAIN BY
WILLIAM CLOWES & SONS, LIMITED
LONDON, BECCLES AND COLCHESTER

LIST OF CONTRIBUTORS

G. R. BEDFORD, *Imperial Chemical Industries Limited, Pharmaceutical Division, Alderly Park, Macclesfield, Cheshire, SK10 4TG, England*

D. R. BUHLER, *Department of Agricultural Chemistry and Environmental Health Sciences Center, Oregon State University, Corvallis, Oregon 97331, U.S.A.*

M. E. A. CUDBY, *Imperial Chemical Industries Limited, Plastics Division, Welwyn Garden City, Hertfordshire, England*

C. W. HAIGH, *Department of Chemistry, University College, Swansea, Wales*

R. HAQUE, *Department of Agricultural Chemistry and Environmental Health Sciences Center, Oregon State University, Corvallis, Oregon 97331, U.S.A.*

K. JONES, *I.B.M. (U.K.) Limited, London Process Branch, Croydon, Surrey, England*

E. F. MOONEY, *Anacon (Instruments) Limited, Bourne End, Buckinghamshire, England*

I. O. SUTHERLAND, *Department of Chemistry, The University, Sheffield, S3.7HF, England*

H. A. WILLIS, *Imperial Chemical Industries Limited, Plastics Division, Welwyn Garden City, Hertfordshire, England*

ACKNOWLEDGMENTS

For permission to reproduce, in whole or in part, certain figures and diagrams we are grateful to the following publishers—

American Chemical Society, American Institute of Physics, Association of Official Analytical Chemists Inc., Chemical Society, Pergamon Press Ltd, Society of Applied Spectroscopy, Taylor and Francis Ltd., Texas A & M University (Thermodynamic Research Centre Data Project).

Detailed acknowledgments are given in the legends to the figures.

PREFACE

For those of us in the world of publishing 1970–1971 will surely go down in history as the year of the impossible. The difficulties arising out of various industrial actions have greatly delayed this volume, but in spite of this delay this volume will prove to be equally useful as the previous volumes in this series.

The chapters on ^{1}H and ^{19}F are both written in the normal pattern of the annual review of the published work on proton and fluorine-19 NMR. The chapter on polymers augments the earlier review in Volume One. Three new chapters appear in this volume, an account of the kinetics of conformational changes as determined by NMR, the NMR of pesticides and an account of computer programmes for the analysis of NMR spectra. This latter chapter will be of interest to all chemists concerned with the abstraction of the correct NMR parameters for structural determination and I feel that it is particularly appropriate that this chapter should have been written at this time.

To all the contributors to this volume, I would like to express my gratitude for their efforts and care with which the manuscripts were prepared.

Anacon (Instruments) Limited,
Buckinghamshire,
June 1971

ERIC F. MOONEY

CONTENTS

General Review of Proton Magnetic Resonance

G. R. BEDFORD

The Investigation of the Kinetics of Conformational Changes by Nuclear Magnetic Resonance Spectroscopy

I. O. SUTHERLAND

Nuclear Magnetic Resonance
Spectroscopy in Pesticide Chemistry

R. HAQUE and D. R. BUHLER

A Simple Guide to the Use of Iterative
Computer Programmes in the Analysis of NMR Spectra

C. W. HAIGH

The Nuclear Magnetic Resonance Spectra
of Polymers

M. E. A. CUDBY and H. A. WILLIS

Fluorine-19 Nuclear Magnetic Resonance Spectroscopy

K. JONES and E. F. MOONEY

THE CHEMICAL SHIFT SCALES

Readers are reminded of the convention for the presentation of chemical shift data introduced into Volume Three of this series. This self-consistent convention has now been used for some two years in various places and is gradually being universally accepted.

Convention adopted for Chemical Shift Scales

1. All shifts will be denoted by the delta scale, low-field shifts being shown as positive and high-field shifts as negative values. In all cases the standard will take the reference shift of δ 0·0.
2. No other symbols to denote shifts at infinite dilution will be used.

General Review of Proton Magnetic Resonance

G. R. BEDFORD

Imperial Chemical Industries Limited, Pharmaceuticals Division, Alderley Park, Macclesfield, Cheshire, SK10 4TG, England

INTRODUCTION

AN ANNUAL REVIEW of such a large subject as proton magnetic resonance spectroscopy has become a mammoth task. The already considerable number of texts on the theory and application of NMR spectroscopy has been added to with the publication of three books[1,2,3] whilst a text on the NMR of polymers[4] has also appeared. Thus, the reviewer, like previous reviewers in this series, has made certain omissions. The task of selecting topics for omission is made easier by the fact that certain subjects are reviewed elsewhere in this volume (e.g. polymers, kinetic processes) and are only considered when they are of extreme relevance to the subject matter of this review (e.g. in conformational analysis). The reader is

1

also referred to the 1969 NMR reviews on inorganic and organometallic compounds,[5] on sugars[6] and monosaccharides[7] and on magnetic double resonance[8]
since these topics are not considered in detail whilst wide line and solid state
studies are not considered at all.

I. EXPERIMENTAL

A. Experimental techniques

The use of reference materials for proton magnetic resonance studies has again
given rise to several papers during 1969. Two suitable new reference standards
have been announced. A new water soluble standard, the sodium salt of 3-tri-
methylsilyltetradeuteropropionic acid (1), is claimed[9] to be superior to the conventional water soluble standard D.S.S., in that it has no undesired resonances
in the region δ 0·5 to 3·0, is more soluble in water and in a series of polar organic
solvents and can be used up to a temperature of at least 200°. A stable internal
standard "cyclosilane-d_{18}" (2) permitting measurements to be carried out up to
200° in a variety of solvents in unsealed sample tubes without loss of the reference material has also been described.[10] The use of the ammonium ion, popular
for studies of aqueous electrolyte solutions, is discouraged since studies of this
ion in methanol has cast some doubts on its suitability as a reference for ion-shift
tables for hydroxylic solvents.[11] The use of external reference samples when

$$(CH_3)_3CD_2CD_2CO \cdot ONa$$

1

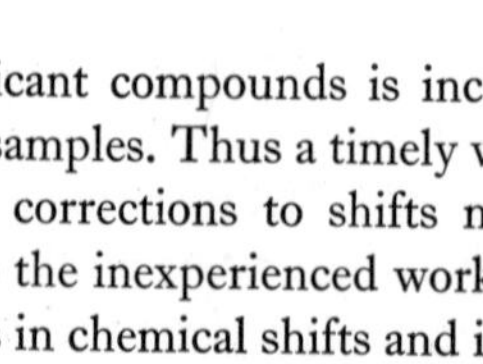

2

studying biologically significant compounds is increasing due to the desire to
avoid contamination of the samples. Thus a timely warning on the importance of
making bulk susceptibility corrections to shifts measured versus an external
reference sample is given to the inexperienced worker in these fields by demonstrating that opposite trends in chemical shifts and inaccurate activation energies
can be obtained by comparing data obtained from variable temperature studies
of uridine-5'-phosphate using both external and internal references.[12] Magnetic
susceptibility measurements, however, may sometimes be difficult and unreliable,
as was found in a study of aqueous solutions of aromatic compounds[13] and a

spherical external water referencing system, for which a theory for non-ideality had been developed, was used.

Although studies of the paramagnetic shifts caused by metal ions have been reported before, the potential use of the coordinative binding of metal ions for conformational studies has not yet been fully exploited. The use of various amounts of $CoCl_2 \cdot 6H_2O$ added to a solution of egg white lysozyme caused systematic induced shifts of the resonance for protons, up to 14 Å away from the postulated binding site of the Co^{2+} ion, without seriously affecting the line shape of the resonances[14] and thus aided the interpretation of the spectrum. A similar study was made of the effect of the dipyridyl adduct of trispivalomethanato europium(III) on the NMR spectrum of cholesterol[15] where the shifts observed appeared to be approximately correlated with the cubed reciprocal distance of the proton from the coordination site. A less rewarding and less specific reagent appears to be the cobalt-acetylacetone complex which, with alcohols and amines, caused a downward shift of the α-methylene resonances but also caused appreciable line broadening.[16] However, the addition of paramagnetic complexes, e.g. nickel-acetylacetone, in low concentration may also remove spin-spin coupling, as has been demonstrated for proton-proton coupling in dimethylformamide and for proton-phosphorus coupling in the case of trialkyl phosphites.[17]

An improved technique for handling milligramme samples in a capillary, which was developed with gas-liquid chromatography in mind, has the advantage that the wobble problem of the free floating capillary is virtually non-existent because the tube is held at both the top and the bottom.[18] A temporary seal for NMR tubes that requires no modification to the tube and will contain liquid sulphur dioxide at room temperature but is blown off at about five atmospheres pressure without damage to the tube could do much to reduce the incidence of broken probe inserts.[19]

The use of Fourier transformation for the sensitivity and resolution enhancement of spectra has already attracted considerable attention. A preliminary account of a new method, called the driven equilibrium Fourier transform (DEFT) spectroscopy[20] suggests that this latter method will mainly have an application to nuclei with long T_1 (e.g. ^{13}C) and will not offer much advantage to proton work. In the field of the specialized superconducting magnet instruments details have been given of a novel probe design in which both the transmitting and receiving coils are coupled to the sample space by a copper loop acting as a single turn transformer.[21] A 250 MHz spectrometer, designed for very low temperature operation,[22] has been described whilst the operation and application of a 220 MHz instrument has been reviewed.[23]

A light-piping technique has been described which directs intense radiation, from a mercury or xeon arc point source, into the NMR probe without alteration of the spectrometer resolution.[24] The *in situ* NMR photochemistry experiment could possibly prove to be as interesting as the present study of free radical reactions by NMR spectroscopy.

B. Derivation of spectral information

The use of iterative computer programmes (e.g. LAOCN and NMRIT) to obtain spectral information, i.e. chemical shifts and coupling constants, is by now well documented (see p. 311). An improvement of the NMRIT programme is called NMRENIT[25] and greatly facilitates the analysis of spin systems having sets of magnetically equivalent nuclei. It is claimed to be superior to LAOCN III in that it offers a more intimate understanding of the nuclear spin system being studied and provides greater facility for analysis involving degenerate closely lying or crossing energy levels and a clearer separation and identification of energies and transitions belonging to each symmetry group.

The method of subspectral analysis[26] has again been demonstrated in the analysis of 1,2,4-trifluorobenzene, an ABCMXZ system, and the parameters reported in this study are quite comparable with those of an independent study employing a full analysis. In the $[AX_n]_3$ system,[27] by deriving the algebraic expressions for the frequency and intensities of some transitions in the X spectrum where $J_{XX}=0$, it is shown that J_{AX} and J_{AX}' with relative signs, can be measured directly from the spectrum and J_{AA} can also easily be found. In comparison with subspectral analysis this is a straightforward way by which the X transitions for the $[AX]_3$ spin system ($J_{XX}=0$) are proved. Diehl and coworkers[28] have also discussed the theory of deceptive simplicity in NMR spectra of orientated molecules in terms of the degeneracy of subspectra. Whereas degeneracy of the spectra in isotropic media means collapse of the subspectra into single lines, degenerate subspectra of orientated molecules in which the chemical shift approaches zero may have a relatively complex appearance. The authors show that the conditions for deceptive simplicity are easily fulfilled for ABX, AA'BB'X and AA'XX' cases but that deceptive simplicity is not so common in AB_2X spectra. Deceptive simplicity in ABX[29] and ABXYM[30] systems has been discussed and has allowed the determination of the relative signs of coupling constants in the case of the ABX spectrum.

One method by which the relative signs of coupling constants have been determined previously is the use of double quantum transitions (D.Q.T.). An interesting new use of D.Q.T. is shown by the determination of the geminal coupling constants of 1-bromo-2-chloroethane.[31] The normal spectrum of this compound exhibits twenty lines but cannot fully be analysed since the four transitions used to derive the parameter $K(=J_{AA}+J_{BB})$ are too weak to be observed. By observing the spectrum under steadily increasing values of the irradiating field H_1, twelve out of the sixteen possible D.Q.T. lines (besides two out of the four possible triple quantum lines and a pair of single combination bands) are found. Since the D.Q.T. lines, which are related to the weak un-observed transitions, could be easily detected it was possible to deduce the positions of these weak lines and hence complete an unambiguous analysis. The method thus shows great promise for the accurate determination of coupling constants although, as has been previously predicted by theory, the movement of the positions of the crucial D.Q.T. lines as H_1 is increased (0·2 Hz in the above case) must be taken into consideration.

The analysis of a tightly coupled system, as in an ABC spectrum, is often difficult since several sets of parameters may fit the experimental data. It has been shown,[32] however, that from a joint treatment of the experimental data for an ABC spectrum recorded at two frequencies it is possible to obtain a set of algebraic equations for the NMR parameters which will yield a unique solution of the analysis. A more interesting method of varying the relative sizes of the chemical shifts and scalar coupling to aid the analysis using only one spectro-meter is described by Ellet and Waugh.[32] They irradiated the sample with equally spaced r.f. pulses in which adjacent pulses differed in phase by 180°. The nuclear signal was sampled once each cycle to obtain a sequence of signal points which resembled a free induction decay. The Fourier transformation of this signal gave a normal spectrum with the chemical shift scaled by an experi-mentally determined factor but where the scalar coupling was unaltered. The practical result is that, by varying the pulse width, a series of spectra can be obtained as if they had been observed at different field strengths with the advan-tage that the sensitivity remains at the high value corresponding to the actual field strength and that the absolute resolution improves as the shifts are scaled down.

The relative signs of coupling constants in AX_3, ABX_2 or ABX_3 can be de-rived in a single experiment by a method using the INDOR technique.[34] A further advantage of the method is that the spectrum does not have to be first order. A detailed study of heteronuclear decoupling on the ammonium ion showed the important consequence that exact resonance in the nitrogen spectrum does not lead to minimum intensity in the outer lines of the proton triplet. Thus, if either of these lines were used as a monitoring point for an INDOR spectrum, a sharp hole would appear in the centre of the INDOR peak.[35]

The derivation of thermodynamic data from the temperature dependence of the spectrum is now well documented. However, several papers dealing with new approaches to the measurement of kinetic processes have appeared of which the most interesting is that presented by Binsch[36] on a unified theory of exchange effects on line shape. He has shown that although experimentalists, because of mathematical difficulties, may pick very simple spin systems for dynamic studies (e.g. AB systems) that collapse into a single resonance line in the fast-exchange limit, much more accurate parameters can be derived from the observation of the numerous changes in a complex spectrum with changing rate. As an example, the

ABC case is considered and it is demonstrated that a whole series of "coalescence points" are being observed for different values of the rate constant. Although the mathematics appear somewhat daunting to the non-specialist a computer programme is being made available. A method has been developed[37] which uses the truncated second moments of exchange-broadened NMR lines to determine exchange rates and this alleviates the need for a full line shape fitting analysis although the data obtained will not be so precise. The method, however, may easily be extended to cover unequal populations, finite linewidths in the absence of exchange, and multiplets collapsing due to chemical exchange.

Calculations for total line shape analysis of systems with chemical exchange and relaxation have also been published and demonstrated for the example where quadrupolar broadening of the NMR spectrum of a nucleus of spin $\frac{1}{2}$ coupled to a nucleus of spin $\frac{3}{2}$ occurs.[38] Such an analysis also gives information about the quadrupolar relaxation time and hence allow estimates to be made of quadrupolar coupling. Information of this type has been derived from the proton spectrum of alkyl nitrates and nitramines and used to define the symmetry of the electron distribution at the site of the nitro group.[39] The derivation of information for fast molecular processes is, however, the most interesting development of the study of quadrupolar relaxation. Line shape analysis of the NMR spectra is used for studying processes in the 1 to 10^4 sec^{-1} frequency range. However, much faster molecular processes, in the 10^8 to 10^{12} sec^{-1} frequency range, can be investigated through the determination of nuclear relaxation times. It has been shown that selective "quadrupolar labelling" may lead to establishing a microdynamic map of molecular behaviour.[40] Thus T_q, the quadrupolar relaxation time, is measured by the line shape analysis of the signal of a proton spin-spin coupled to a deuteron and this leads to the local correlation time τ_q at the site of the deuteron by use of the equation (1) where e^2qQ/h is the quadrupolar coupling

$$T_q^{-1} = \tfrac{3}{8}(e^2qQ/h)^2\tau_q \tag{1}$$

constant. For instance, in molecules such as [^{2}H$_1$] fluorene (3) the correlation time τ_q of the deuteron describes the overall molecular motion and thus the activation parameters for the reorientation process can be derived.[39] When intramolecular motions are present local correlation times have to be considered so that in (4) triple labelling allows the local motions at the CH$_2$D, CHD and COCH$_2$D sites to be studied. The method is claimed to allow a detailed study of overall motions, local intramolecular motions and effects of molecular and steric hindrance as well as the perturbation of local motions by solvent effects or complex formation. It is probable, however, that the information obtained will be more of a semi-empirical nature, although this should not detract from the obvious benefits of the method.

An alternative but more limited method for studying processes in the range 10^{10} to 10^{12} sec^{-1} uses the molecular rotation as a frequency standard for an

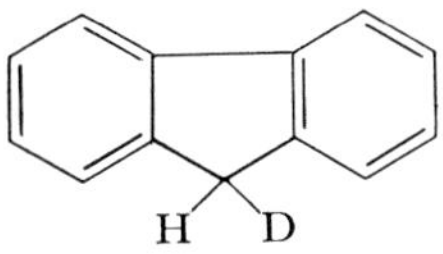

3

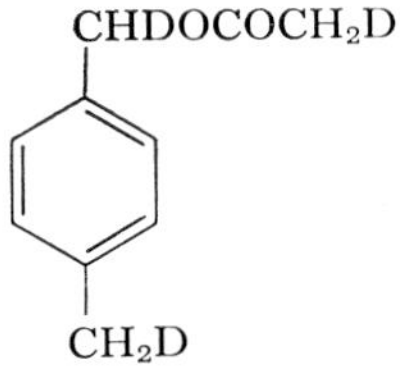

CHDOCOCH$_2$D

CH$_2$D

4

exchange process.[41] The relative rates of exchange and molecular rotation have a profound effect on relaxation behaviour so that systems exchanging more slowly than the rate of molecular rotation may be distinguished from systems experiencing faster exchange. The method has been used in studies of spin lattice relaxation in charge transfer complexes.

The use of a high resolution spectrometer with no ancillary equipment to provide a new method of measuring individual spin-lattice relaxation times (T^{ij}) for each transition (ij) at constant field and frequency has been discussed and applied to an AB spin system.[42] By measuring the peak heights for increasing values of H$_1$ (going through saturation of the line) and plotting a graph of H$_1$/Vij(0), where V = e.m.f., against H$_1^2$, a straight line is obtained with the slope proportional to T$_1$. Absolute values of T$_1$ could be obtained by calibrating the instrument against a sample of known T$_1$. It is claimed that the method is superior to the saturation method which only measures $\sqrt{T_1T_2}$ directly. The relaxation of individual lines of a high resolution spectrum, however, may be studied by employing a Fourier transformation technique. The use of varying r.f. pulses in the sequence 180°-t-90° with variations in t and with subsequent Fourier transformation has proved an alternative method to such "selective" relaxation studies and has been applied to the study of the nuclear spin-lattice relaxation of individual lines of a high resolution spectrum of p-dimethyl-aminobenzaldehyde.[43]

C. Specialized techniques

It is appropriate to discuss under this heading the use of specialized solvents and to review the work on free radical reactions as studied by NMR spectroscopy.

The study of molecules dissolved in the nematic phase of liquid crystals is one of the best known uses of specialized solvents and an article, written by one of the more active workers in the field, summarizes all the experimental results available up to the summer of 1969.[44] The introduction[45] of N-(p-methoxybenzylidene)-p-n-butylaniline (5), which exhibits liquid crystal properties at room temperature, should mean that good spectra will be easily obtained. The determination of the direct spin-spin coupling constants, which are simply related to

$$CH_3O-\langle\ \rangle-CH{=}N-\langle\ \rangle-C_4H_9\text{-}n$$

5

the geometry of the solute molecules, allows direct comparison with and also supplements the data obtained from electron and X-ray diffraction studies as well as from microwave spectroscopy. Thus, the calculated parameters from the spectrum of 1,4-cyclohexadiene,[46] assuming a planar form, agree reasonably well with those derived from earlier electron-diffraction studies but not with the latest data which suggest a boat form with the line H_1H_2 at an angle of $29 \pm 6°$ with the three-fold axis. It is suggested, however, that small deviations from a planar conformation would not seriously influence the parameter $\overline{T_{ZZ}^{(ij)}}$ and thus the NMR data do not completely rule out non-planar forms. Relative bond lengths and orientation parameters have also been derived for pyridazine and pyridine[47] (in which it is suggested that the data would indicate no change in the geometry of the molecule in going from the gas to liquid phase). For spiropentane,[48] the proton coordinates differed by a few percent from those derived from electron diffraction data and it is suggested that this could be due to various effects of non-rigidity. Molecular vibrations, however, do not completely explain why in allene[49] the determined C–C bond length is short relative to the C–H bond length when compared with the electron diffraction results. For *ortho*, *meta* and *para* difluorobenzenes[50] a displacement of the hydrogen atoms, *ortho* to fluorine, from their expected positions was detected from the derived molecular parameters.

Corrections for vibrations have been shown to be difficult to apply in the case of ethane[51] since in general molecular vibrations are known to be anharmonic and cause considerable uncertainties. In the case of the analogous 1,1,1-trifluoroethane, a comparative study with that of ethane showed that the proton chemical shift anisotropies were small.[52] With 1,1-difluoroethylene,[53] however, the large discrepancies, between parameters derived from NMR data and those obtained from microwave data, suggested that a large anisotropy in the indirect couplings ($\geqslant$ 1 KHz in the case of J_{HH}) would be needed to explain the differences. The indirect coupling constant J_{HF} was shown to be positive in fluoromethanes[54] and the fluorine and proton magnetic shielding anisotropies also determined, were shown to be approximately two and a half times greater than

those previously determined in clathrated molecules. No evidence for anisotropic contributions to the geminal indirect spin-spin interaction was reported.
A study of methyl fluoride,[55] enriched with 55% [13]C, showed an unexpectedly
large apparent anisotropy in the ^{13}C–H and ^{13}C–F indirect couplings. A change
in apparent geometry, due to anharmonic vibrations, may again be a contributing factor in these results but it is still considered that this anisotropy may be
much larger than anticipated. Caesar and Dailey,[56] however, have performed
theoretical calculations for the methyl halides and have shown that the frequently used magnetic dipole model gives calculated anisotropies much larger
than those measured. The use of an electric dipole moment and charge density
of the polar substituent produced calculated anisotropies that were worse than
those derived from the magnetic dipole model. They conclude that, at present,
it does not appear that chemical shieldings for small molecules can be understood
from available simple theories. The numerous instances in the literature where
neighbour magnetic anisotropy or electric field mechanisms have been used to
explain observed chemical shifts should thus be viewed with some scepticism.
The anisotropy measured for acetonitrile is more negative than that of methylisocyanate and in comparison with the methyl halides most closely resembles
methyl fluoride. Again electric dipole effects cannot account for these observations and a solvent effect of varying degree on the chemical shift of the acetonitrile and methylisocyanate is proposed.[57]

Interestingly, the assumption previously made that changes in solvent effect
may be neglected in obtaining the anisotropic part of the chemical shielding
tensor σ, even when the medium changes from isotropic to nematic, has now
been proved to be valid[58] for 1,3,5-trichloro- and 1,3,5-tribromo- benzenes.
The method involves a plot of the observed chemical shielding of the protons
against the orientation parameter S_{33} for varying temperatures to obtain the
isotropic contribution to the shielding in the nematic phase.

A study of monodeuteromethane has shown unequivocally that the molecule is
orientated with the H–H–H plane parallel to the conjugated portion of the liquid
crystal molecule.[59] This is explained by the fact that the C–D bond is 0·003 Å
shorter than the C–H bond, so that the crude shape of the molecule is a pyramid
with its symmetry axis along the C–D bond and the molecule would thus be
expected to pack in the direction found. The proton and deuteron spectra of
monodeuterobenzene in a nematic phase have been measured.[60] The values of
the dipole-dipole coupling show minor but significant deviations due to isotopic
substitution from those expected for the regular hexagon geometry.

Of significance is the first observation[61] of two different signals, due to different degrees of order of the solute molecule in two intermediate nematic
phases for 1,1- and 1,2-dichloroethylenes in 4,4′-di-n-hexyloxyazoxybenzene in
the temperature range 70 to 76°. It is considered that the dichloroethylene molecules may be orientated in the two different intermediate phases of the ordered

solvent molecules without destroying the nematic phase because of their small size. That this type of ordering is not a unique observation is shown by an independent spin resonance observation of coexisting modes of solute alignment in nematic solvents.[62]

Another most interesting development has been the first reports[63 to 66] of NMR spectra being obtained from an ordered smectic solution. In a wide-line study it was shown[63] that a sharp peak, in addition to a water peak, is obtained when a solution of 80% by weight of potassium oleate in deuterium oxide is placed between glass plates and orientated at 55° to the applied magnetic field. No experiments with added solutes appear to have been investigated. Thus of more interest has been the recording of an NMR spectrum of a lyotropic mesophase formed by spinning benzene (1%) is an aqueous (D_2O) mixture of sodium sulphate, sodium decylsulphate and decyl alcohol.[64] From the complete analysis it is shown that the orientation of maximum probability for the benzene is that with the six-fold axis parallel and the molecular plane perpendicular to the applied field. This is a similar orientation to that found in a cholesteric mesophase, but at right angles to that found in a conventional mesophase. The orientation of the benzene molecule in this phase and the fact that the sample can be spun in a magnetic field without destroying the orientation suggests that the phase alignment may be one in which the long axis of the surfactant molecules are perpendicular to the long axes of the nematic structure and to the applied magnetic field. A similar study by the same authors[65] on ethanol shows that the C–C–O plane is perpendicular to the magnetic field. Although the structure and behaviour of this mesophase are not fully understood, it should prove a versatile and useful addition to the group of solvents suitable for NMR orientation studies of dissolved molecules, the more so since the rapid spinning of samples can be used to facilitate the recording of well resolved spectra suitable for analysis. Previously, this had only been possible with spectrometers employing superconducting magnets. Of considerable interest also is the observation[66] of an NMR spectrum from a 20 mole % solution of 1,1,1-trifluorotrichloroethane in p-(p-2-n-propoxyethoxybenzylideneamino) acetophenone. It was found, using an assumed molecular geometry, that the parameter S_0 is 0·0148 which is similar in magnitude to the ordering factors for trifluorotrichloroethane in nematic solutions. The ordered smectic solution offers the possibility of arbitrary control of the direction of orientation and also the external field is no longer necessary once the sample has been prepared. This could make smectic solvents the most versatile crystal matrix for orientating molecules.

Any discussion of specialized solvents would, however, not be complete without mention of the well known use of chiral solvents to distinguish enantiomers. Pirkle has extended his studies to an examination of α-amino acids[67] where the use of 2,2,2-trifluorophenylethanol [a convenient method to prepare the resolved alcohol has been described[68]] has induced non-equivalence in α-amino acid methyl esters. The absolute configuration of monosubstituted glycines may be correlated with the spectral non-equivalence. Thus the observed shielding of the carbomethoxy groups and carbinyl protons and deshielding of the C-methyl group of (S)-methyl alanate, relative to the corresponding nuclei in the R isomer, in (R)-2,2,2-trifluorophenylethanol as solvent, has been explained in terms of a model in which the R,S solvate (6) allows closer approach of the carbomethoxy group and carbinyl proton to the shielding region of the phenyl ring than does the R,R solvate (7). The method is also applicable to the determination

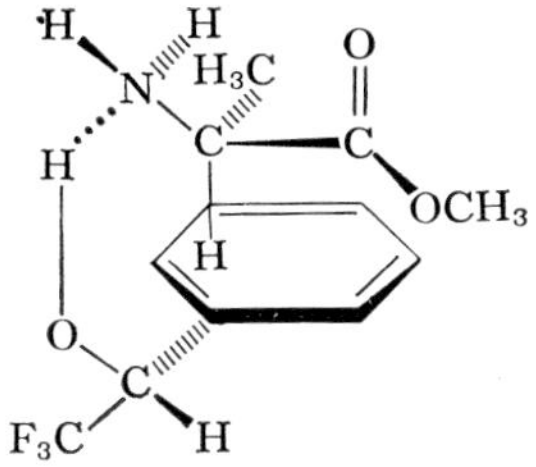

6 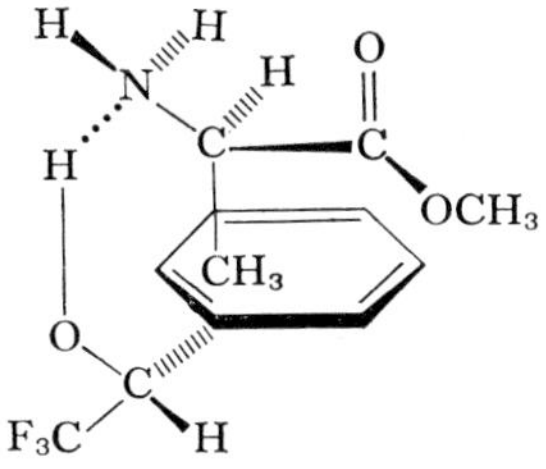   7

of the optical purity of disubstituted glycines and β amino acids. The same solvent has been used to demonstrate NMR enantiomeric spectral non-equivalence of sulphur compounds of type (8) whilst the related solvent 2,2,2-trifluoro-α-naphthylethanol has been used for oxides of type (9).[69]

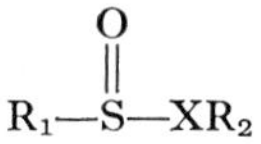

$$R_1\text{---}S\text{---}XR_2$$
$$X = N, O, S$$
8

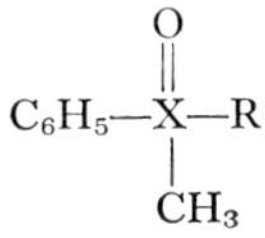

$$C_6H_5\text{---}X\text{---}R$$
$$CH_3$$
$$X = P, N$$
9

It has generally been presumed that the NMR spectrum of a racemate and either of its enantiomers are identical when measured under the same conditions in an achiral solvent. Thus, the report[70] that optically active dihydroquinone and the racemic compound give rise to significantly different NMR spectra at the same concentration in deuterochloroform is most surprising. It is concluded that solute-solute interactions occur such that each individual enantiomer resides in an environment which is diastereomeric.

To conclude this section a review of the use of NMR for the study of radical reactions is included since this has been one of the most interesting recent specialized applications of the technique. The appearance of emission and/or enhanced absorption lines in the NMR spectrum observed during rapid radical reactions in liquids is referred to as chemically induced dynamic nuclear polarization (CIDNP). A qualitative explanation was initially developed based on the theory of the long known physical effect of dynamic nuclear polarization, specified for nuclei of free radicals in solution. This mechanism, a dynamic (longitudinal) polarization, accounted for some of the earlier radical reactions examined and has been outlined in the recent review[71] of CIDNP during the thermal decomposition of peroxide and azo compounds. Many papers have appeared detailing experimental observations of CIDNP. For instance, the thermal decomposition of acyl peroxides in the presence of alkyl iodide,[72] and certain rearrangements,[73,74,75] which could be thought of as concerted ion-pair reactions and which in the case of Stevens[75] rearrangement of (10) to (11) has so been postulated, have indeed been shown to go *via* radical pairs by the application of the CIDNP.

$$O_2N-\langle\!\rangle-CH_2 \qquad \longrightarrow \qquad O_2N-\langle\!\rangle-CH_2$$

$$(CH_3)_2\overset{\oplus}{N}-NCOCH_3 \qquad\qquad CH_3CON-N(CH_3)_2$$

$$\textbf{10} \qquad\qquad\qquad \textbf{11}$$

The mechanism, however, cannot account for the "multiplet-effects" frequently observed in radical transfer and disproportionation reactions such as occur in the overall halogen metal exchange process[76,77,78] given in equation (2).

$$RM + R^1X = RX + R^1M \tag{2}$$

Where R, R^1 = alkyl, M = Li and X = halide

The first examples of strong nuclear polarizations resulting from photochemically induced reactions of the sample in the probe of the spectrometer, e.g. the irradiation of diphenyldiazomethane in toluene[79] or the photoreduction of benzophenone in toluene or ethylbenzene[80] have been observed and explained as a "transversal Overhauser effect" involving singlet-triplet-transitions of radical pairs.[81] A similar mechanism was proposed to account for the radical transfer and disproportionation reactions[82] and a simple qualitative theory developed to account for the observation of both longitudinal and transversal polarizations in reactions involving radical transfer and recombinations.[83] This theory also accounts for the fact that the type of polarization may vary with the intensity of the magnetic field.[83] It may also account for the interesting observation that when radical reactions are conducted outside the spectrometer field, thus enabling the introduction of energy (e.g. light or heat) into the sample, and then introduced quickly into the spectrometer probe after the reaction is essentially complete a different polarization is encountered to that observed when the radical reaction is conducted in the spectrometer probe.[84]

II. COUPLING CONSTANTS

A. Proton-proton coupling

Two significant papers on the theory and correlation of coupling constants have used a theoretical valence bond description of contact nuclear spin-spin coupling. Perturbation theory and Penney-Dirac bond orders were used to obtain a simple form for the average energy valence-bond model of the contact contribution to proton coupling constants.[85] For the most common molecular systems, in which there are only small deviations from a localized bond description, the vicinal and long-range coupling constants were expressed in terms of the bond orders for four-electron fragments. The resulting formulae provided a natural separation into direct and indirect contributions to the coupling. The generalized product approximation formalism has been used to extend the valence bond calculations to molecular fragments with as many as sixteen electrons.[86] This permitted coupling constant calculations to be performed in aromatic and cyclic unsaturated hydrocarbons. Agreement of theoretical results with experiment was best for small, long-range coupling constants.

Several comprehensive reviews of coupling constants have also appeared. Geminal, vicinal and long-range couplings, and couplings in aromatic and heteroaromatic systems, are considered in a most useful review.[87] An empirical approach, which the author justifies on the grounds that it is less likely to lead to errors of interpretation than is the application of theoretical treatments, is used to delineate the usefulness of the better established correlations between the magnitudes of interproton coupling constants and structure. A more comprehensive review on long-range coupling constants[88] places greater emphasis on comparison of experimental and theoretical results, conformational and substituent dependence and the detailed mechanisms which lead to the observed long-range coupling constants. An extensive compilation for the period 1966 to 1968 of geminal coupling in methylene groups is divided between methylene groups adjacent to heteroatoms and $C-CH_2-C$ groups.[89] The factors known to affect J_{gem} such as inductive removal of electrons and back donation of loan pairs, orientation of adjacent substituent, double bonds or lone-pairs and $C-CH_2-C$ angle, are shown to be generally followed. The deviations from these trends are discussed, although many may be attributed to inaccuracies in the reported data.

An addition to the rarely encountered geminal coupling across a heteroatom is a study[90] of $J(H-P-H)$ between protons bonded to phosphorus of different coordinations. The magnitudes of the $J(H-P-D)$ [and hence $J(H-P-H)$] were obtained from the proton spectrum, whilst the signs of $J(H-P-D)$ relative to J_{PD} and J_{HP} were established by a variety of multiple resonance experiments. The results suggest that opening out of the geminal H-P-H angle leads to an algebraic increase in the proton-proton coupling and hence resembles $J(H-C-H)$.

This is not the only factor, however, since the anion O_2PH_2 has the largest $J(H–P–H)$ (i.e. $+35 \cdot 1$ Hz) yet the H–P–H angle is only about $92°$.

The dependence of the vicinal coupling constants on the nature and orientation of substituents is still largely unknown in precise detail. Using a quantitative theory for the effect of solvent on energy differences in substituted ethanes, which has been further developed[91] to take into account dipolar interactions in highly polar media, the coupling constants of the individual rotational isomers in a number of substituted ethanes have been reinvestigated.[92] These results, when combined with those on a number of CH_2CH_2 groups in staggered conformations and in cyclic and acyclic compounds, confirm that all the coupling constants depend on the electronegativity of the substituents and in general decrease with increasing electronegativity. As previously postulated, the predominent effect on the *gauche* coupling occurred when the substituents are in a planar *trans* orientation. It was also shown, however, that when the electronegative substituents are not in a planar *trans* arrangement the *gauche* coupling increases rather than decreases. It is suggested that the predictable values of the coupling in the individual isomers of any $CH_2X \cdot CH_2Y$ compound provide a simple method for the determination of the energy difference between the *gauche* and *trans* isomers. An independent study reported a similar method to evaluate the barrier to internal rotation.[93]

The importance of considering medium effects is emphasized by a study of some halogenated alkanes where the energy differences between rotamers, as determined from the temperature dependence of the coupling constants, were only in agreement with values obtained from IR and Raman spectroscopy when these effects were taken into account.[94] Amongst other studies on the dependence of the coupling constants on the substituent electronegativity, an examination of monosubstituted cyclopropanes has enabled equations to be developed to predict the couplings with a high degree of confidence.[95]

The previously proposed linear correlations between the vicinal (or *ortho*) coupling constants in unsaturated systems and π-bond orders have been reinvestigated using more accurate values for the coupling constants.[96] The relationship, although no longer linear over the whole range of bond orders, is still approximately linear for aromatic hydrocarbons. The deviations can be rationalized in terms of steric interactions, as was also found in a more limited study of 3,4-benzopyrene,[97] and this enables a new correlation, which is linear over the whole range of bond lengths, to be derived. Linear correlations are also found to hold for 5,6,7,8-tetradeuteronaphthalene and 9,10-dideuteroanthracene,[98] whilst the derivation of bond orders in (12) and (13), Z=O, S and NMe, is claimed to indicate a reduction in the aromaticity of these compounds by comparison with that found in naphthalene.[99] Other workers, however, suggest that for (12), Z=O, S and Se, structural factors are important[100] and a tentative correlation between the vicinal coupling constant and changes in internal bond

angle in the benzenoid ring is established.[101] In tropone, tropolone and substituted heptafulvenes correlation of the coupling constants with those of related
systems was used to suggest that tropone and tropolone exhibit bond alternation,
characteristic of polyenones and polyenes, and do not exhibit any appreciable
aromatic character.[102]

It is known that the vicinal couplings in substituted benzenes do not correlate
with π-bond order but show a dependence on substituent electronegativity. A

$$^3J = 7 \cdot 63 + 0 \cdot 0508 \Delta E_\alpha - 0 \cdot 096 \Delta E_\beta \tag{3}$$

linear regression has yielded a correlation[103] given by equation (3), where ΔE_α
and ΔE_β are the changes in electronegativity caused by substitution in the α or β
positions, respectively, to the CH–CH fragment. Related correlations have also
been found in 2-substituted thiophenes,[104] and substituted pyridines.[105] In
pyrimidines,[106] however, the difference in the observed coupling constants for
the neutral and protonated molecules is interpreted in terms of delocalization of
the nitrogen lone-pair since the findings are contrary to that expected from the
effective electronegativity of the nitrogen atom on protonation. It is further
suggested that the effect of substituents on the coupling constants of monosubstituted benzenes may be partially explained in a similar way. The use of
statistical methods has established[107] the best linear correlations between the
couplings and substituent electronegativity values for the monohalobenzenes and
3,5-dihalobenzenes, involving a total of 133 distinct couplings (*ortho*, *meta* and
para). In *meta*- and *para*- disubstituted compounds the substituent effects are
both transferable and additive to a good approximation but in the *ortho*-
dihalobenzenes the adjacent vicinal couplings are additive but not transferable.

On the basis of existing theoretical results[86] it appears that the most important
contributions to the *ortho* and *meta* coupling constants are due to σ-electron
mechanisms, whereas the *para* coupling arises from a π-electron mechanism. A
common assumption has been that the magnitude and sign of the coupling in
aromatic compounds may be used in the analysis of related compounds. This
does not apply to *meta* coupling across a nitrogen atom since it was observed that
in pyrimidine N-oxide $J_{2,4} = -0 \cdot 3$ Hz, whilst in pyrazine N-oxide $J_{3,5} = +0 \cdot 38$
Hz.[108] "Benzylic" coupling (i.e. coupling between an aromatic proton and a
proton centered on the α-carbon atom of a side chain) is mainly discussed in
terms of the σ–π-configuration interaction mechanism.[86,88] The correlation in
para-substituted benzaldehydes[109] between the long-range coupling of the ring

protons and the aldehydic proton and with both the resonance and field constants, derived from Hammett σ_m and σ_p values, is taken as evidence that a σ-electron mechanism is dominant for these couplings, although the argument against a π-mechanism appears to rely solely on a poor correlation of the coupling in *para* alkyl substituted benzaldehydes with the resonance constant. In *di-ortho* substituted benzaldehydes[110] steric interactions force the aldehyde group out of a coplanar conformation and lead to hyperconjugation of the aldehyde proton with the aromatic π-system whilst the sign and magnitude of the long-range coupling constant is used to discuss the conformation of 2,6-dichlorobenzaldoxime on the basis of the σ–π exchange mechanism.

In polycyclic hydrocarbons the long-range couplings observed have been documented[111] as benzylic or inter-ring (*epi*, *bay* or *peri*) and the mechanisms involved reviewed.[112] The coupling between benzylic-methyl protons and ring protons *ortho* or *para* to them is again proposed as a σ–π exchange mechanism, but the small positive values measured for $J(CH_3–m-H)$ are explained purely by a σ-mechanism. For inter-ring couplings π-electrons are shown to dominate five bond *epi*-coupling but to make little contribution to *peri* inter-ring coupling. In benzoxazole[113] the long-range couplings observed are considered to be π-electron transmitted whilst in benzofurans[114] the well documented planar zig-zag path mechanism was invoked to account for all the observed couplings, except that between the 2 and 4 protons. Seven bond methyl-methyl coupling reported in 7,12-dimethyl[*a*]anthracene[111] and estimated at 0·6 Hz was considered not to be stereospecific since an analogous coupling was detected in *para*-methyl-benzylbromide. Theoretical considerations[86] would suggest that "inter-benzylic" couplings would be of the same order of magnitude as benzylic couplings and some examples have been noted.[88] The several examples[114,115,116] of five bond coupling between methoxy protons and the adjacent ring proton can all be rationalized in terms of a restricted rotation of the methoxy group about the C_{aryl}–O bond such that a larger coupling is associated with that conformation in which the methoxy group is *anti* to the *ortho* substituent. A steric factor may also account for the size of the coupling ($J \simeq 0·9$ Hz) of the cyclopropyl hydrogen to *ortho* aromatic protons in some 3-aryl-1,1,2,2-tetracyanocyclopropanes[117] since this coupling is appreciably larger than the comparable coupling in the corresponding arylidenemalonitriles which, because of greater s character in the bonding, would have been expected to have exhibited the larger coupling.

A new type of homoallylic coupling[118] in camphene (**14**) involving five bond coupling in the fragment H–C=C–C–C–H (the more usual type being H–C–C=C–C–H) has been demonstrated. The observed couplings are given in Table I; the data in the last two columns represent values for this new type of homoallylic coupling. The observation that the *syn*-C_4H interaction is larger than the allylic coupling (*syn*-C_1H) and the possibility of a steric dependence, since the *anti*-C_4H coupling is much smaller, suggest that the coupling involves

principally π contributions. A further interesting observation on the allylic couplings (column 3 Table I) was made in camphene in that the "dihedral angle"
(see **15**) is about 80° and the identical values for *cisoid* and *transoid* couplings
disagree with current theories which predict J *cisoid* to be less than J *transoid*.

14   **15**

TABLE I

Proton NMR parameters for exo-methylene protons in camphene (14)

Proton	$\delta_H^{CCl_4}$	J_{gem}[b]	$J(HC_1C-CH)$[b]	$J(HC_4CC-CH)$[b]	$J(M_eCC-CH)$[bc]
syn	4·65	0·9	0·55	0·85	<0·02
anti	4·44	0·9	0·55	<0·1[c]	<0·05

[a] Spectra were obtained on a Varian HA-60 instrument with external audio power for
the decoupling experiments supplied by a GR-1310A and two HP-200CD oscillators,
while the frequencies were measured with a HP-5245L counter.
[b] In hertz with an estimated precision of ±0·1 Hz.
[c] Estimated from line widths at half-height.

An extension of the Pople and Bothner-By theory for geminal coupling
constants is used to discuss the long-range coupling observed in geminal methyl
groups of propane derivatives.[119] It is suggested that variations in four-bond
couplings are controlled by variations in singlet-triplet excitation energies. In
acetone the four bond coupling of +0·55 Hz is considered probably to result
from a −0·5 Hz contribution *via* π electrons with an approximately 1·0 Hz contribution through σ bonds and possibly through space.[120] Long-range coupling
is observed in 2,7,8-trioxa-1-phosphabicyclo[3,2,1]octane (**16**) between the
protons H_A and H_F.[121] A convenient pathway for interaction through the lone-
pair electrons of the three oxygen atoms and the $3d$ orbital of the phosphorus
atom is proposed since previous examples of such long-range couplings suggest
that couplings are enhanced by heteroatoms or cyclopropane rings.

Whilst the general trends of long-range coupling across four and five bonds
have already been reviewed[87,88] it is interesting to note that the observation[122] of
a positive coupling ($J = +1·1$ Hz) between protons H_A and H_B in (**17**) supports
the hypothesis that long-range coupling between protons separated by four
bonds in an M (or, as sometimes referred to, W) configuration, which are not

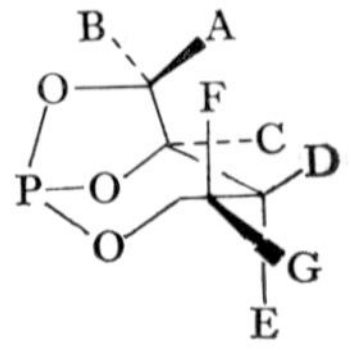

16

coplanar, is positive whilst for other cases the coupling is negative. A remarkable example of a molecule in which both protons of the same methylene group gave rise to two long-range couplings through four bonds was demonstrated[123] in (**18**). It can, however, be demonstrated that an M spatial arrangement exists between the C-1 proton and one of the C-19 methylene protons (H_A) and between the C-5 proton and the other C-19 methylene (H_B).

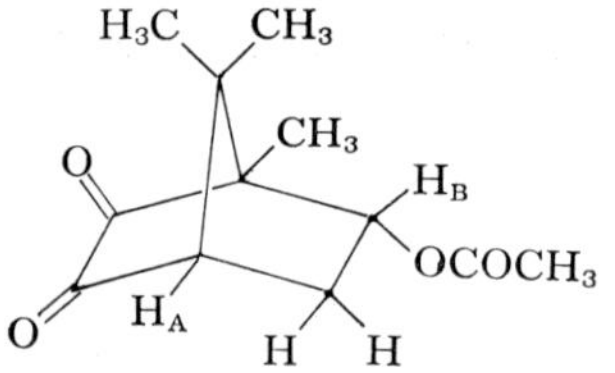

17

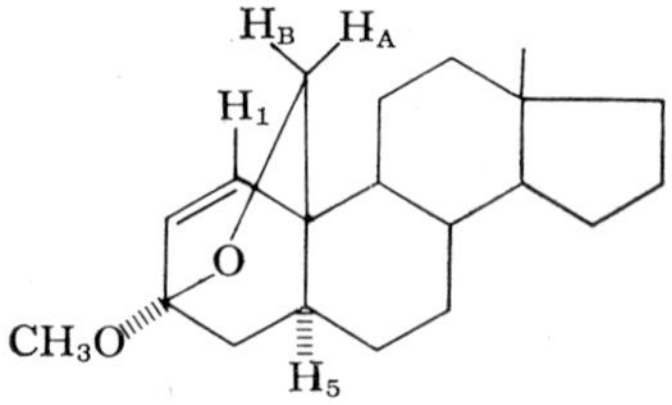

18

To conclude this section, mention is also made of a unique six bond coupling ($J=1$ Hz) observed between those protons of the methylene groups which are *syn* to the olefinic bond in (**19**). The protons are in an extended M configuration and the great sensitivity of the long-range coupling to geometrical changes is demonstrated by the fact that neither (**20**) nor its dihydro derivative showed this six bond coupling.[124]

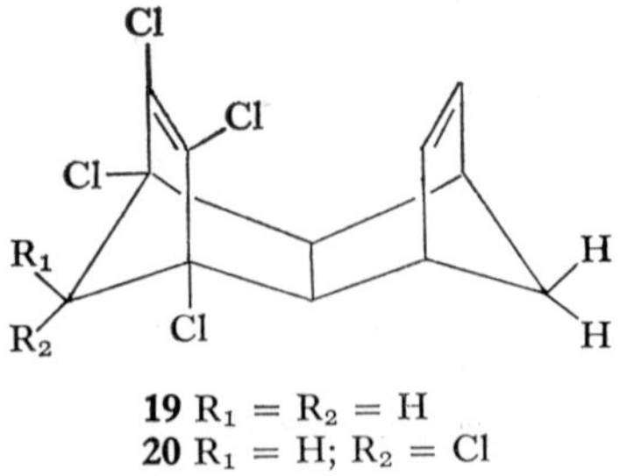

19 $R_1 = R_2 = H$
20 $R_1 = H; R_2 = Cl$

B. Proton-heteroatom coupling

Several theoretical papers and a comprehensive review,[125] which are relevant to the study of proton-heteroatom coupling, have been published on nuclear spin-spin coupling between directly bonded nuclei. Systematic trends in coupling constants of directly bonded nuclei have been examined[126] and a synopsis of the indirect coupling constants for magnetic nuclei in fifty different pairs of directly bonded X–Y atoms is given along with the corresponding reduced constant $K_{XY} = (2\pi/\gamma_X\gamma_Y)J_{XY}$. A model has been proposed which successfully accounts for changes in $^1K_{XY}$ across the periodic table. The changes in signs of $^1K_{PC}$ and $^2K_{PCH}$ over a wide range of phosphorus and selenium compounds as well as the signs of PH, SeC and SeCH couplings are explained by this model.[127] Also, the parameterized L.C.A.O.-S.C.F. molecular-orbital theory[128] has been applied[129] to the calculation of the signs and magnitudes of one and two bond couplings involving the nuclei ^{1}H, ^{11}B, ^{13}C, ^{14}N, ^{19}F, ^{29}Si and ^{31}P.

The geminal proton-deuteron coupling in a number of organic molecules was shown[130] to be both temperature and solvent dependent. Lowering of the temperature leads to decoupling of the nuclei and can be explained in terms of rotational motions of the molecules affecting the quadrupolar relaxation although intermolecular forces, solvent polarity and molecular shape are also important factors. The use of such deuterium quadrupolar relaxation to study local molecular motions[40] has already been mentioned.

Carbon-proton couplings $J(^{13}$C–H) have been reported in unsaturated systems by several workers. A simple additivity relationship which adequately reproduced all reported ^{13}C–H couplings for chloroethylenes has been proposed,[131] whilst a study of monosubstituted ethylenes has revealed that the previous correlation in monosubstituted methanes between electronegativity and C–X bond distance with the $J(^{13}$C–H) can be extended to ethylenes.[132] Thus a unified expression can be obtained which reproduces the ^{13}C–H couplings for saturated and ethylenic systems. The stereospecific effect of the electron lone-pairs of an α-substituent on $J(^{13}$C–H) is demonstrated in (21) where $J[$C(B)–H(A)$]$ is less than that for ethylene.[133] Partial delocalization of the lone-pair electrons into the C–H bond is responsible and in the *trans* arrangement, as in (21), the magnitude of the effect is such as to overcome the effect of the electronegativity of the nitrogen [i.e. to increase $J(^{13}$C–H)].

Methyl ^{13}C–H coupling constants for a series of substituted toluenes, dimethylanilines, anisoles and t-butylbenzenes could be linearly correlated with the Hammett σ constant of the substituent.[134] Since the couplings are a function of the s character of the bond which can be related to electronegativity effects, the relative correlations were said to be a measure of the mode of transmission of substituent effects to the methyl site. Two bond couplings involving the formyl proton have been reported for forty aldehydes.[135] For aliphatic aldehydes the values are of the order 22 to 26 Hz but a notable increase is observed when the hydrogens attached to the ^{13}C atom are substituted by halogens e.g. $J(^{13}C–C–H)=51$ Hz for $Br_3C\cdot CHO$ and for aromatic aldehydes the coupling is 20 to 26 Hz. The sign of the coupling constant was found to be the same as the directly bonded coupling constant. M.O. calculations show that the main contribution to the two bond coupling comes from delocalization of the lone-pair electrons of the carbonyl oxygen atom and the low excitation of these electrons. In acetone a three bond coupling of $2\cdot2\pm0\cdot3$ Hz has been observed.[120] For the case $–HC{=}N–^{13}C$ electron transfer occurs from the nitrogen nonbonding orbital into the anti-bonding CH and NC molecular orbitals and hence the electronegativity of the nitrogen does not influence $^3J_{CH}$ appreciably as demonstrated[133] in (21) where $J[H(A)C(D)]=12\cdot0\pm0\cdot6$ Hz, whereas the expected *cis* coupling in $–HC{=}C\cdot^{13}C$ is approximately $+5$ Hz.

$$H_5C_6$$
$$\underset{(B)}{C}{=}N^{(C)}$$
$$\underset{(A)}{H}\qquad\underset{(D)(E)}{CH_3}$$

21

$$R_nXCH{=}CH_2$$

X = H,C,N,F,Si,P,Sn,Hg,Tl

R = H,Alkyl,Alkoxy,Aryl,vinyl.

n = 0 to 3

22

Nitrogen-proton couplings have been examined by several workers to distinguish structural effects. A consideration of some disubstituted ethanes[136] suggested that $^3J_{NH}$ shows a dependence on the dihedral angle similar to that of $^3J_{HH}$. The orientation of the lone-pair of electrons on the nitrogen atom is an important factor as was also demonstrated for four bond couplings.[137] Comparison of ^{14}N-H and X-H couplings has been made in compounds of type (22) and, although the data are limited, an apparent increase of the "normalized" coupling constant with increasing atomic number occurs.[138] By spin tickling experiments all the $J(^{14}N–H)$ are shown to be positive. Homo- and hetero- nuclear spin tickling experiments were also used to determine the signs of $^2J_{NH}$ and $^3J_{NH}$ in oximes and in quinoline[139] and similarly all three $J(^{15}N–H)$ in formamide are shown to be negative.[140] Two independent linear correlations of $J(^{15}N–H)$ in *meta*- and *para*- substituted anilines with Hammett σ constants have been presented.[141,142] The data may be rationalized in terms of the stereochemical change expected at the nitrogen atom from the known electronic character of the substituents. Although the trends are essentially the same in the two reports, measurements in $CDCl_3$ differ considerably; the source of this discrepancy is not clear.

Proton-fluorine couplings have been obtained from a series of monosubstituted fluorobenzenes and compared with the corresponding couplings in fluorobenzene to derive substituent effects.[143] These substituent effects were shown to be additive for a series of di- and tri- substituted compounds. The effect of the substituent on the proton-proton and proton-fluorine couplings in benzene and pyridine derivatives is suggested to be *via* the σ framework from a comparison of couplings in 2-methyl-3-fluoropyridine with those in fluorotoluene derivatives.[144] Long-range benzylic type coupling in a p-fluorobenzaldehyde and in 2,6-dichlorobenzyl fluoride has been discussed in terms of the $\sigma-\pi$ exchange mechanism. A negative hyperfine interaction constant between the aldehyde proton and the aromatic system is suggested,[145] whereas the fluoromethyl group is assumed to have a stable conformation with the C–F bond perpendicular to the aromatic ring.[146] In alicyclic systems H–F couplings have been extensively investigated in a series of pyranosyl fluorides. The vicinal and geminal couplings have been shown to have the same relative sign[147] whilst in hexopyranosides a marked angular dependence is exhibited.[148] Hence $J_{trans} = ca$ 24 Hz and $J_{gauche} =$ 1·0 to 1·5 Hz for J_{FaHe} and 7·5 to 12·6 Hz for J_{FeHa} whilst $J_{gem} = 49$ to 53 Hz. The gauche couplings probably reflect a configurational electronegative dependence. Similar results were obtained for pentropyranosyl fluorides.[149] Although numerous five bond long-range couplings have been recorded the exact arrangement of nuclei undergoing interaction has not been known since nearly all the examples relate to methyl fluorine coupling. It is thus of interest to observe that in (23)

23

both the $syn(H_S)$ and $anti(H_a)$ protons coupled[150] with the fluorine atom and that the two coupling constants are not remarkably different (i.e. 3·6 and 3·0 Hz respectively). One possibility for the surprising coupling of the $anti$ proton to the fluorine atom is that it may occur through overlap of the fluorine with the small rear lobe of the $anti$ C_8–H bond.

The angular dependence of phosphorus-proton couplings and their relationship to proton couplings has again received considerable attention. A full description of the previously reported angular dependence of two bond coupling in cyclic phosphines and acyclic phosphines exhibiting restricted rotation has been given and it is suggested[151] that dependence may be due to the lone-pair orientation of the phosphorus atom. Three bond phosphorus-proton coupling, which has been shown to have a similar angular dependence to $^3J_{\text{HH}}$,[136,152] is normally greater than the two bond coupling but the reverse is true in β-substituted ethylphosphonates.[153] Four-bond coupling through oxygen may also show an orientation preference since in (24), for which the proton-proton couplings are consistent with a half-chair conformation $^4J(\text{P–H}_{ax}) = 0·5$ Hz and $^4J(\text{P–H}_{eq}) =$

3·6 Hz[154] whilst a large four bond coupling through three sp^3 carbons of 5 Hz in (25) may be an M type coupling.[155]

24   25

Interest in determining the signs of the different phosphorus-proton couplings in various compounds continues since the signs of the coupling constant are known to be sensitive to the valence of the phosphorus and to provide useful structural information. Thus, for example it is found that in *para*-substituted derivatives of triphenyl phosphine[156] all the proton-phosphorus couplings become more positive as the valence of the phosphorus atom is increased whilst in allenic organophosphorus compounds[157] the sign of the four bond coupling varies with both the inductive and resonance effects of the substituents bound to the phosphorus atom. In **26** a triple resonance experiment showed the seven bond coupling to be negative and this is believed to be a unique determination.[156]

$$[p\text{-}CH_3C_6H_4CH_2\overset{\oplus}{P}(C_6H_5)_3]$$
26

The reviewer has made no detailed examination of the literature on proton coupling to heteroatoms, other than those detailed above, and so considers that it would be inappropriate to discuss such couplings.

III. CHEMICAL SHIFTS

A. Theory and correlations

A linear relationship between the proton chemical shifts for substituted aliphatic derivatives and the positive charge density on the hydrogen, as determined by a M.O.-L.C.A.O. method, was obtained.[158] Since the relationship was observed for mono- and poly- substituted methanes and branched aliphatic derivatives, provided that the substituents were of the same row of the periodic table, it was considered that the proton chemical shift is mainly determined by the electronic charge at the hydrogen atom. For methyl esters the electron density at the oxygen atom is considered to be important in determining the chemical shift of the methyl group.[159]

The use of empirically deduced additivity parameters, however, continues to have success. For instance, systematic trends similar to the Zurcher correlations in steroids have been established in pentacyclic triterpenes.[160,161] Caution should be exercised in applying some of the additivity parameters since it was shown in several cases, where hydroxyl and/or acetoxy groups are in a 1,2-diequatorial orientation, that the calculated values deviated somewhat from the observed ones. This was presumably due to restricted rotation of the functional groups or to distortions from the normal chair conformation.

Additive shielding parameters for olefinic protons were derived for thirty-six functional groups by a least squares procedure applied to 4298 chemical shifts[162] and this study allowed the estimation of shielding parameters for a further seven functional groups. A related study restricted to polysubstituted ethylenes was also reported.[163] Some structural features associated with significant deviations from the results calculated on the basis of the additivity principle are: — unusual juxtaposition of remote functional groups, planar conjugated carbonyl derivatives, bicyclic olefines and dienes, vinyl ethers in which the lone pair on the oxygen is constrained into certain conformations and vinyl halides.[164] It can thus be concluded that ground state mesomerism offers the best rationalization of some trends in numerous groups of olefinic compounds.

The modifications by Pople and by McWeeney of London's M.O. theory of π-electron ring currents have been used to calculate the individual currents in a number of tri- and tetra- cyclic hydrocarbons.[165] These calculations and the observed chemical shifts have led to the conclusion that π-electron systems exist which sustain diamagnetic currents in some rings and, at the same time, paramagnetic currents in others. Thus aromaticity cannot be defined in terms of ring currents for such systems. Calculations based on the Johnson-Bovey current loop expressions were used to provide a description of the ring current effect in some silicon and germanium phthalocyanins[166] but the usefulness of such calculations in quantitative structural studies is doubtful. The Johnson-Bovey model, however, has also been used to provide a qualitative interpretation of the systematic progressive shielding of the protons in the homologous series phenanthrene

FIG. 1. The structure of nonahelicene (bis-phenanthro
[3,4.c,4′,3′.g] phenanthrene).

to nonahelicene (bis-phenanthro[3,4,*c*,4′,3′,*g*]phenanthrene) (Fig. 1) caused by successive annelations.[167] The concept of ring currents in aromatic molecules is most useful in studying compounds of the annulene series, as has previously been extensively used. For example, the NMR spectrum clearly showed for the first time[168] a paramagnetic ring current in a [4*n*+1]annulene derivative (27) and a strong paramagnetic effect is suggested in the dianions of *trans* 15,16-dialkyl-dihydropyrenes (28) where the interior protons at the α carbon appeared[169] at δ 21·0 to 21·24 (the lowest downfield value yet recorded for hydrogen bound to carbon).

27

28

It is suggested that ring currents in each hexagon of a polynuclear aromatic hydrocarbon are equal to that of benzene based upon the observation of a good correlation between the methyl chemical shift and the inverse cube of the distances ($\sum R^{-3}$) which separate the methyl group and the centres of the aromatic ring in a series of twenty-nine methylarenes.[170] Deviations from this correlation occurred, where there was either nonplanarity or steric compression of the methyl groups or where compounds contained more than three rings, but a more general correlation with $\sum IR^{-3}$ (where I is a previously calculated relative ring current intensity) could be obtained. Further, a correlation for the chemical shift of the methylene protons, but not for the hydroxyl proton, in some polycyclic arylmethanols with this latter parameter, indicates that the time averaged conformation of compounds is a function of their structure.[171] However, a correlation between the chemical shift of the ring protons of twenty-two alternant and seven non-alternant hydrocarbons[172] and the corresponding values of the L.C.A.O. index of free valence (and hence of other M.O. indices of chemical reactivity) appears to be a fortuitous consequence of the geometry of these molecules. Thus, it is not surprising that the use of proton chemical shifts to predict the reactivity of non-alternant hydrocarbons and their ions[173] could only be used where the π-electron density appeared to be the decisive factor.

Attempts to correlate ring proton shifts in substituted benzenes with various inductive and resonance parameters and with field effects continue e.g. alkyl-benzenes[174] and monosubstituted benzoic acids.[175] However, the theory of aromatic proton chemical shifts is still incomplete as is shown in an attempt to interpret the spectra of substituted benzenes in terms of a combination of π-electron charge density, electric field, diamagnetic anisotropy and van der Waals interaction, and steric effects on each.[176] Several observations could not be explained, such as, the negative *meta* proton substituent shift with electron donating substituents or with halogens. In an attempt to explain the results for halobenzenes, a contribution from some hitherto unknown effect which is transmitted to *ortho* and *meta* protons, but only reluctantly to *para*-protons and to methyl protons in all positions, is postulated.[177] It is suggested that this unknown effect could be a "spin polarization" shift which is caused by Fermi contact interaction of a nucleus with electrons and which is transmitted in a similar manner to that of the indirect spin-spin interaction between nuclei. The correlation of the chemical shift of the protons, of various substituent groups in disubstituted benzene derivatives, with electronic and steric parameters has also continued e.g. *para*-substituted acetanilides,[178] *meta*- and *para*- substituted formanilides,[179] azomethines,[180] and trimethylsilyl benzenes.[181] The variation of the correlation of the chemical shift of the benzylic protons with the Hammett σ value of the *para* substituent in a series of *para*-substituted toluene derivatives bearing different groups at the α position is reported[182] and appears to have a conformational dependence; this again cannot be explained on current theories of substituent effects. The "*ortho*" effect has also been studied e.g. *ortho*-substituted phenols, and *ortho*-substituted fluorobenzenes.[183] The chemical shift of the hydroxyl proton in a large number of *ortho*-substituted phenols in dimethyl sulphoxide solution appeared to be free of steric effects. Hence, it was found possible to assign *ortho*-substituent constants (σ_o^-) for thirty-two substituents and to correlate these constants successfully with reactivity data for *ortho*-substituted compounds where steric factors were not important.[184] It was also claimed that the Taft steric parameters ($\sigma_{o,s}$) may be interpreted as a function of the electronic effects.[185] This claim does not appear to be justified due to the lack of discrimination between the parameters employed in the calculation. In *para*-hydroxydiphenyl sulphide, sulphoxide and sulphone[186] the transmission of electronic effects decreases in the series $S > SO > SO_2$. In a related study, however, it was suggested[187] that in diphenyl sulphide derivatives a transmission mechanism is only operative through sulphur and is not effective when the bridging function is sulphoxide or sulphone. Further, the extent to which the transmission is operative in the sulphides is dependent upon the precise nature of the *para*-substituent. In organo-metallic derivatives of benzene several related studies on the influence of the metal atoms have been made. For example, from

$[XC_6H_4]_n MR_{4-n}$

X = *p*- or *m*- F

M = Si, Ge or Sn

R = CH_3 or C_2H_5

29

C_6H_5XR

30a X = O; R = H, CH_3, SiH_3, GeH_3

30b X = S; R = H, CH_3, SiH_3, GeH_3

a study of the NMR spectra of compounds of type (29), a $p_\pi-d_\pi$ interaction of the metal atom with the aromatic ring is suggested.[188,189] Similarly, results for a number of phosphorylated furan, thiophene and pyrrole derivatives[190] indicated that some degree of $p_\pi-d_\pi$ bonding is present. However, comparison of the spectra of the phenol and thiophenol derivatives (30a) and (30b) lead to the conclusion that any involvement of the silicon or germanium d orbitals in the bond to oxygen or to sulphur does not strongly influence the bonding in the aromatic ring.[191]

Various studies have been made of substituent effects in heterocycles, e.g. in substituted pyridines,[192,193] pyrimidines,[194] quinolines[195] and quinoxalines,[196] but in general the correlations are no more encouraging than in substituted benzenes.[193]

A detailed examination of the relationship $\Delta\sigma = a\Delta q$, where $\Delta\sigma$ is the difference in chemical shift between the proton in an heterocycle and its aromatic polycyclic analogue and where Δq is the excess π-electron density on the carbon atom to which the proton is bound in the heterocycle, revealed quite a satisfactory correlation for the proton *ortho* to a nitrogen atom, as long as only one nitrogen was in that particular ring.[197] The validity of the relationship for other positions was much less satisfactory and hence the determination of charge density from observed chemical shift data appears questionable at present and may certainly lead to serious errors in molecules with two adjacent heteroatoms.

B. Anisotropic effects

The procedure, whereby the magnitude of the magnetic anisotropy of bonds may be calculated from a study of relative chemical shifts, has been employed to estimate the magnetic anisotropy of the acetylenic, nitrile and isonitrile triple bonds[198] although a previous study had suggested that the values of anisotropy obtained for the C–C and C–H bonds are incompatible with those obtained from Colton-Moulton constants. The magnetic anisotropy of the C–H and C–C bonds is employed to rationalize the influence of a methyl substituent on the chemical shift of a vicinal proton since measurements in the gas phase showed that solvent effects were not responsible for the chemical shift changes observed.[199] The magnetic anisotropy of the thioketo group in thioamides has been calculated by a study of the sterically fixed 1-thioacyl piperidine derivatives and has enabled an assignment of the *cis*- and *trans*- N-methyl groups in dimethylthioacetamide and dimethylthioformamide to be made.[200] It is also shown, from a comparative study of the ^{13}C chemical shifts and aromatic solvent induced shift of the proton resonances in camphor and thiocamphor, that the C=S bond, unlike the sulphoxide bond, is similar to the C=O bond in bond order. Similar screening "cones" for these keto and thioketo groups could thus be drawn.[201] For the sulphoxide bond, it is considered that the screening environment will closely resemble that associated with the acetylenic bond. Thus, the assignment

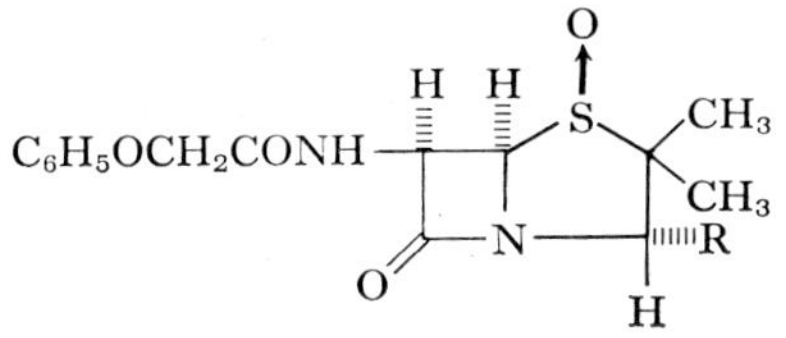

31

of the configuration of phenoxymethyl penicillin sulphoxide as (31) from calculations using this approximation has been partially successful[202] and confirmed by solvent induced chemical shifts and nuclear Overhauser effects on this and related penicillin sulphoxides.[203,204] Similarly configurational assignments in thietan-1-oxides[205] and episulphides[206] and the conformation of some sulphites[207] have been based on calculations of the anisotropy of the S→O bond.

C. Asymmetric effects

This subject has again produced a large number of studies of which one of the most interesting has been the first direct time average chemical shift differences that are exclusively due to an intrinsic diastereotopism.[208] In molecules of type **32** the geminal nuclei, or groups of nuclei, are diastereotopic and hence

$$RCG_2CXYZ \qquad\qquad RCG_2C(X^*)_3$$

32   **33**

anisochronous. Any chemical shift difference observed for the nuclei may be partly due to differences in conformer population and partly due to an intrinsic effect. However, in compounds of general formula (**33**), where the X*'s are identical chiral substituents all having the same configuration, the conformer populations will be exactly equal by symmetry. Thus, an intrinsic diastereotopism is demonstrated in propeller molecules of type (**34**) by the observation of

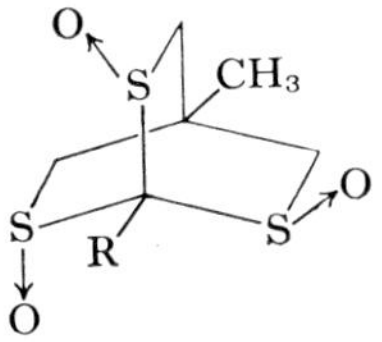

(a) R = $CH_2C_6H_5$
(b) R = $C(CH_3)_2OH$
(c) R = $C(CF_3)_2OH$

34

an AA′A″BB′B″ pattern for the ring methylene protons in a variety of solvents. The first examples of methyl groups which are anisochronous and are not attached to a carbon atom have also been reported.[209] For the species (35),

$$[(CH_3)_2XCH(CH_3)C_6H_5]^{\oplus}Br^{\ominus}$$

35

where X = PhN, PhP, S or Se, the chemical shift difference of the methyl groups in any one species showed a marked solvent and temperature dependence and it is clear that differences in conformer populations are at least as important as intrinsic asymmetry. The observed non-equivalences are strongly concentration dependent and it is suggested that stereospecific ion-pair formation occurs; a conclusion that is supported by observations[210] for the phosphonium salt (36),

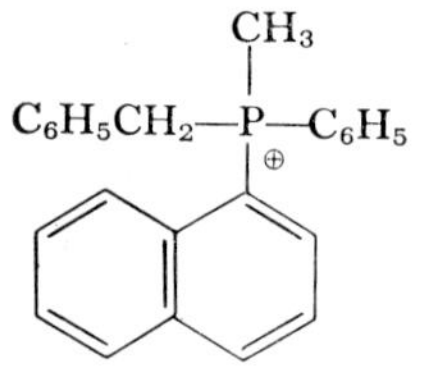

$$
\begin{array}{c}
CH_3 \\
|\\
C_6H_5CH_2-\underset{\oplus}{P}-C_6H_5
\end{array}
$$

36

$$[CH_3NH_2]^{\oplus}[(C_6H_5CO_2)_3BOCH_3]^{\ominus}$$

37

where the anisochronism of the benzyl methylene protons is dependent on the nature of the anion (see Table II). Stereospecific ion-pairing is also attributed to asymmetry associated with the borate salt (37).[211] The unique observation[212] of

TABLE II

Proton NMR data of the methylene protons of (36) in CDCl$_3$

Anion	Chemical shift δ (p.p.m.)		Difference Δv (Hz)
	H$_A$	H$_B$	
chloride	4·75	5·46	42·5
bromide	4·80	5·51	42·5
nitrate	4·62	4·98	21·5
triiodide	4·60	4·60	0
mixture of chloride/triiodide	4·69	5·16	28
mixture of bromide/nitrate	4·71	5·24	30·5

the methyl protons of a methoxy group being anisochronous in (38a) relied on the fact that the signals for the methyl ester and ether methoxy groups were of very unequal height and width at room temperature although being of equal

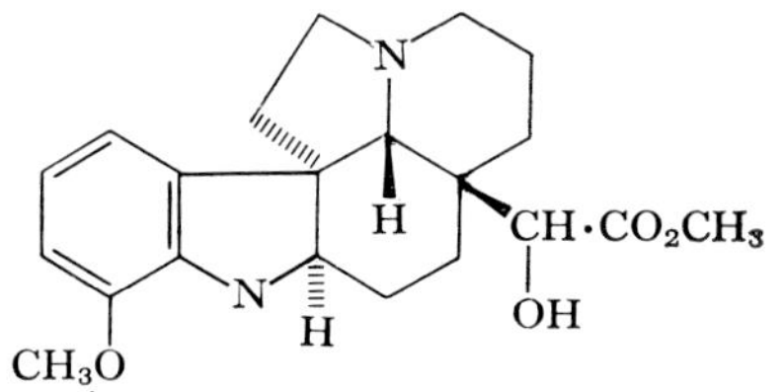

(a) R = COC_6H_5
(b) R = $COCH_3$
(c) R = $COCH{=}CHC_6H_5$

38

height at 70° or in the derivatives (**38b**) and (**38c**). It is suggested, by considering Dreiding models, that only the benzoyl group could interact with the aromatic methoxy-group and the broadening of the signal was produced by the non-equivalence of the methyl protons when in close proximity to the benzene ring. It is a pity the authors did not conduct a low temperature study for this would have distinguished between the proposed theory and the more likely explanation that the phenomenon is due to coalescence of two methoxy resonances due to some molecular process (e.g. amide rotation).

Parameters for anisochronous nuclei have been further investigated. Thus a study of N-benzyl derivatives of methyl piperazines suggested that for N-benzyl groups in cyclic systems non-equivalence of the methylene protons will be observed if the conformer is chiral and the benzyl substituent is vicinal to a single equatorial alkyl substituent.[213] Further, the asymmetry in 2- and 3-pyrazolines, pyrazolidines and pyrazolidones which can give rise to non-equivalence of ethyl, benzyl or isopropyl groups fixed on nitrogen atoms has been defined[214] as either a ring carbon atom, a quaternary nitrogen atom (protonation or quaternization) or a tertiary nitrogen atom (slow inversion). In alicyclic compounds the magnetic non-equivalence of the methylene protons of the ethyl group in acetylenic and allenic ethers and thioethers is related[215] either to the nature of the heteroatom or to the local dissymmetry element, i.e. asymmetric carbon, ketal group or allenic system. In acetals of structure (**39**) the

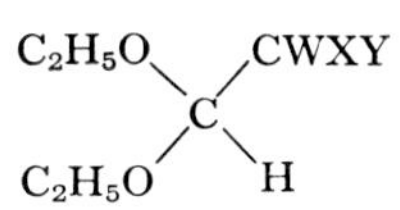

C_2H_5O ╲ ╱ CWXY
 ⟍C⟋
C_2H_5O ╱ ╲ H

W,X,Y = H,Cl,Br

39

$$CH_3$$
$C_6H_5{-}CH{-}CH$ ⟨ $SCH_AH_BC_6H_5$ / $SCH_{A'}H_{B'}C_6H_5$

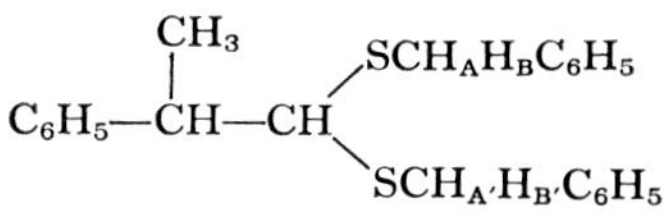

40

non-equivalence of the methylene protons is shown[216] to be dependent on the degree of halogen substitution and to correlate well with the corresponding group electronegativity values, whilst in thioacetals of structure (40) double magnetic non-equivalence has been observed[217] in benzene solution. In other solvents either protons A and B, or both sets of methylene protons, are isochronous. Similar results are reported[218] in the dibenzylmercaptal of type (41).

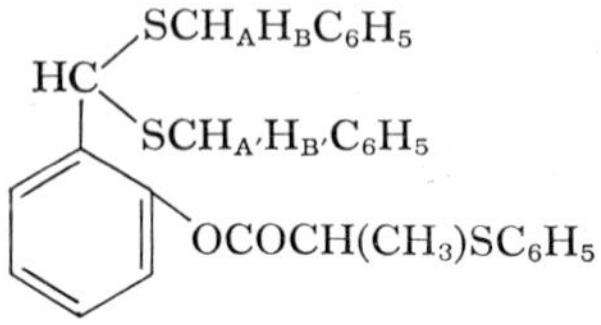

41 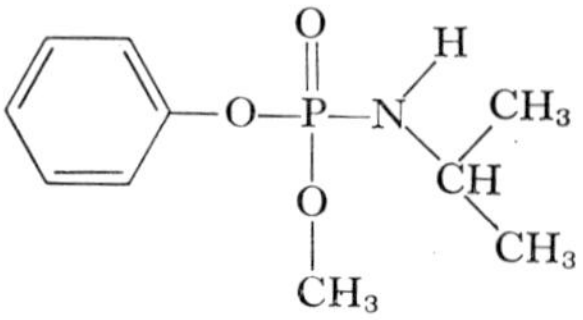   42

Various factors have been attributed to the enhancement of asymmetric effects such as solvent effects, intramolecular hydrogen bonding, diamagnetic anisotropy of an aromatic ring and steric effects. Intermolecular hydrogen bonding has now been proposed as the cause of the enhancement of the non-equivalence exhibited by the methyls of the isopropyl group in (42) and a planar, eight-membered, cyclic dimer is postulated in which restricted rotation of the N–C bond occurs.[219]

Intrinsic asymmetry, due to the pyrimidal configuration of the sulphur atom, continues to attract study and the magnetic non-equivalence of the methylene protons α to the sulphoxide group is well documented. In a study of magnetic non-equivalence of the methylene protons of benzyl para-substituted phenyl sulphoxides (43), it was found that the peaks corresponding to the proton gauche to the lone pair on sulphur H_A are more sensitive to a substituent change.[220] The phenomenon was tentatively attributed to the conformational preference of

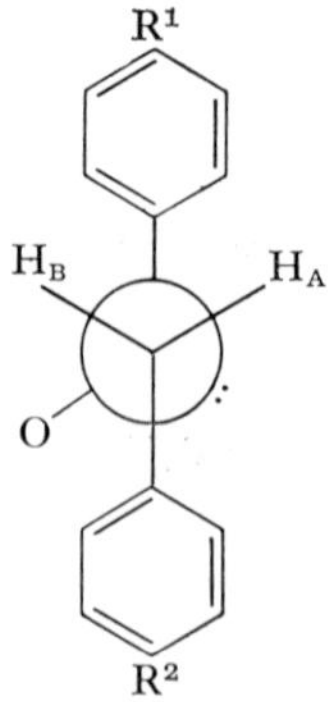

43

the ring A phenyl group[221] and has been applied to configurational assignments of some diastereomeric sulphoxides.[222] The stereospecific transmission of the electronic effect across the sulphoxide bridge, as shown in a series of a methyl benzyl β-substituted phenyl sulphoxides, is attributed to the relative geometry of the proton and the lone-pair.[223]

Asymmetric effects at a sulphoxide centre have also been used to distinguish diastereoisomers. Thus the *dl*-isomer of the sulphoxide (44) was identified by the observation of non-equivalent methine protons and methyl groups, as has previously been observed for the configurationally analogous *dl*-sulphite ester but not for the *meso* ester.[224] Similarly, for sulphites of optically active alcohols

$$R_1R_2HCO—S—OCHR_1R_2$$
$$\overset{\|}{O}$$

$$C_6H_5CH(CH_3)SOCH(CH_3)C_6H_5$$

44

45

having the general formula (45), three of the four possible isomers are distinguishable by NMR spectroscopy due to the pyramidal configuration of the sulphur atom which is *pseudo*-asymmetric in the case of the *meso* isomers.[225]

The asymmetry at a phosphorus centre, augmented by the effect of conformational preference, has again been noted. Thus, a reinvestigation of the spectrum of (46) revealed that the non-equivalence of the isopropyl methyl group could be

$$C_6H_5P(S)[NHCH(CH_3)_2]$$

46

attributed to the effective asymmetry of the phosphorus centre and to a barrier to the inversion of the pyramidal nitrogen.[226] The dependence on the dielectric constant of the solvent, as has been noted in compounds containing an asymmetric carbon atom, was also studied.[227] For methylene protons in (47) and (48), non-equivalence was observed in solvents of low, but not of high, dielectric constant. In phosphonium and arsonium salts the non-equivalence of the methylene protons is dependent on the size of the rest of the substituents.[228]

$$\overset{O}{\overset{\|}{CH_3P(SCH_2SR)OR'}}$$

47

$$O_2N—\langle\underset{=}{\bigcirc}\rangle—O—\overset{\overset{O}{\|}}{\underset{CH_3}{P}}—OCH_2CO—\langle\underset{=}{\bigcirc}\rangle—Y$$

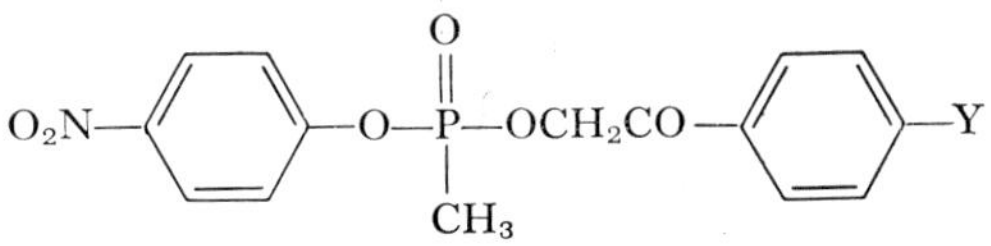

$$Y = H,Cl,CH_3,NO_2,OCH_3$$

48

A new molecular asymmetry defined as "quadratisomerism" is suggested for the positional isomers of (49) due to the triangular double pyramid configuration.[229]

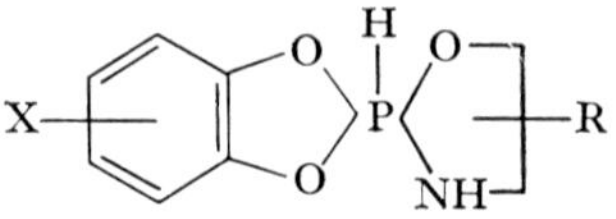

49

D. Molecular association phenomena

One of the best techniques for observing weak interactions is NMR spectroscopy. For instance, although a detailed study of the electronic spectra of chloronitrobenzenes in tetrahydrofuran had provided inconclusive evidence for specific complex formation, the solvent effects observed in the NMR spectra are considered to be evidence for weak hydrogen bonded $1:1$ donor-acceptor complexes existing in solutions of nitrobenzenes in tetrahydrofuran.[230] The association constants are about 0.01 M^{-1} at $23°$. The NMR study of organic charge-transfer complexes has recently been reviewed.[231] For the charge-transfer complexes of hexamethylbenzene and 1-substituted-3,5-dinitrobenzene the association constants, derived by the NMR method, gave a reasonable correlation with the Hammett σ_{meta} constant for the substituent and this was attributed to the electron accepting role of the nitrobenzenes.[232] The observed shifts are explained in terms of an offset (50) or inclined collision (51) complex. It is also

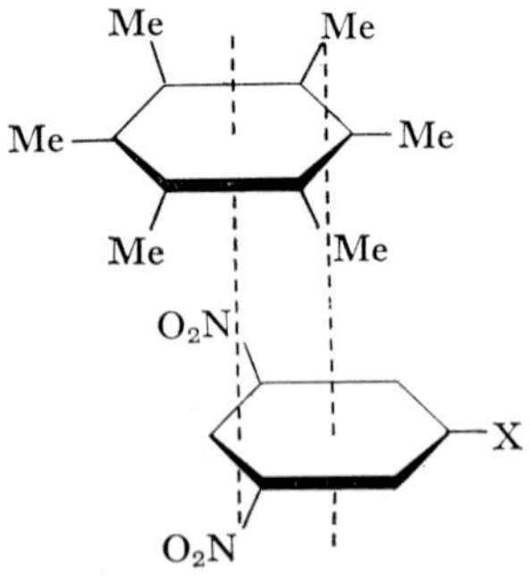

50 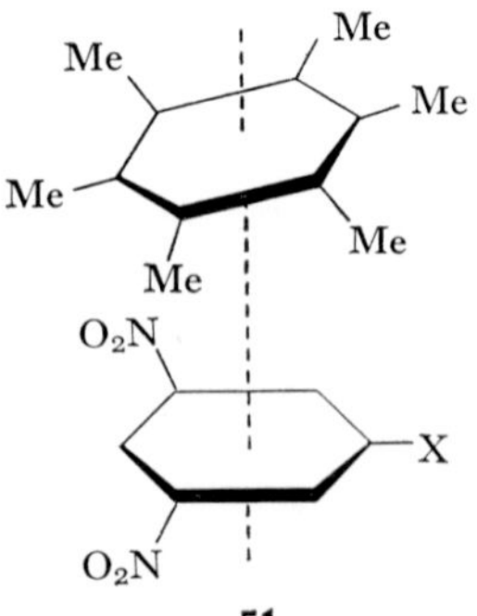   51

noted that, for a range of complexes derived from interaction of electron acceptors with various aromatic hydrocarbons, the association constant increases as the electron donating ability of the hydrocarbon increases and shows an alternating effect with chain length.[233] The formation of free radicals and charge transfer complexes plays an important role in determining the biological activity of diquat (52) and paraquat (53). NMR studies, along with other methods, have been used to show a strong tendency for the association of these cations with

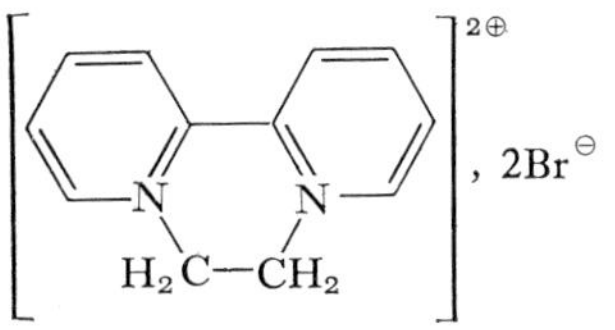

52

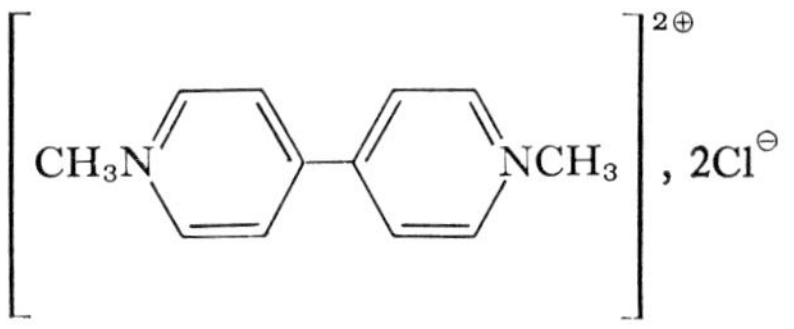

53

electron donating ions[234] and with organic donor molecules.[235] It has been demonstrated, however, that in a number of systems the association constant derived from chemical shift data is dependent on the particular nucleus measured.[236] It is thus possible that the results could be accounted for in terms of isomeric 1 : 1 complexes provided that the ratio of the two (or more) isomers was dependent on the concentration of the component present in excess or that the stoichiometry of the complex species is not restricted to 1 : 1.

The structure of complexes formed by the action of nucleophiles on aromatic systems containing electron accepting groups, now often referred to as Meisenheimer complexes (or salts or compounds), have been readily determined by NMR spectroscopy. Typical of recent investigations has been the conclusion that some nucleophiles attack 1-substituted-3,5-dinitrobenzene at both the 2- and 4- positions as demonstrated by the appearance of two sets of absorptions for the complex.[237] The upfield shift of 2·5 p.p.m. in the absorption of the ring proton of picric acid, dissolved in 1·2 M sodium sulphite solution, from that of the picrate ion is taken as an indication of covalency change at the ring position carrying the proton and, in collaboration with other evidence, as evidence of a most unusual ion (54) which carries five negative charges.[238] Picryl ethers form Meisenheimer complexes with alkoxide ions by attack at the alkoxy bearing carbon atom or at a CH position. Thus of interest were the observations that attack of methoxide ion

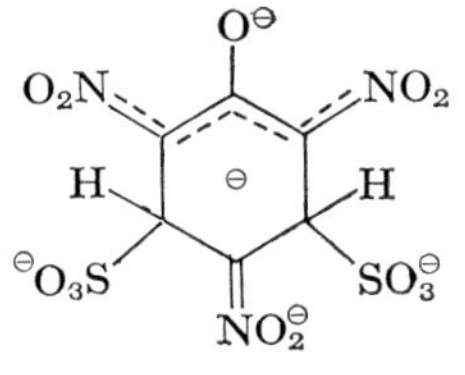

54

in dimethyl sulphoxide solution on 4-methoxy-3,5-dinitropyridine[239] gave rise to (55) [resonances at δ 2·92, 8·78] whilst attack on 2-methoxy-3,5-dinitro-pyridine[240] yielded (56) [resonances at δ 3·26, 3·77, 5·99, 8·59].

Hydrogen bonding is characterized by a large downfield shift of the proton involved and much qualitative and quantitative information has been derived from such studies. For instance, thermodynamic parameters have been derived[241] for the self association of methanol, or its association with trimethylamine in the vapour phase, by measurements of the chemical shift of the hydroxy proton and several discrete complexes of methanol-nitromethane have been postulated to account for the shifts observed in dilution studies of this mixture in carbon tetrachloride.[242] It is of interest to note that in this latter study and in 1-(β-hydroxyethoxy)-2,4-dinitrobenzene,[243] the presence of the nitro group appeared to suppress proton exchange. The chemical shift data have similarly been used to obtain the mole fraction of the solute in monomeric, dimeric or poly-meric forms in the systems ethanol-cyclohexane[244] and N-vinyl carbonate-dimethyl sulphoxide.[245] Proton exchange in hydroxylamines indicated that the hydroxyl group participated to a greater extent in hydrogen bonding than did the amino-group,[246] whilst the association constants and enthalpy data derived for a number of thiophenols suggested that the hydrogen bonding energy is much smaller than that in the corresponding phenols.[247] The dilution shift of the thiol proton in thiophenol was also studied in eighteen organic solvents and a comparison of the data with similar information derived for thiobutanol and a number of acetylenes was interpreted as giving a measure of the relative sensiti-vity of the solutes to interaction with the solvent.[248] It was shown, however, that if an acetylene contains an oxygen function then a significant increase in the dilution shift occurs[249] which suggests that the oxygen is an important proton acceptor site in these compounds. The NMR method may also be of use in studying amine-amide hydrogen bonding since the enthalpy values obtained for the dimerization of δ-valerolactam are in general agreement with those obtained by other methods.[250] For the 2-substituted acetanilides (57) the extent to which the 6-proton (H_6) shifts downfield upon N-acylation in excess of that observed in the absence of an *ortho* substituent is advanced as a measure of the hydrogen bonding ability of the *ortho* substituent.[251] The amino proton *trans* to the

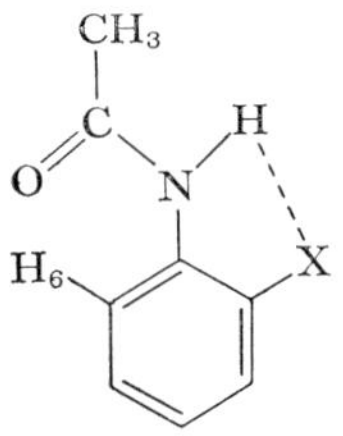

$$CH_3$$

57

carbonyl group forms a hydrogen bond to bromide ion stronger by 0·7 kcal/mole than does the *cis* amide proton and it has been suggested that this may account for the formation of hydrogen-bonded chains by *N*-monosubstituted amides preferentially with the amide hydrogen *trans* to the oxygen.[252] However, from a similar study on alkyl, aryl and arene substituted alcohols an electrostatic interaction of the bromide ion with the hydroxyl group was proposed.[253]

The elucidation of the structure of water and modifications to this structure, caused by dissolved substances, has continued to be extensively studied. Thus, the concentration dependence of the chemical shift of dioxan dissolved in water is suggested as supporting the theory that small amounts of dioxan (i.e. up to 0·1 mole fraction) increase the degree of hydrogen-bonding of the water molecules so that these become organized into cages which envelop the dioxan molecules.[254] Spin lattice relaxation time measurements confirmed that up to concentrations of about 20 mole % the dioxan has a structure promoting effect upon the water but that at higher concentrations of dioxan a dispersion of water molecule clusters in a matrix of dioxan occurred.[255] In some non-ionic surface active agent water systems (i.e. those containing *n*-alkoxypolyoxyethylene glycol monoethers), it is concluded that the extent of motion and hydrogen bonding of the water molecules is independent of the phase (mesomorphic phase or isotropic solution) and is only determined by the temperature and composition of the system.[256] However, it was shown for aqueous solutions of aromatic compounds that chemical shift data alone are insufficient for definite conclusions to be reached and that it was not necessary to postulate either structural changes in the water or hydrophobic bonding to explain the results.[13]

The "clathrate" model is also used to explain the shifts observed in the *t*-butyl alcohol-water system where the alcohol molecules are said to be isolated from each other and only come into contact when there is no longer sufficient water to provide clathrate cavities for all the alcohol molecules. Thus, the effect of added small amounts of solute depends on whether the compound is directly involved in hydrogen bonding with water protons or not.[257] In methanol, ion-solvent interactions can be explained in terms of the relative effects of hydrogen bonding to methanol and bonding to the ions, without any major contribution from structural changes remote from the ions.[258]

In many cases separate resonance signals are obtained for free and bound solvent molecules in electrolyte solutions and thus relative intensity measurements enable solvation numbers to be derived. For example, by this technique it was determined that the solvation number of magnesium in ethanol was six[259] and that the solvation number of the total molecules for hexamethylenephosphotriamide and water was the same for Be^{2+} and Al^{3+}.[260] The hydration number of Ga^{3+} in acetone-water mixture varies from 1·3 to 5·5 depending on the gallium trichloride-water-acetone ratios. This was taken to indicate contact ion-pairing[261] as had been advanced in the case of aluminium perchlorate in a variety of aqueous mixtures.[262] Use of aqueous N-methylacetamide solutions suggests that the relative degree of solvation of certain cations is $Al^{3+} > Th^{3+} > Mg^{2+} > Li^{+}$ and for anions $Cl^{-} > NO_3^{-} > ClO_4^{-}$.[263] The study of the exchange of methanol molecules between the first coordination sphere of the metal ion and the bulk solvent in the presence of Zn^{2+},[264] Ni^{2+},[265] Mn^{2+}, Cu^{2+}, Fe^{2+} and Fe^{3+}[266] has allowed activation parameters to be derived, whilst the determination of the composition of the solvation shell of $K_3[Cr(NCS)_6]$ reveals a strong preference of $Cr(NCS)_4^{3+}$ for acetonitrile in acetonitrile-water mixtures.[267]

A similar type of study has been made to determine the relative complexing ability of a number of ligands[268] by adding BF_3 to an excess of two organic bases and integration of the two signals observed for each base (i.e. complexed and bulk). Evidence was also presented for the formation of mixed boron trihalide adducts of dimethyl ether.[269]

E. Solvent effects

The study of specific association between solute and solvent continues to attract attention.

Thus, a study of the change in chemical shift of a number of non-polar molecules in going from the gas phase to infinite dilution in a series of solvents allowed the displacement, due to van der Waals forces, to be essentially related to the degree of exposure of the solute molecule and not to any simple property of the solvent molecule, such as molecular polarizability.[270] A good correlation between the solvent shift of methane in eleven hydrocarbon solvents and the MacRae term $(n^2-1)/(2n^2-1)$ has been used[271] as indirect support that the London-van der Waals interaction between molecules ought to be additive in terms of atom and bond contributions provided that the electrons remain localized; simple additive rules for halogenated methanes have also been demonstrated.[272] Some confirmation of the suggestion that in a 1:1 molecular complex the participant species are in a van der Waals contact was obtained from a study[273] of chloroethylenes in the system chloroethylene-benzene-cyclohexane.

Furthermore, the mechanism of complex formation of some small polar molecules with benzene was shown[274] to depend on the polarization of the benzene by the electric fields arising from the polar bonds in the compounds and to be independent of whether or not the solute had a resultant electric moment.

The simple collision complex model has also been used to analyse the concentration dependent shifts for hydrogen-bonding, charge-transfer and dipolar solutes in methylbenzenes and in a few non-aromatic solvents and it was suggested that the various modes of interaction could be distinguished.[275] However, equilibrium constants from 0·03 to 4·0 l/mol are reported although it would seem improbable that any reported value less than 0·1 is likely to be reliable since it may represent no more than the van der Waals collision frequency or a medium effect.

Most studies have been concerned with aromatic solvent effects. The theoretical predictions[276] that the anisotropic shifts for non-polar solutes in benzene, based on a geometrical model, would show a systematic decrease with increasing size of the solute molecule were found to be in agreement with experimental observations. The collision complex proposed for polar solutes in benzene in which the dipole axis of the solute is located along the six fold axis of the benzene nucleus is claimed to inadequately rationalize the shifts observed in 5α-androstanols and in phenols.[277] A new model (58) is proposed in which the six fold

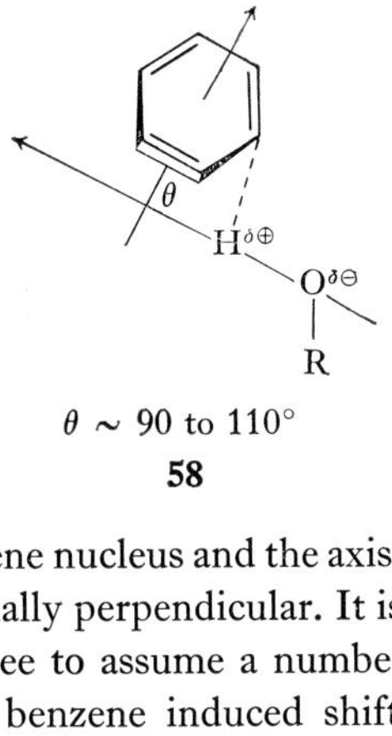

$\theta \sim$ 90 to 110°

58

axis of symmetry of the benzene nucleus and the axis of symmetry of the hydroxyl bond lie approximately mutually perpendicular. It is emphasized that in systems where the solute dipole is free to assume a number of preferred conformations then the magnitude of the benzene induced shift will be dependent on the population of the conformers. It has been pointed out,[278] however, that the shifts induced in hydroxy- and oxo- steroids originate from the superposition of polar and nonpolar effects. For monosubstituted methylbenzenes, the solvent shifts induced by benzene could be rationalized in a terms of a 1 : 1 complex where steric effects are important for protons remote from the substituent and both polar and steric effects are important for protons close to the substituent in forming the complex. In steroids,[279] the shifts have been more specifically defined in that whereas a planar collision complex is energetically favoured for regions of low electron density, "end on" collision complexes are proposed for regions of high electron density. A systematic study of the solvent induced shifts for terpenes[280] was used to either distinguish groups which gave overlapping bands in the spectrum or to determine the relative configuration of polar and remote non-polar groups. Solvent induced shifts were also shown to be configurationally dependent in acetylated monosaccharides[281] and sulphoxides,[282] whilst the conformational analysis of α-cyclopropyl ketones[283] was studied by solvent effects. For oxazoles[284] the 1:1 solute solvent complex with benzene was suggested to occur with the benzene nucleus located near the oxygen of the oxazole nucleus which was surprising since M.O. calculations indicated that the π-electron density of oxazole is greatest at the oxygen nucleus. An attempt to rationalize these observations in terms of canonical forms of oxazole bearing a formal positive charge on the oxygen was made. In the case of 1,3-dimethyluracil and 1,3-dimethylthymine the aromatic solvents were considered to associate with the pyrimidine rings in a vertical stacking arrangement.[285] The aromatic molecules act as electron donors and avoid the negative dipole at C–3 of the pyrimidine ring. The shielding effect produced by changing solvent from $CDCl_3$ to C_6D_6 for the helicenes was also interpreted[167] in terms of a weak complex bringing (a) benzene molecule(s) in a position simulating the building up of the helix. A more detailed study of the solvent induced chemical shift for the sterically hindered lower benzologues phenanthrene (**59**), benzo[c]phenanthrene (**60**) and dibenzo[c,g]phenanthrene (**61**) showed[285] that, relative to the shifts in

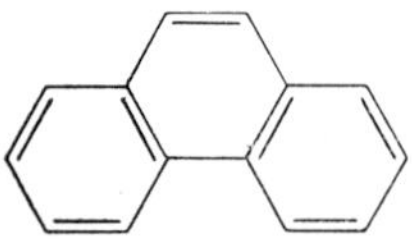

59 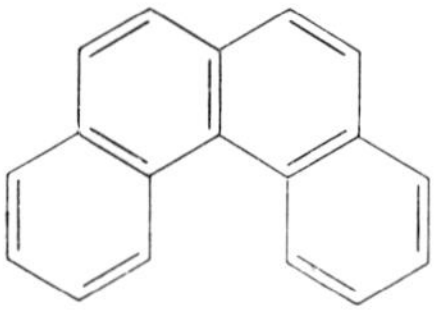   60 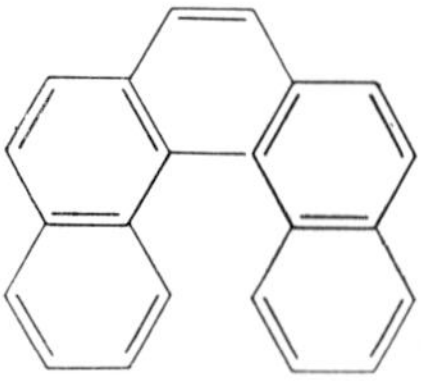   61

cyclohexane, shifts for other solvents are very similar for non-sterically hindered protons. The shifts for the "bay" protons, however, are progressively decreased relative to those of the perimeter protons by increase of the steric hindrance at the latter sites.

Amongst the many other studies of solvent effects made, but not reviewed here, are those on natural products such as flavanoids,[287] colchicine alkaloids[288] and erythromycin aglycones.[289]

IV. CONFORMATIONAL ANALYSIS

Conformational analysis now ranks amongst the most important branches of organic stereochemistry and the derivation of information about the conformation and configuration of molecules from coupling constant and chemical shift data is well documented. Further the use of the nuclear Overhauser effect to derive conformational information is growing rapidly and has been briefly reviewed,[290] whilst the reader is referred to the next chapter for a fuller review of conformational mobility.

A. Alicyclic and heterocyclic compounds

A high energy barrier to inversion at the nitrogen atom is observed in three membered nitrogen heterocycles and this leads to the possibility of an effective asymmetric centre and hence to diastereoisomerism. Thus, it is of interest to note the two recent observations of such an effect, i.e. in N-halo-2-alkylaziridines[291] and in substituted oxaziridines,[292] where the stereochemistry was tentatively assigned from the known anisotropic effect of a *para*-nitrophenyl substituent, from the influence of the lone-pair electrons of the nitrogen atom and from solvent effects. In the case of 1,2,2-trimethylaziridine[293] the rate of inversion of the nitrogen atom could be measured whilst for compounds of type (62) the invertomer ratio (i.e. 62⇌63) could be obtained at room temperature.[294]

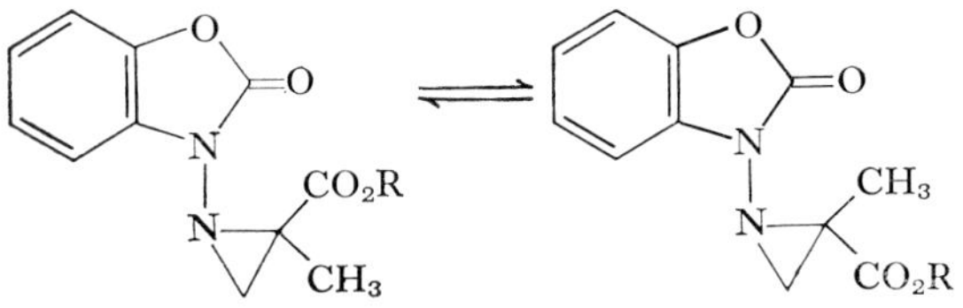

62   63

$R = CH_3, C_2H_5, CH(CH_3)_2, C(CH_3)_3$

In the case of compounds of type (62) an unexpected attraction between the heterocycle and the ester grouping, which increases with the size of R, was postulated to account for the preference of form (62) as R increases.

A detailed analysis of *endo*-bicyclo[2.1.0]pentan-2-ol (64), cyclobutanol and

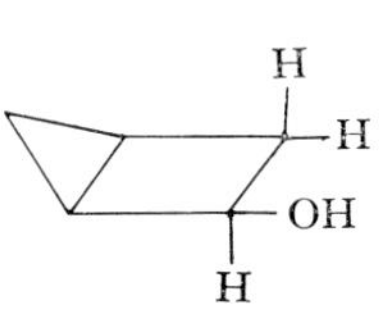

64

cis-1,3-dibromocyclobutane[295] allowed the vicinal coupling constants for planar and puckered cyclobutane rings to be determined. Hence, the planar ring gave values of $J_{cis} = 9$, $J_{trans} = 3\cdot5$ Hz, whilst for the puckered ring $J_{ae} = 9\cdot7$ and $7\cdot9$, $J_{aa} = 10\cdot4$ and $J_{ee} = 2\cdot3$ Hz and these values are said to be in agreement with those expected on the basis of dihedral angles. The magnetic anisotropy of the puckered cyclobutane ring was suggested to account for the observation that the equatorial methyl groups resonated at higher field than did the axial. This observation was used to elucidate the conformation of some *cis* and *trans* pinonic, pinononic and pinic acids.[296] In a series of 1-alkyl-2-phenyl-3-aroylazetidines[297] the observed trends in the chemical shifts were rationalized in terms of a large contribution from intra-molecular van der Waals dispersion forces in such a way as to suggest that the conformation of the azetidine ring was a function of the steric requirement of the *N*-alkyl group and that the greatest puckering occurred when the alkyl group was small.

It has recently been shown that the chemical shifts of the axial and equatorial methine protons in substituted cyclohexanes are effected by the 4-*t*-butyl group which is often used as a conformational retaining group.[298] Similar effects were observed in quaternary salts of 4-alkylpiperidines.[299] By using the McConnell equation, as modified by J. W. ApSimon, the shielding parameters of the C-1 protons of the two chair conformations of cyclohexane carbonitrile, *cis* and *trans* 4-*t*-butylcyclohexane carbonitrile, and the two chair conformations of 4,4-dimethylcyclohexane carbonitrile were calculated[300] as a function of ring angles from 103·5 to 119·5°. The chemical shifts of the methine protons were shown to be sensitive to ring flattening; the equatorial proton became shielded whilst the axial proton became deshielded. Thus it was suggested that the effect of the remote alkyl substituent on the chemical shift of the methine proton probably arises from changes in polarizability of the ring due to deformation and from the inductive effect of the C-1 substituent rather than from the accompanying changes in anisotropic shielding. Therefore calculations of conformational free energy based on the chemical shifts of the unsubstituted cyclohexyl derivative compared with that of the *t*-butyl compound may be in serious error. This is amply illustrated by the determination of the conformational free energy of the hydroxyl group where the values obtained by the NMR method in certain solvents were neither in agreement with the thermodynamic value nor were consistent.[301] Furthermore, the presence of a *t*-butyl substituent cannot be relied upon to render a cyclohexane derivative conformationally homogeneous as was demonstrated in *trans*-3-*t*-butyl-4-hydroxycyclohexanone[302] since consideration of the vicinal coupling constants indicated that nonchair conformations probably predominated.

Conformers of monosubstituted cyclohexanes which have barriers to equilibration less than 11 kcal/mole can be separated and examined in solution as was demonstrated for chlorocyclohexane and trideuteromethoxycyclohexane.[30]

Thus measurements of rate constants for chair-chair interconversions may be made at temperatures very different from those necessary for employing conventional NMR site exchange techniques and therefore it is neither necessary to make the complicated assumptions required for rapidly equilibrating systems nor to introduce large "locking" groups. The conformational preference of twenty-two cyclohexane derivatives has been obtained[304] by peak area measurements at $-80°$ in CS_2 with "A values" claimed to be accurate to ± 20 cal/mole. The possibility of the additivity of conformational energies in polysubstituted cyclohexanes has also been further studied and transannular electrostatic interaction[305] is proposed for the non-additivity of $\Delta G°$ values in cyclohexanes with polar 1,4-disubstituents. However, the rate of inversion of cyclohexane derivatives with one, two or three pairs of geminal alkyl or alkoxy groups appeared to depend on the number and relative positions of the ligand pairs as well as on their size.[306]

The conformational preferences (E_4 values) for 4-fluoro, 4-chloro, 4-bromo and 4-iodo cyclohexenes were determined[307] by low temperature NMR spectro-

TABLE III

The chemical shift (Hz) between axial and equatorial methine protons and fluoride in monosubstituted cyclohexanes and 4-substituted cyclohexenes[307]

Compound		$\nu_{eq} - \nu_{ax}$ Hz[a]
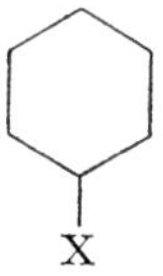	X = H	28
	X = F	1230[b]
	X = Cl	42
	X = Br	43
X	X = I	45
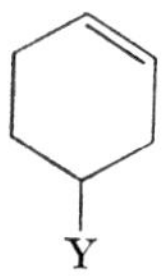	Y = H	19
	Y = F	728[b]
	Y = Cl	27
	Y = Br	27
Y	Y = I	27

[a] For protons, operating frequency = 60 MHz.
[b] ^{19}F NMR spectra (56·4 MHz).

scopy and showed the same trend as A values except for the iodo-compound. This showed a preference for the conformation in which the substituent was axially orientated which was attributed to London attractive forces. In comparison with monosubstituted cyclohexanes, one of the most striking differences was the substantially reduced chemical shift difference between the axial and equatorial C-4 protons and fluorines in cyclohexenyl compounds as shown in Table

III. Changes in bond orientations in cyclohexene, as well as the anisotropic effect of the double bond, are considered to be responsible. Homoconjugation of the double bond with an electronegative substituent, however, is a possibility but in a study of a number of 4-mono and *trans*-4,5-disubstituted cyclohexenes it was shown that such an effect did not alter the conformational equilibrium in any other way.[308]

Conformational preferences in heterocyclic systems have again attracted considerable attention. On the assumption that the vicinal H–P–C–H coupling has the same geometric dependence as the H–C–X–H couplings, where X= C,O,N and for which a reasonable qualitative theoretical treatment has been proposed,[85] it has been shown[309] that phosphacyclohexane exists almost entirely in the conformation with the phosphorus proton axial, i.e. (65). An attractive

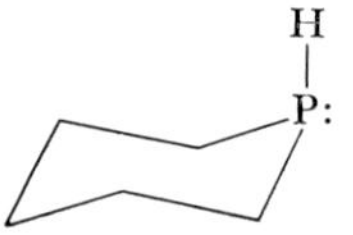

65

axial-axial interaction between protons, as has been discussed for the conformational preference of the proton on the nitrogen atom in piperidine is suggested as an explanation for this observation. In compounds having a $CH_2 \cdot CH_2$ or a $CH_2 \cdot CHR$ moiety it is shown that the ratio of the vicinal coupling constants, i.e. $R = J_{trans}/J_{cis}$ can be used to calculate the ring dihedral angle.[310] The rate of inversion at a nitrogen atom can be reduced by complex formation with sulphur dioxide as was demonstrated for morpholine,[311] where it was also noted from the observed coupling constants that the complex occurred in about 75% of one conformer which was presumed to be with the SO_2 equatorially orientated. Complex formation offers an attractive alternative to protonation for measuring the rates of nitrogen inversion. Such studies can be complicated if two nitrogens are present in an heterocycle, as is shown in the case of the conformational isomerism of N,N'-di-*t*-butylpiperazonium dichloride[312] in acidic solution where the results are interpreted in terms of a double consecutive nitrogen inversion with deuteron transfer. In some tetra- and hexa- hydropyridazines both ring inversion and nitrogen inversion were reported[313] to be slow. A detailed analysis of the spectra, as a function of temperature, indicated that (66)

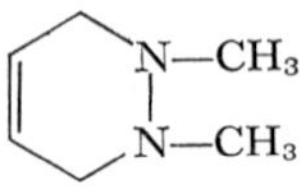

66 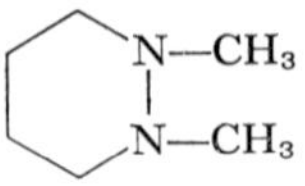   **67**

had a preferred conformation with one methyl group axially orientated and one methyl group equatorially orientated whilst (67) appeared to prefer a conformation with both methyl groups equatorial. The change in the conformation of the N-methyl groups was related to the 1,3-diaxial nonbonded interactions. The deformation of the chair conformation by 1,3 interactions of the substituents was also suggested to account for the fact that the rate constant for ring inversion in some substituted 1,3-dioxans, 1,3-dithians and 1,3-oxathians[314] appeared to depend on the number and position of the substituents. However, the geometry of the ring, the steric requirement of the sulphur atom and the torsional barrier of the C–S bond were all evoked to explain the differences in conformational preferences of alkyl substituents at various positions of the dithian[315] system, whilst a combination of *syn*-axial and *gem*-dialkyl effects is proposed to account for the variation in the chair to twist conformation ratio in a number of multi-sulphur heterocycles.[316] In 1,1,4,4-tetramethyl-1,4-disilacyclohexane (68) the

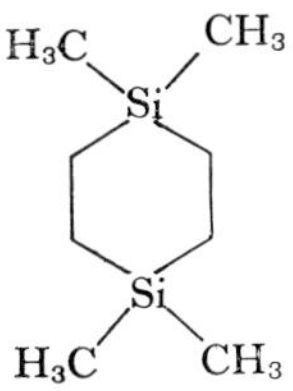

68

lower barrier to inversion, than in the analogous cyclohexane or other six membered rings containing two heteroatoms, is attributed[317] mostly to the greater length of the carbon–silicon bonds. In the conformational equilibration of the dihydrothiazines[318] the conformers (69) and (70) were equally populated when

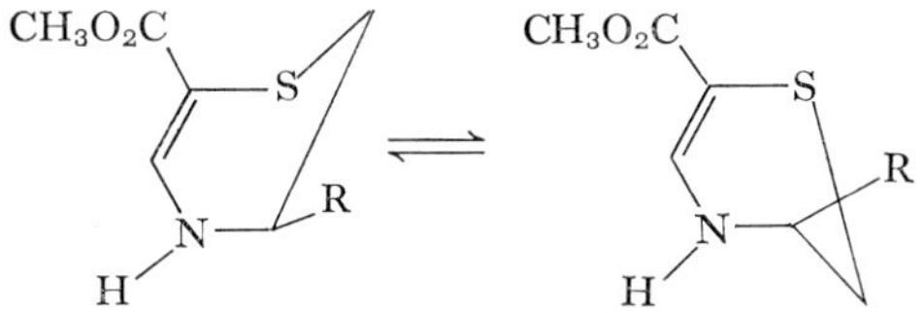

69   70

R = Me irrespective of the solvent, but an axial preference associated with a polar group (i.e. R = CH_2Cl, CH_2OSO_2Me) could be tentatively explained as a dipolar attraction between the sulphur and the electrophilic carbon of the 3-substituent.

Increasing the bond angle strain in the transition state will make a substantial contribution to the barrier of inversion for the six membered ring. This is demonstrated[319] in the case of the spiro system (71) where, for small rings (i.e. n = 4 or 5), a higher barrier to the inversion of the dioxan ring is observed.

In dihydropyran the significant higher barrier to conformational isomerism as compared to cyclohexene is interpreted in terms of increased stabilization of the half chair form by electronic delocalization involving oxygen and the two sp^2 hybridized carbon atoms.[320] The "anomalously" high field shift of the C-5 vinyl proton (δ 4·65) is claimed to support the suggestion that a canonical structure such as (72) contributes to the resonance hybrid of the molecule. In 2-substituted

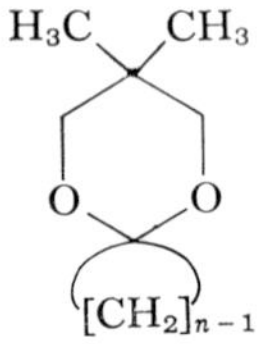

71

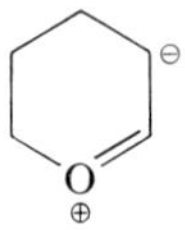

72

cycloheptanols[321] the *cis* and *trans* isomers were distinguished by the different chemical shifts of the C-1 methine proton. However, the different spectra were not due to a preferred conformation of the seven membered ring, as would have been the case for a six membered ring system, but were only due to differences in configuration of the substituent groups. The room temperature spectrum of cycloheptatriene has previously been shown to be consistent with the equilibration of nonplanar conformers (73a) and (73b). A comparison of the observed long-range coupling with calculated values has now suggested[86] that the unsaturated portion of the molecule is very nearly planar in the liquid phase. Slow inversion at room temperature occurs in 7-substituted cycloheptatriene and the determination of a negative sign for the coupling constant between the 2 and 7 protons in the 7-phenyl and 7-*t*-butyl derivatives was used to confirm that these compounds exist with the substituent in the quasi-equatorial position[322] i.e. conformers (74b) and (75b). However, for 1-methyl-7-*t*-butylcycloheptatriene

(a)   (b)

73, R = H
74, R = C(CH$_3$)$_3$
75, R = C$_6$H$_5$

the striking conclusion that the conformer with the *t*-butyl group in the quasi-axial position is more stable is derived[323] from the spectrum recorded at room temperature. Further, at $-104°$ the spectrum is claimed to show three distinct resonances for the *t*-butyl group for the less stable conformer and these resonances are ascribed to the three magnetically nonequivalent methyl groups as depicted in (76). In the seven membered sulphur compounds (77) and (78) it was shown that, in comparison with cycloheptane, the very low energy barrier for pseudo-rotation is not significantly increased even though in (77) a substantial ring inversion barrier occurs.[324]

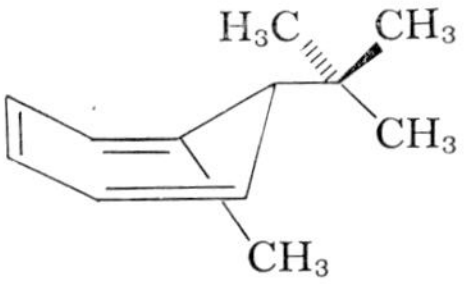

76 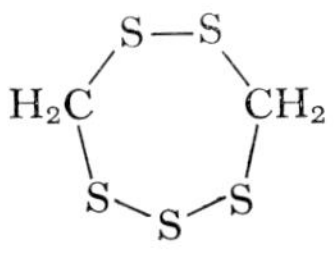   77 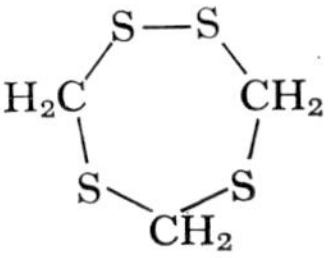   78

The energy profile for ring interconversions in compounds containing more than one ring fused together can be complicated. Thus it is of interest to observe that two characteristic reaction paths were suggested[325] for saturated and unsaturated compounds from an NMR kinetic study of the ring inversion of the three hexalines (79a, b, c) and the two propellane derivatives (80) and (81). It

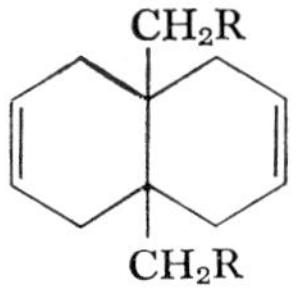

(a) R = CN
(b) R = Br
(c) R = CO$_2$CH$_3$
79

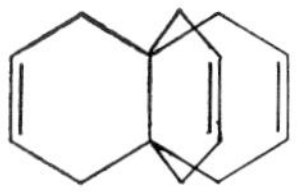

80 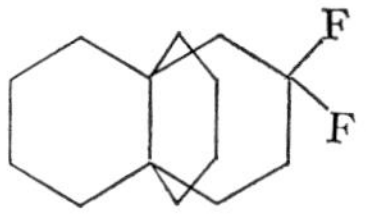   81

is suggested that in saturated compounds the reaction profile had discrete steps involving one ring at a time whilst in unsaturated compounds the reaction profile seemed to contain only one maximum. In the *cis* 1,4-dioxano-1,4-dioxane derivative (82) a lower barrier to inversion, than in the analogous decalin, is

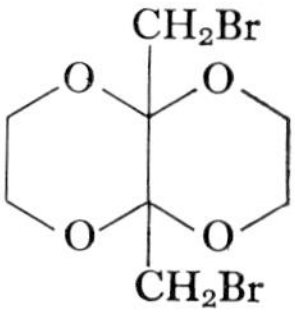

82

attributed[326] to a lower C–O torsional barrier. For decahydroquinazolines four conformations for the *trans* isomer are possible owing to nitrogen inversion whilst for the *cis* isomer eight isomers are possible as a result of both nitrogen and ring inversion processes. It is claimed[327] that the conformers (83) and (84) pre-dominate, i.e. with the lone pair on the nitrogen in the axial orientation, but the evidence partly depends on the fact that the two NH groups give a sharp singlet in $CDCl_3$ solution and thus the conclusion that this supports proton nitrogen lone-pair repulsions being smaller than proton-proton repulsions should be viewed with caution.

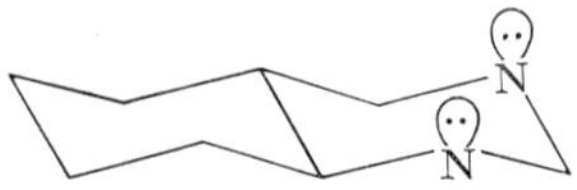

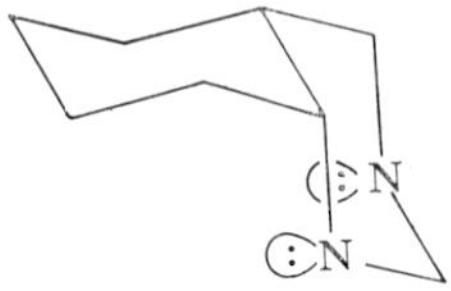

To conclude this section, on conformational effects in alicyclic and hetero-cyclic systems, a short discussion of steric factors involved in conformational aspects of the large ring systems, the cyclophanes, is included. A large study of the phanes, for which nomenclature rules have been proposed,[328] has been made recently and over twenty-five papers containing significant NMR information have appeared during 1969. One interesting facet of this study is that an analysis of the conformational mobility of a related series of metacyclophanes gives some information as to the steric requirements of groups. Typical of such studies is that for a range of the substituted metacyclophanes (85) where measurements of

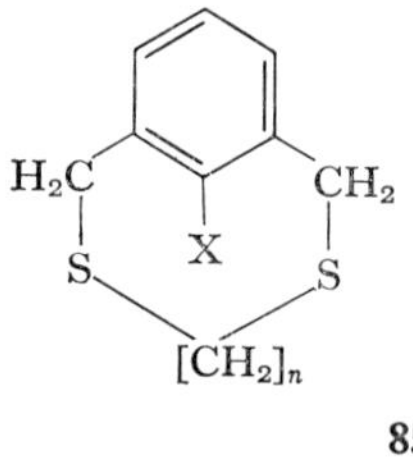

the energy barrier for the inversion process, in which the substituent X passes through the space of the multi-membered ring, were used to deduce[329] that the steric requirements of the groups decrease in the order $Br > Me > Cl$. Studies of the cyclophane (86) when compared with results for the cyclophanes (87) and (88) allowed the direct comparison of large non-bonded interactions between two nitrogen atoms and a nitrogen atom and a C–H group, in comparable geometrical situations,[330] and showed that the relative interactions were CH, $CH > CH, N > N, N$. Independent studies on the related compounds (89) showed similar trends.[331] It was stressed,[330] however, that this order applied to relatively short-range interactions and was not inconsistent with the evidence for quite large interactions between non-bonded electron pairs which probably result

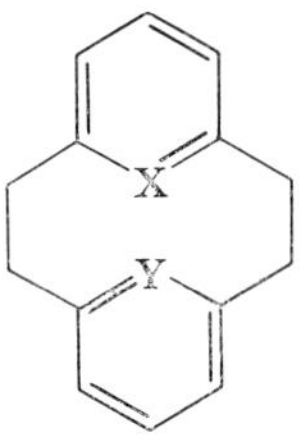

86, X = Y = N
87, X = Y = CH
88, X = N; Y = CH

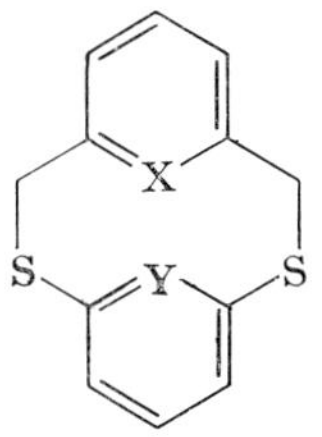

X = Y = CH
X = CH; Y = N
X = N; Y = CH
X = Y = N

89

from dipole-dipole repulsions.[332] In paracyclophanes with a benzylic ring substituent (**90**) a steric hindrance to the process (**91**⇌**92**) gives rise to non-equivalence of the methylene protons. Thus a study of the energy barrier allowed the steric requirement of the group X to be deduced[333] as being OH > Br > CO$_2$Et.

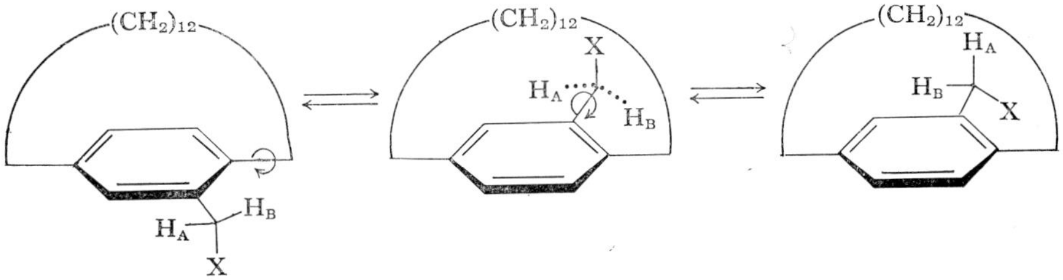

90   **91**   **92**

The chemical shift of the ring protons of the more rigid cyclophanes may also be used to derive information about the conformation of the compound. Thus [2,2](1,4)-naphthaleno(2,5)furanophane was shown[334] to exist predominantly in the *anti*-form (**93**) from a study of the shielding effects expected on the β-furanoid protons whilst in the case of [2]1,4-benzo[2](1,4)-triptycenophane a "skew" structure (**94**) rather than the undistorted structure (**95**) was postulated[335]

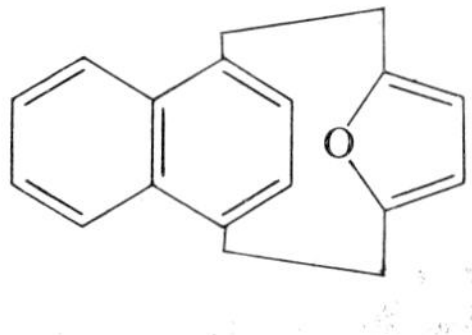

93 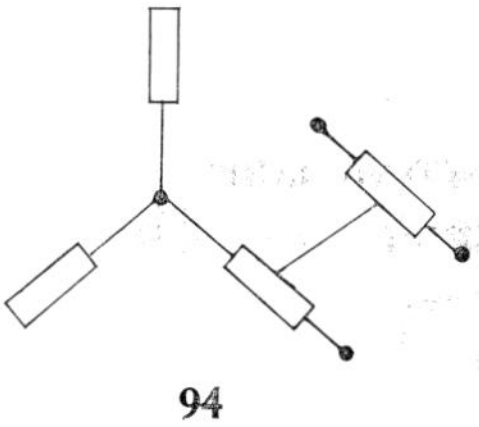   **94** 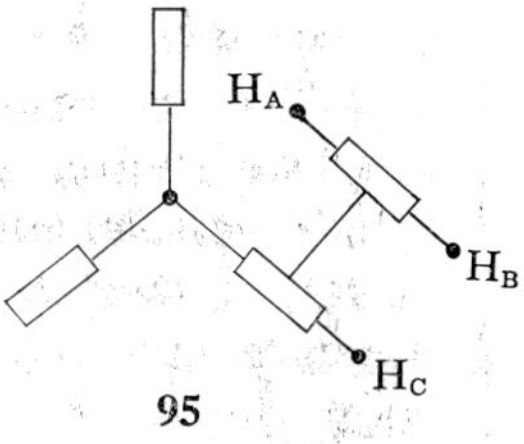   **95**

from the agreement between the observed chemical shifts for the H_A, H_B and H_C protons with those predicted for such a structure from the Johnson-Bovey equations. Other distorted structures, however, could not be excluded.

B. Acyclic compounds

Conformational preferences in acyclic compounds will depend on some energy difference between the possible rotameric conformations of the compound under study. The NMR parameter most valuable in ascertaining information with regard to the conformational preferences of the alkanes is the vicinal coupling constant and some of the factors affecting this parameter have already been discussed under the section dealing with coupling constants. A comprehensive study of heavily chlorinated propanes showed that very few rotational isomers are found compared to the number of theoretically possible conformations with all vicinal interactions staggered. This observation was rationalized[336] by assuming that strong interactions occur between chlorine atoms in conformers where carbon atoms 1 and 3 have parallel C–Cl bonds on the same side of the carbon skeleton. It was further proposed that quite long-range interactions along a polymer chain could be reliably allowed for by taking into account parallel (1 : 3) interactions between like groups and the normal *cis* (1,2) repulsive interactions. The 1,3-eclipsed, rather than 1,2-gauche, interactions have similarly been considered important in the determination of relative conformer populations adopted by acyclic sugar derivatives[337] where the observed conformer distribution was close to that calculated on the basis of these non-bonded interactions. However, conformations involving gauche *t*-butyl groups have been proposed to account for the unexpected values of the vicinal coupling constants in some substituted ethanes[338] and support for these conformations is derived from dipole moment studies. The

$$C_6H_5CH_2CH_2CH_2X$$
96, X = OH
97, X = H

conformational energy difference in (**96**) is quite similar to that observed in the parent hydrocarbon (**97**) from which it is concluded[339] that the hydroxy group plays no important part in influencing the energetics of conformational equilibrium as it might be expected to do if intramolecular hydrogen bonding to the aromatic ring were present.

The stereochemical requirements for the occurrence of four bond coupling in the saturated fragment H–C–C–O–H, which were briefly reported on in 1968, have been fully studied in saturated systems.[340] A coplanarity of the protons and connecting atoms is required, the long-range coupling rapidly diminishing at even slight deviations from coplanarity. Since the magnitude of the ^3J(H–C–O–H) coupling also has a stereochemical dependence new possibilities for the conformational analysis of the hydroxyl proton are apparent. The variation in the magnitude of ^3J(H–C–O–H) in different alcohols in hydrogen-bonding media is also attributed to conformational changes.[341] It is considered that for sterically unhindered primary alcohols the three carbon-oxygen bond rotamers are equally populated whilst for unhindered secondary alcohols it was suggested that the rotamer with the hydroxyl group staggered between the two C–C bonds (98a)

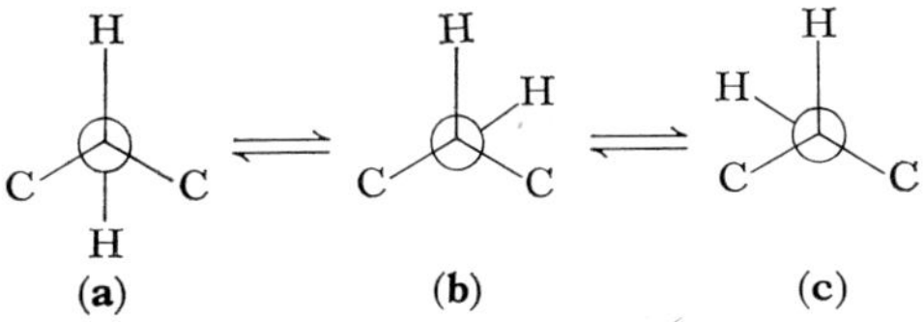

(a)   (b)   (c)

98

is significantly less populated than the other two rotamer conformations (98b, c). A consistent increase of ^3J(H–C–O–H) for both primary and secondary alcohols on substitution of an alkyl group at the β carbon atom was attributed to a slight but significant decrease in the equilibrium H–C–O–H dihedral angle of some of the C–O bond rotamers in which the OH is staggered between a C–H and a C–C bond. Preferred conformations about the bond joining the ring carbon to hydroxyl bearing carbon in some alkyl substituted α-cyclopropyl alcohols[342] and (α-epoxy alkyl)-carbinols[343] were similarly deduced on the basis of steric interactions. Solvent effects, however, can considerably affect the conclusions about the conformation of the CH_2OH group as was demonstrated[344] for 3-β-acetoxy-5β,6β-oxidocholestan-19-ol (99).

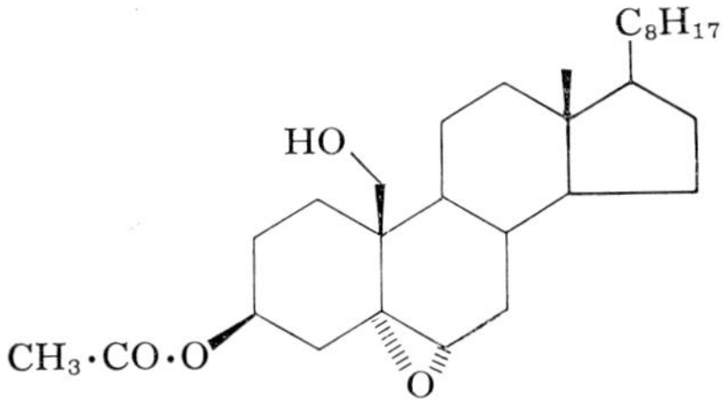

99

The effects of solvent and temperature on the vicinal coupling constant in some substituted aldehydes were used to deduce that the most stable rotamer was the one in which the substituent eclipsed the carbonyl group i.e. (100a) when

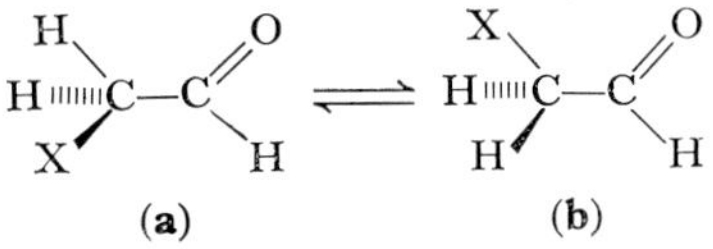

(a)   (b)

100

the substituent X was Cl, Br, OPh or OMe[345] but that when the substituent was SMe, cyclopropyl or epoxide[346] then (100b) is the more stable rotamer. In the case of dichloro- and dibromo- acetaldehyde[347] the conformation preference was more dependent on the nature of the solvent (i.e. aromatic or non-aromatic) and on the dielectric constant of the solvent. Further the dependence upon the solution dielectric constant of the sum and difference of the two vicinal coupling constants of the rotamers of (1,2-dibromoethyl)benzene enabled the relative stabilities of the rotamers to be deduced and showed that dipolar interactions are as important as steric interactions.[348]

The successful determination of the stereochemistry of diastereomers of compounds with two adjacent asymmetric centres, permitting existence of *erythro* and *threo* forms, has continued with a number of related studies on substituted diphenylethanes[349 to 351] where the solvent and temperature dependence of the vicinal coupling constant was used to study the conformational equilibria. A study of β-hydroxy-*dl*-aspartic acids,[352] however, indicated that whilst the *threo* compound preferred a conformer having *anti* carboxyl groups, as has been found to be the case for other dicarboxylic acids, the *erythro* compound preferred a conformation with *gauche* carboxyl functions and no satisfactory explanations were advanced for this anomaly. In systems of type (101) and (102), where G is a chiral group and R=H or Me, the differences in chemical

$$
\begin{array}{ccc}
\text{R} & \text{R} & \text{R} \\
| & | & | \\
G_R\!-\!\overset{|}{\underset{|}{C}}\!-\!G_R \;\; \text{or} \;\; G_S\!-\!\overset{|}{\underset{|}{C}}\!-\!G_S & & G_R\!-\!\overset{|}{\underset{|}{C}}\!-\!G_S \\
\text{R} & \text{R} & \text{R} \\
\end{array}
$$

Threo　　　　　　　　　　　　　*Meso*

101　　　　　　　　　　　　　　102

shift and spin coupling could be rationalized in terms of the configurations of the isomers.[353]

The introduction of a double bond into an acyclic compound gives rise to geometric isomers due to the high activation energy required for isomerization about the ethylenic bond. The configuration of a disubstituted ethylene can often be derived from a consideration of the vicinal coupling constant. However, the configuration of di- and tri- substituted ethylenes was derived[163] by the additivity of vinyl substituent shielding effects on the vinyl protons present. The resonance position of the vinyl proton in (103) was given by equation (4), where -5.27 ppm represented the resonance position of $CH_2\!=\!CH_2$ and

$$
\begin{array}{cc}
X_{cis} & H \\
\diagdown & \diagup \\
C\!=\!C & \\
\diagup & \diagdown \\
Y_{trans} & Z_{gem} \\
\end{array}
$$

103

$\sigma(cis$-X$)$, $\sigma(trans$-Y$)$ and $\sigma(gem$-Z$)$ were the shielding constants of X, Y and Z from the *cis, trans* and *gem* substituent locations. In the styrene derivatives (104) a

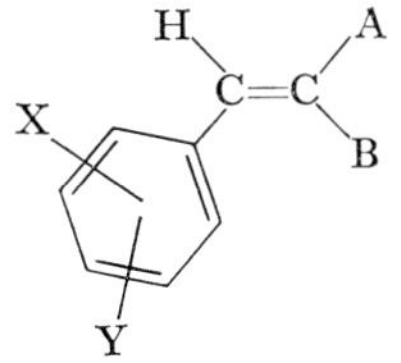

A,B = COCH$_3$,CO$_2$C$_2$H$_5$ or CN

104

$$\delta = -5\cdot27 + \sigma(cis\text{-}X) + \sigma(trans\text{-}Y) + \sigma(gem\text{-}Z) \qquad (4)$$

detailed examination of the chemical shifts of the vinyl proton and protons of the functional groups A and B with change of ring substituents X and Y provided some information on the preferred conformations[354] of the groups A and B.

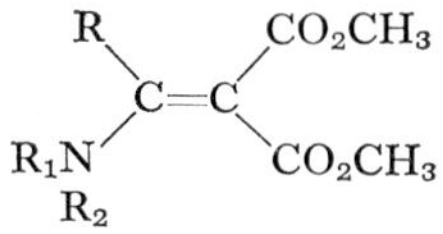

(a) R = H,CH$_3$; R$_1$,R$_2$ = CH$_3$,C$_6$H$_5$
(b) R = SCH$_3$; R$_1$,R$_2$ = CH$_3$,C$_6$H$_5$

105

However, in suitably substituted olefines rotation about the double bond can be detected and activation parameters deduced as has been demonstrated previously for conjugated enamines and conjugated enol ethers. Two rotational processes were found in conjugated enamines of type (105a) which were assigned[355] to a lower energy process for rotation about the carbon-carbon double bond and a higher energy process for rotation about the nitrogen to sp^2 carbon bond, whilst a substantially lower energy barrier was observed[356] in the related ketone-mercaptoaminals (105b). In (106) up to four rotational barriers, in which

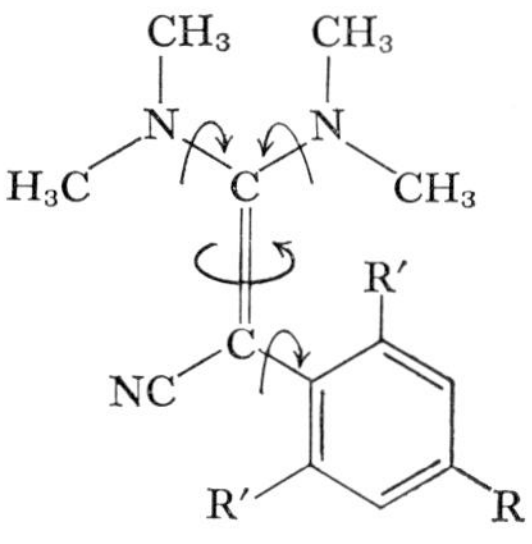

106

the values could be correlated with the Hammett σ_p constant, were detected.[357] The isomerization of configuration about a C–N double bond by inversion or rotation has been discussed for several compounds e.g. guanidinium[358] and thiuronium salts,[359] whilst the boron compounds, which are isoelectronic with ethylenes, amidinium and guanidinium salts, have also been considered.[360] The isomerization often parallels the conjugative ability of the group bonded to the imino nitrogen i.e. $N > S > O > C$ rather than their relative electronegativities i.e. $O > N > S > C$, but both rotational and lateral shift mechanisms were shown to be consistent with the data for imine isomerization.[361]

Alternatively, steric factors may contribute to high energy barriers for rotation about single bonds leading to rotational rates being in the NMR time scale and thus allowing the derivation of thermodynamic parameters as has been found for triarylmethanes[362] and radicals,[363] diarylethanes,[364] 9-arylfluorenes[365] and in aryl substituted cations[366] and anions.[367] An interesting paper[368] considers the steric conditions necessary for the observation of hindrance to rotation about the C_α–C_β or Z–C_β single bonds in compounds of the type (107), (108) and (109).

Z = P,As,Sb,Bi

107   108   109

Although the free activation enthalpies for rotation about the sigma bond were related to different temperatures and solvents the study showed that for compounds of type (107) detection of hindered rotation about the C_α–C_β bond requires that both positions *ortho* to the C_β atom must be occupied by substituents such as Me or OMe. In compounds of type (108) the steric hindrance decreases with increasing bulk of Z whilst, for compounds of type (109), a smaller steric hindrance is required than in compounds of type (107).

Rotational barriers about formal C–N bonds are well documented e.g. in amides, nitroso groups, aromatic and heterocyclic alkylamino groups and in recent studies the factors involved in isomerization about N–N bonds (e.g. in hydrazines where hindered nitrogen inversion is not a prime factor[369]) and in other heterobonds (e.g. in sulphonamides[370] and sulphenamides,[371] where electron repulsion and steric hindrance are dominant factors) have been reported.

The studies on these systems are too numerous to be completely reviewed in this section and the reader is referred to a later chapter for a comprehensive review of the subject of torsional barriers.

V. BIOLOGICAL STUDIES

The recent advent of high field superconducting magnet spectrometers has greatly increased the number of studies of biological systems which have employed NMR spectroscopy and thus it seems appropriate that a short survey of this work should be included in this general review.

A. Structure and conformation of polypeptides and proteins

The use of NMR spectroscopy to study the tertiary structure of polypeptides and proteins is well documented and relies on changes in the chemical shifts of the constituent amino acids or on the dependence of the NH–CH vicinal proton coupling constant upon the dihedral angle between the HNC and NCH planes. Conformational preferences in dipeptides of alanine[372] or of alanine and phenylalanine[373] have been deduced from the vicinal coupling and the suggestion made that in polar media there is an increase in the amount of conformation which probably corresponds to a right-handed helix whilst increase in line width of the oligomers of the tripeptide Leu-Phe-Ala in dimethyl sulphoxide solution is interpreted as showing the possibility of some rigid tertiary structure.[374] However, a study at 220 MHz in combination with C.D. measurements on γ-ethyl-L-glutamate oligopeptides indicated that helix formation would only occur at the heptamer in trimethyl phosphate or in trifluoroethanol solution and not at all in dimethyl sulphoxide solution.[375]

The occurrence of several antibiotic cyclic peptides has promoted an interest in the conformation of cyclic peptides. In cyclic dipeptides the piperazinedione ring departed from planarity in dimethyl sulphoxide solution.[376] In cyclic hexapeptides two of the amide protons are shielded from the solvent and four are exposed to it[378,379] and this evidence was claimed to strongly support the β-model proposed for gramicidin-S. Further, by studying cyclic hexapeptides containing four or five glycyl residues, attempts[379,380] were made to define which amino acid residues were at the "corner" positions and which were at the centre of the extended segment. Gramicidin-S appeared to be conformationally stable in a variety of solvents but valinomycin exhibited a dish like structure with surfactant properties in dimethyl sulphoxide whereas in methanol, with added potassium bromide, it had a "pore" structure with the proper dimensions and character for selective binding of potassium ion.[380] Other studies on the valinomycin-KCNS complex, however, were consistent with valinomycin functioning as a mobile ion carrier in biological membrane systems rather than as the ion channel model.[381] Similarly, changes in chemical shifts and coupling constants were adduced to suggest that the conformation of the nonactin ring when complexed with potassium ion is different from that of the free molecule[382] whilst a rigid structure for the cyclicpeptide rings of actinomycin D was also indicated in non-aqueous solutions.[383] The relevance of these non-aqueous studies to the biological systems of interest is however questionable. Aqueous studies of the cyclic antibiotic decapeptides, the tyrocidines,[384] showed line broadening which was proved to result from self aggregation. The latter appeared to arise chiefly from interactions between the side chains but required the rigid backbone structure of the ring to maintain a definite stereochemical relationship between the side chains of the interacting monomer.

The problem of assigning the peaks in the spectra of proteins has continued to be investigated by several methods. The spectra of a number of random coil proteins has been computed and shown to correspond reasonably well with the actual spectra so that it has been suggested that if a major difference appeared between the computed spectrum and the actual spectrum of a protein in an extended configuration then it might indicate important residual structure in the protein configuration.[385] A characteristic line-width of the resonances has also been used[386] to assess the presence or absence of covalent interaction in proteins, of molecular weight 57,000 to 650,000, in a series of denaturing solvents. The technique of incorporating ^{1}H amino acid residues into fully deuterated algal proteins to simplify the NMR spectrum has continued to be used,[387] but the proteins are large molecules of mainly unknown amino acid sequence thus restricting the application of the technique. The study by this technique of smaller protein molecules, for which the correlation of NMR data with amino acid sequence and X-ray crystallographic structure should be simpler, should prove useful. Deuteration techniques and shifts caused by trifluoroacetylation have enabled the partial analysis of the 220 MHz spectrum of glucagon[388] whilst, as reported earlier in this review, the addition of the paramagnetic Co^{2+} ion to the protein enabled new assignments of the lysozyme spectrum to be made.[14] Further, a combination of deuterium exchange rates, inhibiter perturbation and chemical modification techniques allowed the specific assignment of the indole amino protons for five of the six tryptophan residues of hen egg white lysozyme.[389]

Helix-coil transitions in synthetic polypeptides are characterized by a down-field shift of the α-CH as was shown in poly-γ-benzyl-L-glutamate[390] in strong acids. However, this shift in dichloroacetic acid solution,[391] was shown to be due first to collapse of the helix to an uncharged random coil followed by protonation of the amide group and it was suggested that it existed in the coil conformation because of strong solvation by hydrogen bonding and not because it is protonated. The observation of separate α-CH resonances for helix and random coil conformations of poly-L-alanine in $CHCl_3$/T.F.A. solution suggested no interconversion in times less than 10^{-1} sec. and it was postulated that competition between solvent-peptide and peptide-peptide hydrogen bonds, coupled with a destabilizing effect of the T.F.A. on the helix, was responsible for the helix to coil transformation.[392]

B. Nucleosides, nucleotides and nucleic acids

A review recently published covers much of the earlier contribution of NMR to the study of the structure and electronic aspects of nucleic acids and their constituents.[393] A general conformational model of all dinucleoside mono- and di- phosphates was obtained[394] by observing the shielding effect of the ring current in the neighbouring bases and the specific deshielding effect of the 5'-phosphate on the C-8 proton of the purine nucleotides and C-6 proton of the pyrimidine nucleotides. In this model the nucleosidyl units all have the *anti* conformation with respect to the sugar-base torsion angle, and the turn of the (3'–5') screw axis of the stack is right handed. Other studies also suggest *anti* conformations for the wobble pair UpUpU and UpUpC.[395] Electrolytes, however, can have an important effect on conformations as demonstrated for the uracil nucleotides and nucleosides.[396] Further, nuclear Overhauser experiments were used to suggest that for purine[397] and pyrimidine[398] nucleosides the *syn* conformation as well as intermediate range conformations must also be considered. The implication of these observations to oligo- and poly- nucleotide structure remains to be ascertained since vertical base stacking interactions presumably play an important part in stabilizing the base orientation and the conformation of each furanose residue. Intramolecular stacking interaction between the bases in some ribose dinucleoside monophosphates containing adenosine[399,400] in aqueous solutions was found to have a pronounced effect on the conformation of the ribose moieties in that they adopt a more 3'-*endo* conformation. This work[400] also pointed out the necessity of working at low concentration to obtain meaningful results regarding the intramolecular process because of extensive intermolecular self-association at high concentrations. From a study of 7-methylinosine, it was concluded that electrostatic interactions of monopoles or dipoles do not contribute significantly to stacking interactions[401] whilst, since methylation of the 2'-hydroxy group of ApA caused no substantial change in the three dimensional structure or stability of the ordered conformation, it was concluded that the increased stability of oligo- and poly- ribonucleotides, relative to their deoxyribonucleotide counterparts, was due to the presence of an oxygen atom of the 2'-hydroxy group and not to its hydrogen bond donor capability.[402]

The observation of non-equivalence at 200 MHz of the two C-4 protons in the nicotinamide moiety of NADH has provoked speculation as to the specific recognition of one of two folded forms of the purine dinucleotides by certain enzymes.[403] It has been pointed out, however, that the data can be rationalized by the simpler hypothesis that there is fast interconversion among all forms of NAD and NADH in solution and that one folded form is more stable than the other.[404] It was also demonstrated that the ratio of unfolded to folded form could be changed by the addition of methanol or urea to the aqueous solution.[405] Thus the non-equivalence of the C-4 protons is of doubtful significance in explaining the stereospecificity of dehydrogenase enzymes toward the nicotinamide ring. A similar equilibrium between folded and unfolded states of FAD was confirmed by a 220 MHz study where it was also found that dioxan decreased the fraction of folded molecules by lowering the energy barrier between the two states and also reduced the intermolecular stacking of FAD and FMN.[406]

C. Specific molecular interactions

The possible mechanism of action of ribonuclease continues to be discussed and the positions of histidine-12, histidine-119 and lysine-41 relative to each other and to the phosphate group of the substrate have been derived from the study of RNase inhibitor complexes by NMR and X-ray diffraction methods. The observation that the 2'-hydroxy group of the inhibitor is close to the histidine-12 whilst the phosphate group is fairly close to the histidine-119 has been used to support a linear mechanism for the action of RNase.[407] Conformational isomerization of the enzyme involving a movement of lysine-41 towards the phosphate group also probably occurs.[408] Related NMR studies were, however, reported to still support the alternative hypothesis that histidine-119 and lysine-41 are the binding groups of the enzyme whereas the histidine-12 takes up a proton when being released from its binding to histidine-119.[409]

Studies on human lysozyme indicated that the highly shielded tryptophan residues are at the binding site and are involved identically in the binding of both di- and tri- N-acetylglucosamine.[410] Information about the inhibitor has been obtained from a study of changes in chemical shifts induced in selected nuclei of the inhibitor and has shown that the reducing end pyranose ring of chitobiose, chitotriose and chitotetrose all bind to one end of the three contiguous binding sub-sites on the enzyme with the other pyranose rings occupying the other sub-sites.[411]

The measurement of the enhancement of the effect of paramagnetic ions, when bound to RNase, upon the relaxation rate of solvent water molecules was used to reflect the dynamic properties of the macromolecular structure at the binding site. Thus one strong binding site and another class of weaker sites were inferred from a study of Mn^{II} ion on ^{t}RNA[412] whilst the strong binding site for Cu^{II} was tentatively assigned to histidine-12 with two weaker sites at histidine-105 and histidine-119.[413] However, a study of the relaxation rate of water protons in solutions of E. coil ribosomes containing Mn^{2+} ions showed[414] that as the temperature was reduced T_1 passed through a field-dependent minimum. This is attributed to a change in the relaxation mechanism, a conclusion that is in disagreement with previous studies where the mechanism of the water protons in the manganese hydration sphere was assumed not to change with temperature. The stable free radical spin labels which are proving most useful in ESR studies, have also been used as paramagnetic probes in NMR experiments. Thus the reaction of the sulphydryl groups of creatine kinase with the nitroxide radical (110) has allowed the conformation in the environment of the enzyme-bound free radical and the change in conformation induced upon binding of the substrate, metal adenosine diphosphate, to be monitored by its ESR spectrum and by its contribution to the proton relaxation rate of water.[415] Similarly results from the use of an analogue of NAD (**111**) bearing an unpaired electron in a

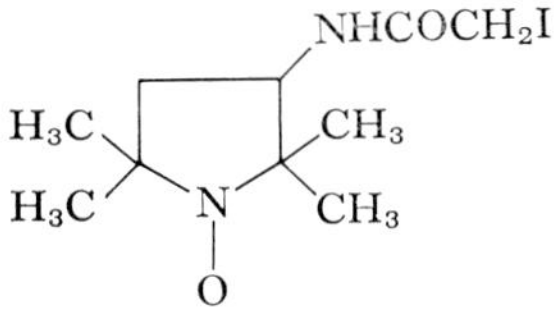

110 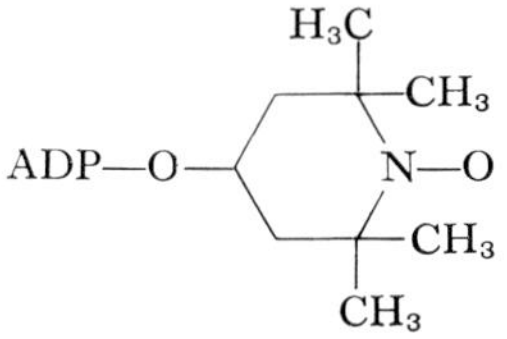   111

region corresponding to the pyridine N-ribose C-1 bond of the enzyme, were interpreted[416] as showing that the substrates bind close to the co-enzyme and on the "water side" of its pyridine ring. The relative positions of the co-enzyme and substrate fitted the idea of direct hydrogen transfer from one to another although the drawing of firm structural conclusions from relaxation data alone is hazardous.

Line-widths for carbon linked protons of analogues of carbamyl phosphate in the presence of the catalytic sub-unit of aspartate transcarbamylase were used as a measure of the rotational freedom of bound analogues.[417] The observation that the signals of the methyl protons of tertiary ammonium salt complexes with DNA are considerably more broadened than those of the corresponding quaternary ammonium salts was used[418] to suggest hydrogen bonding interaction of the DNA with tertiary ammonium salts. The derivation of spin-spin relaxation data from line width broadening, however, can be complicated if long T_2 or line splittings are involved. Therefore, in certain systems the derivation of T_1 by the adiabatic rapid passage method may be more appropriate as was found[419] for relaxation rates of N-methyl protons of a series of aliphatic ammonium salts related to acetylcholine. The results, when compared with theoretical calculations suggested that the contribution to the relaxation rate came from tumbling of the whole molecule whilst for methoxy and acetoxy derivatives the results indicated relatively free group rotation. These results should help to define more precisely the molecular motion in the compounds when bound to enzymes, antibodies or drug receptors.

D. Other studies

The mechanism of non-enzymatic transamination catalyzed by pyridoxal cofactors has been studied in more detail by investigations[420,421] of the structures and equilibria of the tridentate ligands formed from the Schiff bases of amino acids with pyridoxal and metal ions. A new vitamin B_6 catalyzed reaction, β proton exchange of α-amino acids, has also been studied by both proton and metal ion catalysis.[422]

A 220 MHz study at room temperature of high density serum lipoproteins showed[423] that the lipid material present was probably in a magnetically isotropic environment with considerable molecular freedom; similar to the situation when the lipid was dissolved in organic solvents. On increasing the temperature there appeared to be greater mobility of the lipid chains and also of some amino acids of the protein moiety which, therefore, appeared to allow greater mobility of the cholesterol.

Relaxation data have indicated two types of water in brain and muscle tissue[424] and it is suggested that the water exists in at least two ordered phases which can be distinguished by the widths of their NMR signals, by deuterium exchange, and by vacuum drying.[425] However, the previous observation that the splitting of the water signal in the rat phrenic nerve is due to dipole-dipole interactions caused by partial orientation of the bulk water in the nerve has been suggested[426] to be an artefact of the sample geometry from a deuterium broad line study.

REFERENCES

1. R. M. Lynden-Bell and R. K. Harris, "Nuclear Magnetic Resonance Spectroscopy", University Press, Belfast, 1969.
2. F. A. Bovey, "Nuclear Magnetic Resonance Spectroscopy", Academic Press, New York, 1969.
3. E. D. Becker, "High Resolution NMR, Theory and Chemical Applications", Academic Press, New York, 1969.
4. I. Ya. Slonin and A. N. Lgubimov, "The NMR of Polymers", Plenum Press, New York, 1969.
5. Chemical Society Specialist Reports, "Spectroscopic properties of inorganic and organometallic compounds", Vol. I, The Chemical Society, London, 1969.
6. S. J. Angyal, *Angew. Chem. Internat. Edn.*, 1969, **8**, 157.
7. R. J. Ferrier, *Chem. in Britain*, 1969, **5**, 15.
8. E. G. Derouane, *Ind. chim. (Bruxelles)*, 1969, **34**, 103.
9. L. Pohl and M. Eckle, *Angew. Chem. Internat. Edn.*, 1969, **8**, 381.
10. L. Pohl and M. Eckle, *Angew. Chem. Internat. Edn.*, 1968, **8**, 380.
11. R. N. Butler, *Chem. and Ind.*, 1969, 456.
12. B. J. Blackburn, F. E. Hruska and I. C. P. Smith, *Canad. J. Chem.*, 1969, **47**, 4491.
13. D. J. Frost, G. E. Hall, J. G. Lawrence and S. Newham, *J. Chem. Soc. (B)*, 1969, 761.
14. C. C. McDonald and W. D. Phillips, *Biochem. Biophys. Res. Comm.*, 1969, **35**, 43.
15. C. C. Hinckley, *J. Amer. Chem. Soc.*, 1969, **91**, 5160.
16. W. A. Szarek, E. Dent, T. B. Grindley and M. C. Baird, *Chem. Comm.*, 1969, 953.
17. M. Kainosho, *J. Phys. Chem.*, 1969, **73**, 3516.
18. D. W. Mastbrook and E. P. Ragelis, *Appl. Spectroscopy*, 1969, **23**, 376.
19. P. A. Bristow and R. G. Coombes, *Chem. and Ind.*, 1969, 1509.

20. E. D. Becker, J. A. Ferretti and T. C. Farrar, *J. Amer. Chem. Soc.*, 1969, **91**, 7784.
21. J. D. Halliday, H. D. W. Hill and R. E. Richards, *J. Sci. Instr.*, 1969, **2**, 29.
22. F. A. L. Anet, paper presented at the Tenth Experimental NMR Conference Pittsburg, Pa, Feb. 1969.
23. J. K. Becconsall and M. C. McIvor, *Chem. in Britain*, 1969, **5**, 147.
24. T. F. Page, *Chem. and Ind.*, 1969, 1462.
25. M. T. Bowers, T. I. Chapman and S. L. Manatt, *J. Chem. Phys.*, 1969, **50**, 5412.
26. E. Lustig, E. A. Hansen, P. Diehl and H. Kellerhals, *J. Chem. Phys.*, 1969, **51**, 1839.
27. E. G. Finer and R. K. Harris, *J. Chem. Soc.(A)*, 1969, 1972.
28. P. Diehl, C. L. Khetrapal and V. Lienhard, *Org. Magn. Resonance*, 1969, **1** 93.
29. T. J. Batterham, *Tetrahedron Letters*, 1969, 949.
30. T. J. Batterham, N. V. Riggs, A. V. Robertson and W. R. J. Simpson, *Austral. J. Chem.*, 1969, **22**, 725.
31. C. W. Haigh and M. Kinns, *Chem. Comm.*, 1969, 1502.
32. V. Spirko and J. Pliva, *J. Mol. Spectroscopy*, 1969, **29**, 426.
33. J. D. Ellet and J. S. Waugh, *J. Chem. Phys.*, 1969, **51**, 2851.
34. V. J. Kowalewski, *J. Mol. Spectroscopy*, 1969, **31**, 256.
35. W. McFarlane and D. H. Whiffen, *Mol. Phys.*, 1969, **17**, 603.
36. G. Binsch, *J. Amer. Chem. Soc.*, 1969, **91**, 1304.
37. V. P. Heuring and W. S. Brey, *J. Chem. Phys.*, 1969, **50**, 1025.
38. J. R. Yandle and J. P. Maher, *J. Chem. Soc.(A)*, 1969, 1549.
39. J. P. Kintzinger, J. M. Lehn and R. L. Williams, *Mol. Phys.*, 1969, **17**, 135.
40. C. Brevard, J. P. Kintzinger and J. M. Lehn, *Chem. Comm.*, 1969, 1193.
41. J. E. Anderson and P. A. Fryer, *J. Chem. Phys.*, 1969, **50**, 3784.
42. E. G. Finer and R. K. Harris, *Chem. Comm.*, 1969, 42.
43. R. Freeman and H. D. W. Hill, *J. Chem. Phys.*, 1969, **51**, 3140.
44. P. Diehl and C. L. Khetrapal, "NMR Basic Principles and Progress", Vol. I, p. 1, Springer-Verlag, New York, 1969.
45. H. Kelker and B. Scheurle, *Angew. Chem. Internat. Edn.*, 1969, **8**, 884.
46. A. D. Buckingham, E. E. Burnell and C. A. de Lange, *Mol. Phys.*, 1969, **16**, 521.
47. E. E. Burnell and C. A. de Lange, *Mol. Phys.*, 1969, **16**, 95.
48. A. D. Buckingham, E. E. Burnell and C. A. de Lange, *Mol. Phys.*, 1969, **17**, 205.
49. E. Sackmann, *J. Chem. Phys.* 1969, **51**, 2984.
50. C. T. Yim and D. F. R. Gilson, *Canad. J. Chem.*, 1969, **47**, 1057.
51. W. Bovée, C. W. Hilbers and C. Maclean, *Mol. Phys.*, 1969, **17**, 75.
52. D. N. Silverman and B. P. Dailey, *J. Chem. Phys.*, 1969, **51**, 655.
53. A. D. Buckingham, E. E. Burnell and C. A. de Lange, *Mol. Phys.*, 1969, **16**, 299.
54. R. A. Bernheim, D. J. Hoy, T. R. Krugh and B. J. Lavery, *J. Chem. Phys.*, 1969, **50**, 1350.
55. T. R. Krugh and R. A. Bernheim, *J. Amer. Chem. Soc.*, 1969, **91**, 2385.
56. G. P. Ceasar and B. P. Dailey, *J. Chem. Phys.*, 1969, **50**, 4200.
57. D. N. Silverman and B. P. Dailey, *J. Chem. Phys.*, 1969, **51**, 1679.
58. K. Hayamizu and O. Yamamoto, *J. Chem. Phys.*, 1969, **51**, 1676.

59. C. S. Yannoni, *J. Chem. Phys.*, 1969, **51**, 1682.
60. P. Diehl and C. L. Khetrapal, *Canad. J. Chem.*, 1969, **47**, 1411.
61. T. Yonezawa, I. Morishima, K. Deguchi and H. Kato, *J. Chem. Phys.*, 1969, **51**, 5731.
62. G. Havach, P. Ferruti, D. Gill and M. P. Klein, *J. Amer. Chem. Soc.*, 1969, **91**, 7526.
63. J. J. de Vries and H. J. C. Berendsen, *Nature*, 1969, **221**, 1139.
64. P. J. Black, K. D. Lawson and T. J. Flautt, *J. Chem. Phys.*, 1969, **50**, 542.
65. P. J. Black, K. D. Lawson and T. J. Flautt, *Mol. Crystals*, 1969, **7**, 201.
66. C. S. Yannoni, *J. Amer. Chem. Soc.*, 1969, **91**, 4611.
67. W. H. Pirkle and S. D. Beare, *J. Amer. Chem. Soc.*, 1969, **91**, 5150.
68. W. H. Pirkle, S. D. Beare and T. G. Burlingame, *J. Org. Chem.*, 1969, **34**, 470.
69. W. H. Pirkle, S. D. Beare and R. L. Muntz, *J. Amer. Chem. Soc.*, 1969, **91**, 4573.
70. T. Williams, R. G. Pitcher, P. Bommer, J. Gutzwiller and M. Uskokovic, *J. Amer. Chem. Soc.*, 1969, **91**, 1871.
71. H. Fischer and J. Bargon, *Accounts Chem. Res.*, 1969, **2**, 110.
72. H. R. Ward, R. G. Lawler and R. A. Cooper, *Tetrahedron Letters*, 1969, 527.
73. U. Schöllkopf, G. Ostermann and J. Schossig, *Tetrahedron Letters*, 1969, 2619.
74. J. E. Baldwin and J. E. Brown, *J. Amer. Chem. Soc.*, 1969, **91**, 3647.
75. R. W. Jemison and D. G. Morris, *Chem. Comm.*, 1969, 1226.
76. H. R. Ward, R. G. Lawler and R. A. Cooper, *J. Amer. Chem. Soc.*, 1969, **91**, 746.
77. A. R. Lepley and R. L. Landau, *J. Amer. Chem. Soc.*, 1969, **91**, 748.
78. A. R. Lepley, *J. Amer. Chem. Soc.*, 1969, **91**, 749.
79. G. L. Closs and L. E. Closs, *J. Amer. Chem. Soc.*, 1969, **91**, 4549.
80. G. L. Closs and L. E. Closs, *J. Amer. Chem. Soc.*, 1969, **91**, 4550.
81. G. L. Closs, *J. Amer. Chem. Soc.*, 1969, **91**, 4552.
82. F. Gerhart and G. Ostermann, *Tetrahedron Letters*, 1969, 4705.
83. F. Gerhart, *Tetrahedron Letters*, 1969, 5061.
84. H. R. Ward, R. G. Lawler, H. Y. Loken and R. A. Cooper, *J. Amer. Chem. Soc.*, 1969, **91**, 4928.
85. M. Barfield and M. Karplus, *J. Amer. Chem. Soc.*, 1969, **91**, 1.
86. M. Barfield and B. Chakrabarti, *J. Amer. Chem. Soc.*, 1969, **91**, 4346.
87. S. Sternhell, *Quart. Rev.*, 1969, **23**, 236.
88. M. Barfield and B. Chakrabarti, *Chem. Rev.*, 1969, **69**, 757.
89. R. Cahill, R. C. Cookson and T. A. Crabb, *Tetrahedron*, 1969, **25**, 4681, 4711.
90. S. L. Manatt, E. A. Cohen and A. H. Cowley, *J. Amer. Chem. Soc.*, 1969, **91**, 5919.
91. R. J. Abraham, *J. Phys. Chem.*, 1969, **73**, 1192.
92. R. J. Abraham and G. Gatti, *J. Chem. Soc.(B)*, 1969, 961.
93. W. C. Lin, *J. Chem. Phys.*, 1969, **50**, 1890.
94. F. Heatley and G. Allen, *Mol. Phys.*, 1969, **16**, 77.
95. P. A. Scherr and J. P. Oliver, *J. Mol. Spectroscopy*, 1969, **31**, 109.
96. M. A. Cooper and S. L. Manatt, *J. Amer. Chem. Soc.*, 1969, **91**, 6325.
97. C. W. Haigh and R. B. Mallion, *J. Mol. Spectroscopy*, 1969, **29**, 478.
98. J. B. Pawliczek and H. Günther, *Z. Naturforsch*, 1969, **24B**, 1068.

99. A. J. Boulton, P. J. Halls and A. R. Katritzky, *Org. Magn. Resonance*, 1969, **1**, 311.
100. F. L. Tobiason and J. H. Goldstein, *Spectrochim. Acta*, 1969, **25A**, 1027.
101. M. Kamiya, S. Katayama and Y. Akahori, *Chem. and Pharm. Bull. (Japan)*, 1969, **17**, 1821.
102. D. J. Bertelli, T. G. Andrews and P. O. Crews, *J. Amer. Chem. Soc.*, 1969, **91**, 5286.
103. W. Bremsor and H. Günther, *Org. Magn. Resonance*, 1969, **1**, 435.
104. M. J. Bulman, *Tetrahedron*, 1969, **25**, 1433.
105. Y. Sasaki and M. Suzuki, *Chem. and Pharm. Bull. (Japan)*, 1969, **17**, 1104.
106. R. Ditchfield and V. M. S. Gil, *J. Chem. Soc.(A)*, 1969, 533.
107. A. R. Tarpley, H. B. Evans and J. H. Goldstein, *Analyt. Chem.*, 1969, **41**, 402.
108. A. G. Moritz and D. B. Paul, *Austral. J. Chem.*, 1969, **22**, 1305.
109. S. S. Danyluk, C. L. Bell and T. Schaefer, *Canad. J. Chem.*, 1969, **47**, 4005.
110. C. L. Bell, S. S. Danyluk and T. Schaefer, *Canad. J. Chem.*, 1969, **47**, 3529.
111. K. D. Bartle, D. W. Jones and R. S. Matthews, *Tetrahedron*, 1969, **25**, 2701.
112. K. D. Bartle, D. W. Jones and R. S. Matthews, *Rev. Pure. Appl. Chem. (Australia)*, 1969, **19**, 191.
113. M. Kamiya, *Chem. and Pharm. Bull. (Japan)*, 1969, **17**, 1815.
114. L. G. Alexakos and E. N. Givens, *Tetrahedron Letters*, 1969, 4345.
115. R. W. Crecely, K. W. McCracken and J. H. Goldstein, *Tetrahedron*, 1969, **25**, 877.
116. H. A. Gaur, J. Vriend and W. G. B. Huysmans, *Tetrahedron Letters*, 1969, 1999.
117. Y. C. Kim and H. Hart, *Tetrahedron*, 1969, **25**, 3869.
118. S. H. Grover and J. B. Stothers, *J. Amer. Chem. Soc.*, 1969, **91**, 4331.
119. D. J. Sardella, *J. Mol. Spectroscopy*, 1969, **31**, 70.
120. W. H. deJeu and H. A. Gaur, *Mol. Phys.*, 1969, **16**, 205.
121. M. Kainosho and A. Nakamura, *Tetrahedron*, 1969, **25**, 4071.
122. D. Chalier, D. Gagnaire and A. Russat, *Bull. Soc. chim. France*, 1969, 387.
123. A. Guzman, E. Diaz and P. Crabbe, *Chem. Comm.*, 1969, 1449.
124. C. H. M. Adams and K. Mackenzie, *J. Chem. Soc.(C)*, 1969, 480.
125. W. McFarlane, *Quart. Rev.*, 1969, **23**, 187.
126. C. J. Jameson and H. S. Gutowsky, *J. Chem. Phys.*, 1969, **51**, 2790.
127. C. J. Jameson, *J. Amer. Chem. Soc.*, 1969, **91**, 6232.
128. A. H. Cowley and W. D. White, *J. Amer. Chem. Soc.*, 1969, **91**, 1913.
129. A. H. Cowley and W. D. White, *J. Amer. Chem. Soc.*, 1969, **91**, 1917.
130. R. M. Moriarty, J. P. Kim, S. J. Druck and E. Lustig, *Tetrahedron*, 1969, **25**, 1261.
131. K. L. Servis, J. Casanova and M. Geisel, *Org. Magn. Resonance*, 1969, **1**, 209.
132. L. Lunazzi and F. Taddei, *Spectrochim. Acta*, 1969, **25A**, 553.
133. V. M. S. Gil and A. C. P. Alves, *Mol. Phys.*, 1969, **16**, 527.
134. C. H. Yoder, R. H. Tuck and R. E. Hess, *J. Amer. Chem. Soc.*, 1969, **91**, 539.
135. O. Yamamoto, M. Watabe and O. Kikuchi, *Mol. Phys.*, 1969, **17**, 249.
136. A. A. Bothner-By and R. H. Cox, *J. Phys. Chem.*, 1969, **73**, 1830.
137. T. Yonezawa, I. Morishima, K. Fukuta and Y. Olimore, *J. Mol. Spectroscopy*, 1969, **31**, 341.
138. M. Ohtsuru, K. Tori, J. M. Lehn and R. Seher, *J. Amer. Chem. Soc.*, 1969, **91**, 1187.

139. D. Crepaux, J. M. Lehn and R. R. Dean, *Mol. Phys.*, 1969, **16**, 225.
140. R. J. Chuck, D. G. Gillies and E. W. Randall, *Mol. Phys.*, 1969, **16**, 121.
141. T. Axenrod, P. S. Pregosin, M. J. Wieder and G. W. A. Milne, *J. Amer. Chem. Soc.*, 1969, **91**, 3681.
142. M. R. Bramwell and E. W. Randall, *Chem. Comm.*, 1969, 250.
143. J. E. Loemker, K. M. Pryse, J. M. Read and J. H. Goldstein, *Canad. J. Chem.*, 1969, **47**, 209.
144. T. Schaefer, S. S. Danyluk and C. L. Bell, *Canad. J. Chem.*, 1969, **47**, 1507.
145. T. Schaefer and S. S. Danyluk, *Canad. J. Chem.*, 1969, **47**, 4289.
146. T. Schaefer, C. M. Wong and K. C. Tam, *Canad. J. Chem.*, 1969, **47**, 3688.
147. L. D. Hall and J. F. Manville, *Carbohydrate Res.*, 1969, **9**, 11.
148. L. D. Hall, J. F. Manville and N. S. Bhacca, *Canad. J. Chem.*, 1969, **47**, 1.
149. L. D. Hall and J. F. Manville, *Canad. J. Chem.*, 1969, **47**, 19.
150. C. W. Jefford, D. T. Hill, L. Ghosez, S. Toppet and K. C. Ramey, *J. Amer. Chem. Soc.*, 1969, **91**, 1532.
151. J. P. Albrand, D. Gagnaire, J. Martin and J. B. Robert, *Bull. Soc. chim. France*, 1969, 40.
152. L. Evelyn, L. D. Hall, P. R. Steiner and D. H. Stokes, *Chem. Comm.*, 1969, 576.
153. R. H. Cox and R. B. Adelman, *Tetrahedron Letters*, 1969, 4017.
154. J. P. Albrand, D. Gagnaire, J. B. Robert and M. Haemers, *Bull. Soc. chim. France*, 1969, 3496.
155. C. Benezra, *Tetrahedron Letters*, 1969, 4471.
156. W. McFarlane, *Org. Magn. Resonance*, 1969, **1**, 3.
157. M. P. Simonnin, C. Charrier and M.-J. Lecourt, *Org. Magn. Resonance*, 1969, **1**, 27.
158. P. Lazzeretti and F. Taddei, *Tetrahedron Letters*, 1969, 3025.
159. W. McFarlane, *J. Chem. Soc.(B)*, 1969, 28.
160. H. T. Cheung and D. G. Williamson, *Tetrahedron*, 1969, **25**, 119.
161. S. Itô, M. Kodama, M. Sunagawa, T. Ôba and H. Hikino, *Tetrahedron Letters*, 1969, 2905.
162. U. E. Matter, C. Pascual, E. Pretsch, A. Pross, W. Simon and S. Sternhell, *Tetrahedron*, 1969, **25**, 691.
163. S. W. Tobey, *J. Org. Chem.*, 1969, **34**, 1281.
164. U. E. Matter, C. Pascual, E. Pretsch, A. Pross, W. Simon and S. Sternhell, *Tetrahedron*, 1969, **25**, 2023.
165. D. E. Jung, *Tetrahedron*, 1969, **25**, 129.
166. T. R. Janson, A. R. Kane, J. F. Sullivan, K. Knox and M. E. Kenney, *J. Amer. Chem. Soc.*, 1969, **91**, 5210.
167. R. H. Martin, N. Defay, H. P. Figeys, M. Flammang-Barbieux, J. P. Cosyn, M. Grelbcke and J. J. Schurter, *Tetrahedron*, 1969, **25**, 4985.
168. G. W. Brown and F. Sondheimer, *J. Amer. Chem. Soc.*, 1969, **91**, 760.
169. R. H. Mitchell, C. E. Klopfenstein and V. Boekelheide, *J. Amer. Chem. Soc.*, 1969, **91**, 4931.
170. R. J. Ouellette and B. G. van Leuwen, *J. Org. Chem.*, 1969, **34**, 62.
171. R. J. Ouellette and B. G. van Leuwen, *Tetrahedron*, 1969, **25**, 819.
172. K. D. Bartle and D. W. Jones, *J. Phys. Chem.*, 1969, **73**, 293.
173. J. Kuthan, Z. Donnerová and V. Skála, *Coll. Czech. Chem. Comm.*, 1969, **34**, 2398.
174. K. Hayamizu and O. Yamamoto, *J. Mol. Spectroscopy*, 1969, **29**, 183.

175. R. H. Cox, *Spectrochim. Acta.*, 1969, **25A**, 1189.
176. Y. Nomura and Y. Takeuchi, *Org. Magn. Resonance*, 1969, **1**, 213.
177. Y. Nomura, Y. Takeuchi and N. Nakagawa, *Tetrahedron Letters*, 1969, 639.
178. J. Bennett, M. Delmas and J. C. Maire, *Org. Magn. Resonance*, 1969, **1**, 319.
179. J. Niwa, *Bull. Chem. Soc. Japan*, 1969, **42**, 1926.
180. K. Tabei and E. Saitou, *Bull. Chem. Soc. Japan*, 1969, **42**, 1440.
181. H. Sakurai and M. Ohtsuru, *J. Organometallic Chem.*, 1969, **13**, 81.
182. R. R. Fraser, Gurudata, R. N. Renaud, C. Reyes-Zamora and R. B. Swingle, *Canad. J. Chem.*, 1969, **47**, 2767.
183. J. L. Roark and W. B. Smith, *J. Phys. Chem.*, 1969, **73**, 1043 and 1046.
184. M. T. Tribble and J. G. Traynham, *J. Amer. Chem. Soc.*, 1969, **91**, 379.
185. M. Charton, *J. Amer. Chem. Soc.*, 1969, **91**, 6649.
186. E. Z. Katsnel'son, B. I. Ionin and C. S. Frankovskü, *Zhur. org. Khim.*, 1969, **5**, 1099.
187. J. B. Hyne and J. W. Greidanus, *Canad. J. Chem.*, 1969, **47**, 803.
188. J. C. Maire and J. M. Angelelli, *Bull. Soc. chim. France*, 1969, 1311.
189. J. M. Angelelli and J. C. Maire, *Bull. Soc. chim. France*, 1969, 1858.
190. R. H. Kemp, W. A. Thomas, M. Gordon and C. E. Griffin, *J. Chem. Soc.(B)*, 1969, 527.
191. C. Glidewell, D. W. H. Rankin and G. M. Sheldrick, *Trans. Faraday Soc.*, 1969, **65**, 2801.
192. Y. Sasaki, M. Suzuki and M. Hattori, *Chem. and Pharm. Bull (Japan)*, 1969, **17**, 1515; Y. Sasaki and M. Suzuki, *Chem. and Pharm. Bull. (Japan)*, 1969, **17**, 1778; W. B. Smith and J. L. Roark, *J. Phys. Chem.*, 1969, **73**, 1049.
193. J. T. Gerig and J. D. Reinheimer, *Org. Magn. Resonance*, 1969, **1**, 239.
194. O. Teisuke and A. Takadate, *Yakugaku Zasshi*, 1969, **89**, 302.
195. Y. Sasaki, K. Iwasalu, M. Suzuki and N. Nishimolo, *Yakugaku Zasshi*, 1969, **89**, 25.
196. Y. Sasaki, M. Hatanaka and M. Suzuki, *Yakugaku Zasshi*, 1969, **89**, 64.
197. T. B. Cobb and J. D. Memory, *J. Chem. Phys.*, 1969, **50**, 4262.
198. J. M. Jackman and G. Y. Sarkis, *Bull. Chem. Soc. Japan*, 1969, **42**, 1179.
199. E. Pretsch and W. Simon, *Helv. Chim. Acta*, 1969, **52**, 2133.
200. W. Walter, E. Schaumann and H. Pausen, *Annalen*, 1969, **727**, 61.
201. P. V. Demarco, D. Doddrell and E. Wenkert, *Chem. Comm.*, 1969, 1418.
202. R. D. G. Cooper, P. V. Demarco, J. C. Cheng and N. D. Jones, *J. Amer. Chem. Soc.*, 1969, **91**, 1408.
203. R. D. G. Cooper, P. V. Demarco and D. O. Spry, *J. Amer. Chem. Soc.*, 1969, **91**, 1528.
204. D. H. R. Barton, F. Comer and P. G. Sammes, *J. Amer. Chem. Soc.*, 1969, **91**, 1529.
205. C. R. Johnson and W. O. Siegl, *Tetrahedron Letters*, 1969, 1879.
206. K. Kondo, A. Negishi and M. Fukuyama, *Tetrahedron Letters*, 1969, 2461.
207. L. Cazaux and P. Maroni, *Tetrahedron Letters*, 1969, 3667.
208. G. Binsch and G. R. Franzen, *J. Amer. Chem. Soc.*, 1969, **91**, 3999.
209. W. McFarlane and J. A. Nash, *Chem. Comm.*, 1969, 524.
210. G. P. Schiemenz and H. Rast, *Tetrahedron Letters*, 1969, 2165.
211. A. Pelter and T. E. Levitt, *Chem. Comm.*, 1969, 1027.
212. B. V. Milborrow and C. Djerassi, *J. Chem. Soc.(C)*, 1969, 417.
213. R. E. Lyle and J. J. Thomas, *Tetrahedron Letters*, 1969, 897.
214. J. Elguero, C. Marzin and D. Tizané, *Org. Magn. Resonance*, 1969, **1**, 249.

215. M. L. Martin, F. Lefevre, D. Lapeyre, G. J. Martin and R. Mantione, *Org. Magn. Resonance*, 1969, **1**, 19.
216. L. S. Rattet and J. H. Goldstein, *Org. Magn. Resonance*, 1969, **1**, 229.
217. M. Brink, *Tetrahedron Letters*, 1969, 4055.
218. M. Brink, *Tetrahedron Letters*, 1969, 5247.
219. A. W. Garrison, L. H. Keith and A. L. Alford, *Spectrochim. Acta*, 1969, **25A**, 77.
220. M. Nishio, *Chem. and Pharm. Bull. (Japan)*, 1969, **17**, 262.
221. M. Nishio, *Chem. and Pharm. Bull. (Japan)*, 1969, **17**, 274.
222. M. Nishio, *Chem. Comm.*, 1969, 51.
223. M. Nishio, *Chem. Comm.*, 1969, 560.
224. C. Y. Meyers and A. M. Malte, *J. Amer. Chem. Soc.*, 1969, **91**, 2123.
225. R. E. Lack and L. Tarasoff, *J. Chem. Soc.(B)*, 1969, 1095.
226. A. H. Cowley, M. J. S. Dewar, W. B. Jennings and W. R. Jackson, *Chem. Comm.*, 1969, 482.
227. L. Frankel, J. Cargioli, H. Klapper and R. Danielson, *Canad. J. Chem.*, 1969, **47**, 3167; L. S. Frankel, H. Klapper and J. Cargioli, *J. Phys. Chem.*, 1969, **73**, 91.
228. F. Caesar and W. D. Balzer, *Chem. Ber.*, 1969, **102**, 1665.
229. M. Sanchez, L. Beslier, J. Roussel and R. Wolf, *Bull. Soc. chim. France*, 1969, 3053.
230. D. J. Cowley and L. H. Sutcliffe, *Spectrochim. Acta*, 1969, **25A**, 1663.
231. R. Foster and M. I. Foreman, in "Progress in Nuclear Magnetic Resonance Spectroscopy", Vol. 4, p. 1, 1969, Ed. J. Emsley, J. Feeney and L. H. Sutcliffe, Pergamon Press, London.
232. M. I. Foreman and R. Foster, *J. Chem. Soc.(B)*, 1969, 885.
233. P. H. Emslie, R. Foster, I. Horman, J. W. Morris and D. R. Twiselton, *J. Chem. Soc.(B)*, 1969, 1161.
234. R. Haque, W. R. Coshow and L. F. Johnson, *J. Amer. Chem. Soc.*, 1969, **91**, 3822.
235. B. G. White, *Trans Faraday Soc.*, 1969, **65**, 2000.
236. M. I. Foreman, R. Foster and D. R. Twiselton, *Chem. Comm.*, 1969, 1318.
237. M. I. Foreman and R. Foster, *Canad. J. Chem.*, 1969, **47**, 729.
238. M. R. Crampton and M. El-Ghariani, *J. Chem. Soc.(B)*, 1969, 330.
239. P. Bemporad, G. Illuminati and F. Stegel, *J. Amer. Chem. Soc.*, 1969, **91**, 6742.
240. C. Abbolito, C. Iavarone, G. Illuminati, F. Stegel and A. Vazzoler, *J. Amer. Chem. Soc.*, 1969, **91**, 6746.
241. A. D. H. Clague, G. Govil and H. J. Bernstein, *Canad. J. Chem.*, 1969, **47**, 625.
242. N. F. Hepfinger and P. A. Clark, *J. Org. Chem.*, 1969, **34**, 2572.
243. C. E. Griffin, E. J. Fendler and B. D. Martin, *Spectrochim. Acta*, 1969, **25A**, 710.
244. W. L. Chandler and R. H. Dinius, *J. Phys. Chem.*, 1969, **73**, 1596.
245. W. C. Meyer and J. T. K. Woo, *J. Phys. Chem.*, 1969, **73**, 2989.
246. H. Feuer, D. Pelle, D. M. Braunstein and C. N. R. Rao, *Spectrochim. Acta*, 1969, **25A**, 1393.
247. V. K. Pogoreli and I. P. Gragerov, *Doklady Akad. Nauk S.S.S.R.*, 1969, **186**, 610.
248. S. H. Marcus and S. I. Miller, *J. Phys. Chem.*, 1969, **73**, 453.

249. W. E. Bentz and L. D. Colebrook, *Canad. J. Chem.*, 1969, **47**, 2473.
250. J. M. Purcell, H. Susi, J. R. Cavanaugh, *Canad. J. Chem.*, 1969, **47**, 3655.
251. B. D. Andrews, I. D. Rae and B. E. Reichert, *Tetrahedron Letters*, 1969, 1859.
252. R. D. Green, *Canad. J. Chem.*, 1969, **47**, 2407.
253. R. D. Green, J. S. Martin, W. B. McG. Cassie and J. B. Hyne, *Canad. J. Chem.*, 1969, **47**, 1639.
254. C. J. Clemett, *J. Chem. Soc.(A)*, 1969, 455.
255. C. J. Clemett, *J. Chem. Soc.(A)*, 1969, 458.
256. J. M. Corkill, J. F. Goodman and J. Wyer, *Trans. Faraday Soc.*, 1969, **65**, 9.
257. R. G. Anderson and M. C. R. Symons, *Trans. Faraday Soc.*, 1969, **65**, 2550.
258. R. N. Butler and M. C. R. Symons, *Trans. Faraday Soc.*, 1969, **65**, 2559.
259. T. D. Alger, *J. Amer. Chem. Soc.*, 1969, **91**, 2220.
260. C. Beguin, J. J. Delpuech and A. Peguy, *Mol. Phys.*, 1969, **17**, 317.
261. A. Fratiello, R. E. Lee and R. E. Schuster, *Chem. Comm.*, 1969, 37.
262. A. Fratiello, R. E. Lee, V. M. Nishida and R. E. Schuster, *Inorg. Chem.*, 1969, **8**, 69.
263. J. F. Hinton, E. S. Amis and W. Mettetal, *Spectrochim. Acta*, 1969, **25A**, 119.
264. S. A. Al-Baldawi and T. E. Gough, *Canad. J. Chem.*, 1969, **47**, 1417.
265. Z. Luz, *J. Chem. Phys.*, 1969, **51**, 1206.
266. F. W. Breivogel, *J. Chem. Phys.*, 1969, **51**, 445.
267. S. Behrendt, C. H. Langford and L. S. Frankel, *J. Amer. Chem. Soc.*, 1969, **91**, 2236.
268. A. Fratiello and R. E. Schuster, *Inorg. Chem.*, 1969, **8**, 480.
269. D. E. Hamilton, J. S. Hartman and J. M. Miller, *Chem. Comm.*, 1969, 1417.
270. W. T. Raynes and M. A. Raza, *Mol. Phys.*, 1969, **17**, 157.
271. P. Laszlo, A. Speert and W. T. Raynes, *J. Chem. Phys.*, 1969, **51**, 1677.
272. W. T. Raynes, *J. Chem. Phys.*, 1969, **51**, 3138.
273. J. Homer and M. C. Cooke, *J. Chem. Soc.(A)*, 1969, 773.
274. J. Homer and M. C. Cooke, *J. Chem. Soc.(A)*, 1969, 779.
275. M. D. Johnston, F. P. Gasparro and I. D. Kuntz, *J. Amer. Chem. Soc.*, 1969, **91**, 5715.
276. J. K. Becconsall, T. Winkler and W. von Philipsborn, *Chem. Comm.*, 1969, 430.
277. P. V. Demarco and L. A. Spangle, *J. Org. Chem.*, 1969, **34**, 3205.
278. T. Winkler and W. von Philipsborn, *Helv. Chim. Acta*, 1969, **52**, 796.
279. R. G. Wilson, D. E. A. Rivett and D. H. Williams, *Chem. and Ind.*, 1969, 109.
280. R. G. Wilson and D. H. Williams, *Tetrahedron*, 1969, **25**, 155.
281. M. H. Freemantle and W. G. Overend, *J. Chem. Soc.(B)*, 1969, 547.
282. E. T. Strom, B. S. Snowden and P. A. Toldan, *Chem. Comm.*, 1969, 50.
283. C. Agami and J. L. Pierre, *Bull. Soc. chim. France*, 1969, 1963.
284. J. H. Bowie, P. F. Donaghue and H. J. Rodda, *J. Chem. Soc.(B)*, 1969, 1122.
285. I. Rosenthal, *Tetrahedron Letters*, 1969, 3333.
286. K. D. Bartle, D. W. Jones and R. S. Matthews, *J. Chem. Soc.(A)*, 1969, 876.
287. A. Pelter, R. Warren, J. N. Usmani, M. Ilyas and W. Rahman, *Tetrahedron Letters*, 1969, 4259.
288. G. Severini Ricca and B. Danieli, *Gazzetta*, 1969, **99**, 133.
289. P. V. Demarco, *Tetrahedron Letters*, 1969, 383.
290. G. Moreau, *Bull. Soc. chim. France*, 1969, 1770.
291. R. G. Kostyanovsky, Z. E. Samojlova and I. I. Tchervin, *Tetrahedron Letters*, 1969, 719.

292. D. R. Boyd, R. Spratt and D. M. Jerina, *J. Chem. Soc.(C)*, 1969, 2650.
293. M. Jautelat and J. D. Roberts, *J. Amer. Chem. Soc.*, 1969, **91**, 642.
294. D. J. Anderson, D. C. Horwell and R. S. Atkinson, *Chem. Comm.*, 1969, 1189.
295. K. B. Wiberg and D. E. Barth, *J. Amer. Chem. Soc.*, 1969, **91**, 5124.
296. L. R. Subramanian and G. S. Krishna Rao, *Tetrahedron*, 1969, **25**, 1749.
297. E. Doomes and N. H. Cromwell, *J. Org. Chem.*, 1969, **34**, 310.
298. F. A. L. Anet and P. M. Henrichs, *Tetrahedron Letters*, 1969, 741.
299. R. Brettle, D. R. Brown, J. McKenna and J. M. McKenna, *Chem. Comm.*, 1969, 696.
300. G. E. Hawkes and J. H. P. Utley, *Chem. Comm.*, 1969, 1033.
301. E. L. Eliel and E. C. Gilbert, *J. Amer. Chem. Soc.*, 1969, **91**, 5487.
302. R. D. Stolow, T. Groom and D. I. Lewis, *Tetrahedron Letters*, 1969, 913.
303. F. R. Jenson and C. H. Bushweller, *J. Amer. Chem. Soc.*, 1969, 91, 3223.
304. F. R. Jensen, C. H. Bushweller and B. H. Beck, *J. Amer. Chem. Soc.*, 1969, **91**, 344.
305. G. Wood, E. P. Woo and M. H. Miskow, *Canad. J. Chem.*, 1969, **47**, 429.
306. H. Friebolin, H. G. Schmid, S. Kabuss and W. Faisst, *Org. Magn. Resonance*, 1969, **1**, 147.
307. F. R. Jensen and C. H. Bushweller, *J. Amer. Chem. Soc.*, 1969, **91**, 5774.
308. N. S. Zefirov, V. N. Chekulaeva and A. I. Belozerov, *Tetrahedron*, 1969, **25**, 1997.
309. J. B. Lambert, W. L. Oliver and G. F. Jackson, *Tetrahedron Letters*, 1969, 2027.
310. H. R. Buys, *Rec. Trav. chim.*, 1969, **88**, 1003.
311. R. K. Harris and R. A. Spragg, *Org. Magn. Resonance*, 1969, **1**, 329.
312. J. J. Delpuech, Y. Martinet and B. Petit, *J. Amer. Chem. Soc.*, 1969, **91**, 2158.
313. J. E. Anderson, *J. Amer. Chem. Soc.*, 1969, **91**, 6374.
314. H. Friebolin, H. G. Schmid, S. Kabuss and W. Faisst, *Org. Magn. Resonance*, 1969, **1**, 67.
315. E. L. Eliel and R. O. Hutchins, *J. Amer. Chem. Soc.*, 1969, **91**, 2703.
316. C. H. Bushweller, *J. Amer. Chem. Soc.*, 1969, **91**, 6019.
317. R. W. Murray and M. L. Kaplan, *Tetrahedron*, 1969, **25**, 1651.
318. A. R. Dunn and R. J. Stoodley, *Tetrahedron Letters*, 1969, 2979.
319. J. E. Anderson, *Chem. Comm.*, 1969, 699.
320. C. H. Bushweller and J. W. O'Neil, *Tetrahedron Letters*, 1969, 4713.
321. H. Baumann, H. Möhrle and A. Dieffenbacker, *Tetrahedron*, 1969, **25**, 135.
322. H. Gunther, *Z. Naturforsch*, 1969, **24B**, 680.
323. W. E. Heyd and C. A. Cupas, *J. Amer. Chem. Soc.*, 1969, **91**, 1559.
324. R. M. Moriarty, N. Ishibe, M. Kayser, K. C. Ramey and H. J. Gisler, *Tetrahedron Letters*, 1969, 4883.
325. H. Gilboa, J. Altman and A. Loewenstein, *J. Amer. Chem. Soc.*, 1969, **91**, 6062.
326. B. Fuchs, *Tetrahedron Letters*, 1969, 3571.
327. W. L. F. Armarego and T. Kobayashi, *J. Chem. Soc.(C)*, 1969, 1635.
328. F. Vögtle and P. Neumann, *Tetrahedron Letters*, 1969, 5329.
329. F. Vögtle, *Tetrahedron Letters*, 1969, 3193.
330. J. R. Fletcher and I. O. Sutherland, *Chem. Comm.*, 1969, 1504.
331. F. Vögtle and A. H. Effler, *Chem. Ber.*, 1969, **102**, 3071.
332. R. A. Y. Jones, A. R. Katritzky and A. C. Richards, *Chem. Comm.*, 1969, 708.

333. M. Nakazaki, K. Yamamoto and S. Okamoto, *Tetrahedron Letters*, 1969, 4597.
334. H. H. Wasserman and P. M. Keehn, *Tetrahedron Letters*, 1969, 3227.
335. D. T. Longone and G. R. Chipman, *Chem. Comm.*, 1969, 1358.
336. A. B. Dempster, K. Price and N. Sheppard, *Spectochim. Acta*, 1969, **25A**, 1381.
337. J. B. Lee and B. F. Scanlon, *Tetrahedron*, 1969, **25**, 3413.
338. D. C. Best, G. Underwood and C. A. Kingsbury, *Chem. Comm.*, 1969, 627.
339. E. I. Snyder, *J. Amer. Chem. Soc.*, 1969, **91**, 2579.
340. J. C. Jochims, W. Otting, A. Seeliger and G. Taigel, *Chem. Ber.*, 1969, **102**, 255.
341. C. P. Rader, *J. Amer. Chem. Soc.*, 1969, **91**, 3248.
342. J. L. Pierre, R. Perraud and P. Arnaud, *Bull. Soc. chim. France*, 1969, 1322.
343. J. L. Pierre, R. Perraud, P. Chautemps and P. Arnaud, *Bull. Soc. chim. France*, 1969, 1325.
344. R. R. Fraser, M. Kaufman, P. Morand and G. Govil, *Canad. J. Chem.*, 1969, **47**, 403.
345. G. J. Karabatsos and D. J. Fenoglio, *J. Amer. Chem. Soc.*, 1969, **91**, 1124.
346. G. J. Karabatsos and D. J. Fenoglio, *J. Amer. Chem. Soc.*, 1969, **91**, 3577.
347. G. J. Karabatsos, D. J. Fenoglio and S. S. Lande, *J. Amer. Chem. Soc.*, 1969, **91**, 3572.
348. W. F. Reynolds and D. J. Wood, *Canad. J. Chem.*, 1969, **47**, 1295.
349. G. Heublein, H. Schütz and A. Zschunke, *Tetrahedron*, 1969, **25**, 4225.
350. S. L. Spassov, *Tetrahedron*, 1969, **25**, 3631.
351. J. N. Stefanovsky, S. L. Spassov, B. J. Kurter, M. Balla and L. Olvos, *Chem. Ber.*, 1969, **102**, 717.
352. C. W. Jones, D. E. Leyden and C. H. Stammer, *Canad. J. Chem.*, 1969, **47**, 4363.
353. R. Le Gaoller, J. L. Pierre and P. Arnaud, *Org. Magn. Resonance*, 1969, **1**, 337.
354. W. M. Phillips and D. J. Currie, *Canad. J. Chem.*, 1969, **47**, 3137.
355. Y. Shvo and H. Shanan-Atidi, *J. Amer. Chem. Soc.*, 1969, **91**, 6683.
356. Y. Shvo and I. Belsky, *Tetrahedron*, 1969, **25**, 4649.
357. H. Kessler, *Angew. Chem. Internat. Edn.*, 1969, **8**, 905.
358. H. Kessler and D. Leibfritz, *Tetrahedron*, 1969, **25**, 5127.
359. H. Kessler and D. Leibfritz, *Tetrahedron Letters*, 1969, 427.
360. M. J. S. Dewar and P. Rona, *J. Amer. Chem. Soc.*, 1969, **91**, 2259.
361. N. P. Marullo and E. H. Wagener, *Tetrahedron Letters*, 1969, 2555.
362. M. J. Sabacky, S. M. Johnson, J. C. Martin and I. C. Paul, *J. Amer. Chem. Soc.*, 1969, **91**, 7542.
363. H. Kessler, A. Moosmayer and A. Rieker, *Tetrahedron*, 1969, **25**, 287.
364. A. J. M. Reuvers, A. Sinnema, F. van Rantwijk, J. D. Remijnse and H. van Bekkum, *Tetrahedron*, 1969, **25**, 4455.
365. T. H. Siddall and W. E. Stewart, *J. Org. Chem.*, 1969, **34**, 233.
366. J. W. Rakshys, S. V. McKinley and H. H. Freedman, *Chem. Comm.*, 1969, 1180.
367. C. A. Fyfe, *Canad. J. Chem.*, 1969, **47**, 2331.
368. A. Rieker and H. Kessler, *Tetrahedron Letters*, 1969, 1227.
369. J. R. Fletcher and I. O. Sutherland, *Chem. Comm.*, 1969, 706; J. E. Anderson, D. L. Griffith and J. D. Roberts, *J. Amer. Chem. Soc.*, 1969, **91**, 6371.
370. M. Raban and F. B. Jones, *J. Amer. Chem. Soc.*, 1969, **91**, 2180.

371. M. Raban, G. W. J. Kenney and F. B. Jones, *J. Amer. Chem. Soc.*, 1969, **91**, 6677.
372. V. F. Bystrov, S. L. Portnova, V. I. Tsetlin, V. T. Ivanov and Y. A. Ovchinnikov, *Tetrahedron*, 1969, **25**, 493.
373. V. F. Bystrov, S. L. Portnova, T. A. Balashova, V. I. Tsetlin, V. T. Ivanov, P. V. Kostetzky and Y. A. Ovchinnov, *Tetrahedron Letters*, 1969, 5225.
374. K. D. Kopple, T. Saito and M. Ohnishi, *J. Org. Chem.*, 1969, **34**, 1631.
375. M. Goodman, A. S. Verdini, C. Toniolo, W. D. Phillips and F. A. Bovey, *Proc. Nat. Acad. Sci. U.S.A.*, 1969, **64**, 444.
376. K. D. Kopple and M. Ohnishi, *J. Amer. Chem. Soc.*, 1969, **91**, 962.
377. K. D. Kopple, M. Ohnishi and A. Go, *J. Amer. Chem. Soc.*, 1969, **91**, 4264.
378. R. Schwyzer and U. Ludescher, *Helv. Chim. Acta*, 1969, **52**, 2033.
379. K. D. Kopple, M. Ohnishi and A. Go, *Biochemistry*, 1969, **8**, 4087.
380. M. Ohnishi and D. W. Urry, *Biochem. Biophys. Res. Comm.*, 1969, **36**, 194.
381. D. H. Haynes, A. Kowalsky and B. C. Pressman, *J. Biol. Chem.*, 1969, **244**, 502.
382. J. H. Prestegard and S. I. Chan, *Biochemistry*, 1969, **8**, 3921.
383. T. A. Victor, F. E. Hruska, K. Hikichi, S. S. Danyluk and C. L. Bell, *Nature*, 1969, **233**, 303; T. A. Victor, F. E. Hruska, C. L. Bell and S. S. Danyluk, *Tetrahedron Letters*, 1969, 4721.
384. A. Stern, W. A. Gibbons and L. C. Craig, *J. Amer. Chem. Soc.*, 1969, **91**, 2794.
385. C. C. McDonald and W. D. Phillips, *J. Amer. Chem. Soc.*, 1969, **91**, 1513.
386. J. H. Bradbury and N. L. R. King, *Austral. J. Chem.*, 1969, **22**, 1083.
387. H. L. Crespi and J. J. Katz, *Nature*, 1969, **224**, 560.
388. B. Bak, J. J. Led and E. J. Pedersen, *J. Mol. Spectroscopy*, 1969, **32**, 151.
389. J. D. Glickson, C. C. McDonald and W. D. Phillips, *Biochem. Biophys. Res. Comm.*, 1969, **35**, 492.
390. J. H. Bradbury and M. D. Fenn, *Austral. J. Chem.*, 1969, **22**, 357.
391. J. Steigman, A. S. Verdini, C. Montagner and L. Strasorier, *J. Amer. Chem. Soc.*, 1969, **91**, 1829.
392. J. A. Ferretti and L. Paolitto, *Biopolymers*, 1969, **7**, 155.
393. P. O. P. Ts'o, M. P. Schweizer and D. P. Hollis, *Ann. New York Acad. Sci.*, 1969, **158**, 256.
394. P. O. P. Ts'o, N. S. Kondo, M. P. Schweizer and D. P. Hollis, *Biochem.*, 1969, **8**, 997.
395. I. C. P. Smith, B. J. Blackburn and T. Yamane, *Canad. J. Chem.*, 1969, **47**, 513.
396. J. H. Prestegard and S. I. Chan, *J. Amer. Chem. Soc.*, 1969, **91**, 2843.
397. P. A. Hart and J. P. Davis, *J. Amer. Chem. Soc.*, 1969, **91**, 512.
398. P. A. Hart and J. P. Davis, *Biochem. Biophys. Res. Comm.*, 1969, **34**, 733.
399. S. I. Chan and J. H. Nelson, *J. Amer. Chem. Soc.*, 1969, **91**, 168.
400. B. W. Bangerter and S. I. Chan, *J. Amer. Chem. Soc.*, 1969, **91**, 3910.
401. P. O. P. Ts'o, N. S. Kondo, R. K. Robins and A. D. Broom, *J. Amer. Chem. Soc.*, 1969, **91**, 5625.
402. A. M. Bobst, F. Rottman and P. A. Cerutti, *J. Amer. Chem. Soc.*, 1969, **91**, 4603.
403. D. J. Patel, *Nature*, 1969, **221**, 1239; R. H. Sarma and N. O. Kaplan, *J. Biol. Chem.*, 1969, **244**, 771.
404. D. P. Hollis, *Org. Magn. Resonance*, 1969, **1**, 305.

405. W. A. Catterall, D. P. Hollis and C. F. Walter, *Biochem.*, 1969, **8**, 4032.
406. G. Kolowyez, N. Teng, M. P. Klein and M. Calvin, *J. Biol. Chem.*, 1969, **244**, 5656.
407. G. C. K. Roberts, E. A. Dennis, D. H. Meadows, J. S. Cohen and O. Jardetzky, *Proc. Nat. Acad. Sci. U.S.A.*, 1969, **62**, 1151.
408. G. C. K. Roberts, D. H. Meadows and O. Jardetzky, *Biochemistry*, 1969, **8**, 2053.
409. H. Ruterjans and H. Witzel, *European J. Biochem.*, 1969, **9**, 118.
410. J. S. Cohen, *Nature*, 1969, **223**, 43.
411. F. W. Dahlquist and M. A. Raftery, *Biochemistry*, 1969, **8**, 713.
412. M. Cohn, A. Danchin and M. Grunberg-Manago, *J. Mol. Biol.*, 1969, **39**, 199.
413. B. K. Joyce and M. Cohn, *J. Biol. Chem.*, 1969, **244**, 811.
414. A. R. Peacocke, R. E. Richards and B. Sheard, *Mol. Phys.*, 1969, **16**, 177.
415. J. S. Taylor, J. S. Leigh and M. Cohn, *Proc. Nat. Acad. Sci. U.S.A.*, 1969, **64**, 219.
416. A. S. Mildvan and H. Weiner, *J. Biol. Chem.*, 1969, **244**, 2465.
417. P. G. Schmidt, G. R. Stark and J. D. Baldeschwieler, *J. Biol. Chem.*, 1969, **244**, 1860.
418. E. J. Gabbay, B. L. Guffney, R. Glaser and D. Z. Denney, *Chem. Comm.*, 1969, 1507.
419. T. Nogrady and A. S. V. Burgen, *J. Amer. Chem. Soc.*, 1969, **91**, 3890.
420. O. A. Gansow and R. H. Holm, *J. Amer. Chem. Soc.*, 1969, **91**, 573, 5984.
421. E. H. Abbott and A. E. Martell, *J. Amer. Chem. Soc.*, 1969, **91**, 6866.
422. E. H. Abbott and A. E. Martell, *J. Amer. Chem. Soc.*, 1969, **91**, 6931.
423. D. Chapman, R. B. Leslie, R. Hirz and A. M. Seanu, *Nature*, 1969, **221**, 260.
424. F. W. Cope, *J. Biophys.*, 1969, **9**, 303.
425. C. F. Hazlewood, B. L. Nichols and N. F. Chamberlin, *Nature*, 1969, **222**, 747.
426. M. P. Klein, D. E. Phelps, *Nature*, 1969, **224**, 70.

The Investigation of the Kinetics of Conformational Changes by Nuclear Magnetic Resonance Spectroscopy

I. O. SUTHERLAND

Department of Chemistry, The University, Sheffield, S3 7HF, England

I. INTRODUCTION

NMR Spectroscopy, in addition to providing valuable data in the for   of chemical shifts and coupling constants, has been used extensively in the study of certain types of rapid equilibria. These must be processes involving the exchange of nuclei between different magnetic sites with first order rate constants falling in the range of approximately 1 sec.$^{-1}$ to 10^3 sec.$^{-1}$, in the temperature range (103°K to 473°K) available within the probe of modern NMR spectrometers. The associated free energies of activation for these processes may therefore range from 5 to 25 kcal. mole^{-1}, and most of the studies which have been made deal with examples of two general types of unimolecular processes. The first type involves changes of molecular geometry without major changes in bonding while the second type involves rapid bond reorganization in so called fluxional molecules. The first type of process is for the most part restricted to conformational changes in organic molecules associated with rotation about single and double bonds, inversion of the conformation of cyclic compounds and of the configuration of certain tricovalent atoms. These processes will be discussed in some detail. The fluxional molecules have been particularly widely recognized in inorganic chemistry and organometallic chemistry, in addition quite a large number of organic compounds undergo electrocyclic bond reorganizations which are sufficiently fast to be studied by NMR line-shape methods. This review will be restricted to the conformational changes of organic compounds.

The first section of the review deals with the elementary theory of the effects of site exchange on NMR line-shapes; the more sophisticated quantum mechanical methods have not been included although the results of the density matrix treatment for coupled systems have been briefly described. The subject is treated at a level believed to be suitable for chemists who are unfamiliar with NMR theory. The second part of the review is a survey of some of the very large number of examples which have appeared in the literature since 1956. The topics chosen for discussion are, for the most part, those which have attracted attention within the last two or three years but some attempt has been made to cover the early literature within the general area of the review. This is extensive and the author hopes that not too many important contributions have been omitted.

Several important reviews have appeared on the use of NMR line-shape methods in kinetic studies, two of these are quite comprehensive[1,2] and cover much of the literature up to 1966 and early 1967. In addition a third review deals with the theory of line-shape equations,[3] and two other reviews[4,5] deal with specialized aspects of the application of line-shape methods. Much of the theory dealt with in the first section of this review is covered by the standard text-books on NMR spectroscopy, but it is included here in the belief that a self-contained review is better than one which deals only with limited aspects of the subject.

II. THE DERIVATION OF LINE-SHAPE EQUATIONS

In order to understand the way in which rate processes may be studied by NMR spectroscopy it is necessary to consider the characteristic shapes of NMR lines in the absence of exchange effects, and then examine the effects of site exchange processes upon these line shapes. Of the two approaches that may be used, classical and quantum mechanical, the rather simpler classical approach, first developed by Bloch,[6] will be described, and this will then be modified to allow for the effects of the exchange of nuclei between different sites. This approach is not suitable for deriving line-shape equations for coupled systems, for which the quantum mechanical approach must be used. The results obtained from this approach will be discussed and the application of the general line-shape equation to a number of specific problems will be described.

A. The Bloch equations

NMR spectrometers detect a change in the macroscopic magnetization of a sample, containing nuclei with non-zero spin, in a plane at right angles to the direction of a large field H_0 (defined as the z direction) in which the sample is placed. This change in magnetization is caused by subjecting the sample to a further linearly oscillating field H_1 along the x axis; this second field behaves effectively as two equal rotating fields in the xy plane with angular velocities of equal magnitude but opposite sign. A convenient classical description of the behaviour of the nuclear magnetic moments in the fields H_0 and H_1 has been given by Bloch,[6] and the resulting equations, known as the Bloch equations, provide a relatively simple approach to the consideration of NMR line-shapes in addition to other phenomena associated with the method. These equations may then be further modified to allow for the effects of processes which cause rapid changes of the magnetic environments of the nuclei.

A nucleus having spin $\mathbf{I}$, and therefore a magnetic moment $\mu = \gamma\mathbf{I}$, where γ is the gyromagnetic ratio characteristic of the nuclear type, placed in a magnetic field H_0 in the z direction experiences a torque which causes it to move in a manner described by the vector equation:

$$d\mu/dt = \gamma[\mu \times \mathbf{H}] \tag{1}$$

where $\qquad \mu = (\mu_x, \mu_y, \mu_z) \qquad$ and $\qquad \mathbf{H} = (0, 0, H_0)$

Developing the vector product $\mu \times \mathbf{H}$ in the usual way, this equation may be written more fully as:

$$d\mu_x/dt = \gamma[\mu_y H_z - \mu_z H_y] = \gamma H_0 \mu_y \tag{1a}$$

$$d\mu_y/dt = \gamma[\mu_z H_x - \mu_x H_z] = \gamma H_0 \mu_x \tag{1b}$$

$$d\mu_z/dt = \gamma[\mu_x H_y - \mu_y H_x] = 0 \tag{1c}$$

The equations (1a–c) describe the precession of a nuclear dipole about the z axis with angular frequency $\gamma H_0 = \omega_0$ in a clockwise direction, provided that $\gamma > 0$; ω_0 is generally referred to as the Larmor frequency. The equations (1) apply to the motion of a single nuclear moment, for a sample containing many nuclei of the same type they will all precess about the z axis with the same angular frequency ω_0, but the phases of the precession will generally be randomly distributed among the nuclei as shown in Fig. 1. The resulting macroscopic magnetization in the sample $\mathbf{M}$ is therefore $\mathbf{M}_0 = (0, 0, M_0)$ with a resultant only in the z direction. The frequency

ω_0, the Larmor frequency, is in radians sec.$^{-1}$ and should be replaced by $2\pi\nu_0$ when it is desired to express the frequency in Hz.

The observation of an NMR spectrum requires that this system, of randomly phased precessing nuclei, should be disturbed by the second smaller field H_1, rotating with angular frequency ω in the same sense as the angular precession of the nuclei. It can then be shown that the x and y components of the induced magnetization become significantly different from zero as the frequency ω approaches the Larmor frequency ω_0. In practice, as has already been mentioned,

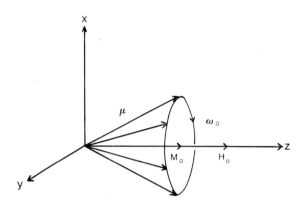

FIG. 1. The movement of nuclei with magnetic moment μ when placed in a magnetic field $\mathbf{H}_0$ in the z direction.

the rotating field H_1 is provided by a linear radiofrequency field in the x direction which is produced along the axis of a suitably oriented coil in the spectrometer probe. This field may be decomposed into two components rotating in the xy plane with angular frequency ω in opposite senses, only the component with the correct sense of rotation interacts with the precessing nuclei to a detectable extent, as the following treatment will show. The equation of motion for this situation is now;

$$dM/dt = \gamma[\mathbf{M} \times \mathbf{H}] \tag{2}$$

where
$$\mathbf{H} = (H_1 \cos \omega t, -H_1 \sin \omega t, H_0)$$

$$\mathbf{M} = (M_x, M_y, M_z)$$

which may be written more fully as in equations (2a–c)

$$dM_x/dt = \gamma(M_y H_0 + M_z H_1 \sin \omega t) \tag{2a}$$

$$dM_y/dt = \gamma(-M_x H_0 + M_z H_1 \cos \omega t) \tag{2b}$$

$$dM_z/dt = \gamma(-M_x H_1 \sin \omega t - M_y H_1 \cos \omega t) \tag{2c}$$

These equations are in a rather inconvenient form for further development, and a more useful set of equations results if the original Cartesian axes are replaced by a set of axes with angular velocity ω about the z axis in a clockwise direction. Then u and v are defined as the components of $\mathbf{M}$ along and perpendicular to the direction of H_1, which is stationary in this new reference frame. The components u and v correspond to the in-phase and out-of-phase components of $\mathbf{M}$ as shown in Fig. 2. It should be noted that the transformation equations used in Bloch's original description imply a direction for the component v which is shifted in phase by π from the direction consistent with M_y. This phase shift does not affect the line-shape and, since the use of a v component in the opposite direction results in sign changes in the right-hand side of the resulting equations for terms in v, the axes chosen by Bloch will be used in this review. The accounts of the Bloch equations given in books and reviews generally, but not always,[2,7] introduce this phase shift.

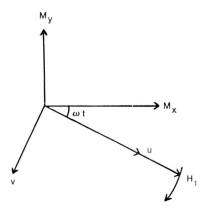

FIG. 2. Transverse components of the magnetic moment $\mathbf{M}$ (M_y and M_x) referred to the fixed axes and u and v referred to the rotating axes.

Using the relationship $\gamma H_0 = \omega_0$, and remembering that in the system of rotating axes (Fig. 2) the magnetic field is given by $\mathbf{H} = (H_1, 0, H_0)$ and the magnetic moment by $\mathbf{M} = (u, -v, M_z)$ and that ω_0 should be replaced by $(\omega_0 - \omega)$ the equations (2) may be rewritten as

$$du/dt = -(\omega_0 - \omega)v - u/T_2 \tag{3a}$$

$$dv/dt = (\omega_0 - \omega)u - \gamma M_z H_1 - v/T_2 \tag{3b}$$

$$dM_z/dt = \gamma H_1 v - (M_z - M_0)/T_1 \tag{3c}$$

The additional term on the right-hand side of each of these equations allows for the decay of the induced macroscopic magnetic moment $\mathbf{M}$ by relaxation processes to its original value $\mathbf{M}_0 = (0, 0, M_0)$. These decays are assumed to be first-order processes with the rate constants $1/T_2$ for relaxation in the transverse xy plane and $1/T_1$ for relaxation in the z direction. The transverse relaxation process results in the dephasing of the nuclear spins, which effectively become phased as ω approaches ω_0 and the transverse component of the magnetization becomes non-zero. This dephasing is a result of variations in the local magnetic environments of individual nuclei, and it will become apparent that T_2 is of major importance in determining the shape of NMR lines under normal conditions of spectrometer operation. The longitudinal relaxation time T_1 depends upon the rate at which excess nuclear Zeeman energy is exchanged with the other degrees of freedom of the system.

The solution of the differential equations (3) allows the determination of the magnitudes of the in-phase, u, and out-of-phase, v, components of the induced magnetization as ω is varied through ω_0. The change in M_z, and thus the Zeeman energy of the system, depends upon the out-of-phase component of the magnetic moment v, and the latter therefore corresponds to the absorption mode of the spectrum, and the in-phase component u corresponds to the dispersion mode. The change in magnetization in the xy plane, the component detected by the spectrometer, may conveniently be considered as a complex magnetization G where

$$G = u + iv \quad \text{and} \quad dG/dt = du/dt + i\, dv/dt \tag{4}$$

and the imaginary component of G describes the absorption spectrum.

Combining the equations (3) and (4) we obtain the Bloch equations (5) in a form suitable for the consideration of the effects of chemical exchange upon the line-shapes

$$dG/dt = i(\omega_0 - \omega)G - i\gamma H_1 M_z - G/T_2 \tag{5}$$

$$dM_z/dt = \gamma v H_1 - (M_z - M_0)/T_1 \tag{5a}$$

B. The effects of site exchange upon the Bloch equations

The variation in the complex magnetization G as the frequency ω changes may be obtained from the Bloch equations (5), the imaginary component of G is then proportional to the absorption intensity at ω. In practice NMR spectra are measured under "steady state conditions", which means that the spectra are swept sufficiently slowly so that the time derivative in equations (5) may be set equal to zero. In addition, the oscillating field H_1 is set sufficiently small for the equilibrium value M_0 to be used for the z component of the magnetization M_z. Then, replacing $\gamma H_1 M_0$ by a constant C, equation (5) becomes

$$G/T_2 - i(\omega_0 - \omega)G = -iC \tag{6}$$

The absorption intensity at frequency ν Hz† is then proportional to the imaginary part, Im(G), of the complex magnetization, and from equation (6) the resulting line-shape equation is‡

$$\text{Im}(G) = -CT_2/[1 + T_2^2 4\pi^2(\nu_0 - \nu)^2] \tag{7}$$

Equation (7) describes a Lorentzian curve centred at ν_0 with a full width w Hz at half maximum intensity given by:

$$w = 1/\pi T_2 \tag{8}$$

It should be stressed that equation (7) and other line-shape equations introduced in this section only apply for a pure absorption mode signal produced under steady-state conditions.

Equation (7) refers to the NMR absorption of a nucleus with non-zero spin which occupies a single magnetic environment, or as will be shown below undergoes exchange between a number of different magnetic environments or sites at a rate that is very fast on the NMR time scale, that is $k \gg 2\pi\delta\nu$ where k is the site exchange rate and $\delta\nu$ is the separation in Hz between sites. For cases in which the nucleus may occupy either of two sites, and the rate at which the nucleus can exchange between the sites is of the same order as the site separation, the use of an independent line-shape equation of a form analogous to (7) for each of the two sites is no longer valid. A correct line-shape equation, for these conditions, can be obtained by first modifying the Bloch equations (5) to allow for the effects of the exchange process upon the complex magnetization G associated with each of the sites.

An example of a situation where a proton or group of equivalent protons may occupy two different magnetic environments A and B is provided by the N-methyl groups of dimethylformamide (1). The protons in site A have the chemical shift $\nu_A = \omega_A/2\pi$ and the protons in site B the chemical shift $\nu_B = \omega_B/2\pi$. An exchange of the groups of three equivalent protons in the methyl groups labelled 1 and 2 between the two sites occurs as a result of rotation about the N–CO

---

† In this section NMR frequencies and line-widths are given the symbols ν and w when the units are Hz, and ω refers to frequencies in radians sec.$^{-1}$; the former units are used where this is convenient. Rate constants k are in sec.$^{-1}$ units and the symbol τ refers to a reciprocal rate constant or average residence time in sec.

‡ For those not familiar with the manipulation of complex numbers the quotient of two complex numbers may be obtained using the relationship

$$(a + ib)/(c + id) = [(ac + bd) + i(bc - ad)]/(c^2 + d^2)$$

It will also be noticed that line-shape equations such as (7) give negative values for Im(G). This is due to the choice of rotating axes referred to on p. 75 (Fig. 2), the sign of Im(G) must therefore be changed before the results are printed or the line-shape plotted for all equations for Im(G) which are derived using the Bloch equation (5a).

bond. An exchange process of this type, where only a single configurational or conformational type is involved [that is $(1) \equiv (1a)$], may be termed a mutual site exchange.

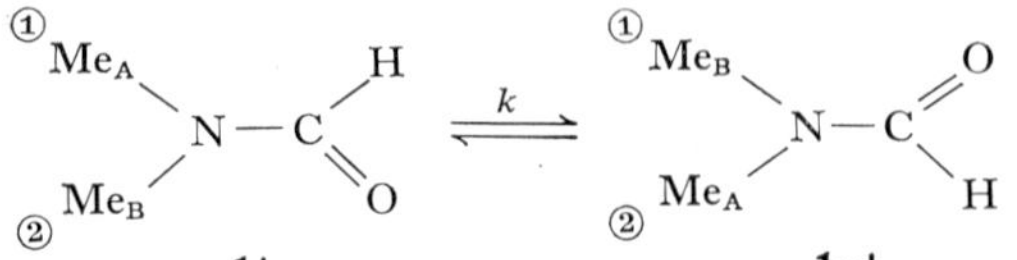

1†   1a†

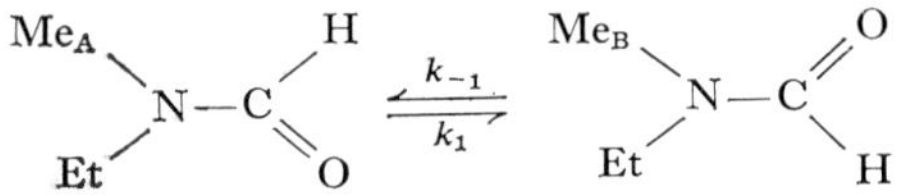

2   2a

The process $(2) \rightleftharpoons (2a)$ exemplifies a slightly different type of process, which involves diastereomeric configurations or conformations of the same constitutional type. In this case the methyl group (and the ethyl group) undergo exchange between two different environments, each environment being associated with one of the diastereomers, and as might be expected the effects on the NMR spectrum are similar to those found for the process $(1) \rightleftharpoons (1a)$. No distinction will be made between these two types of process in this section but, for systems where spin-spin coupling is important, it is convenient to make a distinction between the two types of process.

For the general situation in which proton(s) are exchanged between two sites A and B, the site populations are designated p_A and p_B and kinetics of the process are described in terms of two first-order rate-constants, k_A for transfer from site A to site B and k_B for transfer from site B to site A. Then for equilibrium the relationship between these rate constants is:

$$k_A p_A = k_B p_B \qquad (9)$$

The literature on site exchange effects frequently refers to the average residence

† In (1) and other diagrams of this type the subscripts A and B refer to the NMR sites appropriate to the molecular environment of the proton(s), and the encircled superscripts are used to denote the identity of the proton(s). The line-shape equations discussed in this section refer to the combined absorption of nuclei in the sites A, B, etc., and although p_A and p_B refer to the distribution of a single type of proton in the discussion they may equally well refer to the distribution of the six N-methyl protons in (1) between the sites A and B or the three N-methyl protons of (2) between two similar sites.

times τ_A and τ_B of the proton(s) in each of the sites. These times may simply be considered as reciprocal rate constants so that

$$k_A = 1/\tau_A; \qquad k_B = 1/\tau_B; \qquad \tau_A p_B = \tau_B p_A \qquad (10)$$

The relationship(s) between the rate constants for site exchange k_A and k_B and the rate constants for the conformational change causing the site exchange is usually easily recognized. Thus for $(1)\rightleftharpoons(1a)$, $k_A = k_B = k$, and for $(2)\rightleftharpoons(2a)$, $k_A = k_1$ and $k_B = k_{-1}$.

The effects of these exchange processes upon the NMR spectrum will now be considered following the general approach described by Hahn, Maxwell and McConnell (HMM)[8,9] since this is mathematically simpler than the earlier method of Gutowsky, McCall and Slichter[10,11] or the more general approach of Kubo and Sack.[12] Jumps of nuclei from site A to site B, which are sufficiently fast for no nuclear precession to occur during the jump, will result in a decrease in the transverse magnetization of site A at a rate $k_A G_A$ and an increase in the magnetization of site B at the same rate. Similarly transfer of nuclei from site B to site A will increase the complex magnetization in site A at a rate $k_B G_B$ and decrease that in site B at the same rate. The changes may be incorporated into the Bloch equation (5) which must be written in a suitable form for both sites A and B separately to give the equations (11) in which the subscripts A and B refer to the sites A and B respectively.

$$dG_A/dt + \alpha_A G_A = -i\gamma H_1 M_{zA} + k_B G_B - k_A G_A \qquad (11)$$

$$dG_B/dt + \alpha_B G_B = -i\gamma H_1 M_{zB} + k_A G_A - k_B G_B \qquad (11a)$$

where
$$\alpha_A = 1/T_{2A} - 2\pi i(\nu_A - \nu)$$

$$\alpha_B = 1/T_{2B} - 2\pi i(\nu_B - \nu)$$

The equations (11) require that the average time for a jump from site A to site B is much smaller than T_2, a condition which is usually met by such an exchange process since T_2 is of the order of a second or more. Exchange processes that involve low-energy intermediates may occur relatively slowly, and in these cases the line-shape equations discussed in this section may not apply, particularly when k is small.

For steady-state conditions, as previously defined, the M_z components of the magnetization are not appreciably changed from their equilibrium value M_0 and in particular

$$M_{zA} = M_{0A} = p_A M_0 \qquad (12)$$

$$M_{zB} = M_{0B} = p_B M_0$$

The time derivatives in equations (11) may also be set equal to zero so that these become:

$$\alpha_A G_A + k_A G_A - k_B G_B = -i p_A C \tag{13}$$

$$\alpha_B G_B + k_B G_B - k_A G_A = -i p_B C \tag{13a}$$

where
$$C = \gamma H_1 M_0$$

From the simultaneous equations (13) an expression for the total complex magnetization in the xy plane $G = G_A + G_B$ may be obtained, which is conveniently expressed in terms of the site lifetimes τ_A and τ_B. The measured absorption intensity at a frequency ν is then proportional to the imaginary component of G given by the line-shape equation:[10]

$$G = G_A + G_B = -iC\frac{[\tau_A + \tau_B + \tau_A \tau_B(\alpha_A p_B + \alpha_B p_A)]}{(1 + \alpha_A \tau_A)(1 + \alpha_B \tau_B) - 1} \tag{14}$$

This form of the line-shape equation is suitable for direct insertion into a computer programme since the imaginary part of a complex solution may readily be obtained by standard computing techniques. A theoretical line-shape is obtained by plotting $\text{Im}(G)$ against ν, usually after a normalization procedure to make the comparison of observed and computed spectra easier to carry out. The computation is faster if the imaginary part of equation (14) is extracted before computation[13] and the resulting equation is therefore reproduced below—

$$\text{Im}(G) = \frac{-C\{P[1 + \tau(p_B/T_{2A} + p_A/T_{2B})] + QR\}}{P^2 + R^2} \tag{15}$$

$$\tau = p_B \tau_A = p_A \tau_B; \qquad \delta\nu = \nu_A - \nu_B; \qquad \Delta\nu = \tfrac{1}{2}(\nu_A + \nu_B) - \nu$$

$$P = \tau\left[\frac{1}{T_{2A} T_{2B}} - 4\pi^2 \Delta\nu^2 + \pi^2 \delta\nu^2\right] + \frac{p_B}{T_{2B}} + \frac{p_A}{T_{2A}}$$

$$Q = \tau[2\pi \Delta\nu - \pi \delta\nu(p_A - p_B)]$$

$$R = 2\pi \Delta\nu[1 + \tau(1/T_{2A} + 1/T_{2B})] + \pi \delta\nu\tau(1/T_{2B} - 1/T_{2A}) + \pi \delta\nu(p_A - p_B)$$

Equation (15) allows rapid computation of spectra for appropriate input values of k_A, k_B, ν_A, ν_B, p_A, p_B, T_{2A}, and T_{2B}. Thus a single spectrum consisting of $\text{Im}(G)$ calculated for 500 different values of ν is obtained in 1·5 sec. using an ICL-1907 computer and a FORTRAN IV programme. Typical line-shapes generated for different exchange rates between two sites using the stated input parameters are shown in Fig. 3. Methods used for comparing observed and computed spectra will be discussed in a later section of this review.

In addition to general line-shape equations such as (14) and (15) a number of closed form relationships have been deduced relating observed spectral para-meters to exchange rates.[14] The validity of these methods has been checked by computation[15] and it has been shown that in several cases they are subject to

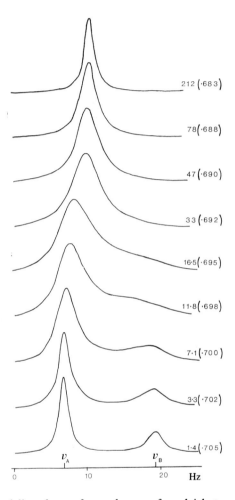

FIG. 3. Calculated line-shapes for exchange of nuclei between two unequally populated sites, A and B. The rate constants for site exchange (k_{AB} in sec.$^{-1}$) are shown by each spectrum, the figures in brackets refer to the value of p_A; $\nu_A = 6.9$ Hz, $\nu_B = 19.4$ Hz, $w_{A0} = 1.1$ Hz, $w_{B0} = 1.3$ Hz.

serious systematic errors. The more commonly used methods, and the conditions under which they are valid, will be discussed briefly since they have been used to produce a considerable amount of the data discussed later in this article.

When k_A and k_B are small compared with $(\nu_A - \nu_B)$, equations (14) and (15) describe two signals situated at ν_A and ν_B. Thus if the observing frequency ν is close to ν_A then G_B becomes effectively zero, implying that the A and B lines do not overlap, and equation (13) becomes

$$G_A = -iCp_A\tau_A/(1+\alpha_A\tau_A) \tag{16}$$

and extracting the imaginary part of G_A gives a line-shape equation closely analogous to equation (7)

$$\text{Im}(G_A) = -Cp_A T'_{2A}/[1+(T'_{2A})^2 4\pi^2(\nu_A-\nu)^2] \tag{17}$$

where
$$1/T'_{2A} = 1/T_{2A}+1/\tau_A.$$

Equation (17) describes a resonance line which has a half-height width $w_A = 1/\pi T'_{2A}$ and the apparent line broadening due to the exchange process is therefore $1/\pi\tau_A$ or expressing the result in a more convenient form

$$k = \pi(w_A-w_{A0}) \tag{18}$$

where w_{A0} is the half-height line-width of the A resonance line for a zero exchange rate. This simple relationship is valid when both the A and B signals give distinct lines which do not appreciably overlap. The determination of w_{A0} may present some difficulties since the low temperature often required for negligible values of k_A may result in line broadening due to factors other than exchange, for example increased solvent viscosity. Suggestions have been made concerning possible ways of allowing for these changes in low-temperature line-widths,[16 to 18] but in general in these circumstances the use of equation (18) gives no more than a very approximate indication of exchange rates. In more favourable circumstances it may be reasonably accurate.

For intermediate rates of exchange, $k \sim (\nu_A - \nu_B)$, the spectrum is observed as broad overlapping peaks which coalesce to a broad singlet at faster exchange rates. The only accurate method for obtaining exchange rates in this region is by the comparison of observed and computed spectral line-shapes. The comparison may be made either in terms of spectral parameters such as half-height line-widths, peak-through ratios, or signal separations, or by a least-squares comparison of observed and computed normalized absorption intensities at suitable frequency intervals and over an appropriate frequency range. The latter method of comparison[19 to 23] has the advantage of providing a technique suited for computers, this ideally requires a digital spectrum output from the spectrometer which is likely to be readily available on future commercial spectrometers, but may at present be obtained using devices such as multi-channel analysers. The major disadvantage of this type of comparison may lie in its thoroughness, it requires a good spectral line-shape over the whole frequency range to be compared and in particular the spectrometer should give a good Lorentzian line-shape[23,24] and the spectrum must of course be a pure absorption spectrum free from any distortion by the dispersion mode.

Other procedures have been suggested using closed form solutions of the line-shape equation for k in the region of intermediate exchange rates, particularly the "peak separation method"[11] and the "intensity ratio method".[13] For various reasons both of these methods are very prone to systematic errors and are no longer used. The only important relationship that has survived the test of time is that between the signal separation $(\nu_A - \nu_B)$ and the exchange rate k_c, which is the rate that just results in coalescence of the A and B signals into a single, rather broad, flat-topped absorption. By differentiation of the line-shape equation it is possible to derive the simple relationship:

$$k_c = \pi(\nu_A - \nu_B)/\sqrt{2} \qquad (19)$$

which is applicable only for cases in which $p_A = p_B = 0.5$ and $\nu_A - \nu_B$ is large compared with the half-height line-widths w_{A0} and w_{B0}.

When these conditions are not fulfilled it is advisable to use computed line-shapes even to obtain k_c. The use of the approximation (19) to obtain free energy barriers to conformational changes at the coalescence temperature only is very widespread, and there is little doubt that the relatively error free values of $\Delta G^\ddagger$ so obtained are useful. Nevertheless, it is generally better to carry out a more complete kinetic study of exchange processes when this is possible, provided that the activation enthalpies and entropies so obtained are sufficiently accurate to be meaningful. This has certainly not always been the case but, with the present availability of computers and programmes for generating line-shapes, kinetic studies by the NMR method should become increasingly accurate.

For the region of fast exchange where $k \gg (\nu_A - \nu_B)$ two relatively simple expressions have been derived which in one case may also be used for rates as low as k_c. Although the use of computed line-shapes is preferable to the use of these relationships they will be briefly discussed here so that their limitations may be recognized. When τ_A and τ_B are very small, the line-shape equation (14) reduces to equation (20) as a result of dropping all terms involving the products of τ_A and τ_B.

$$G = \frac{-iC(\tau_A + \tau_B)}{\alpha_A \tau_A + \alpha_B \tau_B} \qquad (20)$$

and using the relationship $p_A/\tau_A = p_B/\tau_B$, the imaginary part of (20) is given by the expression:

$$\mathrm{Im}(G) = \frac{-C(p_A/T_{2A} + p_B/T_{2B})}{(p_A/T_{2A} + p_B/T_{2B})^2 + 4\pi^2(p_A\nu_A + p_B\nu_B - \nu)^2} \qquad (21)$$

The comparison of equation (21) with equation (7) shows that the former describes a Lorentzian line with an apparent width $w^* = p_A w_{A0} + p_B w_{B0}$ situated at the weighted average of ν_A and ν_B. It has been shown,[25] by similar methods, that where τ_A and τ_B are too large to ignore the product terms in (14), but $k \gg (\nu_A - \nu_B)$, that the resulting line-shape equation describes a line of width w, and that this width is related to k_A and k_B by the simple expressions:

$$k_A = \frac{p_A p_B^2 4\pi(\nu_A - \nu_B)^2}{(w - w^*)}, \qquad k_B = \frac{p_A^2 p_B 4\pi(\nu_A - \nu_B)^2}{(w - w^*)} \qquad (22)$$

In the simplest case where $p_A = p_B = 0\cdot5$, $k_A = k_B = k$ these equations reduce to the single relationship:

$$k = \frac{\pi(\nu_A - \nu_B)^2}{2(w - w^*)} \qquad (23)$$

These equations, generally referred to as the Piette and Anderson equations, have been checked by computation and are accurate for fast exchange rates.[15] Serious systematic errors result, however, if they are used to obtain rates of the same order as k_c and a more suitable equation has been derived[15,26] for this region for the cases in which $p_A = p_B = 0\cdot5$.

$$k = \frac{\pi(\nu_A - \nu_B)^2 \{w^* + w[1 + 2(w/(\nu_A - \nu_B))^2 - (w/(\nu_A - \nu_B))^4]^{\frac{1}{2}}\}}{2(w^2 - w^{*2})} \qquad (24)$$

This equation reduces to equation (23) when $w \ll (\nu_A - \nu_B)$. For cases in which $w \gg w^*$, that is at coalescence and just above, equation (24) may be simplified[15] by the omission of the w^* terms to give

$$k = 0\cdot5\pi[(\nu_A - \nu_B)^4/w^2 + 2(\nu_A - \nu_B)^2 - w^2]^{\frac{1}{2}} \qquad (25)$$

This last equation together with equation (19) give the interesting result that at coalescence $w = (\nu_A - \nu_B)$, a result that has been shown to be accurate for cases in which $w^* \ll (\nu_A - \nu_B)$. This has the advantage that for cases in which $(\nu_A - \nu_B)$ is temperature dependent due to factors other than the exchange process, or for cases in which it is not possible to attain sufficiently low temperatures to measure $(\nu_A - \nu_B)$ directly, it is still possible to measure $(\nu_A - \nu_B)$ at the coalescence temperature.

C. Exchange between more than two sites

Inspection of the equations (13a) and (13b) and consideration of the HMM approach by which they were developed suggests that it is a simple matter to extend these equations to cases involving more than two sites. The general equation for an n site problem may be written[9] for the complex moment G_j of the jth site under steady-state conditions as

$$\alpha_j G_j - \sum_{k \neq j} (k_{kj} G_k - k_{jk} G_j) = -ip_j C \qquad (26)$$

where k_{kj} is the rate constant for exchange from site k to site j and is given a value appropriate to the situation being examined. The resulting n simultaneous equations may be readily solved by standard computing procedures to give the complex moments G_j, then the observed absorption intensity at any frequency ν is obtained by the summation of the imaginary components of the G_j's.

A more elegant and general procedure has been suggested by Binsch[2,27] who represents the equation (26) in matrix form, rather more suitable for direct insertion

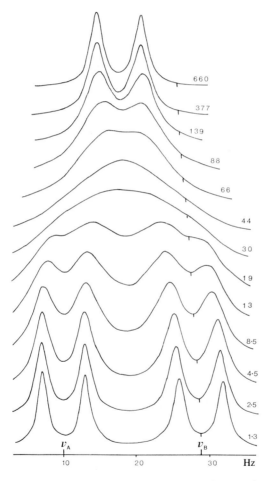

FIG. 4. Calculated line shapes for the methyl signals of $CHMe_A^1Me_B^2$ showing the effects of an exchange of the methyl groups (Me^1 and Me^2) between the two sites A and B. The exchange rate (sec.$^{-1}$) is shown by each curve; $\nu_A = 10.0$ Hz and ν_B varies from 28.75 to 25.65 Hz as indicated by the short vertical line intersecting the right hand side of each spectrum, $J_{CH-Me} = 6.0$ Hz, $w_{A0} = 1.3$ Hz, $w_{B0} = 1.5$ Hz.

into a computer programme. The same author has also suggested methods[27] whereby the solution of the n simultaneous equations (26) for every value of ν is avoided, and this undoubtedly results in more rapid computation. Nevertheless, for a four-site problem, involving the solution of four complex simultaneous equations for every value of ν and not using the more rapid procedure outlined by Binsch, the computing time required is not excessive. Thus a spectrum consisting of the calculated absorption intensity at 400 different values of ν may be obtained in 27 sec. using a FORTRAN IV programme and an ICL-1907 computer.

The line-shape equations and derived expressions for site exchange rates discussed in this section are not applicable to cases where the exchanging nuclei interact by strong spin–spin coupling and quantum mechanical methods (the results of which are outlined in the next section) are required. First-order coupling to a third nucleus may, however, be accommodated by an obvious extension of these equations. Thus for the site exchange (3), which might involve the methyl

$$\text{Me}_A{}^{①} + \text{Me}_B{}^{②} \rightleftharpoons \text{Me}_A{}^{②} + \text{Me}_B{}^{①}$$

3

doublet signals resulting from Me_A and Me_B of a prochiral isopropyl group CHMe_AMe_B, the calculation of line-shapes may be achieved by simply using equations (14) or (15) and generating the resulting spectrum for both the high- and low-field components of the coalescing doublets. Typical examples of spectra computed by this procedure are shown in Fig. 4.

D. Exchange in coupled systems

The extension of the Bloch phenomenological equations by the HMM treatment, which was described in the previous section, makes possible the derivation of line-shape equations for systems in which the exchanging nuclei do not interact by mutual spin–spin coupling. The derivation of line-shape equations for the many cases encountered in the laboratory, which do involve significant spin–spin coupling, requires a quantum mechanical treatment. This has been carried out successfully using the density matrix methods which had, at an early stage in the development of NMR theory, been found useful[28] in the treatment of NMR phenomena. A review has appeared[29] on the calculation of line-shapes using density matrix methods, and the methods have been briefly reviewed[2,3] in some of the articles dealing with exchange processes.

In the density matrix notation the equation of motion for nuclear spins in a magnetic field becomes:[30]

$$d\rho/dt = -i[\mathscr{H}\rho] \tag{27}$$

where ρ is the density matrix describing the system, $\mathscr{H}$ is the Hamiltonian for the system and the energy is in frequency units (radians sec.$^{-1}$). In the account which follows we will consider only the case of protons, or other nuclei with $I_z = \pm \frac{1}{2}$, and the account will generally be restricted to a discussion of the line-shape equations that have been derived elsewhere. For a molecule containing interacting nuclear spins which are all of one nuclear type in a single molecular species, the Hamiltonian in angular frequency units, in the absence of exchange or relaxation processes, is:

$$\mathcal{H} = \sum I_z^i(\omega_i - \omega) + \sum_{i<j} J_{ij} I^i I^j + \sum \gamma I_x^i H_i \qquad (28)$$

where
$$\omega_i = \gamma \hbar H_0 (1 - \sigma_i)$$

The different molecular environments of the nuclei are indicated by the screening constants σ_i, the subscripts i (superscripts i in the spin operators) refer to the ith nucleus of the system. H_0 refers to a permanent field in the z direction, and the oscillating field H_1 lies along the x axis in a co-ordinate system which rotates about the z axis with angular frequency ω. The general method for developing equation (27) into a description of a system in which some of the nuclear spins undergo mutual exchanges of their environments was originally described by Kaplan[31] and it has been further developed by Alexander[32] and Johnson.[3,33] The method used resembles the HMM treatment of the Bloch equations, and the results given here apply only to a mutual intramolecular exchange of environments; the methods may easily be extended to other types of intramolecular processes and also to intermolecular processes. The method consists essentially of modifying equation (27) by the addition of terms allowing for relaxation processes and for exchange. Then, for steady-state conditions, the total complex magnetization for a system of nuclei with $I_z = \pm \frac{1}{2}$ described by the density matrix ρ may be obtained from a solution of the equation (29).†

$$\frac{d\rho_{kl}}{dt} = \frac{1}{\tau} \left[\sum_{n,m} R_{kn} \rho_{nm} R_{ml} - \rho_{kl} \right] - \frac{\rho_{kl}}{T_2}$$
$$- i\rho_{kl} \{ \sum_i 2\pi(\nu_i - \nu)[(I_z^i)_{kk} - (I_z^i)_{ll}]$$
$$+ \sum_{i<j} 2\pi J_{ij}[(I_z^i I_z^j)_{kk} - (I_z^i I_z^j)_{ll}] \}$$
$$+ i \sum_{i<j} \pi J_{ij} \sum_m \{ \rho_{km}(I_+^i I_-^j)_{ml} - \rho_{ml}(I_+^i I_-^j)_{km}$$
$$+ \rho_{km}(I_-^i I_+^j)_{ml} - \rho_{ml}(I_-^i I_+^j)_{km} \}$$
$$+ 2\pi i \nu_r (\rho_{kk} - \rho_{ll}) \sum_i (I_x^i)_{kl} = 0 \qquad (29)$$

† This is a slightly extended form of equation (65) of the review by Johnson[3] and, in this form, may be used with relative ease. Equation (29) is suitable for ν and J in Hz and differs slightly from the analogous equation discussed by Binsch[2,27] in that the spin raising operator has been used, that is $\Delta F_z = +1$ for allowed transitions. This does not affect the final form of the equations but does have the effect of changing the sign of the J's associated with some of the ρ_{kl} values.

In equation (29) the subscripts k, l, m, n refer to the basis functions and the superscripts and subscripts i, j identify the individual spins. The correct basis functions to use are those with the spin states $I_z = +\frac{1}{2}(\alpha)$ and the $I_z = -\frac{1}{2}(\beta)$. In general, equation (29) represents a set of simultaneous equations with one equation corresponding to each of the allowed spectral transitions ($\Delta F_z = +1$, where F_z is the total z component of the nuclear spins in the states k, l, etc.)

The exchange operator R_{kn} permits the inclusion of the density matrix elements ρ_{nm} in a fashion which is appropriate for the exchanging system. Thus, if the basis functions ϕ_k and ϕ_n are interchanged by the exchange process then $R_{kn}=1$, otherwise it takes a zero value. The parameter τ is the mean lifetime of each of the two exchanging states. It is possible to modify equation (29) for other types of exchange involving more than one value of τ, this is discussed below. The absorption intensity at frequency ν is proportional to the imaginary components of ρ_{kl} summed over all allowed transitions.

The application of equation (29) may readily be illustrated for the case of an AB system which is modified by exchange of nuclei between the A and B environments. An example, involving such an exchange, is provided by the bridged biphenyl systems (4) which undergo ring inversion, accompanied by the exchange of ①H and ②H and ③H and ④H between the A and B environments, at rates which result in modification of the line shapes of the resonances of these nuclei.

4

The two AB systems in (4) are equivalent and may therefore be dealt with as a single AB system. The AB system is described by a 4×4 density matrix with the basis functions $\phi_1 = \alpha\alpha$, $\phi_2 = \alpha\beta$, $\phi_3 = \beta\alpha$ and $\phi_4 = \beta\beta$. On mutual exchange of the nuclei between the A and B environments the basis functions exchange as follows $\phi_1 \rightarrow \phi_1$, $\phi_2 \rightarrow \phi_3$, $\phi_3 \rightarrow \phi_2$ and $\phi_4 \rightarrow \phi_4$. Using the notation of equation (29) this means that $R_{11}=R_{23}=R_{32}=R_{44}=1$ and that all the other R's take a zero value. The only transitions for which $\Delta F_z = +1$ are $3 \rightarrow 1$ and $4 \rightarrow 2$ (lines associated with environment A) and $2 \rightarrow 1$ and $4 \rightarrow 3$ (corresponding to B lines); equation (29) then gives four simultaneous equations, two of which, (30a) and (30b), are as follows, and the other two in ρ_{24} and ρ_{34} are analogous, differing only in a reversal of the signs of the J values.

$$d\rho_{12}/dt = k(\rho_{13} - \rho_{12}) - \rho_{12}/T_{2B} - 2\pi i \rho_{12}(\nu_B - \nu + \tfrac{1}{2}J) + i\rho_{13}\pi J + iC = 0 \qquad (30a)$$

$$d\rho_{13}/dt = k(\rho_{12}-\rho_{13})-\rho_{13}/T_{2A}-2\pi i\rho_{13}(\nu_A-\nu+\tfrac{1}{2}J)+i\rho_{12}\pi J+iC = 0 \qquad (30b)$$

where
$$k = 1/\tau$$

The last term in equation (29) involves the diagonal elements of the density matrix, this term $(\rho_{kk}-\rho_{ll})$ corresponds to the difference in the thermal equilibrium populations of the states k and l and therefore becomes a constant for nuclei of a single species. Comparison of equations (30a) and (30b) with equations (13), for the uncoupled two-site exchange, shows that the former may be considered as giving line-shapes resulting from the exchange of spins occupying a pair of sites with populations and frequencies appropriate to the $2 \to 1$ and $3 \to 1$ transitions of the AB spectrum. The other two equations in ρ_{24} and ρ_{34} would represent the exchange of spins occupying sites appropriate for the $4 \to 2$ and $4 \to 3$ transitions. This result is shown diagrammatically in Fig. 5; it might have been anticipated intuitively from the earlier consideration of the results of the exchange process upon the basis functions. The intuitive approach fails, however, in a three-spin system where the effects of combination lines must also be considered.

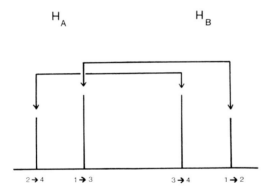

H_A $\qquad$ H_B

$2 \to 4$ $\quad$ $1 \to 3$ $\qquad$ $3 \to 4$ $\quad$ $1 \to 2$

FIG. 5. Exchange between the A and B sites of an AB system, apparent site exchanges are indicated by arrows.

The solution of the complex simultaneous equations (30a) and (30b), and the similar pair of equations in ρ_{24} and ρ_{34}, gives the total complex transverse magnetization $G=\rho_{12}+\rho_{13}+\rho_{24}+\rho_{34}$. For the case where $T_{2A}=T_{2B}=T_2$ this may be represented[2] by the complex equation:

$$G = C\left[\frac{R_++F}{(A_++iF)(B_++iF)-Q_+} + \frac{R_-+F}{(A_-+iF)(B_-+iF)-Q_-}\right] \qquad (31)$$

where C is a constant

$$
\begin{aligned}
A_\pm &= -2\pi i(\nu_A \pm J/2) - 1/T_2 - k \\
B_\pm &= -2\pi i(\nu_B \pm J/2) - 1/T_2 - k \\
Q_\pm &= (\pm \pi i J + k)^2 \\
R_\pm &= -2\pi(\nu_0 \pm J) + 2ik + i/T_2 \\
F &= 2\pi\nu \\
k &= 1/\tau; \qquad \nu_0 = (\nu_A + \nu_B)/2
\end{aligned}
$$

Equation (31) may be inserted into a computer programme and the imaginary part of G extracted after computation. Alternatively the imaginary part of G may be extracted algebraically before computation to give[34] the alternative line-shape equation:

$$
G(\mathrm{Im}) = C\left[\frac{r_+ b_+ - sa_+}{a_+^2 + b_+^2} + \frac{r_- b_- - sa_-}{a_-^2 + b_-^2}\right] \tag{32}
$$

where

$$
\begin{aligned}
a_\pm &= 4\pi^2(\nu_0 - \nu \pm J/2)^2 - (k+1/T_2)^2 - \pi^2(\nu_A - \nu_B)^2 - \pi^2 J^2 + k^2 \\
b_\pm &= 4\pi(\nu_0 - \nu \pm J/2)(k+1/T_2) \mp 2\pi Jk \\
r_\pm &= 2\pi(\nu_0 - \nu \pm J) \\
s &= 2k + 1/T_2 \\
\nu_0 &= (\nu_A + \nu_B)/2
\end{aligned}
$$

The use of equation (32) in a FORTRAN IV programme on an ICL-1907 computer gives a spectrum consisting of 500 values of $G(\mathrm{Im})$ in 2 sec., computation is thus only slightly slower than for the uncoupled two site equation (15). The results of a computation of this type, are shown in Fig. 6. Direct line-shape comparison of observed and computed spectra is thus not unduly laborious for the AB system with mutual site exchange, nevertheless some closed form solutions of the lineshape equation are available. These solutions apply to the slow and fast exchange limits and to the coalescence point and have been quite widely used, particularly the coalescence relationship; these are therefore reproduced here and the limitations associated with their use are noted.

For the cases where $(\nu_A - \nu_B)$ is quite large compared with J the low-temperature line broadening,[35] in Hz, is equal to $k(1 \pm J/A_0)/\pi$, where the plus sign refers to the two outer lines and the minus sign to the two inner lines and $A_0 = [(\nu_A - \nu_B)^2 + J^2]^{1/2}$. The relationship is more conveniently expressed as:

$$
k = \frac{\pi(w - w_0)}{\{1 \pm J/[(\nu_A - \nu_B)^2 + J^2]^{1/2}\}} \tag{33}
$$

where w is the observed line-width and w_0 is the line-width in the absence of exchange. For the fast exchange limit, where $k \gg (\nu_A - \nu_B)$, the equation (23) is found to hold. At the coalescence point[36,37] the rate k_c is given by:

$$k_c = \pi[(\nu_A - \nu_B)^2 + 6J^2]^{1/2}/\sqrt{2} \qquad (34)$$

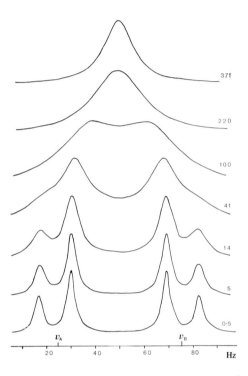

FIG. 6. Calculated line-shapes for exchange of mutually coupled nuclei between two sites, A and B. The rate constants for site exchange (sec.$^{-1}$) are shown by each spectrum; $\nu_A = 24 \cdot 6$ Hz, $\nu_B = 75 \cdot 4$ Hz, $J_{AB} = 13 \cdot 5$ Hz, $w_{A0} = w_{B0}$ is varied from $4 \cdot 0$ to $3 \cdot 15$ Hz as the exchange rate is increased.

The use of these simplified expressions may lead to serious errors in cases where they are not applicable, it is therefore advisable, if accuracy is required, to use equations (31) and (32). For cases where $T_{2A} \neq T_{2B}$ equations analogous to (31) and (32) may be constructed, or alternatively line-shape computation may be based directly upon the pairs of equations (30).

It is also instructive to consider the expansion of equation (29) for a three-spin case, since this includes allowed transitions involving more than one spin flip (combination lines), in addition to the normal single-spin transitions. The exchange between the A and B environments in an ABC system, with a rate constant k, gives rise to fifteen simultaneous equations (35, a to p), each one corresponding to one of the fifteen lines of the ABC spectrum. The formulation of these equations, using equation (29) will be briefly discussed.

Line shape for ABC system with exchange between A and B sites
(rate constant $1/\tau$)

$$
\begin{aligned}
d\rho_{12}/dt = \rho_{12}\{&-1/\tau-1/T_{2C}-2\pi i(\nu_C-\nu+\tfrac{1}{2}J_{AC}+\tfrac{1}{2}J_{BC})\} \\
&+\rho_{13}(\pi i J_{BC})+\rho_{14}(\pi i J_{AC})+iC = 0
\end{aligned} \tag{35a}
$$

$$
\begin{aligned}
d\rho_{13}/dt = \rho_{13}\{&-1/\tau-1/T_{2B}-2\pi i(\nu_B-\nu+\tfrac{1}{2}J_{AB}+\tfrac{1}{2}J_{BC})\} \\
&+\rho_{12}(\pi i J_{BC})+\rho_{14}(1/\tau+\pi i J_{AB})+iC = 0
\end{aligned} \tag{35b}
$$

$$
\begin{aligned}
d\rho_{14}/dt = \rho_{14}\{&-1/\tau-1/T_{2A}-2\pi i(\nu_A-\nu+\tfrac{1}{2}J_{AB}+\tfrac{1}{2}J_{AC})\} \\
&+\rho_{12}(\pi i J_{AC})+\rho_{13}(1/\tau+\pi i J_{AB})+iC = 0
\end{aligned} \tag{35c}
$$

$$
\begin{aligned}
d\rho_{25}/dt = \rho_{25}\{&-1/\tau-1/T_{2B}-2\pi i(\nu_B-\nu+\tfrac{1}{2}J_{AB}-\tfrac{1}{2}J_{BC})\} \\
&+\rho_{26}(1/\tau+\pi i J_{AB})+\rho_{27}(\pi i J_{AC})+\rho_{35}(-\pi i J_{BC}) \\
&+\rho_{45}(-\pi i J_{AC})+iC = 0
\end{aligned} \tag{35d}
$$

$$
\begin{aligned}
d\rho_{26}/dt = \rho_{26}\{&-1/\tau-1/T_{2A}-2\pi i(\nu_A-\nu+\tfrac{1}{2}J_{AB}-\tfrac{1}{2}J_{AC})\} \\
&+\rho_{25}(1/\tau+\pi i J_{AB})+\rho_{27}(\pi i J_{BC})+\rho_{36}(-\pi i J_{BC}) \\
&+\rho_{46}(-\pi i J_{AC})+iC = 0
\end{aligned} \tag{35e}
$$

$$
\begin{aligned}
d\rho_{27}/dt = \rho_{27}\{&-1/\tau-1/T_{2}-2\pi i(\nu_A+\nu_B-\nu_C-\nu)\} \\
&+\rho_{25}(\pi i J_{AC})+\rho_{26}(\pi i J_{BC})+\rho_{37}(-\pi i J_{BC}) \\
&+\rho_{47}(-\pi i J_{AC}) = 0
\end{aligned} \tag{35f}
$$

$$
\begin{aligned}
d\rho_{35}/dt = \rho_{35}\{&-1/\tau-1/T_{2C}-2\pi i(\nu_C-\nu+\tfrac{1}{2}J_{AC}-\tfrac{1}{2}J_{BC})\} \\
&+\rho_{36}(+\pi i J_{AB})+\rho_{37}(\pi i J_{AC})+\rho_{25}(-\pi i J_{BC}) \\
&+\rho_{45}(-\pi i J_{AB})+\rho_{46}(1/\tau)+iC = 0
\end{aligned} \tag{35g}
$$

$$
\begin{aligned}
d\rho_{36}/dt = \rho_{36}\{&-1/\tau-1/T_{2}-2\pi i(\nu_A-\nu_B+\nu_C-\nu)\} \\
&+\rho_{35}(\pi i J_{AB})+\rho_{37}(\pi i J_{BC})+\rho_{26}(-\pi i J_{BC}) \\
&+\rho_{46}(-\pi i J_{AB})+\rho_{45}(1/\tau) = 0
\end{aligned} \tag{35h}
$$

$$
\begin{aligned}
d\rho_{37}/dt = \rho_{37}\{&-1/\tau-1/T_{2A}-2\pi i(\nu_A-\nu-\tfrac{1}{2}J_{AB}+\tfrac{1}{2}J_{AC})\} \\
&+\rho_{35}(\pi i J_{AC})+\rho_{36}(\pi i J_{BC})+\rho_{27}(-\pi i J_{BC}) \\
&+\rho_{47}(1/\tau-\pi i J_{AB})+iC = 0
\end{aligned} \tag{35i}
$$

$$
\begin{aligned}
d\rho_{45}/dt = \rho_{45}\{&-1/\tau-1/T_{2}-2\pi i(-\nu_A+\nu_B+\nu_C-\nu)\} \\
&+\rho_{46}(\pi i J_{AB})+\rho_{47}(\pi i J_{AC})+\rho_{25}(-\pi i J_{AC}) \\
&+\rho_{35}(-\pi i J_{AB})+\rho_{36}(1/\tau) = 0
\end{aligned} \tag{35j}
$$

$$
\begin{aligned}
d\rho_{46}/dt = \rho_{46}\{&-1/\tau-1/T_{2C}-2\pi i(\nu_C-\nu-\tfrac{1}{2}J_{AC}+\tfrac{1}{2}J_{BC})\} \\
&+\rho_{45}(\pi i J_{AB})+\rho_{47}(\pi i J_{BC})+\rho_{26}(-\pi i J_{AC}) \\
&+\rho_{36}(-\pi i J_{AB})+\rho_{35}(1/\tau)+iC = 0
\end{aligned} \tag{35k}
$$

$$dp_{47}/dt = \rho_{47}\{-1/\tau-1/T_{2B}-2\pi i(\nu_B-\nu-\tfrac{1}{2}J_{AB}+\tfrac{1}{2}J_{BC})\}$$
$$+ \rho_{45}(\pi i J_{AC})+\rho_{46}(\pi i J_{BC})+\rho_{27}(-\pi i J_{AC})$$
$$+ \rho_{37}(1/\tau-\pi i J_{AB})+iC = 0 \tag{35l}$$

$$dp_{58}/dt = \rho_{58}\{-1/\tau-1/T_{2A}-2\pi i(\nu_A-\nu-\tfrac{1}{2}J_{AB}-\tfrac{1}{2}J_{AC})\}$$
$$+ \rho_{68}(1/\tau-\pi i J_{AB})+\rho_{78}(-\pi i J_{AC})+iC = 0 \tag{35m}$$

$$dp_{68}/dt = \rho_{68}\{-1/\tau-1/T_{2B}-2\pi i(\nu_B-\nu-\tfrac{1}{2}J_{AB}-\tfrac{1}{2}J_{BC})\}$$
$$+ \rho_{58}(1/\tau-\pi i J_{AB})+\rho_{78}(-\pi i J_{BC})+iC = 0 \tag{35n}$$

$$dp_{78}/dt = \rho_{78}\{-1/\tau-1/T_{2C}-2\pi i(\nu_C-\nu-\tfrac{1}{2}J_{AC}-\tfrac{1}{2}J_{BC})\}$$
$$+ \rho_{58}(-\pi i J_{AC})+\rho_{68}(-\pi i J_{BC})+iC = 0 \tag{35p}$$

The eight basis functions for the ABC system, ϕ_1 to ϕ_8, are listed below, and the effects of the exchange process upon these basis functions are included.

Before exchange		After exchange
ϕ_1 $\alpha\alpha\alpha$	$\longrightarrow$	$\alpha\alpha\alpha$ ϕ_1
ϕ_2 $\alpha\alpha\beta$	$\longrightarrow$	$\alpha\alpha\beta$ ϕ_2
ϕ_3 $\alpha\beta\alpha$	$\longrightarrow$	$\beta\alpha\alpha$ ϕ_4
ϕ_4 $\beta\alpha\alpha$	$\longrightarrow$	$\alpha\beta\alpha$ ϕ_3
ϕ_5 $\alpha\beta\beta$	$\longrightarrow$	$\beta\alpha\beta$ ϕ_6
ϕ_6 $\beta\alpha\beta$	$\longrightarrow$	$\alpha\beta\beta$ ϕ_5
ϕ_7 $\beta\beta\alpha$	$\longrightarrow$	$\beta\beta\alpha$ ϕ_7
ϕ_8 $\beta\beta\beta$	$\longrightarrow$	$\beta\beta\beta$ ϕ_8

From the above scheme it can be seen, following the definition of the R's of equation (29), that $R_{11}=R_{22}=R_{34}=R_{43}=R_{56}=R_{65}=R_{77}=R_{88}=1$ and that all the other R's are zero. The second term of equation (29) simply introduces a relaxation time appropriate to the low-temperature line-width of the spectral line (T_{2A}, T_{2B} and T_{2C} for all A, B and C transitions and T_2 for the combination lines). The third term may be evaluated directly from equation (29) and the results turn out to be the energy differences, in frequency units, between the pure basis states k and l, that is the difference between the diagonal matrix elements $\mathscr{H}_{ll}$ and $\mathscr{H}_{kk}$ of the normal Hamiltonian, less the observing frequency ν. Similar rules may therefore be formulated for evaluating this term as for the evaluation of the Hamiltonian representing the spectrum without exchange. A rule suitable for the evaluation of this third term is expressed in equation (36) for all allowed transitions $[\Delta F_z(l \to k)=+1]$.

$$\text{Term 3} = -i\rho_{kl}2\pi\{(\sum_i a\nu_i)-\nu+\tfrac{1}{2}\sum_{i<j} bJ_{ij}\} \tag{36}$$

where $a = +1$ if nucleus i has spin state α in ϕ_k and β in ϕ_l.

$a = -1$ if nucleus i has spin state β in ϕ_k and α in ϕ_l; this condition will only be found for combination lines.

$a = 0$ if nucleus i has the same spin state in both ϕ_k and ϕ_l.

$b = \pm 1$ if one nucleus i or j has an α spin state in ϕ_k and a β spin state in ϕ_l. The plus sign applies if the other nucleus j or i has the α spin state in both ϕ_k and ϕ_l and the minus sign to the second nucleus having the β spin state in ϕ_k and ϕ_l.

$b = 0$ if the basis functions ϕ_k and ϕ_l are not related by a change of spin of one nucleus i or j with the second nucleus having the same spin state in both ϕ_k and ϕ_l.

It is quite laborious to obtain the fourth term directly from equation (29), evaluation indicates that the result may be summarized by the expression (37) where ρ_{km} and ρ_{nl} refer *only* to allowed transitions.

$$\text{Term } 4 = \sum_{m \neq l} \rho_{km} i\pi c J_{ij} - \sum_{n \neq k} \rho_{nl} i\pi c J_{ij} \tag{37}$$

where $c = +1$ if the pairs of basis functions ϕ_m and ϕ_l or ϕ_k and ϕ_n differ only by an interchange of the spins of nuclei i and j and if the pairs of basis functions ϕ_m and ϕ_l or ϕ_k and ϕ_n have the same value for F_z.

$c = 0$ for all other cases.

Inspection of the results obtained from the evaluation of Term 4 shows that it is related to the off-diagonal elements of the normal spin Hamiltonian.

The fifth, and final, term of equation (29) may be simply set equal to i for an allowed transition involving only a single nuclear spin flip, or equal to zero for a combination line. The use of these rules enables equation (29) to be evaluated quite readily for any set of basis functions of the type $\alpha\alpha\alpha$, etc.

Inspection of the equations (35, a to p) shows that they fall into two sets of three (a set for ρ_{12}, ρ_{13} and ρ_{14} and the other for ρ_{58}, ρ_{68} and ρ_{78}) and one set of nine equations (for ρ_{25}, ρ_{26}, ρ_{27}, ρ_{35}, ρ_{36}, ρ_{37}, ρ_{45}, ρ_{46} and ρ_{47}). They may therefore be solved in these three sets and, since for steady-state conditions the equations are linear, the solution is readily achieved by standard programming techniques. As in the case of multi-site systems the solution is inconveniently slow unless the computational procedure suggested by Binsch[27] is followed, and the co-efficient matrix for the ρ_{kl} values is decomposed into frequency dependent and independent components. The imaginary part of $\sum \rho_{kl}$ is proportional to the absorption intensity at any point in the spectrum corresponding to the frequency ν of the oscillating field H_1. It is interesting to note that in the first-order limit, where $(\nu_A - \nu_B)$, $(\nu_B - \nu_C)$ and $(\nu_A - \nu_C)$ are all large compared with J_{AB}, J_{AC} and J_{BC}, the off-diagonal elements in the Hamiltonian are neglected and the situation may be described as AMX, with apparent site exchanges corresponding to those shown in Fig. 7. Thus the slow exchange AMX system changes as expected into a fast exchange A_2X system with an apparent coupling constant $(J_{AX}+J_{MX})/2$. The AMX system is rarely observed in practice but cases are more commonly encountered with J_{AB} comparable with $(\nu_A - \nu_B)$, that is the ABX case. Then in this case an approximate solution may be obtained for the AB portion by treating it as two AB systems with coupling constants J'_{AX} and J'_{BX} appropriate for the ABX system. This treatment ignores the off-diagonal terms in J_{AC} and J_{BC} and results in pairs of equations in ρ_{13} and ρ_{14}, ρ_{25} and ρ_{26}, ρ_{37} and ρ_{47}, and ρ_{58} and ρ_{68}. The sum of the imaginary components of the solutions of these four pairs of simultaneous equations describes the absorption spectrum of the AB system, but the X-resonance is more complex since it involves combination lines in addition to pure X lines. This type of simplified treatment of coupled systems has been described for a number of cases.[38 to 43]

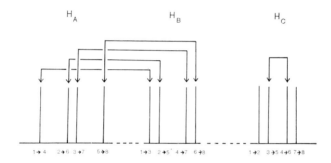

FIG. 7. Exchange between the A and M environments in a first order AMX system.

Extension of equation (29) to exchange in coupled systems of four or more protons is relatively straight forward, and the use of suitable computing procedures makes it possible, in principle, to deal with exchange in systems of up to six spins. There appears, at the present time, to be no account of the complete density matrix treatment of exchange in coupled systems of more than three spins, and most multi-spin problems encountered have been dealt with either very approximately or by the use of simplified computational procedures. Alternatively the problems have been simplified by substituting deuterium for some of the hydrogen atoms of the coupled system, a notable example being the study of the ring inversion of cyclohexane.[24] The definition of R in equation (29) makes it suitable only for those cases which involve mutual intramolecular exchange of the nuclei in a coupled system. Thus it is an equation particularly suited for application to degenerate processes such as the ring inversion process (4) or the bond rotation depicted in (5) which involves exchange of pairs of nuclei between the pairs of sites A and D and B and C of an ABCD system. The

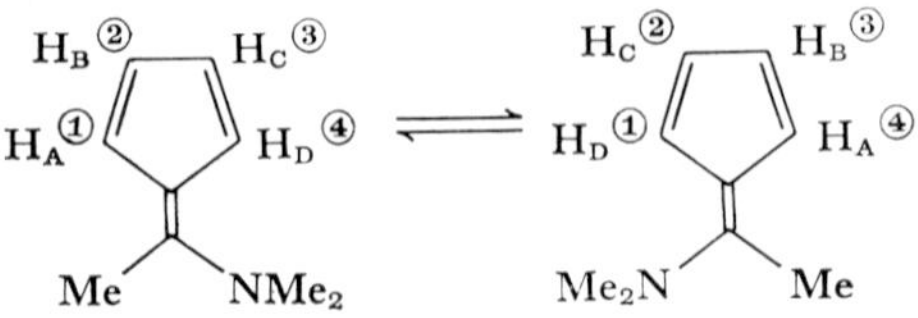

5

equation is not, however, suitable for dealing with cases involving the interconversion of diastereomers, such as the process (**6**) which involves chair and boat (or
twist boat) conformations of the dibenzodithiocin system. This involves two
different two spin systems A^1B^1 and A^2B^2, and cases of this type may be treated
by an obvious modification of equation (29). This modification involves the introduction of an R operator to allow for the exchange of multi-spin systems between different environments r, s, etc.

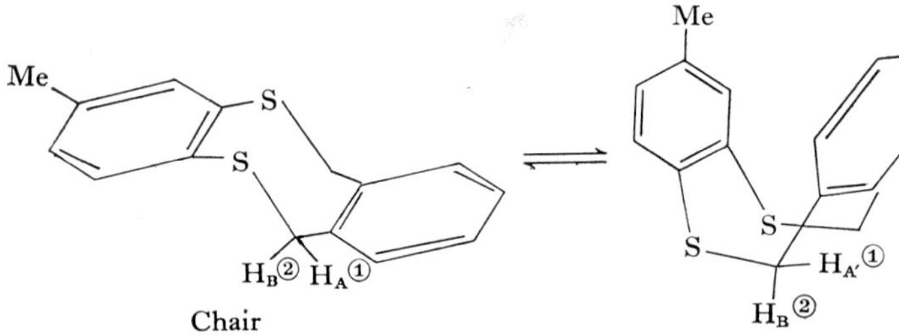

Chair   Boat

6†

Thus, if we consider a system of nuclear spins, denoted by the subscripts i, j,
etc., with basis functions ϕ_k, ϕ_l, etc. undergoing exchange between environments
denoted by the superscripts r, s, etc., this may be described by a more general
form of equation (29) in terms of all of the elements of each of the density
matrices ρ^r, etc. corresponding to the magnetic environments r, s, etc. Rather
general methods for doing this have been devised[27,33] using the Liouville representation of quantum mechanics but we shall restrict the discussion here to a
simple treatment which, although lacking elegance, demonstrates how these
more complex problems may be tackled in some cases. A term is introduced into
equation (29) to allow for exchange between environments r and s with the rate
constants k^{sr} (for s to r) and k^{rs} (for r to s), using the parameter R^{sr} which has
the same significance with respect to exchange between the environments r and s
as R^r has with respect to exchange between the different basis functions within
the environment r. In addition the last term of equation (29) must be modified by
a population factor p^r to allow for different populations of different environ-

† In (**6**) the different environments are denoted by A and A′, B and B′ but in the
equations which follow environments are denoted by superscripts r and s.

ments. Then, for the density matrix element ρ^r_{kl} involving the spin states k and l in the rth environment, we have:

$$
\begin{aligned}
d\rho^r_{kl}/dt = & \left[\sum_{s \neq r} k^{sr} \sum_{nm} R^{sr}_{kn}\rho^s_{nm}R^{sr}_{ml} - k^{rs}\rho^r_{kl}\right] \\
& - i\rho^r_{kl}\Big\{\sum_i 2\pi(\nu^r_i - \nu)\left[(I^i_z)^r_{kk} - (I^i_z)^r_{ll}\right] \\
& \qquad + \sum_{i \neq j} 2\pi J^r_{ij}\left[(I^i_z I^j_z)^r_{kk} - (I^i_z I^j_z)^r_{ll}\right]\Big\} \\
& + i \sum_{i < j} \pi J^r_{ij} \sum_{lm} \Big\{\rho^r_{km}(I^i_+ I^j_-)^r_{ml} - \rho^r_{ml}(I^i_+ I^j_-)_{km} \\
& \qquad + \rho^r_{km}(I^i_- I^j_+)^r_{ml} - \rho^r_{ml}(I^i_- I^j_+)_{km}\Big\} \\
& + 2\pi\rho^r i\nu_0(\rho^r_{kk} - \rho^r_{ll}) \sum_i (I^i_x)^r_{kl} = 0
\end{aligned}
\tag{38}
$$

The use of equation (38) is readily illustrated by considering the conformational change (6) involving the two AB systems AB and A'B' with populations p^1 and p^2, and in which ①H is transferred between the sites A and A' and ②H between the sites B and B'. Two sets of four simultaneous equations are obtained by evaluation of equation (38) in a manner appropriate for this situation. One set is in ρ^1_{12}, ρ^1_{13}, ρ^2_{12} and ρ^2_{13}, and the other set in ρ^1_{24}, ρ^1_{34}, ρ^2_{24} and ρ^2_{34} differs from the first only in that the signs of the J values are reversed. The basis functions for the two AB systems are represented by the usual multiple spin functions so that values for the various R^{rs} terms may be obtained directly from the scheme given below, in which the effect of the exchange process upon the basis functions is considered.

Before exchange		After exchange	
ϕ^1_1	$\alpha\alpha$	$\alpha\alpha$	ϕ^2_1
ϕ^1_2	$\alpha\beta$	$\alpha\beta$	ϕ^2_2
ϕ^1_3	$\beta\alpha$	$\beta\alpha$	ϕ^2_3
ϕ^1_4	$\beta\beta$	$\beta\beta$	ϕ^2_4

From this scheme it can be seen that $R^{12}_{11} = R^{21}_{11} = R^{12}_{22} = R^{21}_{22} = R^{12}_{33} = R^{21}_{33} = R^{12}_{44} = R^{21}_{44} = 1$ and that all the other R^{rs} terms are zero. Then the resulting simultaneous equations in ρ^1_{12}, ρ^1_{13}, ρ^2_{12} and ρ^2_{13} are:

$$
\begin{aligned}
d\rho^1_{12}/dt = & \; k^{21}\rho^2_{12} - k^{12}\rho^1_{12} - \rho^1_{12}/T^1_{2B} \\
& - 2\pi i\rho^1_{12}(\nu^1_B - \nu + \tfrac{1}{2}J^{(1)}) + i\rho^1_{13}\pi J^{(1)} + p^1 iC = 0
\end{aligned}
\tag{39a}
$$

$$
\begin{aligned}
d\rho^1_{13}/dt = & \; k^{21}\rho^2_{13} - k^{12}\rho^1_{13} - \rho^1_{13}/T^1_{2A} \\
& - 2\pi i\rho^1_{13}(\nu^1_A - \nu + \tfrac{1}{2}J^{(1)}) + i\rho^1_{12}\pi J^{(1)} + p^1 iC = 0
\end{aligned}
\tag{39b}
$$

$$d\rho_{12}^2/dt = k^{12}\rho_{12}^1 - k^{21}\rho_{12}^2 - \rho_{12}^2/T_{2B}^2$$
$$- 2\pi i\rho_{12}^2(\nu_B^2 - \nu + \tfrac{1}{2}J^{(2)}) + i\rho_{13}^2\pi J^{(2)} + p^2 iC = 0 \quad (39c)$$

$$d\rho_{13}^2/dt = k^{12}\rho_{13}^1 - k^{21}\rho_{13}^2 - \rho_{13}^2/T_{2A}^2$$
$$- 2\pi i\rho_{13}^2(\nu_A^2 - \nu + \tfrac{1}{2}J^{(2)}) + i\rho_{12}^2\pi J^{(2)} + p^2 iC = 0 \quad (39d)$$

Inspection of the equations (39, a to d) and consideration of the analogous set that may be written in ρ_{24}^1, ρ_{34}^1, ρ_{24}^2 and ρ_{34}^2 shows that the results of the exchange process may be summarized by the four, two-site, exchanges denoted by the arrows in Fig. 8. Several studies have been reported of this type of exchange involving two AB systems [43 to 48] and obviously the approach may be extended to all types of intramolecular exchange and the appropriate set of simultaneous equations compiled.

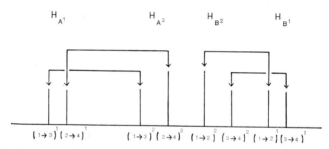

FIG. 8. Exchange of nuclei between A sites of environments 1 and 2 and B sites of environments 1 and 2.

The approach described by Johnson[33] and developed in more detail by Binsch[27] is more suited to a general computer programme, but a successful programme requires an efficient method of dealing with the large number of simultaneous equations which may be generated in a multi-spin problem. The variable parameter ν appears only in the diagonal elements of the matrix $\mathbf{M_0}$ which contains the left-hand side coefficients of the ρ_{kl}^r values,† this means that this matrix may be decomposed (in the notation used by Binsch) as:

$$\mathbf{M_0} = \mathbf{B} - 2\pi i\nu\mathbf{E} \quad (40)$$

where $\mathbf{B}$ is a matrix independent of ν, and $\mathbf{E}$ is the unit matrix. Then the same transformation matrix which will convert $\mathbf{M_0}$ into a diagonal matrix $\mathbf{D}$, that is:

$$\mathbf{U^{-1}M_0U} = \mathbf{D} \quad (41)$$

will also diagonalize $\mathbf{B}$ to give the diagonal matrix $\mathbf{\Lambda}$.

† This is using the notation of equation (38) and keeping all the terms in the off diagonal density matrix elements on the left-hand side, and the constant term in the diagonal density matrix elements ρ_{kk}^r, etc., in the right-hand side vector.

Since **B** and **E** commute:

$$\mathbf{U}^{-1}\mathbf{B}\mathbf{U} = \mathbf{\Lambda} \tag{42}$$

We therefore obtain the relationships:

$$\mathbf{U}^{-1}\mathbf{M}_0\mathbf{U} = \mathbf{U}^{-1}\mathbf{B}\mathbf{U} - 2\pi i\nu\mathbf{U}^{-1}\mathbf{E}\mathbf{U} = \mathbf{\Lambda} - 2\pi i\nu\mathbf{E} = \mathbf{D} \tag{43}$$

and

$$\mathbf{M}_0^{-1} = \mathbf{U}\mathbf{D}^{-1}\mathbf{U}^{-1} = \mathbf{U}(\mathbf{\Lambda} - 2\pi i\nu\mathbf{E})^{-1}\mathbf{U}^{-1} \tag{44}$$

The eigenvalues and right and left eigen vectors for the relatively large complex matrix **B** may be found by computation. Then inversion of the matrix $\mathbf{M}_0$ reduces to the trivial problem of inverting the diagonal matrix $\mathbf{D} = \mathbf{\Lambda} - 2\pi i\nu\mathbf{E}$ together with the matrix multiplication indicated in (44). This procedure, together with methods for setting up the matrix and the right-hand side vector for systems of up to four spins exchanging between two environments, has been incorporated into a FORTRAN IV programme DNMR by Binsch,[27] and this appears to represent the most advanced computational procedure for dealing with exchange in coupled systems which has yet been developed.

E. The determination of site exchange rates using transient NMR phenomena

The previous sections of this review have described the determination of exchange rates by examination of NMR line-shapes obtained under "steady-state conditions", that is, conditions for which the time derivatives of the magnetization may be set to zero, and the z component of the magnetization M_z may be set equal to M_0. If spectra are obtained under conditions where these relationships do not hold time dependent NMR phenomena are observed, which are sensitive to the effects of exchange processes. Methods of this type have been used less widely, than steady-state methods, to examine the kinetics of site-exchange processes, but the two principal examples of techniques employing transient phenomena will be briefly discussed since these may be applied to measure rates of site-exchange which are outside the range which can be studied by steady state methods.

1. *Double resonance techniques*

This method, which has been developed by Forsén and Hoffman,[49,50,51] may be carried out using a commercial spectrometer equipped with a good spin-decoupler. The method consists of irradiating one site of a system undergoing exchange of nuclear spins between two or more sites, and observing the time dependence of the signals from the other sites when they are irradiated with the normal R.F. field H_1. The principle of the method may be illustrated by first considering the Bloch equations for the z components of the magnetization M_{zA} and M_{zB} for nuclei distributed between two sites A and B.

These equations, analogous to equation (5a), are further modified by exchange terms so that we have:

$$\frac{dM_{zA}}{dt} = \frac{-(M_{zA}-M_{0A})}{T_{1A}} - \frac{M_{zA}}{\tau_A} + \frac{M_{zB}}{\tau_B} + \gamma v_A H_1 \qquad (45a)$$

$$\frac{dM_{zB}}{dt} = \frac{-(M_{zB}-M_{0B})}{T_{1B}} - \frac{M_{zB}}{\tau_B} + \frac{M_{zA}}{\tau_A} + \gamma v_B H_1 \qquad (45b)$$

where $1/\tau_A$ and $1/\tau_B$ are the first-order rate constants for site exchange.

If the magnetization of the nuclei in site B is destroyed by irradiation with a strong oscillating R.F. field H_2 of frequency v_B, and the magnetization of the nuclei in site A is investigated by a weak R.F. field H_1, the time dependence of the z magnetization associated with site A is now described by the equation:

$$dM_{zA}/dt = M_{0A}/T_{1A} - M_{zA}/\tau_{1A} \qquad (46)$$

where
$$1/\tau_{1A} = 1/\tau_A + 1/T_{1A}$$

The term in M_{zB} in equation (45a) is dropped because complete saturation of the B signal is assumed, the term in v_A is also dropped because it is assumed that H_1 is sufficiently weak to cause negligible saturation. Under these conditions the strength of the A signal is proportional to M_{zA} if the spectrum is recorded under slow passage conditions.

For a full discussion of these conditions the original paper[49] should be consulted, it will simply be stated here that slow passage conditions in this context require that the conditions of equations (47) and (47a) are satisfied:

$$\tau_{2A} \ll \tau_{1A} \qquad (47)$$

$$T_{2A} \ll \tau_A \qquad (47a)$$

where
$$1/\tau_{2A} = 1/T_{2A} + 1/\tau_A$$

The line width of the A signal is $1/\tau_{2A}$ so that several slow passage recordings of this signal can be obtained during a time of approximately τ_{1A}. The conditions implied in equations (47) and (47a) can usually be met by deliberately increasing $1/T_{2A}$ (and hence $1/\tau_{2A}$) by introducing inhomogeneity into the magnetic field H_0. Under these conditions signal A is recorded in a time that is long compared with τ_{2A} and short compared with τ_{1A}, so that the time dependence of M_{zA} may be followed by studying successive absorption mode signals of the A resonance. The saturation of the nuclei in site B is assumed to occur instantaneously at $t=0$ (the time at which H_2 is switched on) when $M_{zA}=M_{0A}$. The decay of M_{zA}, due to the transfer of magnetization by the exchange process, then follows from the integration of equation (46) to give:

$$M_{zA}(t) = M_{0A}[(\tau_{1A}/\tau_A) \exp(-t/\tau_{1A}) + (\tau_{1A}/T_{1A})] \qquad (48)$$

From this it follows that the new equilibrium value of M_{zA} will be

$$M_{zA}(t \to \infty) = M_{0A}(\tau_{1A}/T_{1A}) \qquad (49)$$

attained through an exponential decay of M_{zA} with a time constant τ_{1A}. The ratio of the initial and final values of M_{zA} gives the quotient T_{1A}/τ_{1A}, and by plotting $\log [M_{zA}(t) - M_{zA}(t \to \infty)]$ a straight line is obtained with the slope τ_{1A}, hence the values of T_{1A} and τ_A may be readily calculated. The reverse experiment involving observation of the nuclei in the B site while irradiating site A may also be carried out to give T_{1B} and τ_B. The ratio of τ_A to τ_B, which should equal the ratio of the site populations, provides a check on the validity of the method. Further checks of the method have also been devised, and these are described in the original paper by Forsén and Hoffman,[49] in which the method is applied to the acid catalysed exchange of the hydroxyl protons of salicylaldehyde and 2-hydroxyacetophenone. In a later paper by the same authors[50] the extension of the method to exchange involving several sites is discussed and two alternative procedures are considered by which the nuclei in all but one of the sites are saturated. Experimental work on a three-site problem, involving proton exchange in the keto–enol system of acetylacetone, has been described.[50] The method has been modified, by Anet and Bourn,[24] for the study of ring inversion of deuterated cyclohexane. In this case a spectrometer with an internal field-frequency lock was used, which enabled the method to be applied even though the separation of the two sites was less than 30 Hz. Furthermore, the spectrometer was operated at high resolution so that complete saturation of the unobserved resonance was achieved with relatively small values of H_2, the decoupling field, both the decay of M_{zA} after turning on the decoupling field, and its recovery after turning off H_2 were studied and analysed in terms of τ_A and T_{1A}. These experiments[24] extended the range of observed rate constants in the slow exchange region from $\tau_A = 3 \cdot 6$ to 236 sec. and an excellent straight line relationship was found in an Arrhenius plot based upon rate constants obtained by steady-state methods in the fast exchange region and by the multiple resonance technique in the slow exchange region.

These studies indicate the potential utility of the multiple resonance technique to measure relatively large values of τ_A and τ_B, which are beyond the range of steady-state methods. The method has the further advantage of experimental simplicity and the availability of the necessary equipment in modern NMR spectrometers. In spite of these advantages few examples of its application to the study of intramolecular exchange have been described. Apart from the study of cyclohexane-d_{11},[24] the only work of which the author is aware is a qualitative study of [18] annulene and p-nitrosodimethylaniline.[52] In addition to the studies of intramolecular exchange carried out by Forsén and Hoffman,[49,50,51] the qualitative use of the method to characterize hydroxyl signals[53] has been suggested.

2. Spin-echo techniques

The use of this method to measure exchange rates has been developed largely by

Gutowsky and his co-workers,[54 to 63] the technique has been reviewed else-where[1,2] and, in view of its rather specialized nature, the discussion here will be very brief. The method consists of irradiating the sample to be examined with a series of R.F. pulses which gives rise to a characteristic series of echo signals, the decay envelope of these echo signals contains the information concerning site-exchange rates.[54] The first pulse is produced by switching on a strong R.F. field H_1 oscillating with a frequency ω which satisfies the resonance condition. This first pulse lasts for a short time t_ω sec. where:

$$H_1 t_\omega = \pi/2 \tag{50}$$

From this relationship the time t_ω is so short that the system does not appreciably relax during this first 90° pulse and the total magnetization ends up in the v direction of the rotating frame. After the pulse is switched off the y component of the magnetization decays, due to loss of phase coherence, and after a time p sec. a second pulse of duration $2t_\omega$ is applied. This second 180° pulse reverses the direction of all the individual spins so that relaxation in the next interval causes them to move together and refocus at $t = t_\omega + p + 2t_\omega + p$ sec. to produce a strong signal called the echo. Some of the magnetization is lost between pulses and as time goes on, and the 180° pulses are repeated at $2p$ sec. intervals, the decrease in the echo-amplitude is controlled largely by T_2. If magnetization is transferred to another site during this process an additional detectable irreversible loss of magnetization occurs. The experimental technique, which requires appropriate modification of the spectrometer, consists of a single 90° pulse followed by a long sequence of equally spaced 180° pulses referred to as the Carr-Purcell spin-echo pulse train,[64] and exchange rates may be obtained by analysis of the envelope of the decaying series of echo signals.

The theory of the method for a single two-site exchange may conveniently be considered[54] using Bloch equations. The decay of magnetization between pulses may be described by these equations by omitting the term in H_1, since the rotating field is turned off between pulses, and adding terms in the exchange rates k_A and k_B in a similar fashion to the treatment of the steady-state exchange phenomena. The resulting modified Bloch equations for nuclei exchanging between the two sites A and B are:

$$dG_A/dt = -\alpha_A G_A + k_B G_B \tag{51}$$
$$dG_B/dt = -\alpha_B G_B + k_A G_A \tag{51a}$$

where, as before, the complex magnetization G is defined by $G = u + iv$, but the α's are conveniently defined as $\alpha_A = 1/T_{2A} + k_A - 2\pi i(\nu_A - \nu)$, with a similar definition for α_B. For the general case in which $(\alpha_A - \alpha_B)^2 + 4k_A k_B \neq 0$ the solutions of equations (51) and (51a) are:

$$G_A(t) = A_+ \exp(-\phi_+ t) + A_- \exp(-\phi_- t) \tag{52}$$
$$G_B(t) = A_+ \beta_+ \exp(-\phi_+ t) + A_- \beta_- \exp(-\phi_- t) \tag{52a}$$

where A_+ and A_- are integration constants determined according to the particular pulse interval used and

$$2\phi_\pm = (\alpha_A + \alpha_B) \pm [(\alpha_A - \alpha_B)^2 + 4k_A k_B]^{1/2}$$

$$\beta_\pm = -(\phi_\pm - \alpha_A)/k_B$$

Two further equations may also be obtained for the special case in which $(\alpha_A - \alpha_B)^2 + 4k_A k_B = 0$.

A procedure was described in detail by Gutowsky and Allerhand[54] whereby equations (52) could be used in a suitable computer programme to calculate the successive echo intensities by obtaining the values of u_A and u_B and v_A and v_B at the times $t = n \cdot 2p(n = 1, 2, 3,$ etc., $p \gg \omega$ so that the duration of the pulses may be neglected). The analysis used requires that the following conditions are observed:

$$\gamma H_1, \; 1/t_\omega \gg 1/T_{2A}, \; 1/T_{2B}, \; 1/T_{1A}, \; 1/T_{1B}, \; k_A, \; k_B, \; 2\pi(\nu_A - \nu), \; 2\pi(\nu_B - \nu), \; 2\pi(\nu_A - \nu_B)$$

These conditions mean that t_ω should be very short compared with the relaxation times, and that the pulse intensity H_1 must be large to provide the required 90° and 180° pulses. The computational procedures provide a set of echo-decay curves for given input values of p_A, p_B, p, $(\nu_A - \nu_B)$, k_A and k_B, these curves were found to be approximately exponential. The apparent time constant T_2 for the decay of the amplitudes of successive echoes was found to be a function of the site populations p_A and p_B, the chemical shift between the sites $(\nu_A - \nu_B)$, the transverse relaxation times T_{2A} and T_{2B}, the exchange rates k_A and k_B, and the pulse separation $2p$. The last variable could be controlled experimentally and for the case in which $p_A = p_B = 0.5$ and $T_{2A} = T_{2B} = T_2^0$ it was possible to obtain not only the site-exchange rate but also the site separation $(\nu_A - \nu_B)$ and T_2^0 by measuring T_2 as a function of the pulse interval $2p$. In a second paper Allerhand and Gutowsky[55] derived closed expressions for the decay of successive echo-amplitudes for the case where $p_A = p_B = 0.5$ and $T_{2A} = T_{2B} = T_2^0$, but in order to obtain exchange rates in the absence of information about $(\nu_A - \nu_B)$ and T_2^0 it was still necessary to fit experimental data to computed decay curves to obtain rate constants. The method has also been extended by Gutowsky's group and others[65,66] to systems involving exchange between many sites, and exchange in systems where spin–spin coupling is important.[60]

The author does not have personal experience of the spin-echo method but it appears to suffer from the disadvantages that it requires a specially modified spectrometer and that the computational procedures are more laborious than those used for the steady-state method. In addition the information obtained relates to all of the nuclei, of the particular species studied, in the molecule. It is therefore necessary that, for example, all non-exchanging protons in the molecule must be exchanged for deuterium. The method, however, has important advantages in that it extends the kinetic studies to much faster exchange rates than can be studied by steady-state methods, and therefore lower energy barriers may be measured. Furthermore, because T_2^0 and $(\nu_A - \nu_B)$ may be obtained independently, errors due to the temperature dependence of these parameters are avoided. Probably, as a result of the rather specialized techniques required, the method has been used by relatively few groups interested in kinetic studies.[54 to 68]

III. THE DETERMINATION OF RATE CONSTANTS AND ACTIVATION PARAMETERS

A. Rate constants

The determination of rate constants from spectra obtained under steady-state conditions only will be discussed. A large proportion of the papers cited in this review, dealing with the examination of the kinetics of rate processes by NMR line-shape methods, include a discussion of the methods used by the authors to obtain rate constants. From the preceding section, outlining the theory of the method, it is clear that it is important that spectra be obtained under conditions where the line-shape equations are valid. In general this means that reasonably slow scan rates should be used to avoid transient effects, particularly for narrow resonance lines. The irradiating field H_1 should be set as low as possible to avoid saturation, the limitation normally being the quantity of sample available and its solubility. The homogeneity of the static field H_0 should also be optimized at each temperature, since for most spectrometers the field homogeneity is degraded when the probe temperature is changed. The field adjustment can be made either on the basis of a sharp signal in the spectrum, from the internal reference for example, or in spectrometers with an internal locking system by monitoring the lock signal. The availability of automatic shim controls on modern spectrometers considerably assists in maintaining good field homogeneity as the temperature is changed. Good spectral line-shapes also depend upon the careful adjustment of the spectrum phase for each temperature setting and this is particularly important if total line-shape comparison is used to obtain exchange rates. Line-shapes in the absence of exchange are generally not truly Lorentzian, and methods for correcting errors of this type have been discussed.[3,24,69] In general, errors due to non-Lorentzian line-shapes are not important if the low intensity portions of the spectrum, for example those parts with $< 5\%$ of the maximum intensity, are ignored.[24,69] The measurement of temperature is usually carried out by examining the peak separations of methanol (in the low temperature range) and ethylene glycol (in the high temperature range) samples, this, combined with the use of a thermocouple, probably ensures an accuracy of $\pm 2°C$ in most work. Temperature calibration should be carried out for each set of spectra recorded, since the temperatures of the sample probably depend upon a number of factors which may vary slightly from time to time. For the older type of spectrometer, with no internal field-frequency lock, spectra tend to vary appreciably from scan to scan and several recordings of each spectrum should be made and average values used for the examination of line-shapes. Modern spectrometers with internal locking systems, such as the Varian HA 100, show so little change in line-shapes for successive sweeps that two superimposable spectra run at each temperature should provide good spectral data provided that the spectrometer controls are properly adjusted.

Assuming that a good set of spectra are recorded over a range of temperatures it is then necessary to obtain kinetic data from the spectra. This may be done in a number of ways as has been discussed briefly in Section I; this discussion will be developed a little further here. If the examination is restricted to the determination of coalescence data, followed by the application of equations (19) or (34), values of $(\nu_A - \nu_B)$ and J may readily be obtained from the low temperature spectra and k_c calculated by inserting these values into the appropriate formula. Exchange rates, at the coalescence temperature, obtained in this way are generally accurate to ± 20 to 30% and the corresponding error in $\Delta G^{\ddagger}$ is quite small. In cases where $(\nu_A - \nu_B)$ is strongly temperature dependent the value at T_c may either be obtained from low temperature data, since it is usually possible to obtain a linear relationship by plotting $(\nu_A - \nu_B)$ or $\log_{10} (\nu_A - \nu_B)$ against T, or by using the relationship of equation (25). This method is limited to either exchange between two equally populated sites in an uncoupled system or to an AB system in which the nuclei exchange mutually between the A and B environments. For all other cases the best method of obtaining the rate at coalescence is from computed spectral line-shapes. In spite of these limitations a high proportion of the results published continue to be based on equations (19) and (34).

For a more complete, and therefore more satisfactory, kinetic study involving the estimation of site-exchange rates at a large number of temperatures it now seems clear that the only method worth using is the comparison of observed and computed line-shapes. Although the account of line-shape changes in Section II included the closed formulae (18), (19), (22 to 25), (33) and (34), which in principle permit the calculation of rate constants under defined conditions for measurable spectrum parameters, these formulae (with the two exceptions noted above) are probably hardly worth using except as a very rough guide. The only recommended method for obtaining rate constants is by use of the appropriate line-shape equation (13 to 15), (26), (29), (31), (32) or (38) for the spectral change under examination. The use of these line-shape equations requires in general good input values for the spectral parameters T_{2i}, $(\nu_A - \nu_B)$ or ν_i in the more general case, J_{ij} and p. The other input parameters are the rate constants, which are varied over the range examined, and if more than one rate constant is involved the relationship between them must be consistent with the rate-process being studied. The spectral parameters present problems since these may well be temperature dependent, and many of the unreliable results obtained in early work may be due to the failure to take this into account. The general procedure used by the author's group to obtain rate constants from spectral data will be discussed here, for the procedures used by other groups the original publications should be consulted.

The relaxation time T_2 fed into the line-shape equations is normally based upon the signal line-width at half maximum intensity in the absence of exchange. This presents no problem, except when measurements are made at rather low temperatures, and may readily be obtained by inspection of the low temperature spectra. In certain cases, however, very considerable changes in line-width may occur over the temperature range used for the examination, often the result of low temperature line broadening due to an increase in solvent viscosity and changes in the molecular correlation time. In the actual computation of line-shapes T_2 is usually not very critical, as the examination of equations (18), (22) and (23) will show, but in a few cases in which T_2 does become a critical input parameter, methods have been suggested[16 to 18] allowing for this temperature dependence. The variation of $(\nu_A - \nu_B)$ with temperature is much more serious and a method for dealing with this variation by extrapolation from low temperature data has been suggested. In general both T_2 and $(\nu_A - \nu_B)$ (or the ν_i values) should be treated as variable input parameters and the effects of the variation of both parameters, as well as the exchange rates, should be investigated. The use of T_2 as essentially a line-width parameter, including for example the effect of long-range coupling in addition to the normal transverse relaxation effects, does not appear to lead to errors when checked by computation. The comparison of observed and computed line-shapes may be made either by comparing line-shape parameters or by comparing the line-shapes by a least squares procedure as has been outlined in Section I. The latter method is more convenient as the comparison routine can be made a part of the same computer programme used to calculate line-shapes. The relative reliability of the two methods is difficult to assess.

B. Activation parameters

Assuming that the kinetic data, extracted preferably from line-shape comparison studies, and temperature data are reasonably accurate a number of courses are open to the chemist who wishes to present such data in the most useful way. The early literature in physical organic chemistry often restricted the discussion of kinetic results to a comparison of rate constants, obtained at a single standard temperature. This procedure has the advantage that it is based entirely upon experimental data and does not rely upon any of the theories of reaction rates. It has the considerable disadvantage that it is rather difficult to relate relative rates to structural changes, particularly when these are to be discussed in terms of steric and electronic effects, since it has become customary to think of the magnitudes of these effects in terms of energy units (kcal.mole^{-1} will be used throughout this article) which may be directly related to the results of calculations using quantum mechanical or other methods.

The more recent literature in physical organic chemistry has therefore tended to relate rate constants k to the Arrhenius activation parameters, A and E_a, using the empirical relationship:

$$k = A \exp(-E_a/RT) \tag{53}$$

It has also become customary to discuss reactions in terms of the transition state theory of reaction rates[70] which is summarized by the Eyring equation:

$$k = (\mathbf{k}T/h)[\exp(-\Delta H^\ddagger/RT) \cdot \exp(\Delta S^\ddagger/R)] \tag{54}$$

Where $\mathbf{k}$ is Boltzmann's constant, h is Planck's constant and $\Delta H^\ddagger$, the enthalpy of activation, and $\Delta S^\ddagger$, the entropy of activation, are the differences in the appropriate thermodynamic functions between the initial and the transition state. Comparison of equations (53) and (54) shows that for unimolecular processes with $\Delta S^\ddagger \sim 0$ the Arrhenius frequency factor A should be equal to kT/h ($\sim 10^{13}$ sec.$^{-1}$). The Eyring equation (54) was originally developed as an approximation for bimolecular processes in the gas phase, but it has been argued that it is also valid for unimolecular processes. The observation of frequency factors of about 10^{13} sec.$^{-1}$ for quite a large number of first-order reactions in the gas phase and in solution supports this view. Unimolecular isomerizations, which are the only type of rate process discussed in this review, may be less suited to the Eyring treatment, which supposes that every molecule crossing the barrier leads to products, and it has been suggested that low frequency factors (or negative entropies of activation) may result from molecules which initially cross the barrier but subsequently return without having reached the product state. The Eyring treatment in addition makes assumptions, probably valid in solution, about energy distribution in the molecular degrees of freedom and energy transfer between molecules. Equation (54) therefore represents an ideal relationship between the rate constant and the thermodynamic activation parameters which may not be realized in practice. For the types of process discussed in this article the failure of this relationship would lead to frequency factors very different from 10^{13} sec.$^{-1}$ or very large negative or positive entropies of activation.

Experimental results obtained at an early stage in the application of NMR line-shape methods did indeed suggest a failure of the Eyring relationship for the processes of geometrical isomerism which were studied. More recent work has, however, shown that these early results were affected by systematic errors, and frequency factors for most of the unimolecular rate processes studied by full line-shape comparison techniques, as discussed in section III A, have generally been encouragingly close to 10^{13} sec.$^{-1}$ Furthermore, linear free energy relationships have now been found for quite a large number of these unimolecular rate processes, which are similar to those which have been extensively documented for bimolecular processes.[71] These experimental results support the validity of the Eyring treatment, and the agreement between the calculated and observed inversion barriers for cyclohexane[24] and the calculated and observed barriers for a number of examples of nitrogen inversion[72,73] suggest that, in general, it should be possible to compare calculated and observed magnitudes of energy barriers for conformational changes.

The generally used method to obtain activation parameters is therefore to carry out a complete line-shape study of the kinetics over as wide a temperature range as is possible, and then to obtain the Arrhenius activation parameters from a plot of $\log_{10} k$ against $1/T$. The activation energy E_a is obtained from the slope of the best straight line relating the experimentally obtained points; normally this is obtained by a linear regression technique and deviations for 90% confidence limits are probably realistic estimates of the random errors in activation parameters based upon NMR line-shape measurement of rate constants. The value of A may then be obtained from E_a and a single value of k using equation (53). Alternatively activation parameters may be expressed in terms of $\Delta H^{\ddagger}$ and $\Delta S^{\ddagger}$, and preferably also $\Delta G^{\ddagger}$ at a standard temperature, for all of the compounds within the series studied. The $\Delta H^{\ddagger}$ and $\Delta S^{\ddagger}$ parameters should correctly be obtained from the temperature dependence of $\Delta G^{\ddagger}$ using the relationships:

$$k = (\mathbf{k}T/h)[\exp(-\Delta G^{\ddagger}/RT)] \tag{55}$$

$$\Delta G^{\ddagger} = \Delta H^{\ddagger} - T\,\Delta S^{\ddagger} \tag{56}$$

Frequently, however, $\Delta H^{\ddagger}$ is obtained from the approximation:

$$\Delta H^{\ddagger} = E_a - RT \tag{57}$$

and $\Delta G^{\ddagger}$ and $\Delta S^{\ddagger}$ are then obtained from k at the chosen standard temperature.

Unless the determination of rate constants is likely to be sufficiently accurate, to justify the time required for full line-shape comparison studies, results are probably best compared (e.g. in the comparison of the relative electronic and steric effects of substituents) in terms of the free energies of activation at a standard temperature. Furthermore, since entropies of activation are difficult to measure reliably, unless very accurate measurements of both rate constants and temperatures can be made, quite a high proportion of workers using NMR methods estimate the free energies of activation at the coalescence temperature only using equation (55). This approach, although saving considerable time, is only useful if the entropies of activation are small since otherwise comparison of the magnitudes of $\Delta G^{\ddagger}$ for different compounds measured at different temperatures would be meaningless.

In this review and discussion of experimental results which follows free energies of activation will generally be quoted, and it will generally be assumed that entropies of activation are small so that results will be compared in terms of these free energies of activation even if they relate to different temperatures. This, in many cases, provides some insight into the steric and electronic effects of substituents on the energetics of the conformational change. In order to form a more critical view the reader should consult the original papers and examine closely the techniques which have been used. In recent work the results may also be worth considering in terms of the entropies and enthalpies of activation, within the error limits of both parameters, but it is not clear at the present time whether a discussion of entropies of activation for rate processes in solution can be extended quantitatively beyond the discussion, for example, of simple statistical features of the reaction pathway.

IV. RING INVERSION PROCESSES

Probably the best known application of NMR line-shape methods is to the study of ring inversion processes,† since the free energies of activation frequently fall within the appropriate range (5 to 25 kcal.mole^{-1}). Four general approaches to the study of ring inversion processes may be considered (see examples **7** to **10**). The first two involve the study of the exchange of environments of diastereotopic protons or groups within a prochiral group CX_2Y. This group may form part of the ring system, as for example the methylene group of a cyclohexane ring (**7**) in which the ring inversion exchanges the protons H and H′ between the equatorial (A) and axial (B) environments. Alternatively, where this is not possible, as for example in certain unsaturated ring systems such as cyclo-octatetraene, the presence of a prochiral ring substituent such as CMe_2OH may allow the inversion process to be studied since it results in the exchange of the methyl groups Me and Me′ between the geometrically different environments A and B (see **8**).

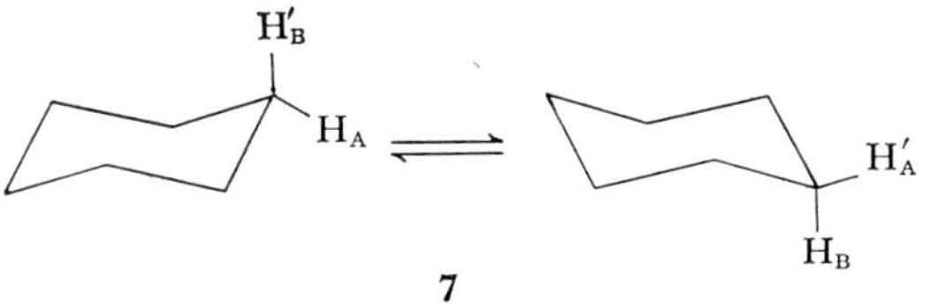

7

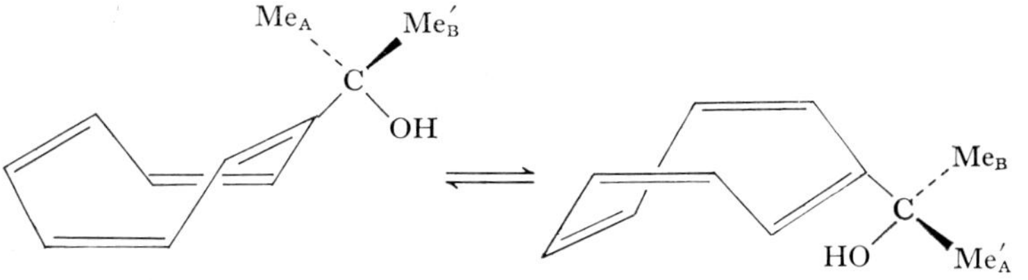

8

† The term "ring inversion" implies the inversion of the conformation of a ring system as exemplified by the processes (**7**) to (**10**).

These two methods may be used to examine degenerate ring inversion processes involving identical or enantiomeric pairs of conformations, but in other examples the original conformation and the conformation resulting from its inversion may be related as diastereomers, as in the case of a mono-substituted cyclohexane (9), or even the case of a cyclo-octatetraene with a chiral substituent (10). The detection of ring inversion for a situation analogous to (10) does not fortunately require the use of a substituent of a single chirality, since the invertomers are of two types (10a and 10b) distinguishable by, for example, the Cahn-Ingold-Prelog nomenclature as the diastereomeric pairs of enantiomers *RR* and *SS*, and *RS* and *SR*. Situations of the first type have been used most frequently to study ring inversion and the fourth type of situation has rarely been recorded.

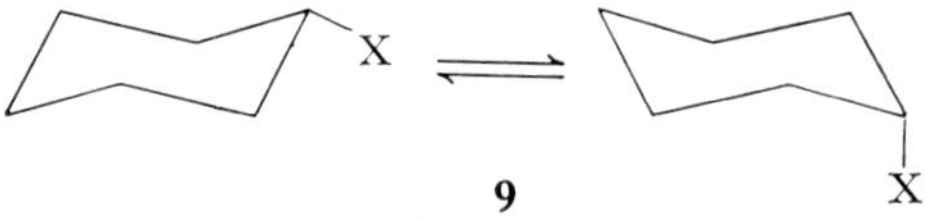

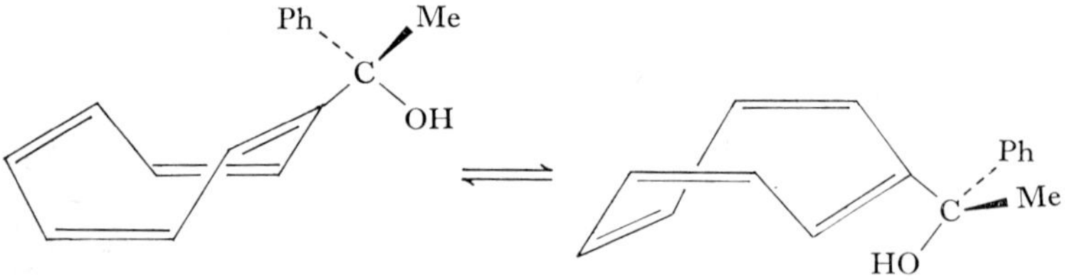

The study of ring inversion by NMR methods has been reviewed several times;[2,4,74,75] the present article will summarize the information available and discuss the significance of some of the results. A complete account is beyond the scope of this review and the more recent results will therefore be stressed. It is convenient to classify the ring systems according to size, and since inversion of conformation is virtually unhindered in four- and five-membered ring systems the account will necessarily be restricted to rings of six or more atoms in both monocyclic and, in a few cases, polycyclic systems.

A. Six-membered ring systems

Many studies have been made of conformational inversion in monocyclic six-membered rings. Accurate inversion rates, based upon line-shape methods, are difficult to obtain in extensively coupled systems and in many cases spectral simplification has been achieved by deuteration of some of the ring methylene groups. Alternative approaches include the use of fluorine substituents or of ring systems with geminal dimethyl or dimethoxyl substituents. It is noteworthy in this respect that some seven papers[24] have dealt with the kinetics of ring inversion of cyclohexane. The results of these studies, summarized in Table I, show that a reasonable measure of agreement has been reached between different research groups by using cyclohexane-d_{11} and examining the temperature dependence of the axial and equatorial proton signals with simultaneous irradiation of the deuterium resonances to eliminate errors due to H–D coupling. The discrepancy between the results obtained by steady-state and spin-echo studies is, however, disturbing.

TABLE I

Activation parameters for the ring inversion of cyclohexane

Compound	$\Delta G_{cb}^{\ddagger}$ kcal.mole^{-1}	$\Delta H_{cb}^{\ddagger}$ kcal.mole^{-1}	$\Delta S_{cb}^{\ddagger}$ e.u.	Reference
C_6H_{12}	10·1	11·5 ± 2	4·9	76
C_6H_{12}	10·3	9·0 ± 0·2	−6·5 ± 1·0	77
C_6H_{12}	10·7	11·5	4·9	78
C_6HD_{11}	10·3	10·9 ± 0·6	2·9 ± 2·3	79
C_6HD_{11}	10·2	10·5 ± 0·5	1·4 ± 1·0	80
C_6H_{12}[a]	10·3	9·1 ± 0·5	−5·8 ± 2·4	56
C_6HD_{11}[a]	10·3	9·1 ± 0·1	−5·8 ± 0·4	56
C_6HD_{11}	10·2	10·8	+2·8	24

[a] These results are based on spin-echo studies, the other results in the table are based on steady-state methods.

The inversion process[81] for the low-energy chair conformation of cyclohexane (*ch*, **11a**) is generally believed to involve one of six possible† twist-chair transition states (*tc*, **11b**) followed by a twist-boat intermediate (*tb*, **11c**), which may then enter a pseudo-rotational itinerary involving six possible boat conformations (**11d**) and five further twist-boat conformations. Each twist-boat intermediate may be converted either back to the original chair conformation (*ch*, **11a**) or into the inverted chair conformation (*ch**, **11e**) by way of the appropriate twist-chair transition state. This complex system of related conformations is conveniently described using a notation[82] based upon the torsion angle about each of the ring C–C single bonds. In this notation the torsional angle about each bond is indicated as positive (**12a**), negative (**12b**) or zero (**12c**) as defined by the Newman projection formulae (**12a, b** and **c**) in which the large curved bond represents the remainder of the ring system.

The various conformations (**11a** to **e**) may then be described by a sequence of six signs referring successively from left to right to the 1,2-bond, the 2,3-bond,

† This discussion makes a distinction between each of the methylene groups of the six-membered ring, this distinction is most easily indicated by numbering the ring positions as in (**11**).

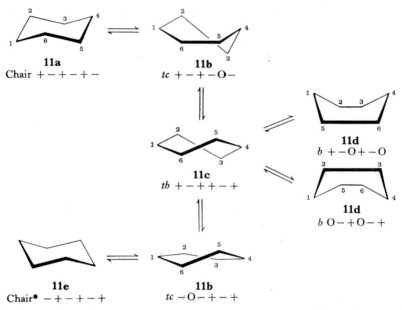

etc., this symbolism is applied to each of the conformations (**11**) to illustrate its use. The full conformational itinerary of a six-membered ring system is then summarized, using this symbolism, in Fig. 9. This figure is included because the

$$- + - + - +$$
$$ch^*$$
$$\updownarrow$$
$$- + - + - +$$
$$ch^*$$
$$\updownarrow$$

		$- + - + -$			$- + - + - +$		$- + - + -$

FIG. 9. Conformational changes for six-membered ring systems; *ch* and *ch** refer to chair, *tc* to twist chair, *b* to boat, and *tb* to twist boat conformations.

inversion of the chair conformation of any six-membered ring system may be considered by its use. The statistics of the inversion of cyclohexane, illustrated in **11** and Fig. 9, are consistent with a positive entropy of activation for the process

$ch \rightarrow tb$, $\Delta S_{cb}^{\ddagger}$, since there are six degenerate pathways available for the process $ch \rightarrow tc$, leading to the expectation that $\Delta S_{cb}^{\ddagger}$ would be $+R \ln 6$. In general, in ring inversion processes[80] involving intermediates and possibly degenerate path-

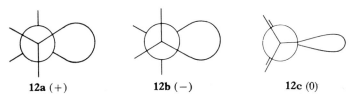

12a $(+)$ **12b** $(-)$ **12c** (0)

ways, allowance should be made for similar statistical features when the observed values of activation parameters are compared with those obtained from a theoretical model. Free energies of activation for the inversion of the chair conformations, $\Delta G_{cc}^{\ddagger}$,† have been determined for cyclohexane and a large number of its derivatives and the results are summarized in Table II. Although for a number of examples listed in Table II entropies and enthalpies of activation have been determined the reliability of these parameters is difficult to assess and therefore have not been included in the Table. Values of $\Delta G_{cc}^{\ddagger}$ are considered to be the most reliable when derived from a complete kinetic study using the comparison of observed and computed line-shapes, these cases have therefore been indicated in Table II.

TABLE II

Ring inversion barriers for cyclohexane derivatives

Compound	Solvent	$\Delta G^{\ddagger}$ kcal.mole^{-1}	Reference
Cyclohexane	CS_2	10·6[a]	24
1,1-Difluorocyclohexane	CS_2	9·7[b]	57, 83
	Propene	9·8[a]	46
1,1-Difluoro-4,4-dimethylcyclohexane	Propene	10·2[a]	46
1,1,2,2-Tetrafluorocyclohexane	Propene	10·9[a]	46
1,1-Difluoro-4-methyl-4-ethylcyclo-	Propene	9·9[a,c]	46
hexane		9·7[a,d]	
1,1-Difluoro-4-chlorocyclohexane	Propene	10·2[a,c]	46
		9·9[a,d]	
cis-1,2-Di-t-butylcyclohexane	CDCl$_3$	16·3[e]	84
	CS_2	10·1[f]	
Perfluorocyclohexane	CFCl$_3$	9·9	85
Chlorocyclohexane	CS_2	ca. 10·5	86
	CS_2	ca. 11·7	87

† $\Delta G_{cc}^{\ddagger} = \Delta G_{cb}^{\ddagger} + RT \ln 2$, since the $ch \rightarrow ch^*$ process involves the tb intermediate for which there is an equal probability for the processes $tb \rightarrow tc$ and $tb \rightarrow tc^*$.

TABLE II—*continued*

Compound	Solvent	$\Delta G^{\ddagger}$ kcal.mole^{-1}	Reference
Bromocyclohexane	CS$_2$	*ca.* 10·8	86
	CS$_2$	*ca.* 11·7	87
Fluorocyclohexane	CFCl$_3$	9·8[a,c]	88
		9·6[a,d]	
trans-1,2-Dichlorocyclohexane	CS$_2$	*ca.* 11·8	89
trans-1,2-Dibromocyclohexane	CS$_2$	*ca.* 11·9	89
trans-1,3-Dichlorocyclohexane	CS$_2$	9·8	90
trans-1,3-Dibromocyclohexane	CS$_2$	9·9	90
cis-Inositol hexa-acetate (**13**)		15·4	91
Allo-inositol hexa-acetate (**14**)		12·6[c]	91
Muco-inositol hexa-acetate (**15**)		10·5	91
γ-Hexachlorocyclohexane (**16**)		*ca.* 13·0	92
cis-1,2-Dimethoxycarbonylcyclo-hexane-d_6 (**17**)		10·7	93
cis-anti-cis-4-5-Dichloro-1,2-dimethoxycarbonylcyclohexane-d_4 (**18**)		13·4	93
cis-syn-cis-1,2,4,5-Tetra-acetoxy-cyclohexane-d_4 (**19**)		12·4	94
cis-anti-cis-1,2,4,5-Tetra-acetoxy-cyclohexane-d_4 (**20**)		13·5	94
1,1-Dimethylcyclohexane-d_4 (**21**)	CS$_2$	10·6	95
1,1-Dimethoxycyclohexane	CS$_2$	10·8	95
1,1,4,4-Tetramethylcyclohexane	CS$_2$	11·4	95
1,1-Dimethyl-4,4-dimethoxycyclo-hexane	CS$_2$	11·3	95
1,1,4,4-Tetramethoxycyclohexane	CH$_2$Cl$_2$	10·5	95
1,1,3,3-Tetramethylcyclohexane	CS$_2$	9·6	95
1,1-Dimethyl-3,3-dimethoxycyclohexane	CH$_2$Cl$_2$	10·4	95
Cyclohexan-1,3-dione bis-ethylene ketal (**22**)	CH$_2$Cl$_2$	*ca.* 9·5	95
2,2,5,5-Tetramethylcyclohexanone ethylene ketal (**23**)	CS$_2$	12·0	95

[a] Result based upon line-shape comparison study from which enthalpies and entropies of activation were also obtained.

[b] Spin-echo technique used.

[c] For major conformer → minor conformer.

[d] For minor conformer → major conformer.

[e] The stable conformation is the twist boat, this barrier is for twist boat pseudo-rotation.

[f] Probably the barrier for twist boat → chair, but could be for hindered rotation about the C–CMe$_3$ bonds.

The effects of substituents on the rates of inversion of the cyclohexane chair conformation are in general not very marked, but two general effects have been noted, which have been discussed briefly in a number of papers.[91,93,94] Recently a rather complete discussion of cyclohexane inversion barriers has been pub-

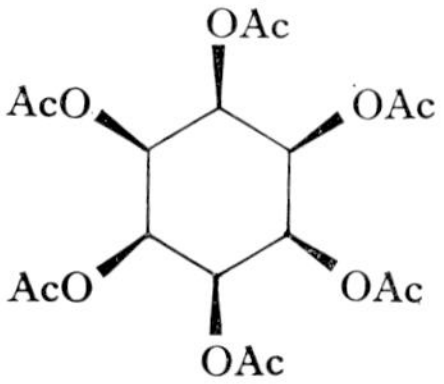

13

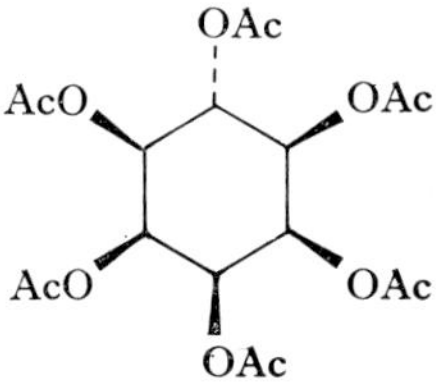

14

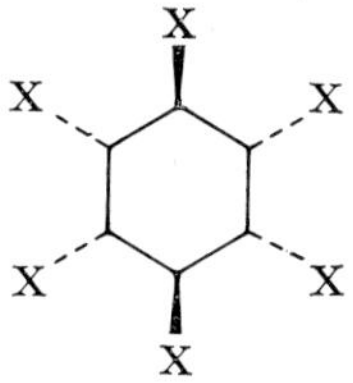

15 X = OAc
16 X = Cl

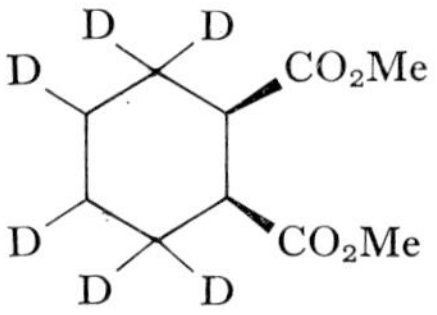

17

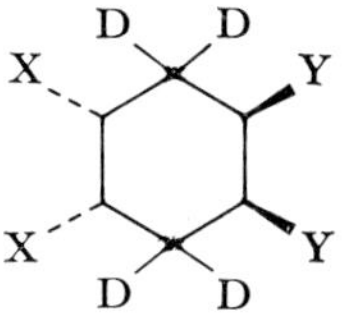

18 X = Cl,
    Y = CO$_2$Me
20 X = Y = OAc

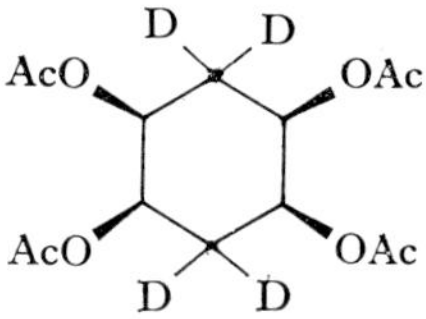

19

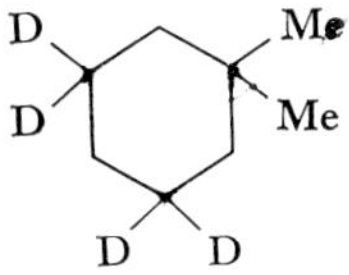

21

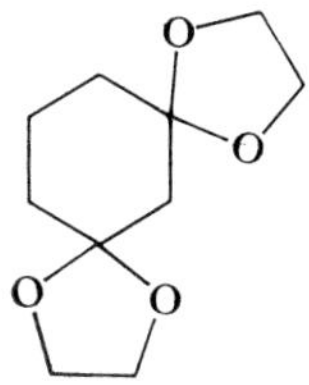

22

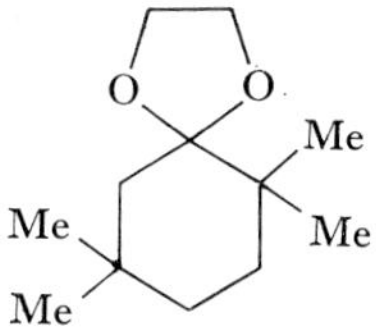

23

lished,[95] which has been supported by the results of calculations[96] of conformational energies using the approach originally adopted by Hendrickson.[81] In some cases the transition state for the inversion process, $ch \rightarrow ch^*$ (see **11**) may not be the half-chair form (tc, **11b**) as generally postulated, but the scheme shown in Fig. 9 serves as a reasonable general description of the conformational changes of six-membered rings, although the form of the energy profile for these changes may require separate consideration for each case. The energy barrier for ring inversion is lowered by syn-axial interactions, as in 1,1,3,3-tetrasubstituted cyclohexanes, since these are generally of more importance in the ground state chair conformation than in the transition state. It does not, however, appear that this effect permits the measurement of syn-axial interactions in the ground state chair conformation as was at one time suggested.[93] Two pairs of geminal substituents in the 1- and 4- positions increase the barrier to ring inversion,[94] this is a consequence of an increase in strain for the process $ch \rightarrow tc$ (**11a** $\rightarrow$ **b**) and the effect may be associated with an increase in the barrier to rotation about the ring C–C single bonds. As would be expected, the magnitudes of the two types of substituent effects depend directly upon the effective size of the substituents, methyl substituents, for example, having more effect than methoxyl substituents. The results for 1,2-*cis*-di-*t*-butylcyclohexane are particularly interesting.[84] The barrier for the process *ch* → *tb* is normal, but the chair conformation is thermodynamically destabilized by the requirement that one *t*-butyl substituent should be axial, and the ring accordingly adopts, largely at least, the twist-boat conformation. The normally rapid pseudorotational process which results in inversion of boat conformations is, in this case, slow because it involves the passage of one *t*-butyl substituent past the other, generating a very high torsional barrier for the C(1)–C(2) bond.

The dependence of ring inversion barriers upon the torsional barriers of individual ring bonds is not simple, as would be expected from the scheme summarized in Fig. 9. It would also be expected that the lowering of ring inversion barriers by lowered torsional barriers would be much easier to detect than increases in torsional barriers leading to increased barriers. These effects are demonstrated[97] by the very low inversion barriers found for six-membered rings containing one[97,98] or two sp^2 hybridized carbon atoms[99] (see Table III). The relationship between these inversion barriers and the corresponding rotational barriers in propene and acetaldehyde has been discussed.[97] The introduction of the second sp^2 hybridized carbon atom[99] [compounds (26) and (27)] does not lower the barrier more than for the first [compounds (24) and (25)],[97,98] and this is consistent with the torsional effects discussed briefly above.

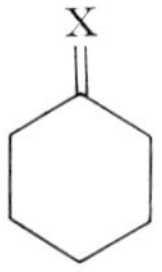

24 X = CH$_2$ 26 X = CH$_2$
25 X = NOMe   27 X = CF$_2$

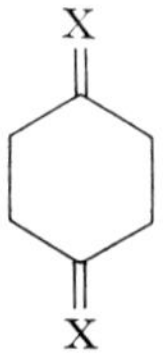

The inversion of the half-chair conformation (32a) of cyclohexene systems[100,101] is more readily understood, and the transition state is probably the conformation (32b) in which five of the ring carbon atoms are coplanar. This type of transition state and the involvement of an intermediate boat conformation are consistent with both the low magnitude of the inversion barrier and the effects of substituents[100] in the 4- and 5- positions (see Table III).

28 X = F, Y = H
29 X = Cl, Y = H
30 X = Br, Y = H
31 X = I, Y = H
32 X = Y = CO$_2$Me

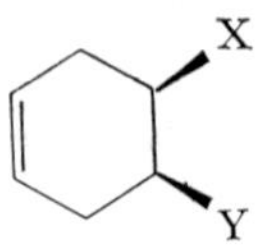

32a   32b

TABLE III

Ring inversion barriers for six-membered monocarbocyclic systems containing trigonal atoms

Compound	$\Delta G_{cc}^{\ddagger}$ [a] kcal.mole^{-1}		Reference
Methylenecyclohexanone (24)	7·7	(158)	97
	ca. 7.7	(168)	98
O-Methylcyclohexanone oxime (25)	5·6	(121)	97
Cyclohexanone	<5·1	(<103)	97
Cyclohexanone [2,2,6,6-^{2}H$_4$]	<5.2	(<105)	97
1,4-Dimethylenecyclohexane (26)	7·5	(155)	99
1,4-Bisdifluoromethylenecyclohexane (27)	6·5	(139)	99
Cyclohexane-1,4-dione	(T_c <113)		99
Cyclohexene [2,3,3,4,5,5,6,6-^{2}H$_8$]	5·4	(107)	100
Cyclohexene [3,3,4,5,6,6-^{2}H$_6$]	5·3	(109)	101
4-Fluorocyclohexene (28)	5·3[b], 5·0[c]	(107)	100
4-Chlorocyclohexene (29)	6·3[b], 5·8[c]		100
4-Bromocyclohexene (30)	6·3[b], 5·8[c]		100
4-Iodocyclohexene (31)	6·6[b], 6·0[c]		100
cis-4,5-Dimethoxycarbonylcyclohexene (32)	7·4		100

[a] In all cases based upon the coalescence temperature (given in brackets in °K).
[b] Major conformer → minor conformer.
[c] Minor conformer → major conformer.

TABLE IV

Ring inversion barriers for six-membered heterocyclic systems

Compound	Solvent	$\Delta G_{cc}^{\ddagger}$ kcal.mole^{-1}	Reference
Piperdine [3,3,5,5-^{2}H$_4$] (33)	CD$_3$OD	8·9[a]	102
N-Methylpiperdine [3,3,5,5-^{2}H$_4$] (33a)	CD$_3$OD	11·6[a]	102
N-t-Butylpiperdine [3,3,5,5-^{2}H$_4$] (33b)	CD$_3$OD	10·7[a]	102
4,4-Difluoropiperdine (33c)	CDCl$_3$	9·1[a]	109
Tetrahydropyran (34)	CD$_3$OD	9·3[a]	47
	CS$_2$	9·9[a]	110

TABLE IV—*continued*

Compound	Solvent	$\Delta G_{cc}^{\ddagger}$ kcal.mole^{-1}	Reference
Pentamethylene sulphide (**34a**)	CH_2Cl_2	8·7	47
Pentamethylene sulphoxide (**34b**)	CH_2Cl_2	9·8	47
Pentamethylene sulphone (**34c**)	CH_2Cl_2	E_a 14·9, T_c 210°K	47
1,3-Dioxan (**35**)	$(CD_3)_2CO$	9·9[a]	105, 106
5,5-Dimethyl-1,3-dioxan (**35a**)	$(CD_3)_2CO$	11·0[a], 10·5	105, 106, 108
2,2-Dimethyl-1,3-dioxan (**35b**)	Me_2O	8·4[a]	105, 106
2,2,5,5-Tetramethyl-1,3-dioxan (**35c**)	Me_2O	9·0[a]	105, 106
4,4-Dimethyl-1,3-dioxan (**35d**)	Me_2O	9·1[a]	105
4,4,6,6-Tetramethyl-1,3-dioxan (**35e**)		< 7·0	105
2,2-Dimethoxy-5,5-dimethyl-1,3-dioxan (**35f**)	CS_2	*ca.* 8·6[a]	105
2,2-Diphenyl-5,5-dimethyl-1,3-dioxan (**35g**)	CS_2	9·6[a]	105
2,2-Trimethylene-5,5-dimethyl-1,3-dioxan (**36**)	CCl_2F_2	9·2	107
2,2-Tetramethylene-5,5-dimethyl-1,3-dioxan (**36a**)	CCl_2F_2	8·8	107
2,2-Pentamethylene-5,5-dimethyl-1,3-dioxan (**36b**)	CCl_2F_2	8·1	107
2,2-Hexamethylene-5,5-dimethyl-1,3-dioxan (**36c**)	CCl_2F_2	7·9	107
2,2-Heptamethylene-5,5-dimethyl-1,3-dioxan (**36d**)	CCl_2F_2	8·0	107
5,5-Dimethylene-1,3-dioxan (**37**)	CCl_2F_2	9·3	108
5,5-Dimethylene-2,2-trimethylene-1,3-dioxan (**38**)	CCl_2F_2	8·6	108
5,5-Dimethylene-2,2-tetramethylene-1,3-dioxan (**38a**)	CCl_2F_2	8·7	108
1,3-Dithian (**39**)	CH_2Cl_2	10·3[a]	105
5,5-Dimethyl-1,3-dithian (**39a**)	CS_2	10·6[a]	105
2,2-Dimethyl-1,3-dithian (**39b**)	CS_2	10·1[a]	105
2,2,5,5-Tetramethyl-1,3-dithian (**39c**)	CH_2Cl_2	11·1[a]	105
1,3-Oxathian (**40**)	CS_2	9·4[a]	105
5,5-Dimethyl-1,3-oxathian (**40a**)	CS_2	10·4[a]	105
2,2-Dimethyl-1,3-oxathian (**40b**)	Me_2O	8·4[a]	105
4,4-Dimethyl-1,3-oxathian (**40c**)	CS_2	9·4[a]	105
6,6-Dimethyl-1,3-oxathian (**40d**)	CS_2	9·3[a]	105
2,2,5,5-Tetramethyl-1,3-oxathian (**40e**)	CS_2	11·6[a]	105
N,N'-Dimethylhexahydropyrimidine (**41**)	$CDCl_3$	11·6	103
	$CDCl_3$	11·6[a]	104
N,N'-Diethylhexahydropyrimidine (**41a**)	$CDCl_3$	10·9	103

TABLE IV—*continued*

Compound	Solvent	$\Delta G_{cc}^{\ddagger}$ kcal. mole^{-1}	Reference
N-Methylhexahydro-1,3-oxazine (42)	CF_2Cl_2	10·8	111
N-Methyl-5,5-dimethylhexahydro-1,3-oxazine (42a)	CH_2Cl_2	10·4[a]	111
N,N'-Dimethylpiperazine (43)		13·0	112
		12·8	74
Piperazine (43a)	CH_2Cl_2	10·3	74
N-Methylpiperazine (43b)	CH_2Cl_2	11·5	74
cis-2,5-Dimethylpiperazine (43c)	CH_2Cl_2	9·6	74
Morpholine (44)	CH_2Cl_2	9·9	74
N-Methylmorpholine (44a)	CH_2Cl_2	11·5	74
trans-2,6-Dimethylmorpholine (44b)	CH_2Cl_2	9·0	74
3,3,6,6-Tetramethyl-1,2-dioxan (45)	CS_2	14·6[a]	113
1,2-Dithian[4,4,5,5-$^2H_4$] (46)	CS_2	11·6	114
cis-4,5-Diacetoxy-1,2-dithian (46a)	CS_2	13·9	115
3,3,6,6-Tetramethyl-1,2-dithian (45a)	CS_2	13·8	113
1,3-Diselenan (47)	CS_2	8·2	116
Tri-N-methylhexahydro-1,3,5-triazine (48)	$CDCl_3$	13·0[a,c]	18, 104, 61
Tri-N-ethylhexahydro-1,3,5-triazine (48a)	$CDCl_3$	12·3[a,c]	18, 104
Tri-N-propylhexahydro-1,3,5-triazine (48b)	$CDCl_3$	11·4[a]	104
Tri-N-isopropylhexahydro-1,3,5-triazine (48c)	n-C_5H_{12}	10·8[a]	18
Tri-N-t-butylhexahydro-1,3,5-triazine (48d)	n-C_5H_{12}	10·2[a]	18
2,2,4,4,6,6-Hexamethyl-1,3,5-trithian (49)		*ca.* 8[b]	61
Cyclopentamethylenedimethylsilane (34d)		5·5	117
Duplodithio-acetone (50)	CS_2	15·6[a,d]	118
	CS_2	16·0[a,e]	
Diacetoneperoxide (50a)	$CDCl_3$	15·4	119
Tetra-N-methyl-hexahydro-1,2,4,5-tetrazine (51)	$CDCl_3$	11·7	120
Dihydropyran (52)		6·6	121

[a] Results based on complete examination using total line-shape comparison.
[b] Determined by spin-echo techniques.
[c] Examined in several solvents, see references cited for details.
[d] For chair → twist boat.   [e] For twist boat → chair.

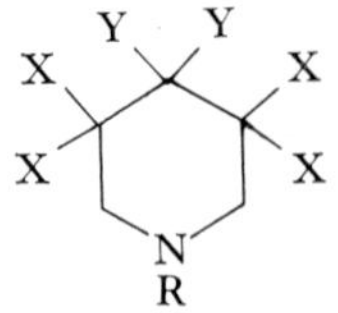

	R	Y	X
33	H	H	D
33a	Me	H	D
33b	CMe₃	H	D
33c	H	F	H

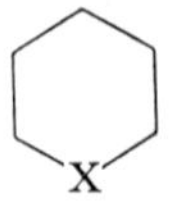

34 X = O
34a X = S
34b X = SO
34c X = SO₂
34d X = SiMe₂

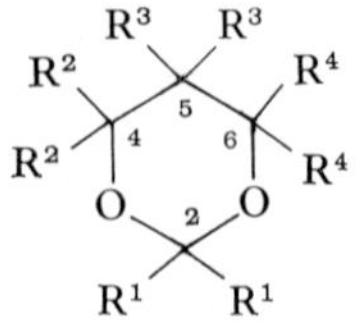

	R¹	R²	R³	R⁴
35	H	H	H	H
35a	H	H	Me	H
35b	Me	H	H	H
35c	Me	H	Me	H
35d	H	Me	H	H
35e	H	Me	H	Me
35f	OMe	H	Me	H
35g	Ph	H	Me	H

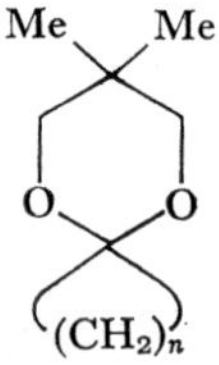

36   n = 3
36a n = 4
36b n = 5
36c n = 6
36d n = 7

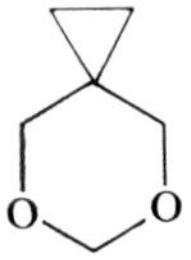

37

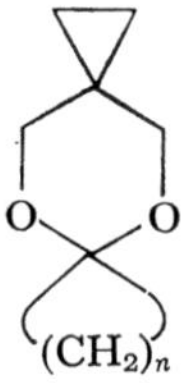

38 n = 3
38a n = 4

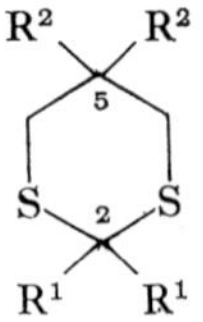

39 R¹ = R² = H
39a R¹ = H, R² = Me
39b R¹ = Me, R² = H
39c R¹ = R² = Me

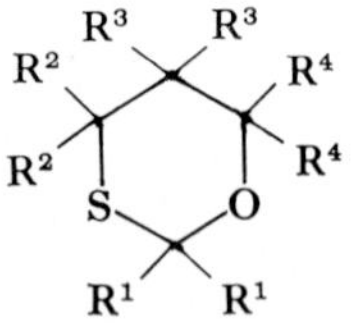

	R¹	R²	R³	R⁴
40	H	H	H	H
40a	H	H	Me	H
40b	Me	H	H	H
40c	H	Me	H	H
40d	H	H	H	Me
40e	Me	H	Me	H

41 R = Me
41a R = Et

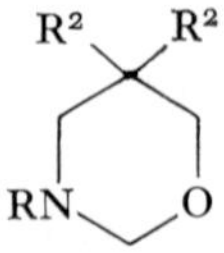

42 R¹ = Me, R² = H
42a R¹ = R² = Me

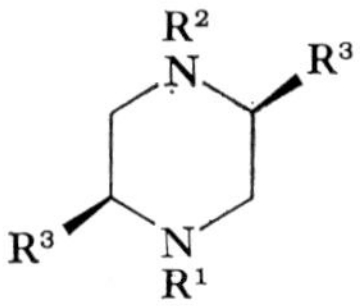

43 $R^1 = R^2 = $ Me, $R^3 = $ H
43a $R^1 = R^2 = R^3 = $ H
43b $R^1 = R^3 = $ H, $R^2 = $ Me
43 $R^1 = R^2 = $ H, $R^3 = $ Me

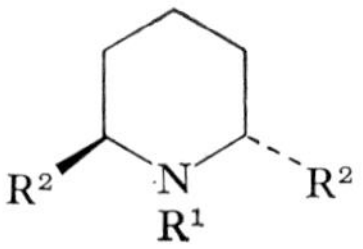

44 $R^1 = R^2 = $ H
44a $R^1 = $ Me, $R^2 = $ H
44b $R^1 = $ H, $R^2 = $ Me

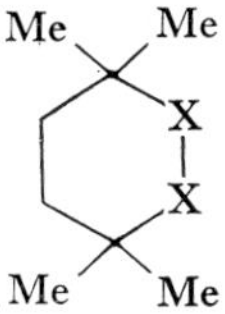

45 X = O
45a X = S

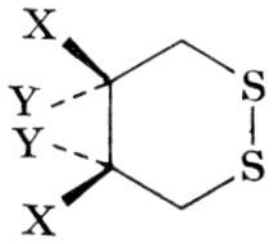

46 X = Y = D
46a X = OAc, Y = H

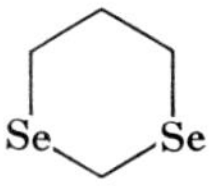

47

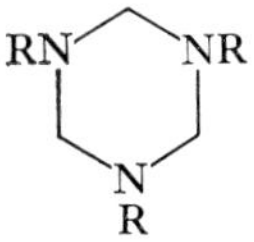

48 R = Me
48a R = CH$_2$Me
48b R = Ch$_2$CH$_2$Me
48c R = CHMe$_2$
48d R = CMe$_3$

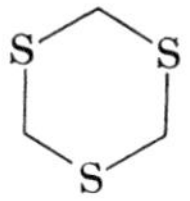

49

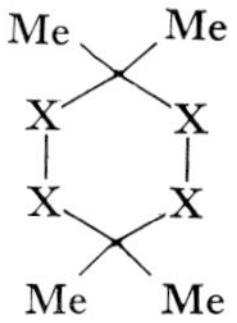

50 X = S
50a X = O

51

52

Ring inversion barriers have also been measured for a very large number of heterocyclic six-membered ring systems using NMR line-shape techniques, and the results of these examinations are reported in Table IV. The relative magnitudes of these inversion barriers have been discussed[74] in terms of the torsional contribution to the strain enthalpy in the various possible twist-chair (*cf* **11b**) transition states for inversion of a chair conformation (*cf* **11a**). This method gave quite good agreement between observed and calculated ring inversion barriers in a number of cases, supporting the idea that the relative magnitudes of the torsional barriers for the individual single bonds of the ring system are of prime importance in the energetics of the ring inversion process. Nitrogen-containing ring systems present additional difficulties in that it is difficult to allow for the effects of the low barrier to nitrogen inversion upon the ring inversion barrier and it has been shown, in a number of cases that, in systems containing nitrogen, the ring inversion barrier is sensitive to the size of the substituents on the nitrogen atoms.[18,102,103,104]

Detailed studies have been made of substituent effects for 1,3-dioxans,[105 to 108] 1,3-oxathians,[105] and 1,3-dithians.[105] In these systems it has been found that the inversion barrier is generally increased by geminal substituents in the 5- position and decreased by geminal substituents in the 2- or 4- positions. This contrasts with the situation in cyclohexane where a single pair of geminal substituents has little effect upon the ring inversion barrier. It is well known, however, that in 1,3-dioxans and analogous ring systems the conformational properties may differ from those of cyclohexane systems owing to the absence of axial hydrogen substituents on the hetero-atoms. The lone pair electrons on the hetero-atoms do not have marked steric requirements, in contrast with hydrogen atoms with considerable space-filling properties. As expected 4,4,6,6-tetrasubstituted systems have reduced inversion barriers arising from the relief of the ground state *syn*-axial interactions in the half-chair transition state.

Ring inversion barriers in six-membered heterocyclic systems, which contain two hetero-atoms in adjacent positions, may be affected by the enhanced torsional barrier for the bond joining the two hetero-atoms. This is certainly the case for certain cyclic hydrazine and hydroxylamine derivatives, which will be discussed in a later section, and is probably also a relevant factor in the rather large barriers associated with some 1,2-dioxan and 1,2-dithian derivatives [e.g. compounds **(45)**, **(45a)** and **(46a)**], duplodithio-acetone **(50)** and diacetoneperoxide **(50a)**. The tetrathian **(50)** provides a particularly interesting example of conformational changes.[118] The NMR spectrum of **(50)** recorded at low temperature shows separate signals which may be associated with a rigid (on the NMR time-scale) chair conformation and a rapidly inverting twist-boat conformation. The kinetics of the equilibration of these conformations has been measured, both by NMR line-shape methods and also by direct observation of the NMR spectrum of the isolated twist-boat form, using a solution of the crystalline compound dissolved in carbon disulphide at $-80°$. The agreement between the activation parameters obtained by the two procedures was good. The only heterocyclic six-membered ring system containing unsaturation for which ring inversion rates have been obtained is dihydropyran **(52)**;[121] the inversion barrier is rather low as might be expected by analogy with cyclohexene.

B. Polycyclic systems containing six-membered rings

The results discussed in this section will include inversion barriers for six-membered ring systems which form part of a polycyclic system. These are of two types, (i) those in which one ring only undergoes inversion and (ii) those in which two or more rings undergo consecutive or synchronized inversion.

The first type of system includes the 9,10-dihydrophenanthrenes (53).[122] Although the inversion barrier in 9,10-dihydrophenanthrene itself (53) would be very low[36,123] the presence of *cis*-alkyl substituents in the 9- and 10- positions raises the torsional barrier for the 9-10 bond so considerably[122] that the ring inversion barriers come within the range suitable for NMR study. The relative heights of the inversion barriers for the 9,10-dihydrophenanthrene derivatives (53a to c) are clearly related to the magnitude of the interaction between the substituents R when these are in an eclipsed relationship.

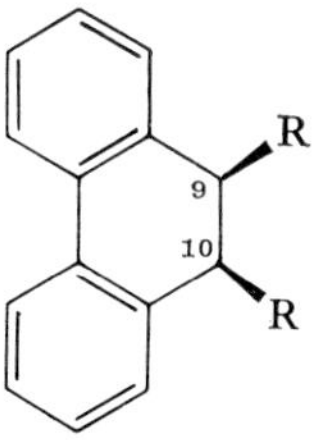

53 R = H
53a R = Me $\Delta G^{\ddagger}_{226}$ 10·8 kcal.mole^{-1}
53b R = Et $\Delta G^{\ddagger}_{290}$ 14·9 kcal.mole^{-1}
53c R = Ph $\Delta G^{\ddagger} < 9\cdot7$ kcal.mole^{-1}

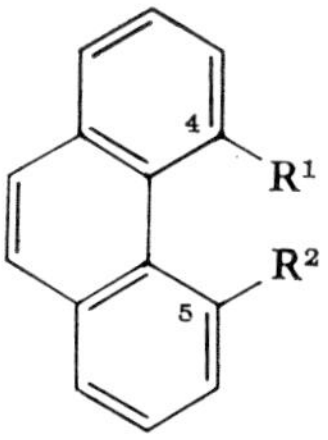

	R^1	R^2	$\Delta G^{\ddagger}_{273}$ kcal.mole^{-1}	Solvent
54	CO$_2$Me	CO$_2$CHMe$_2$	14·5	CDCl$_3$
54a	CH$_2$OAc	CH$_2$OAc	18·1	C$_6$D$_5$NO$_2$

The unsubstituted phenanthrene molecule is planar but the presence of bulky substituents in the 4- and 5- positions (see **54**) is known to cause out-of-plane deformation, which in extreme cases may result in the isolation of optically active non-planar conformations;[124] some very interesting examples of this phenomenon are provided by the helicenes.[125] The substituted phenanthrenes (**54**) have inversion barriers, for their non-planar conformations, which are of the right magnitude for study by NMR line-shape methods, using the temperature dependence[128] of the signals of the prochiral substituents, CO_2CHMe_2 and CH_2OAc. This technique provides a potentially rather convenient method for studying the dynamics of the out-of-plane deformation of similar polycyclic aromatic systems.

The inversion barrier for the cyclohexadiene ring in the 9,10-dihydronaphthalene derivatives (**55**) is clearly raised[126,127] by the interaction between the substituents (X and Y) in the 9-methylene group and the adjacent substituents (Z) on the aromatic rings at positions 1 and 8. The kinetics of conformational inversion have been examined for a number of cases;[126,127] it is of interest that the interaction between X = Cl and Z = H in the transition state for inversion of compound (**55c**) is evidently larger than the analogous interaction between X = H and Z = Cl in compound (**55b**) showing the differing ease of molecular deformation in the two cases.

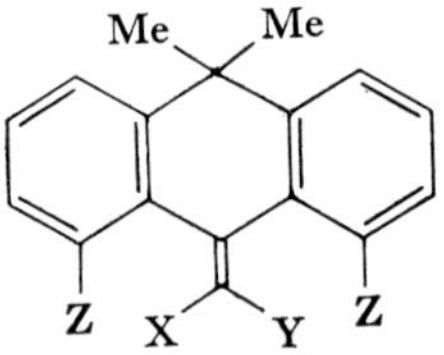

	X	Y	Z	$\Delta G^{\ddagger}$ kcal.mole^{-1}
55	Br	CO_2Me	H	15·1[126]
55a	Br	Ph	H	15·7[126]
55b	H	H	Cl	15·9[127]
55c	Cl	Cl	H	17·4[127]
55d	Br	Br	H	18·1[126], 19·3[127]

The NMR spectrum of *cis*-decalin was originally thought[129] not to show temperature dependence and, although this might have meant a very low barrier for the inversion process (**56a**⇌**56b**), this has been shown not to be the case by the examination of suitably substituted derivatives of *cis*-decalin. The failure to obtain precise results for unsubstituted *cis*-decalin arises from the small chemical shift difference between the equatorial and axial protons.[130]

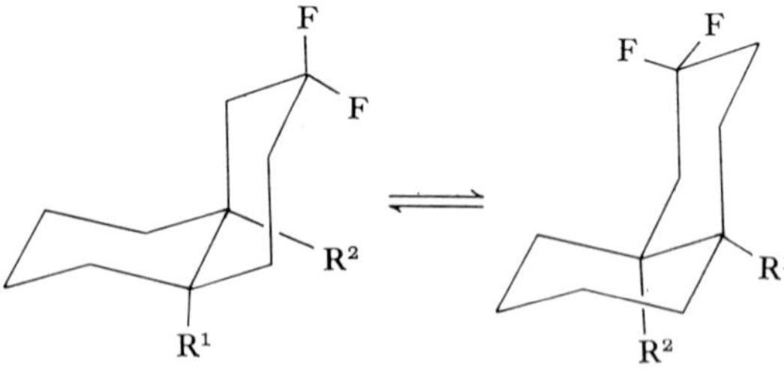

59a   59b 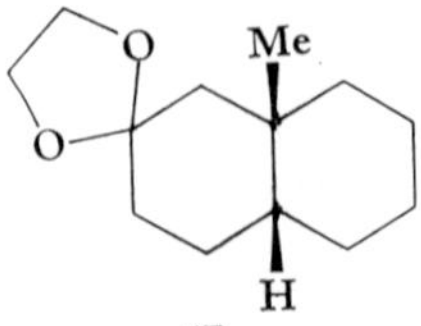   57

Thus the spectrum of the derivative (**57**) showed two methyl signals below 231°K giving $\Delta G^{\ddagger}$ *ca.* 12·5 kcal.mole^{-1} for interconversion of the two double chair conformations.[130] More precise results for the inversion barriers in *cis*-decalin systems were subsequently obtained[131] using the substituted compounds (**58**); in these cases, although the ring inversion is degenerate for (58) and (58a), the methylene groups of the substituents give AB systems at low temperatures which coalesce to singlets at higher temperatures when the inversion process, analogous to (56a⇌56b), becomes fast on the NMR time scale. These spectral changes were examined by line-shape comparison methods to give the activation parameters listed with the formulae (58).

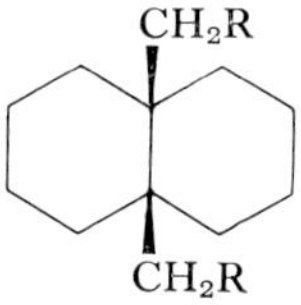

		R^1	R^2	$\Delta G^{\ddagger}_{303}$ kcal.mole^{-1}
58		CO$_2$Me	CO$_2$Me	15·9
58a		Br	Br	14·7
58b		Br	CN	15·0

The ^{19}F resonance spectra of the fluorodecalins (60) were examined by Gerig and Roberts[44] to give the results shown for the populations of the diastereomeric conformations (59a) and (59b) and also the energy barriers separating these two conformations. For a complete discussion the original papers[44,130,131] should be consulted, but the magnitudes of the energy barriers for inversion of the *cis*-decalin systems discussed above are consistent with an inversion process involving consecutive chair → twist-boat changes for each ring in turn.

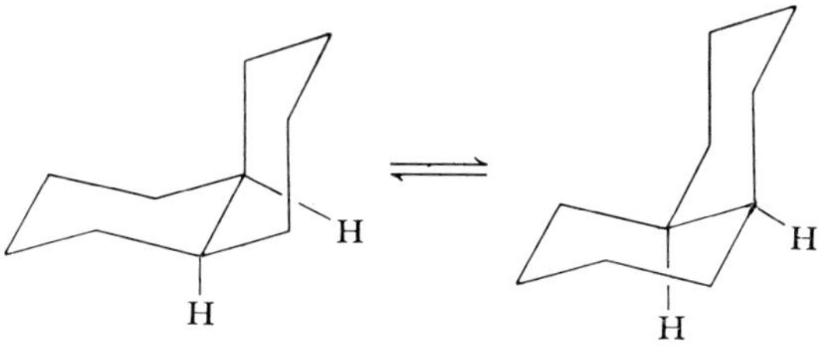

56a   56b

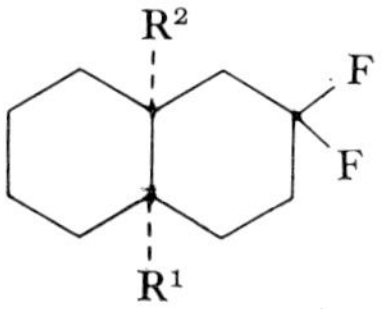

$\Delta G^{\ddagger}$ (major → minor)

	R^1	R^2	kcal.mole^{-1}	% Major conformer
60	H	H	12·3	74
60a	H	Me	12·1	52
60b	Me	H	12·8	77
60c	H	Et	11·8	50

The work of fluorodecalin systems has been extended[45] to the fluorodecalones (61); again two diastereomeric conformations were found to be present, but separated in this case by a rather lower energy barrier than for the fluorodecalins (60). The smaller magnitude of this barrier reflects the much lower inversion barrier of the cyclohexanone ring relative to the cyclohexane ring, and even the ^{19}F spectrum of 4,4-difluorocyclohexanone remains unaffected[45] by the ring inversion process down to 93°K. The inversion barriers for the difluoro-*cis*-hydrindan systems (62) were found to be even smaller,[132] possibly a reflection of the ground state strain in the six-membered ring owing to the fused five-membered ring system.

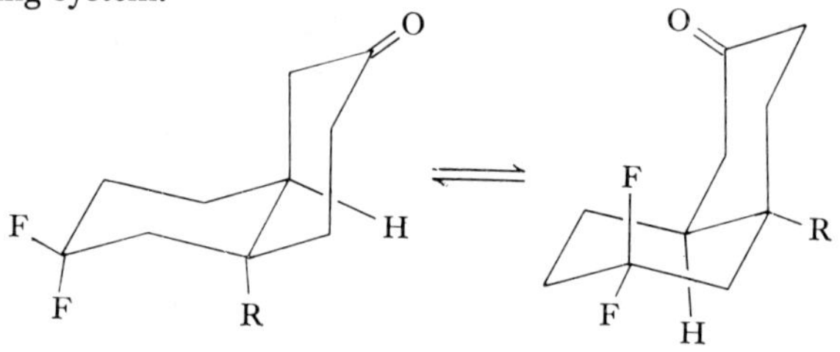

61

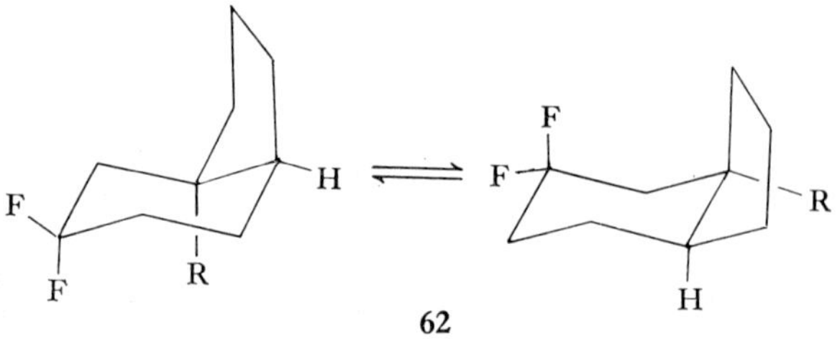

62

R	$\Delta G^{\ddagger}$ (major → minor) kcal.mole^{-1}	% Major conformer
61 H	10·1	65
61a Me	11·6	75
62 H	7·6	70
62a Me	7·8	67

The *cis*-fused 1,4-dioxan (63), analogous to the *cis*-decalins (58), has also been studied[133] by examination of the temperature dependent signals of the bromomethyl substituents. In this case the inversion barrier ($\Delta G^{\ddagger}$ 11·5 kcal.mole^{-1}) was rather lower than in the analogous *cis*-decalin system. The [4,4,4] propellane derivatives (64) and (65) are particularly interesting since, in these cases, inversion of all three six-membered rings must be synchronized to the extent that it involves pseudo-rotation in an intermediate having all three rings in boat or twist-boat conformations. The rather higher energies of activation found[131] for the inversion of (64) and (65) as compared with cyclohexane and cyclohexene are consistent with this synchronized inversion mechanism. Similarly the *cis-$\Delta^{2,6}$-*hexalin derivatives (**66**) also have substantial inversion barriers,[134] in marked contrast with the very low inversion barrier found in monocyclic cyclohexene derivatives.

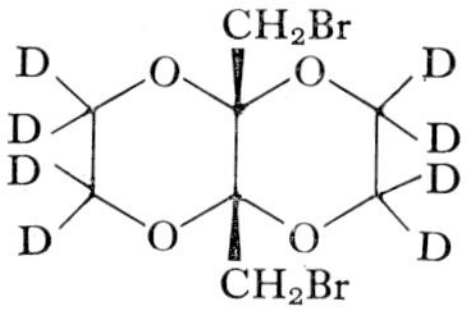

63

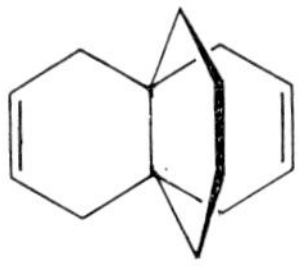

64
$\Delta G^{\ddagger}$ 15·7 kcal.mole^{-1}

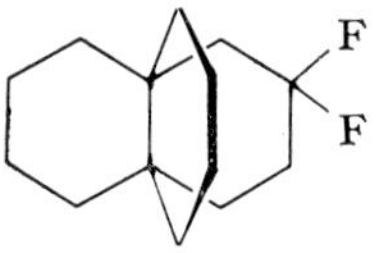

65
$\Delta G^{\ddagger}$ 16·7 kcal.mole^{-1}

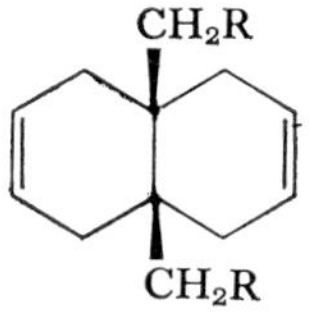

	R	$\Delta G^{\ddagger}$ kcal.mole^{-1}
66	Br	12·2
66a	CN	13·4
66b	CO$_2$Me	14·2

C. Rings larger than six-membered

Although the conformations of six-membered ring systems are generally well defined and qualitatively understood, both in terms of conformational equilibria and dynamics and chemical reactivity, the situation in larger saturated ring systems is less well defined, although it may become clearer in certain cases when double bonds are introduced into the ring system.

According to Hendrickson[135] the cycloheptane ring may adopt either twist-chair (**67**) or twist-boat (**68**) conformations, and either of those conformational types would be consistent with the ^{19}F NMR spectrum of the dibromo-compound (**69**), which shows[136] two singlet ^{19}F signals at low temperatures coalescing to a single signal above 159°K ($\Delta G^{\ddagger}$ 7·4 kcal.mole^{-1}). The two diastereomeric conformations, deduced to be present in a ratio of 3:1 from the low temperature spectrum, were assumed to be the two possible twist-boat conformations rather than, for example, a mixture of two different conformational types such as twist-chair and twist-boat. The spectroscopic results require an equilibrium between two conformational types having time-averaged C_2 symmetry with respect to the axis indicated by a broken line in (**69**) but the result does not further define the conformational species involved.

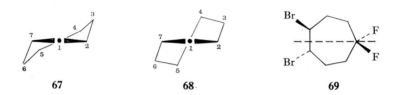

67   68   69

The situation in cycloheptene is, however, more easily understood and the possible conformational changes of this ring system, summarized in Fig. 10, have

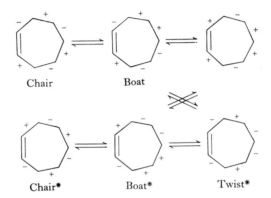

FIG. 10. The conformational changes of the cycloheptene ring system.

been discussed. Different conformations in this scheme are distinguished by the same system, defining the bond torsional angles, that was used for cyclohexane; the conformations have been designated chair (**70**), boat (**71**), and twist (**72**) by analogy with the conformations of cyclohexane. The ^{19}F NMR spectrum of 5,5-difluorocycloheptene (**73**) shows[136] an AB system at low temperature which coalesces to a singlet above 181°K. The inversion barrier associated with this change ($\Delta G^{\ddagger}$ 7·4 kcal.mole^{-1}) probably involves inversion of the chair conformation with the process chair⇌boat being the rate-determining step.

70 Chair   **71** Boat   **72** Twist

The spectrum of the tetramethylbenzocycloheptene (**74**) is more definitive[137] since in this case the low temperature NMR spectrum shows two pairs of signals from each of the CMe$_2$ groups, corresponding with two conformational types, each undergoing inversion at a slow rate on the NMR time scale. These two diastereomeric conformations, which must be chair and boat types, are rapidly interconverted at higher temperatures ($\Delta G^{\ddagger}$ 11·8 kcal.mole^{-1} at 250°K) where each CMe$_2$ group is represented by just a pair of equal intensity signals. At still higher temperatures the process boat⇌boat* also becomes fast on the NMR time scale ($\Delta G^{\ddagger}$ 12·3 kcal.mole^{-1} at 250°K) and each CMe$_2$ group gives just a single signal. The latter process is hindered by the interaction between pairs of methyl substituents in the intermediate twist conformation (75).

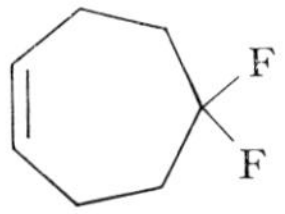

73	74	75

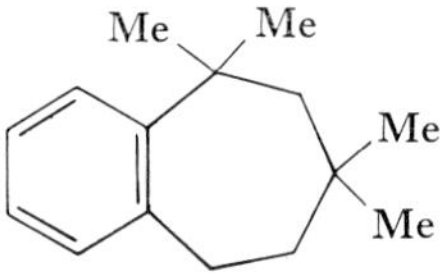

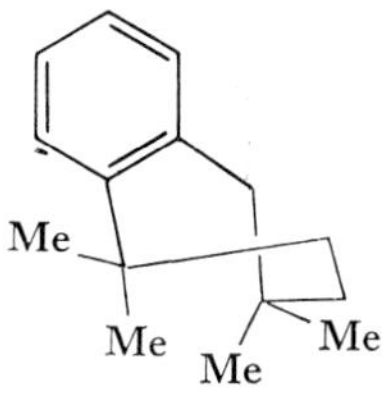

The conformational changes of other benzocycloheptene systems[137] and heterocyclic analogues[138,139] have been studied in considerable detail, and the results of the experimental examination have been compared[140] with theoretical estimates of the relative enthalpies of the chair, boat and twist conformations. From coupling constant and chemical shift data, together with an analysis of molecular symmetry, it was concluded from the NMR spectra of the benzocyclo-heptenes (76 to 76d) at 193°K that the only conformation detectable in solution was the chair conformation; this result was in agreement with model calculations. Conformational inversion barriers for the benzocycloheptenes (76), (76a) and (76d) were obtained from coalescence data,[137] but a complete study of sub-

	R^1	R^2	R^3	R^4	$\Delta G^{\ddagger}$ kcal.mole^{-1}
76	D	H	D	H	10·9
76a	H	Me	H	H	11·8
76b	H	Me	H	Me	
76c	Me	H	Me	H	
76d	Me	H	H	H	11·4

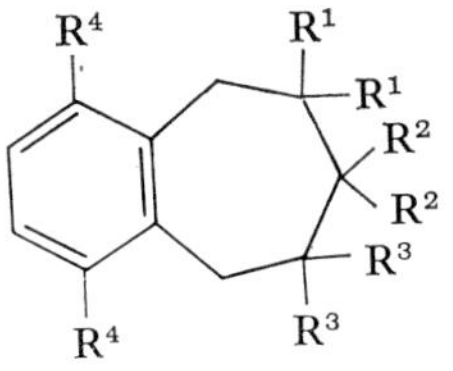

stituent effects in this system has not been reported. The analogous 1,3-dithiepin derivatives (77) and (78) have also been examined[138] and the barriers to con-formational inversion determined from coalescence data. Compound (77a)

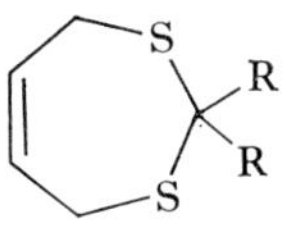

77   R = H, $\Delta G^{\ddagger}$ 8·5 kcal.mole^{-1}
77a R = Me, $\Delta G^{\ddagger}$ 8·2 kcal.mole^{-1}

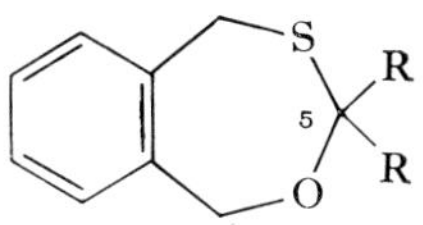

78   R = H, $\Delta G^{\ddagger}$ 10·9 kcal.mole^{-1}
78a R = Me, $\Delta G^{\ddagger}$ 12·1 kcal.mole^{-1}

clearly exists in both chair and boat conformations in the ratio of 2:1 from its NMR spectrum at low temperature. The corresponding 1,3-dioxepin systems are in general more conformationally mobile,[138] and the only reported observation of a temperature dependent NMR spectrum was for the benzodioxepin (79) for which the inversion barrier ($\Delta G^{\ddagger}$ 9·7 kcal.mole^{-1}) is somewhat lower than for the analogous benzodithiepin (78a); in both cases the inversion barrier is evidently increased by the geminal methyl substituents at position 5. The 1,2-dithiepin (80)

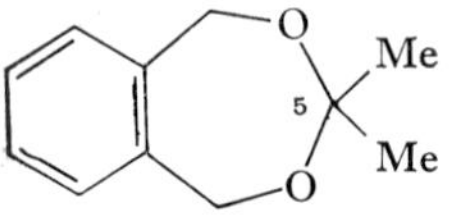

79

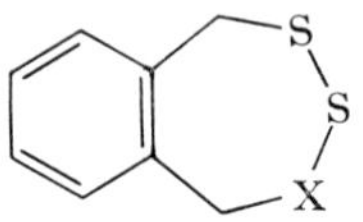

	R	X	$\Delta G^{\ddagger}_{c \to b}$	$\Delta G^{\ddagger}_{b \to b}*$ kcal.mole^{-1}	$\Delta G_{c \to b}$ kcal.mole^{-1}
80	Me	S	19·8	11·5	−0·1
80a	H	S	17·4	ca. 10	+1·0
80b	H	CH$_2$	13·5	10·4	+0·5

and 1,2,3-trithiepin (80a, 80b) systems show a relatively high degree of conformational rigidity. In all three cases the NMR spectra recorded for solutions at low temperature are consistent with the presence of both chair and twist (or boat) conformations. From the observed temperature dependence of these spectra it was possible to obtain values for the energy barrier separating the chair and boat conformations ($\Delta G^{\ddagger}_{c \to b}$) and also the energy barrier for inversion of the twist (or boat) conformation ($\Delta G^{\ddagger}_{b \to b*}$), as well as the energy difference between the chair and twist (or boat) conformations ($\Delta G_{c \to b}$). The high barriers for conformational change in these di- and tri- thiepin systems are in part a consequence of the larger torsional barrier in S–S bonds as compared with C–C bonds. A similar tendency is seen for the pentathiepin derivative (81)[141] Two sharp singlets are observed in the NMR spectrum at 183°K which coalesce to a singlet at higher temperatures (E_a 12·9 ± 0·4 kcal.mole^{-1} from line-shape studies). This

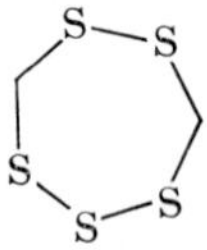

81 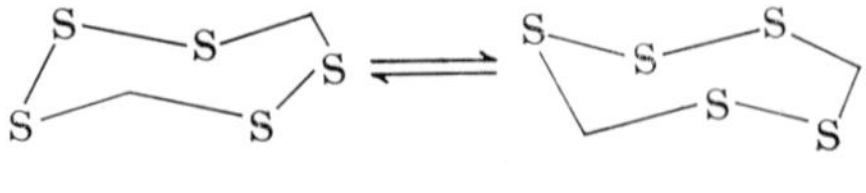   82   82a

result, together with the known crystal structure of (81), is believed to indicate that conformations such as (82) and (82a) are involved in the equilibrium.

Simple cycloheptadiene derivatives do not appear to have been examined by NMR line-shape methods, but a number of papers have described studies of conformational changes in various types of dibenzo-derivatives of seven-membered ring systems. These include the bridged biphenyl systems (83 to

86)[37,123,142,143] which are closely related to a number of compounds for which conformational changes have been followed by the longer established polarimetric methods. The conformational mobility of these systems (83 to 86) is, however, too fast to be studied by polarimetry and NMR line-shape methods must be used. The results obtained[37,142] for the bridged biphenyls (83) are in quite good agreement with calculated inversion barriers for these compounds, the calculations being based upon the angle strain in the transition state (87b) for the conformational inversion process (87⇌87a) which results in the exchange of the

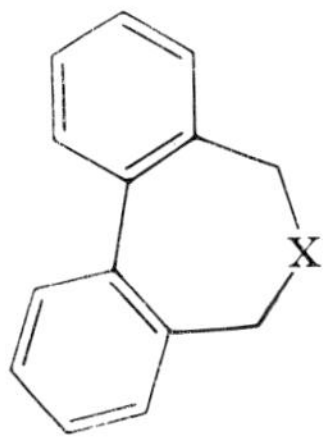

	X	$\Delta G^{\ddagger}$ kcal.mole^{-1}
83	O	9·2[37]
83a	C=NOH	13·4[142]
83b	C(CO$_2$Et)$_2$	14·0[142]
83c	S	16·1[37]
83d	SO$_2$	18·2[142]

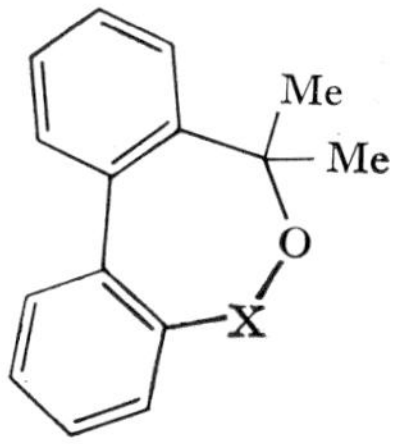

84 X = CMe$_2$, $\Delta G^{\ddagger}$ 13·3 kcal.mole^{-1}
84a X = CO, $\Delta G^{\ddagger}$ 12·3 kcal.mole^{-1}

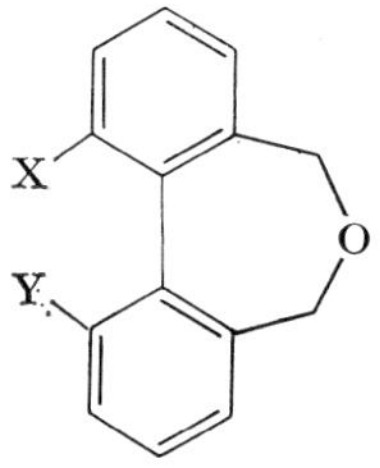

	X	Y	$\Delta G^{\ddagger}$ kcal.mole^{-1}
85	H	NO$_2$	16·5
85a	—(CH$_2$)$_2$—		10·8

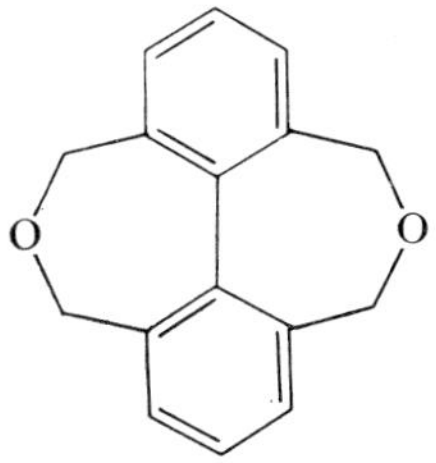

86

methylene protons H and H′ between the environments A and B (see 87). This work on biphenyl systems involves an early application[37] of Alexander's density matrix approach to the line-shape of an exchanging AB system. The doubly bridged biphenyl (86) had some years ago been prepared in an optically active form[144] and the barrier to conformational inversion obtained from a study of

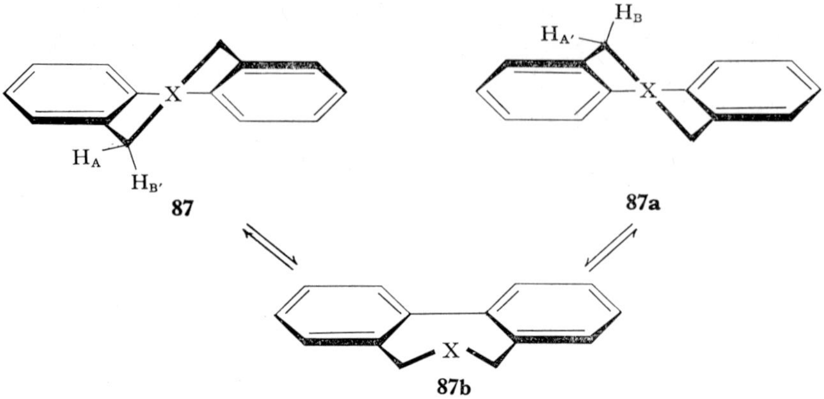

87   87a

87b

racemization rates (E_a 20·5 kcal.mole^{-1}, $\log_{10}A$ 12·1 in o-xylene), a recent study[143] of the inversion of (86) using NMR line-shape methods gave results in extremely close agreement with those obtained in the racemization study (E_a 19·9 kcal.mole^{-1}, $\log_{10}A$ 12·0 in C_4Cl_6 and E_a 21·1 kcal.mole^{-1}, $\log_{10}A$ 12·2 in DMSO-d_6). The agreement between the two studies is very encouraging, particularly since the NMR approach was based on closed form solutions of the line-shape equation, which is generally a less reliable approach than the comparison of observed and computed line-shapes.

The cycloheptatriene system has also been extensively studied. In this case the only conformational change of the ring system is inversion of the boat-like conformation (88). In the unsubstituted system the inversion process may be followed[145,146] by the temperature dependence of the 7-methylene group signals (see H_A and H_B in 88). In more highly substituted cycloheptatrienes, such as (89)[147] and (90),[148] the rather low inversion barrier found for cycloheptatriene itself (88, $\Delta G^{\ddagger}$ 6·1 kcal.mole^{-1} in CF_2Cl_2[145] or $\Delta G^{\ddagger}$ 5·7 kcal.mole^{-1} in CF_3Br) is considerably raised on account of the increase in the interactions between adjacent substituents in the transition state for the inversion process. The

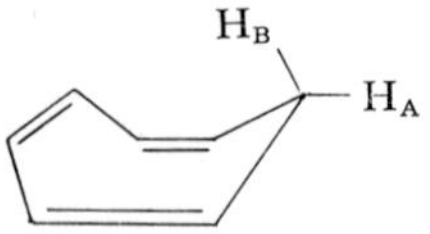

88 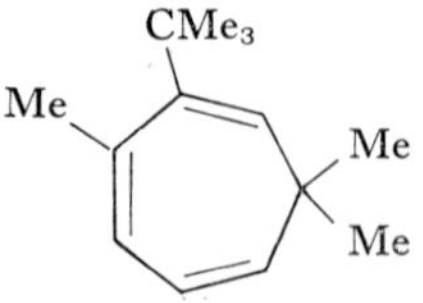   89 $\Delta G^{\ddagger}$ 9·2 kcal.mole^{-1} 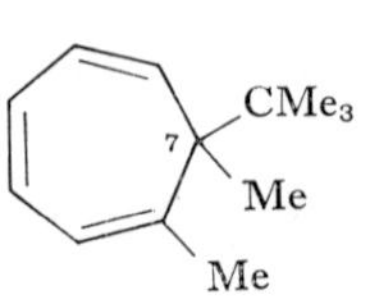   90 $\Delta G^{\ddagger}$ 15·1 kcal.mole^{-1}

less stable conformation of (90), in which the t-butyl substituent occupies the *endo*-position, shows further temperature dependence of the t-butyl group signals, and at $-40°$ the NMR spectrum of this conformer shows three equal intensity singlet signals for this group indicating that rotation about the C(7)–CMe₃ bond is also slow on the NMR time-scale at this temperature. The conformational mobility of 7,7-bistrifluoromethylcycloheptatriene appears to be even greater than that of cycloheptatriene since it shows only a single CF_3 resonance in the ^{19}F spectrum even at 88°K.[149]

Dibenzo-derivatives of cycloheptatriene show, as might be expected, lower conformational mobility than cycloheptatriene itself. Thus 2,3:6,7-dibenzo-cycloheptatriene[150] (**91**) has an inversion barrier ($\Delta G^{\ddagger}$ 9·1 kcal.mole^{-1} in CS_2) which is about 3 kcal.mole^{-1} higher than that of cycloheptatriene. This inversion barrier in dibenzocycloheptatrienes is raised by substituents in a qualitatively predictable manner, the effects of substituents at position-1 (see **91**) being particularly marked.[151] Compounds analogous to (**91**) in which the methylene group at position-1 is replaced by atoms or groups making the seven-membered ring potentially pseudo-aromatic (C=O and C=CR₂) or anti-aromatic (NR,S and O) are also of interest. Measurements of the inversion barriers for the compounds (**92a** to **92e**), using the prochiral CMe₂OH substituent as a probe, and comparison of the results with that for the cycloheptatriene derivative (**92**), shows[150] that in all cases, except the azepin (**92c**), the increase in conjugation, in the seven-membered ring in the planar transition state relative to the non-planar ground state, is the result of increased Ar–X–Ar conjugation unaffected by the cyclic system. The azepin (**92c**) has a rather higher inversion barrier than would be expected by comparison with the other compounds in the series (**92**), suggesting that the nitrogen atom is unable to participate in normal Ar–NEt–Ar conjugation in the transition state. The dibenzoheptafulvene derivative (**93**) has a

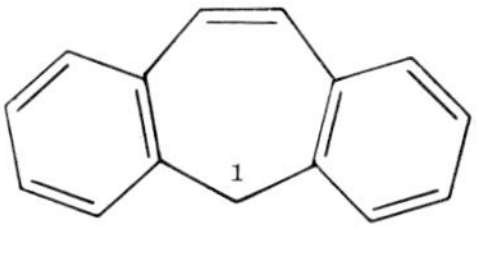

91 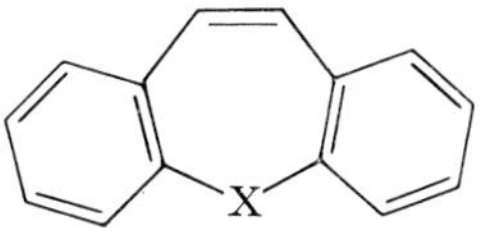 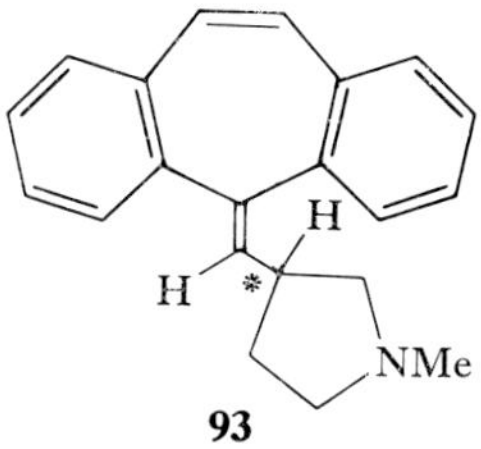   **93**

X	$\Delta G^{\ddagger}$ kcal.mole^{-1}
92 CH₂	17·1
92a O	10·3
92b S	17·7
92c NEt	21·7
92d C=O	<9
92e C=CH₂	21·2

chiral carbon atom in the side chain (indicated by an asterisk) and hindered ring inversion gives two diastereomeric forms in solution. The temperature dependence of the NMR signals of these diastereomers show[152] that they are separated by a free energy barrier ($\Delta G^{\ddagger}$ 25·0 kcal.mole^{-1}) which is similar to the free energy barrier for the racemization[153] of the optically active heptafulvene derivative (**94**). ($\Delta G^{\ddagger}$ 22·6 kcal.mole^{-1}) Monocyclic seven-membered ring systems, analogous to compounds (**92a** to **92e**), would be of greater interest since in these

cases conjugation effects would not be reduced by the effects of benzene annulation. The recent report[154] of an examination of the monocyclic thiepin dioxide derivative (**95**) shows that this compound has a very low barrier to ring inversion ($\Delta G^{\ddagger}$ 6·4 kcal.mole^{-1} at $-150°$), indicating that conjugation in the planar transition state is more important than in planar cycloheptatriene, but not indicating a degree of conjugation in the transition state which would justify the description "aromatic". The study of the thiepin dioxide (**95**) was carried out using a 250 MHz spectrometer, and the advantages of the high operating frequency for this type of work are demonstrated by the report that lower operating frequencies (e.g. 100 MHz) did not result in a detectable separation of the methyl signals of the prochiral isopropyl substituent at low temperatures.[154] The 2,3;4,5-dibenzocycloheptatriene systems (**96**) have also been examined[142] and the expected enhancement of the inversion barrier, by the interaction between the *ortho*-hydrogen atoms of the fused benzene rings in the planar transition state, is observed. This effect is doubly important for the tribenzocycloheptatrienes (**97**), and not surprisingly the inversion barriers are very large.[150] The unsubstituted system (**97**) and the tropone (**97a**) may be examined by line-shape methods, but the substituted tribenzocycloheptatrienes (**97b**) and (**97c**) are too rigid for the successful application of NMR methods. The considerably lower energy barrier for conformational inversion of the tropone derivative (**97a**), compared with the cycloheptatriene (**97b**), demonstrated very clearly the importance of increased Ar–CO–Ar conjugation in stabilizing the planar transition state for the former. Other compounds of this type have been examined by the more traditional polarimetric methods in an extensive study by Tochtermann's group.[155]

Inversion of the seven-membered ring of the dihydropleiadene system (**98**) may also be examined by NMR line-shape methods and several such studies have been reported.[156 to 158] The inversion barriers found for a number of substituted dihydropleiadenes (**98** to **98e**, **99** to **99b**, **100** and **101**) show the effects of

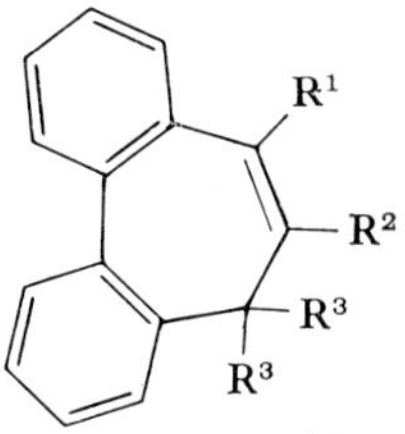

	R^1	R^2	R^3	$\Delta G^{\ddagger}$ kcal.mole^{-1}
96	Me	H	Me	18·8
96a	CN	NH$_2$	H	17·9

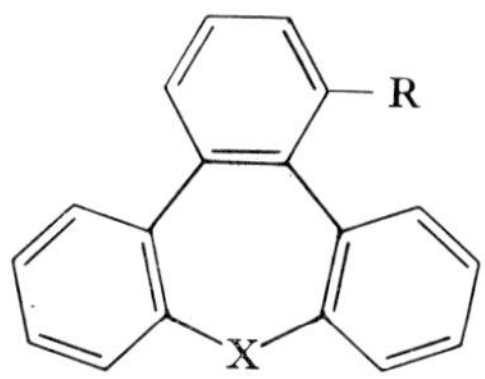

	X	R	$\Delta G^{\ddagger}$ kcal.mole^{-1}
97	CH$_2$	H	23·9
97a	C=O	Et	20·0
97b	CH$_2$	Et	> 27·7
97c	C(OMe)$_2$	H	

substituents upon the barrier. The results obtained for the most part are based upon the coalescence temperatures only,[156,158] but one study has been reported based upon total line-shape comparison.[157]

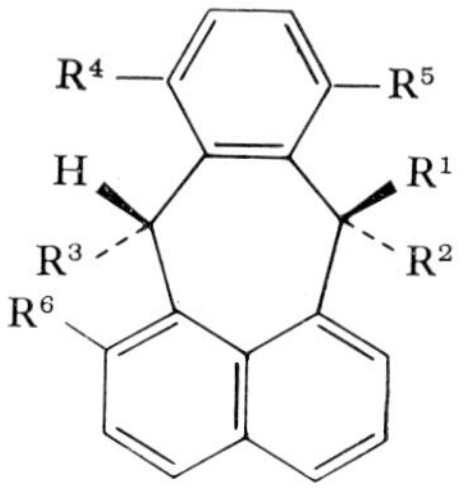

	R^1	R^2	R^3	R^4	R^5	R^6	$\Delta G^{\ddagger}$ kcal.mole^{-1}
98	H	H	H	H	H	H	14·0[157], 13·6[156]
98a	D	D	H	Me	H	H	14·5[156], 13·5[158]
98b	H	H	H	Me	Me	H	15·6
98c	D	D	H	H	H	OMe	13·7
98d	OAc	H	OAc	H	H	H	14·3
98e	OMe	H	OMe	H	H	H	15·2

The fully saturated cyclo-octane system poses a complex conformational problem, and of the large number of possible ground state conformations[81,82] it has been concluded[159] that the crown (**102**) or extended crown, twisted crown (**103**), and boat-chair (**104**) conformations, the latter undergoing rapid pseudo-rotation, must be considered as possible low-energy conformations. These conclusions follow from an examination of the low-temperature NMR spectra of deuteriated cyclo-octanes having two hydrogen substituents in (i) a geminal relationship (**105**), (ii) a *cis*-1,2-relationship (**106**), and (iii) a *trans*-1,2-relationship (**107**). From the temperature dependence of the ^{1}H spectrum of C$_8$D$_{15}$H it

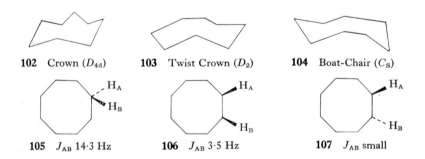

99
$\Delta G^{\ddagger}$ 13·4 kcal.mole^{-1}

	X	$\Delta G^{\ddagger}$ kcal.mole^{-1}
100	O	$T_c < 213°$K
100a	CH$_2$	15·2
100b	CMe$_2$	$T_c > 473°$K

101
$\Delta G^{\ddagger}$ 13·5 kcal.mole^{-1}

was also concluded[160] that the barrier to conformational inversion for cyclo-octane ($\Delta G^{\ddagger}$ 8·1 kcal.mole^{-1}) is considerably smaller than the inversion barrier for cyclohexane. The NMR spectra of fluorocyclo-octanes at low temperatures are also consistent with these general conclusions. Thus the ^{19}F spectrum (with ^{1}H decoupling) of 1,1-difluorocyclo-octane suggests that two conformational types are in equilibrium[161] since, although only a single AB system is observable below 173°K, at 123°K two separate AB quartets are seen. This result indicates the presence of an equilibrium between two diastereomeric conformational types with a rather higher barrier for conformational inversion ($\Delta G^{\ddagger}$ 7·5 kcal.mole^{-1}) than for the interconversion of the diastereomeric conformations. This last result demonstrates the advantages of using ^{19}F substituents as a probe for conformational changes but it is still not definitive regarding the actual conformational species present in the equilibrating system.

102   Crown (D_{4d})   **103**   Twist Crown (D_2)   **104**   Boat-Chair (C_S)

105 J_{AB} 14·3 Hz   **106** J_{AB} 3·5 Hz   **107** J_{AB} small

The inversion barriers in certain heterocyclic analogues (**108**) of cyclo-octane have also been measured;[162] in these compounds only a single AB system is seen for the ring methylene groups at low temperatures. The simplest, but not exclusive, explanation of this observation is that these compounds (**108** to **108d**) adopt the crown conformation in solution, analogous to the known crystal structures of octasulphur, octaselenium and $Se_4(NH)_4$.

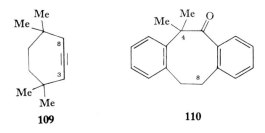

	X	R	$\Delta G^{\ddagger}$ kcal.mole^{-1}
108	S	Me	14·8
108a	S	Et	14·6
108b	S	CHMe$_2$	14·1
108c	S	Ph	13·4
108d	S	Me	14·4

A preliminary examination[163] of the temperature dependence of the NMR spectra of cyclo- octanone, octene, and octa-1,3-diene showed that in all three cases changes in the spectra occurred in the temperature range 153 to 173°K. The results suggested the presence of ring inversion barriers comparable in magnitude with that of cyclo-octane, but the changes were complex and a complete analysis could not be made. The spectrum of tetramethylcyclo-octyne (109) at low temperatures shows[164] two non-equivalent methyl group signals and an AB system from the 3- and 8- methylene groups. From the coalescence temperatures for both sets of signals, measured at 60 and 220 MHz, free energies of activation for the ring inversion process were obtained over the temperature range 217 to 273°K ($\Delta G^{\ddagger}$ 13·1 ± 0·5 kcal.mole^{-1} at 273°K). This technique of measurement of coalescence data at two frequencies is not likely to be sufficiently precise to give reliable enthalpies and entropies of activation. The eight-membered ring

109

110

of 1,2;5,6-dibenzocyclo-octadienes may adopt either a chair conformation or a number of related boat conformations. The NMR spectrum of the derivative (110) shows[165] only two methyl singlets at low temperature, but the observed coalescence of these signals at higher temperatures (> 339°K) gives a free energy of activation ($\Delta G^{\ddagger}$ 17 kcal.mole^{-1}) which may be assigned to an inversion barrier, increased by the *trans*-annular interactions between the C-4 methyl and the C-8 hydrogen substituents in the transition state for ring inversion. This result does not, however, distinguish between a ground state chair or boat conformation for (110), since the equilibrium between these two types may have

been too fast to affect the NMR spectrum. The inversion of 3,5,7-cyclo-octat-
rienone (111) has been studied by a complete examination[38] of the AB portion, of
the ABX system (see 111), given by the C-8 protons. The activation energy for
the inversion process ($\Delta G^{\ddagger}$ 11.4 kcal.mole^{-1}) is comparable with that observed[166]
for the interconversion of the *endo*- (112) and *exo*- (112a) conformations of
cis-1,2-dibromo-3,5,7-cyclo-octatriene ($\Delta G^{\ddagger}$ 13 kcal.mole^{-1}). In both cases the
cyclo-octatriene inversion barrier is rather similar to that observed for cyclo-
octatetraene (see Section E).

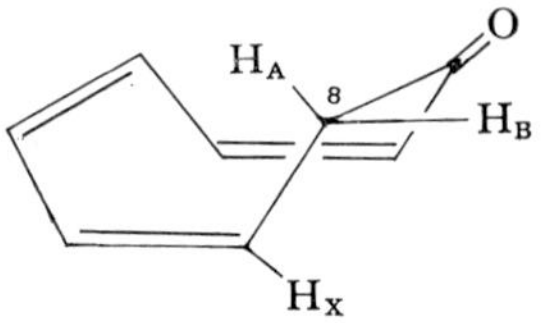

111

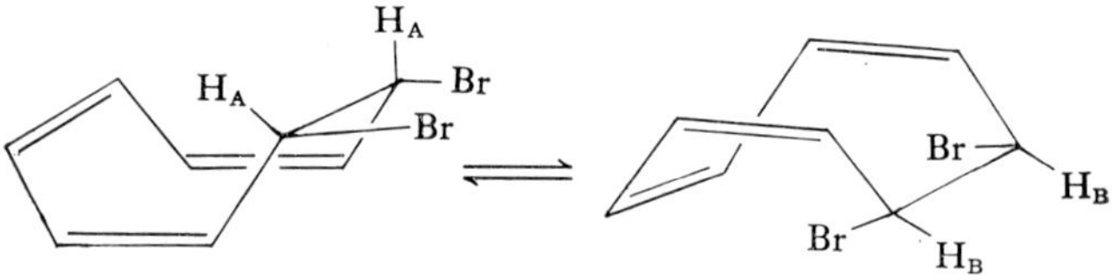

112   *exo*   112a   *endo*

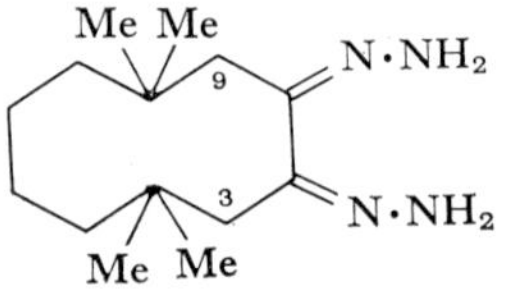

113

Inversion barriers in nine-membered rings are likely to be rather low unless the
processes which interconvert various possible conformational types are blocked
by suitable substituents[167] such as geminal methyl groups. The bis-hydrazone
(113) appears to provide an example of this phenomenon,[168] the spectrum of
(113) at low temperatures shows two methyl signals and a single AB system from
the C-3 and C-9 methylene protons, these coalesce to singlets at 403°K and 415°K
respectively, consistent with a substantial barrier to a ring inversion process. The
corresponding di-ketone is reported to have a temperature independent NMR
spectrum, but this is almost certainly a consequence of small chemical shift
differences between geometrically non-equivalent groups rather than rapid ring
inversion. The *trans*-cycloalkenes (114) are an interesting group of compounds
which exist in non-planar chiral conformations,[17,169] and the enantiomeric
conformations of each cycloalkene are interconverted by rotation of the *trans*-

double bond so that one of the substituent hydrogen atoms (see **114**) passes through the ring system. The energy barrier to this process will obviously decrease as the ring-size increases and the estimated half-lives for this process at room temperature show a remarkable variation with ring size (see **114**). The magnitudes of this energy barrier for *trans*-cyclo-octene and *trans*-cyclo-nonene were obtained by measuring racemization rates for the optically active compounds. For the deuteriated *trans*-cyclodecene (**115**) the kinetic study was

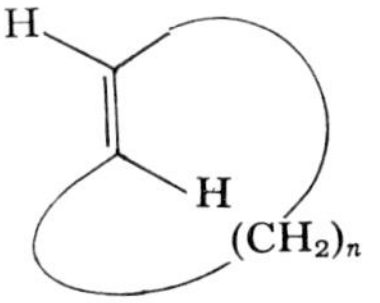

114
$n = 6$ t½ 10^5 years
$n = 7$ t½ 10 sec.
$n = 8$ t½ 10^{-4} sec.

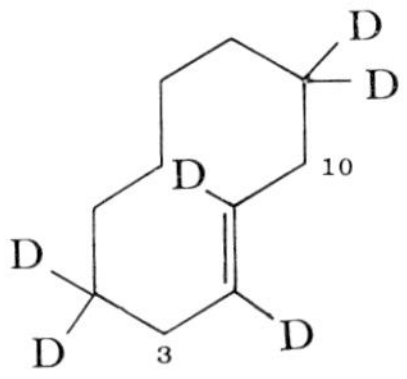

115

116   **116b**   **116a**

carried out by NMR line-shape analysis,[17] using the temperature dependence of the AB spectrum given by the C-3 and C-10 methylene groups ($\Delta G^{\ddagger}_{300}$ 12·2 kcal.mole^{-1}). The conformational situation in *cis-cis*-cyclodeca-1,6-diene is

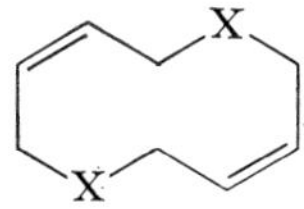

		$\Delta G^{\ddagger}$
	X	kcal.mole^{-1}
117	C = O	10·6 (300°K)[171], *ca.* 10^{172}
117a	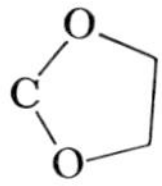	18·8[170,171]
117b	C=CH^2	12·1[170]
117c	CH$_2$	
117d	S	12·3[172]
117e	O	10^{172}

rather simpler than that for other ten-membered ring systems, and the temperature dependent NMR spectra of the unsubstituted diene (117c)[170] and the
derivatives (117 to 117b) are consistent[170,171] with the inverting chair[171] (or
armchair[170]) conformation (116), known to be present in the crystal structure of
the dione,[171] with the boat[171] (or hammock[170]) conformation (116b) an intermediate in the inversion process (116⇌116a). From a line-shape analysis of the
AB spectrum, given by the four equivalent allylic methylene groups, which
coalesces to a singlet at higher temperatures, energy barriers for the conformational change (116⇌116a) have been obtained[170,171] for the carbocyclic systems
(117), (117a), and (117b) and also[172] for the heterocyclic analogues (117d) and
(117e).

Inversion barriers have been measured[173] for the eleven-membered rings
found in the sesquiterpenes humulene (118) and zerumbone (118a) and the
humulene isomer (119); the significance of the relative magnitudes of the inversion barriers and the details of the conformational changes are, however, obscure in systems of this complexity. Whereas the nine-membered ring system of

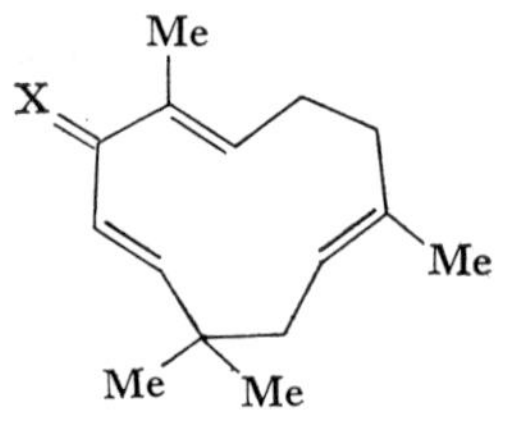

118 X = H_2, $\Delta G^{\ddagger}$ 10·6 kcal.mole^{-1}
118a X = O, $\Delta G^{\ddagger}$ 15·9 kcal.mole^{-1}

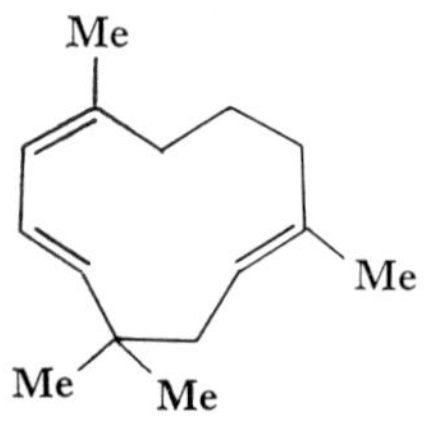

119 $\Delta G^{\ddagger}$ 11·9 kcal.mole^{-1}

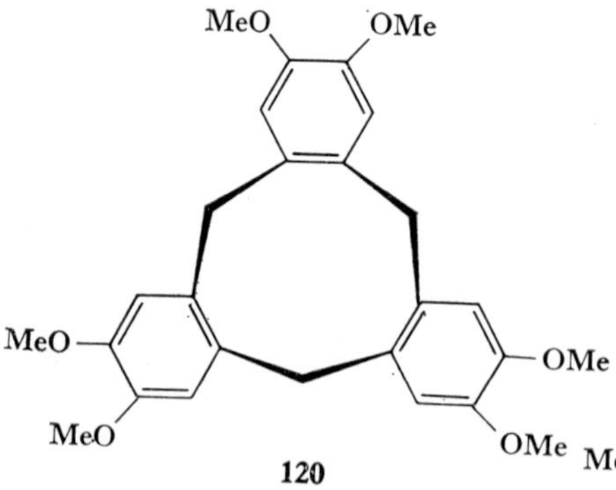

120

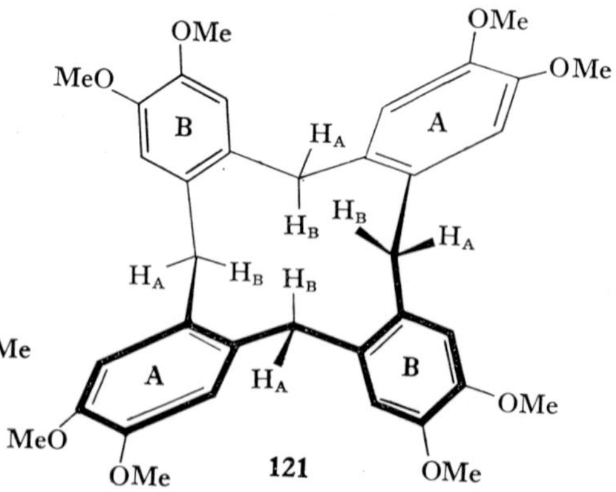

121

cyclotriveratrylene (120) is known[174] to be rigid on the NMR time scale up to
473°K, cyclotetraveratrylene (121) is a mobile structure[175] in which the twelve-
membered ring appears to adopt the chair-like conformation shown, which has

C_{2h} symmetry. This is consistent with the spectrum at low temperatures which shows two aryl-hydrogen signals and two methoxyl signals, corresponding to the aromatic rings of types A and B in (121), and a single AB system for the methylene groups. At higher temperatures the spectrum shows just three singlets for these three types of protons. The barrier to the interconversion of enantiomeric chair conformations, obtained by a study of the spectral changes, is quite low ($\Delta G^{\ddagger}$ 13·2 kcal.mole^{-1}). There should be a two-fold rate difference between the inversion process which exchanges the methylene protons between the A and B environments and that which exchanges the benzene rings between the environments labelled A and B in (121); this was not detected in the line-shape examination.

The trisalicylide system (122) also contains a conformationally mobile twelve-membered ring, and with suitable substituents on the aromatic rings (see R^1 and R^2 in 122) the conformational changes are sufficiently hindered to be examined

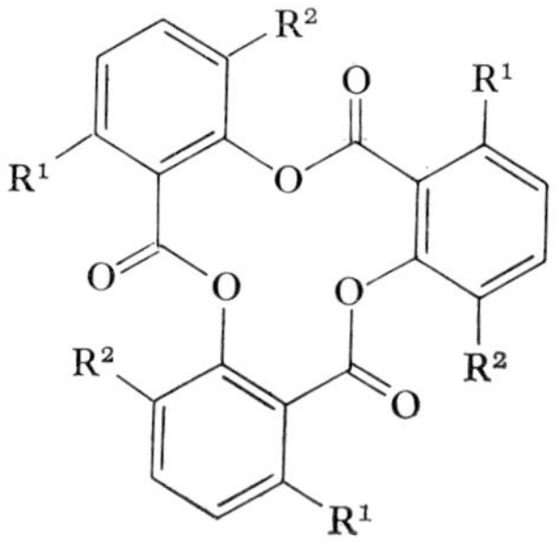

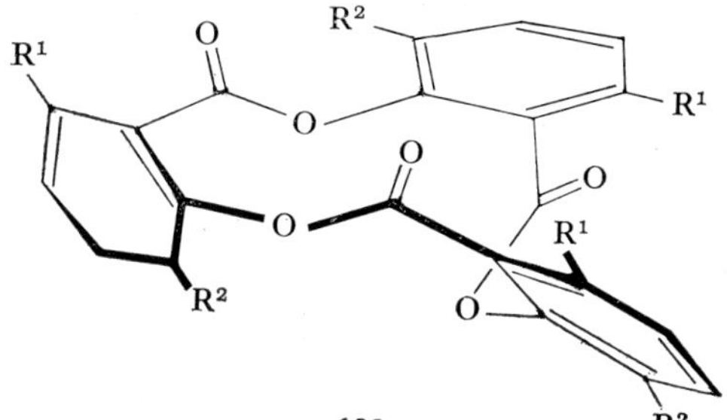

123

122 R^1 = CHMe$_2$, R^2 = Me
122a R^1 = Me, R^2 = CHMe$_2$
122b R^1 = R^2 = Me

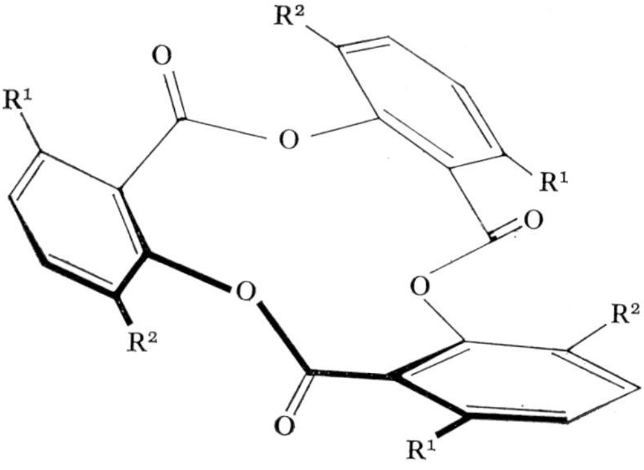

124

Compound	$\Delta G^{\ddagger}_{123\rightarrow124}$ kcal.mole^{-1}		$\Delta G^{\ddagger}_{124\rightarrow123}$ kcal.mole^{-1}	$\Delta G^{\ddagger}_{\text{inversion of 124}}$ kcal.mole^{-1}
122	20·6		20·3	17·6
122a	21·4		20·7	
122b		ca. 18·0		ca. 14·3

by NMR line-shape methods.[176] It was found that these compounds adopt two different chiral conformations in solution, the major conformation designated propeller (123) has C3 symmetry, and the minor conformation designated helix (124) has C1 symmetry. The interconversion of enantiomeric propeller conformations proceeds by way of two enantiomeric helical conformations, and the complete details of the kinetics of these processes have been determined for tri-o-carvacrotide (122) together with partial details for tri-o-thymotide (122a) and tri-dimethylsalicylide (122b). For tri-o-thymotide (122a) the kinetics of conformational change have been examined by three methods, (i) NMR line-shape methods, (ii) measurement of the racemization rate of optically active tri-o-thymotide, and (iii) the direct examination of the interconversion of the propeller and helical conformations. The agreement between the activation parameters obtained by all three methods is quite good. The results are summarized in tabular form below formulae (122 to 124). The cyclic oligo-peptides of sarcosine (125) are similar to the tri-salicyclide system by showing complex temperature dependent changes in the NMR spectra[177] which may be associated both with conformational inversion and also with cis-trans-isomerism of the amide CO–N bonds. The kinetics of these complex processes have not yet been elucidated.

$$\left[\begin{array}{c} Me \\ | \\ N-CH_2-CO \end{array}\right]_n$$

125 n = 3,4,5,6, and 8

D. Cyclophanes

Because of the frequently well-defined geometry the study of the conformational changes of cyclophanes has attracted considerable attention. Thus the study[178,179] of the relative magnitudes of the inversion barriers in the series of dithiametacyclophanes (126 to 126n) permits the assignment of the relative sizes to halogen atoms, methyl groups and hydrogen atoms in the order $Br > CH_3 > Cl > F > H$ and the extension of these results to the series of dithiacyclophanes (127 to 127b) and (128 to 128b) confirms the same sequence for the relative steric requirements of halogen and hydrogen substituents. In all cases the inversion barriers are approximate, being based only upon the coalescence of the low-temperature AB system from the $ArCH_2S$-groups. Cyclophanes of type (126), in which the substituent X is a hydrogen atom, undergo inversion at rates too fast to be studied by NMR line-shape methods unless $n \leqslant 3$. Thus the spectrum of the $ArCH_2S$ group in (126) is a temperature independent singlet[178 to 180] down to 193°K but the spectrum of [7]-(2,6)-dithiametacyclophane (129) shows temperature dependence that may be associated with the interconversion of two different conformational types in addition to conformational inversion.[181] The quintet from H_A and H_B in (129), observable in the spectrum at 283°K, collapses

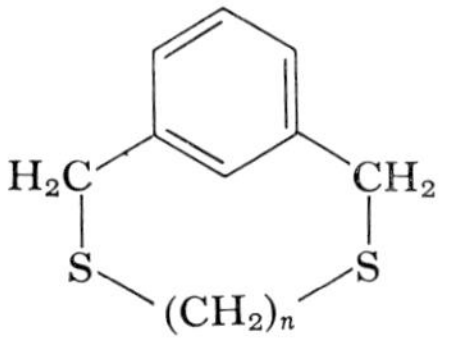

H_2C ... CH_2

S ... S

$(CH_2)_n$

	n	X	$\Delta G^{\ddagger}$ kcal.mole^{-1}
126	4	H	$T_c < 203°K$
126a	4	F	22·6
126b	4	Cl	$T_c > 473°K$
126c	7	F	$T_c < 223°K$
126d	7	Cl	23·5
126e	7	Me	$T_c > 473°K$
126f	7	Br	$T_c > 473°K$
126g	8	F	$T_c < 223°K$
126h	8	Cl	15·4
126i	8	Me	16·6
126j	8	Br	22·5
126k	9	F	$T_c < 223°K$
126l	9	Cl	11·6
126m	9	Me	12·0
126n	9	Br	15·4

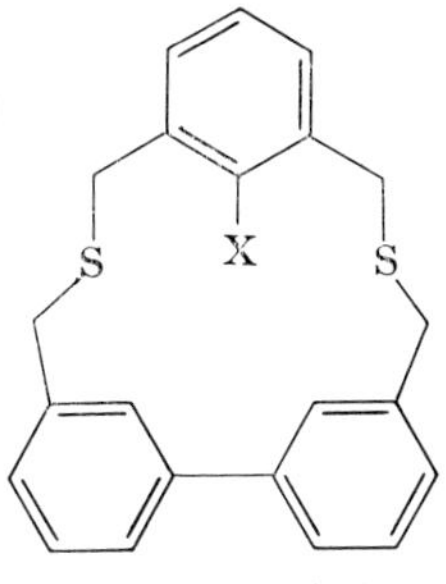

S X S

	X	$\Delta G^{\ddagger}$ kcal.mole^{-1}
127	F	$T_c < 223°K$
127a	Cl	19·4
127b	Br	$T_c > 463°K$

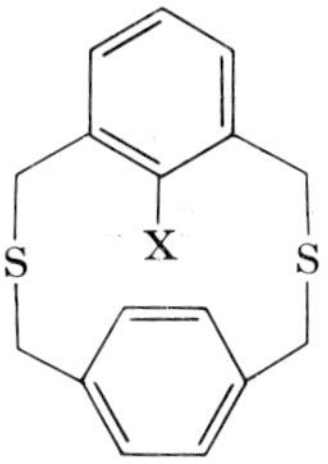

S X S

	X	$\Delta G^{\ddagger}$ kcal.mole^{-1}
128	H	$T_c < 223°K$
128a	F	18·1
128b	Cl	$T_c > 463°K$

on cooling the solution and re-appears as two peaks at δ 1·71 and δ −0·21 ($\Delta G^{\ddagger}$ *ca.* 10·2 kcal.mole^{-1} from the coalescence data). Further cooling of the solution results in the appearance of four signals for this methylene group at lower temperatures ($\Delta G^{\ddagger}$ *ca.* 8·7 kcal.mole^{-1}, from the coalescence data for pairs of signals). Over the same temperature range in which this second change occurs the other two methylene groups of the $S(CH_2)_3S$ unit also show temperature dependence, H_C and H_D (see **129**) appearing as separate signals at low temperatures. The conformational changes consistent with these observations are hindered inversion of conformations such as (**129a**) and (**129b**) together with a restricted rotational process in the $S(CH_2)_3S$ unit, which is required for the interconversion of (**129a**) and (**129b**). These changes particularly involve the relationship between H_A and H_B and the π-system of the benzene ring resulting in large chemical shift differences between these two proton resonances. In the low-temperature spectrum one of the proton environments gives rise to the largest chemical shift to high field (δ $-1\cdot36$) yet observed in a metacyclophane in which the protons on the bridge experience a shielding effect due to their proximity to a benzene ring.

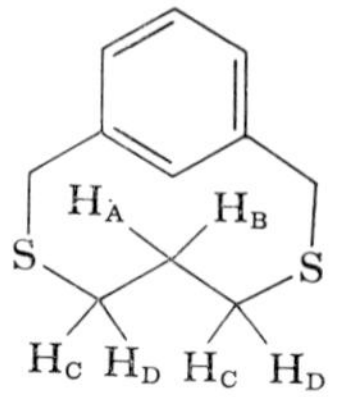

129

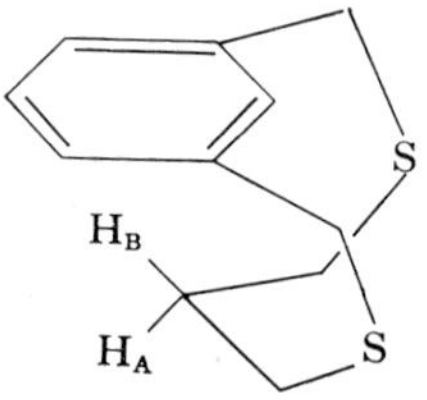

129a

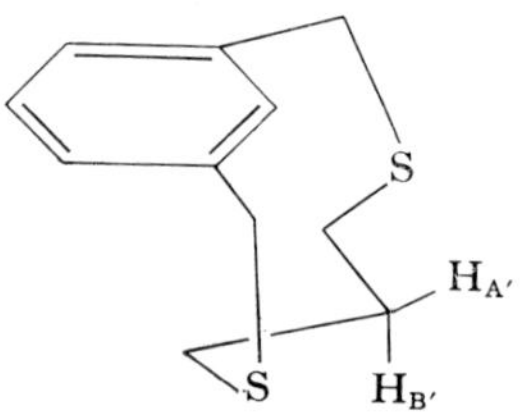

129b

There is some evidence[182] that analogous conformational changes may also be detectable in the meta-heterocyclophanes (**130**), but the observed spectral changes have not been analysed in terms of the conformational types involved or the rates of their interconversion.

The recent studies of paracyclophane systems are related to the observation,[183] made some years ago, that the paracyclophane derivative (**131**) could be resolved, the enantiomers of (**131**) owe their optical stability to the steric hindrance of the rotation of the bridging $-(CH_2)_{10}-$ system about the aromatic ring which is required for interconversion of the enantiomers (**131**) and (**131a**). The same

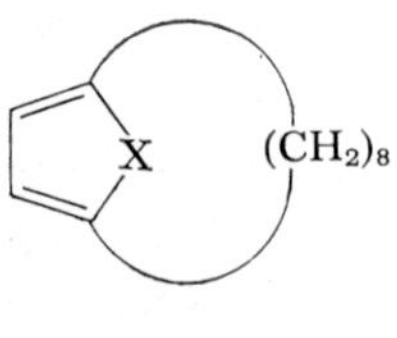

130

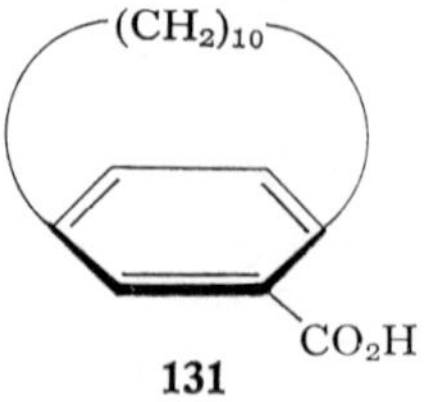

131

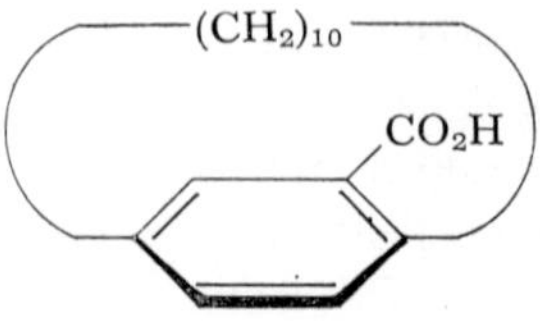

131a

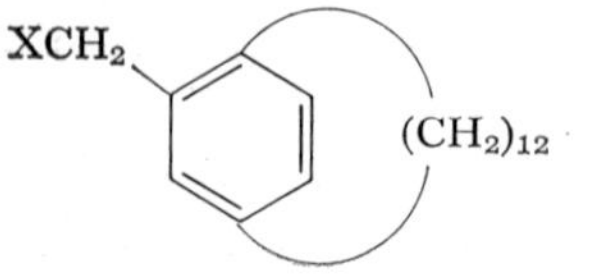

	X	$\Delta G^{\ddagger}$ kcal.mole^{-1}
132	Br	17·1
132a	CO$_2$Et	16·6
132b	OH	17·3

phenomenon of hindered rotation may be studied by NMR methods[184] if the benzene ring has a prochiral substituent, such as CH_2X, which could be used as a probe for the hindered rotation process. The [10]- and [11]- paracyclophanes are too rigid for application of the NMR method but results have been obtained for the [12]paracyclophanes (132 to 132b); as expected the magnitude of the inversion barrier does not depend upon the nature of the group X.

The related [8]paracyclophanes (133 to 135) have also been studied,[185] but in these cases the rate process which can be followed by NMR line-shape methods is quite distinct from the inversion process exemplified by (131)⇌(131a). The temperature dependence of the spectra of compounds (133 to 135) involves both the aromatic and aliphatic proton signals, and is a consequence of a rotational process within the eight-membered bridge which interconverts enantiomeric conformations having C_2 symmetry, for example the process (136)⇌(136a), or, in the case of the furan derivative (133), the conformational change involves rotation of the furan ring [cf [2,2]metaparacyclophane (137)].

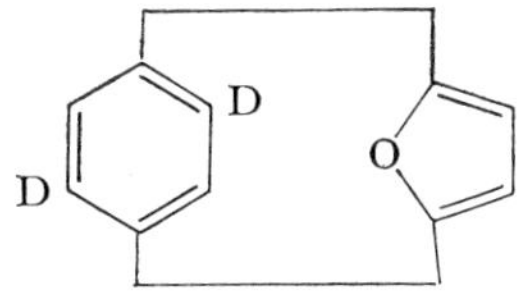

133 $\Delta G^{\ddagger}_{273}$ 13·8 kcal.mole^{-1}

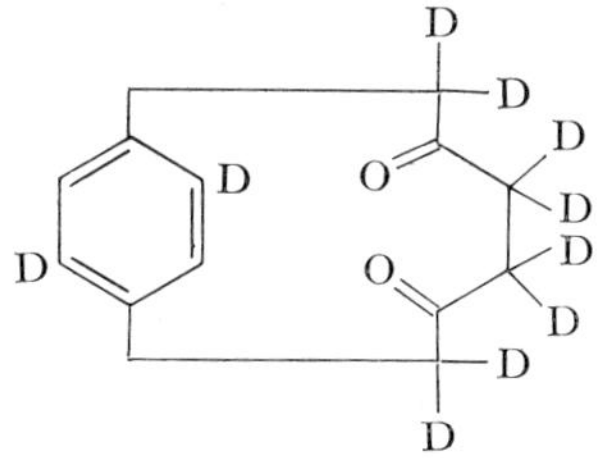

134 $\Delta G^{\ddagger}_{273}$ 13·1 kcal.mole^{-1}

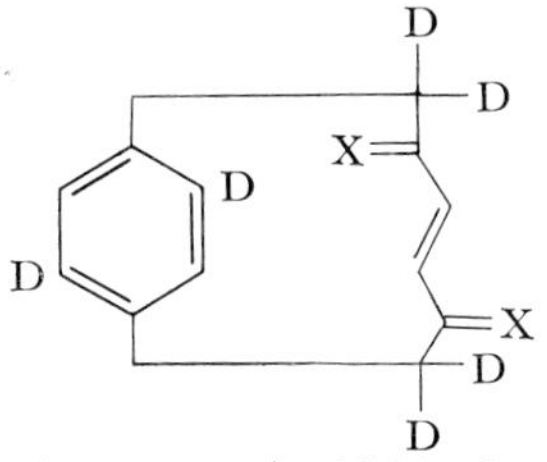

135 X = 0, $\Delta G^{\ddagger}_{273}$ 14·7 kcal.mole^{-1}
135a X = H$_2$, $\Delta G^{\ddagger}_{273}$ 15·9 kcal.mole^{-1}

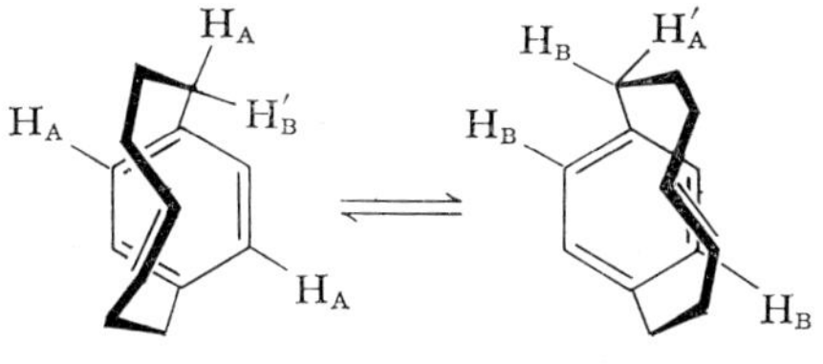

136   136a

Rather similar conformational changes (138)⇌(138a) account for the temperature dependence of the NMR spectrum of [2,2]metaparacyclophane (137).[186 to 188] This process results in the averaging of the environments of each of the pairs of geminally non-equivalent methylene protons in the $(CH_2)_2$ bridging groups in (137), but it may more conveniently be followed by the simultaneous changes of the aromatic proton signals due to exchange of these protons between the environments A and B as indicated in (138) and (138a). The free energy barrier to this change ($\Delta G^{\ddagger}$ 21·8 kcal.mole^{-1},[186] $\Delta G^{\ddagger}$ 20·2 kcal.mole^{-1} in

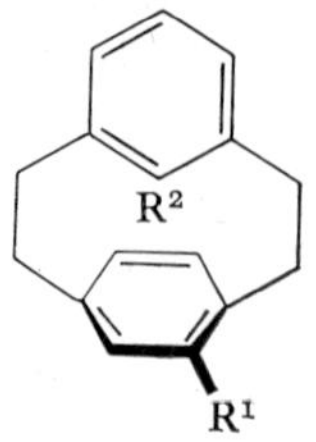

137 $R^1 = R^2 = H$
137a $R^1 = CHO$, $R^2 = H$
137b $R^1 = CO_2H$, $R^2 = H$
137c $R^1 = H$, $R^2 = F$

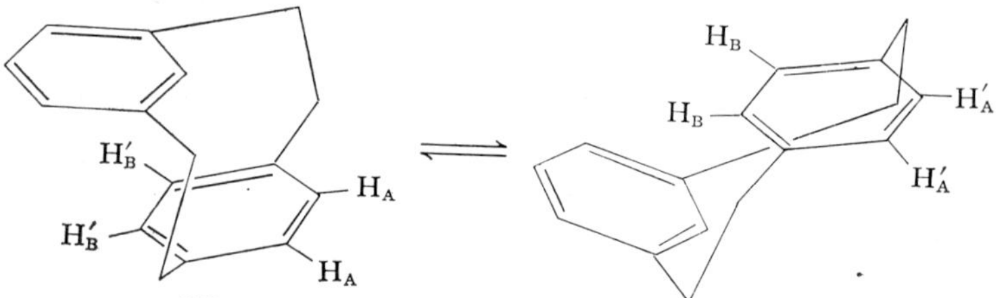

138   138a

DMSO-d_6[188]), determined by NMR methods for the unsubstituted compound
(**137**), agrees quite closely with the analogous energy barrier for the interconversion of the similarly related diastereomers of the aldehyde (**137a**) determined[187] by direct methods for the isolated diastereomers ($\Delta G^{\ddagger}$ 20·8 kcal.mole^{-1}

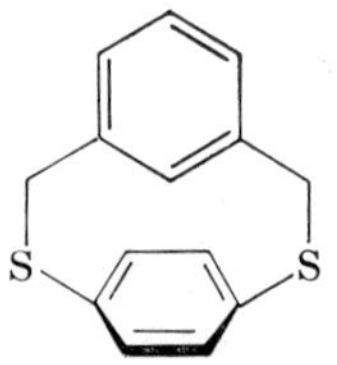

139 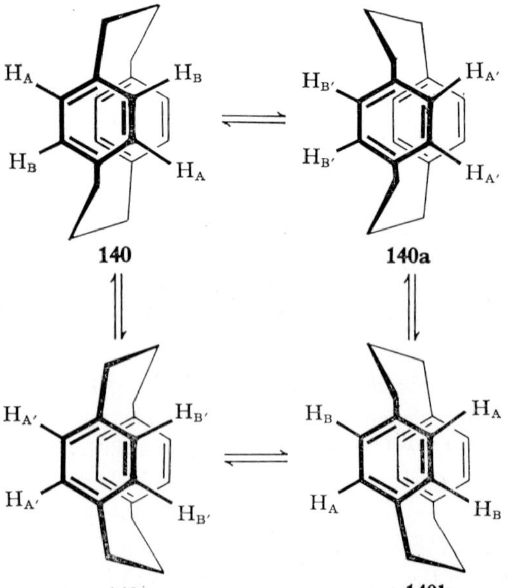   140   140a

140c   140b

for major conformer → minor conformer and $\Delta G^{\ddagger}$ 20·2 kcal.mole^{-1} for minor conformer → major conformer). In agreement with the conclusion that this conformational change involves only the process (138)⇌(138a), and that the p-disubstituted benzene ring cannot rotate through the cyclophane ring system, the resolved acid (137b) shows no loss of optical activity when left in solution at 298°K. The NMR spectrum of the fluoro[2,2]metaparacyclophane (137c) is temperature independent up to 463°K showing[188] that the fluorine substituent considerably increases the barrier to the process analogous to (138)⇌(138a). The rotational barrier for the dithia[2,2]metaparacyclophane (139) is predictably lower ($\Delta G^{\ddagger}$ 14·7 kcal.mole^{-1})[188] than for (137).

[3,3]Paracyclophane (140), in which the aromatic protons are replaced randomly to the extent of 90% by deuterium, has a spectrum at 193°K which is consistent with the presence of both chair (140) and boat (140a) conformations in a 1:2 equilibrium mixture.[189] The spectral changes at higher temperatures provide evidence for both rapid conformational interconversion (140)⇌(140a) and conformation inversion [(140)⇌(140b) and (140a)⇌(140c)] involving exchange of the aromatic protons between the sites A,A', B and B' ($\Delta G^{\ddagger}$ 11·7 kcal.mole^{-1} for the process boat → chair).

The [2,2]metacyclophane system (141), as normally prepared exists[190,191] in the rigid chair-like conformation (142) and there is evidently a substantial barrier to conformational inversion ($\Delta G^{\ddagger}$ > 27 kcal.mole^{-1}) from the lack of line-broadening[191] in the AA'BB' system, given by the bridging methylene groups, at 473°K. [2,2]Metacyclo-2,6-pyridinophane (141a) also has a very rigid structure ($\Delta G^{\ddagger}$ > 27 kcal.mole^{-1} for conformational inversion)[192] but the inversion of [2,2]-2,6-pyridinophane (141b) can be studied by NMR methods and the inversion barrier is quite low ($\Delta G^{\ddagger}$ 14·8 kcal.mole^{-1}),[193] clearly demonstrating the much lower interaction between two nitrogen atoms as compared with the interaction between a nitrogen atom and a CH group or between two CH groups at comparable distances. The relative magnitudes of the interactions N,CH < CH,CH have been similarly established by comparison[194,195] of the inversion barriers of the dithiametacyclophane (143) [no change in the AB spectrum of the ArCH$_2$S group up to 453°K] and the dithiametacyclopyridinophane (143a) ($\Delta G^{\ddagger}$ 20·5 kcal.mole^{-1} in DMSO-d_6). The dithiacyclopyridinophane (143b) apparently has a higher inversion barrier than (143a),[195] but the reason for this difference is not clear. The inversion barrier for the dithiapyridinophane (143c) is low as expected ($\Delta G^{\ddagger}$ < 13·7 kcal.mole^{-1}), but the actual value has not yet been measured.[195] The furanophane (144) is also conformationally mobile[193] ($\Delta G^{\ddagger}$ ca. 16·8 kcal.mole^{-1} for conformational inversion), but the thiophenophane (144a) and even the furanothiophenophane (144b) show no spectral changes up to 473°K ($\Delta G^{\ddagger}$ > 27 kcal.mole^{-1}).[192] Inversion rates in [2,2]metacyclophane analogues therefore show a high structural dependence. [3,2]Metacyclophanes (145), as might be expected, are found to be conformationally more mobile than

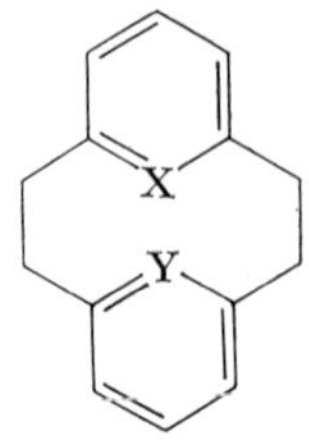

141 X = Y = CH
141a X = CH, Y = N
141b X = Y = N

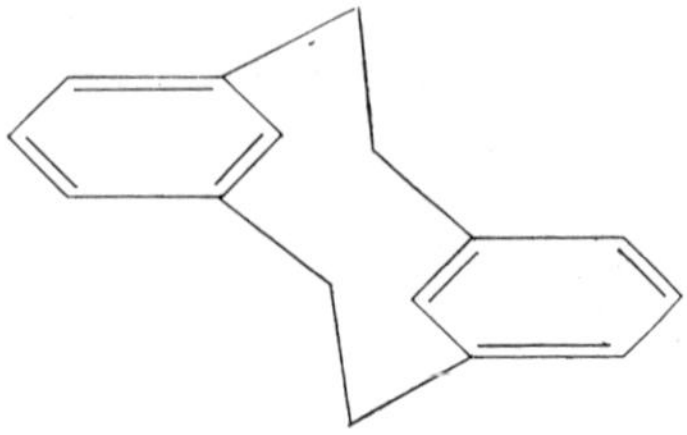

142

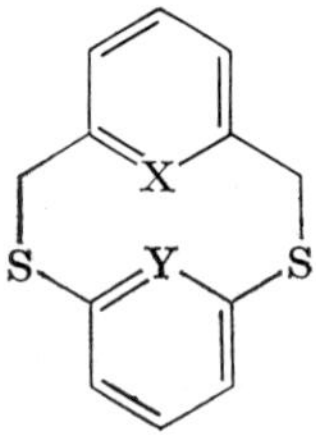

143 X = Y = CH
143a X = N, Y = CH
143b X = CH, Y = N
143c X = Y = N

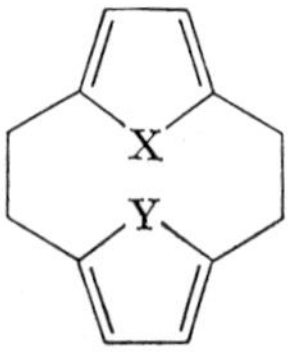

144 X = Y = O
144a X = Y = S
144b X = O, Y = S

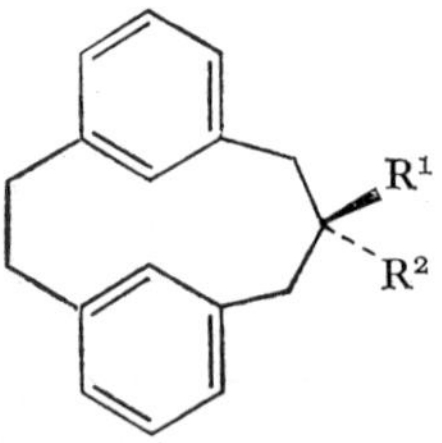

	R^1	R^2	$\Delta G^{\ddagger}$ kcal.mole^{-1}
145	CO_2Et	CO_2Et	19·3
145a	=CPh$_2$		17·3
145b	CO_2H	H	16·8
145c	CO_2Me	H	16·8
145d	CMe_2OH	H	16·2
145e	CPh_2OH	H	15·7

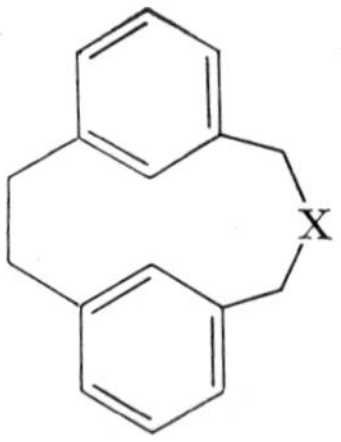

	X	$\Delta G^{\ddagger}$ kcal.mole^{-1}
146	S	12·9
146a	SO	15·4
146b	SO_2	15·5

the [2,2]metacyclophanes. The inversion process may be studied,[196] either by the coalescence of the AB systems given by the benzyl methylene groups (compounds **145** and **145a**), or alternatively by the exchange of the C-9 and C-17 protons be-

tween their non-identical environments in less symmetrical systems, such as
(**145b** to **e**), in which these protons form part of a prochiral system. The analogous
[3,2]thiametacyclophane (**146**) and the derivatives (**146a** and **b**) are also suitable
for NMR studies of their inversion rates.[197] The barriers to inversion in the
thiametacyclophane (**146**) are rather lower than those for the carbocyclic systems
(**145**) because the C–S bond is longer than the C–C bond. This mobility is
further enhanced in the [3,3]dithiametacyclophane system (**147**) in which the
methylene protons are observed as a singlet.[198] The NMR spectra of the halogenated derivatives (**147a** to **d**) are rather more interesting and in some cases
show two AB systems for the methylene groups at low temperatures, consistent
with the presence of two diastereomeric conformations (**148**) and (**148a**), both
inverting slowly on the NMR time scale. Other compounds of this type show an
AB system and an A_2 system for these protons at low temperature, consistent with
slow inversion of one conformational type and fast inversion of the other. These
complex spectral changes have not yet been fully analysed in terms of the kinetics
of the conformational changes, but energy barriers separating the diastereomeric
conformational types (**148**) and (**148a**) generally seem to be measurable ($\Delta G^{\ddagger}$
ca. 21 to 23 kcal.mole^{-1}) for the monofluoro compounds (**147a**) and (**149**) and
difluoro-derivative (**147b**), but are rather too high for NMR measurement for
(**147c** and **147d**).

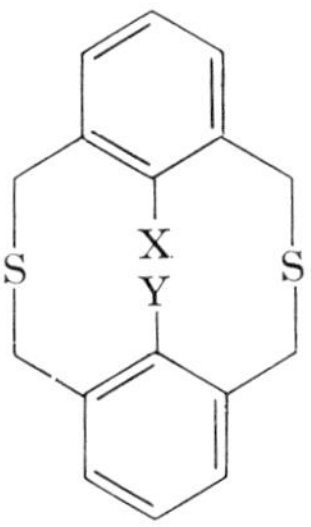

147   X = Y = H   149
147a X = H, Y = F
147b X = Y = F
147c X = F, Y = Cl
147d X = Y = Cl

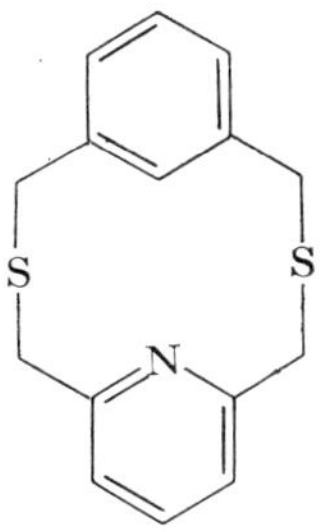

More complex metacyclophane systems have also been studied. Thus a preliminary report[199] discusses the spectrum of [2,2,0]metacyclophane (**150**) which
shows an ABCD system for the methylene protons at low temperatures coalescing
to a singlet above 253°K, whereas the methylene protons of [2,0,2,0]metacyclo-
phane (**151**) give a singlet down to 2·28°K. The spectrum of the [1,1,1,1]meta-
paracyclophane (**152**) shows a temperature dependence which has been
associated[200] with hindered rotation of the durene rings [indicated by an en-
closed asterisk in (**152**)] probably in the boat-like conformation shown. This

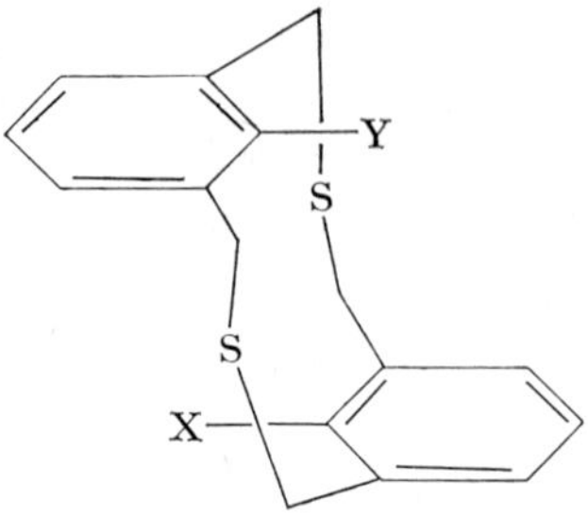

148 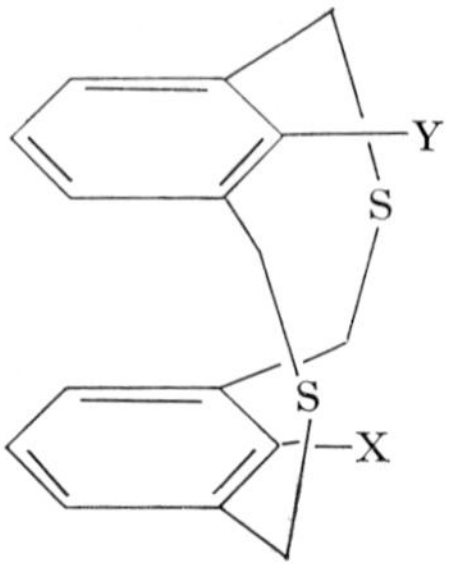   **148a**

process results in the exchange of the durene methyl groups between the environments A and B (see **152**).

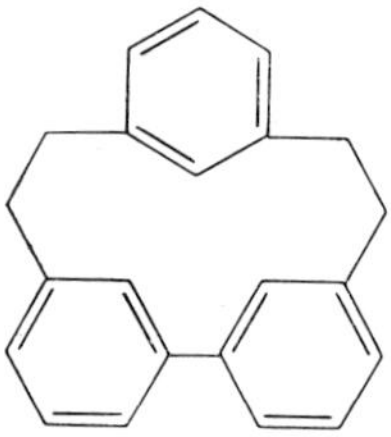

150

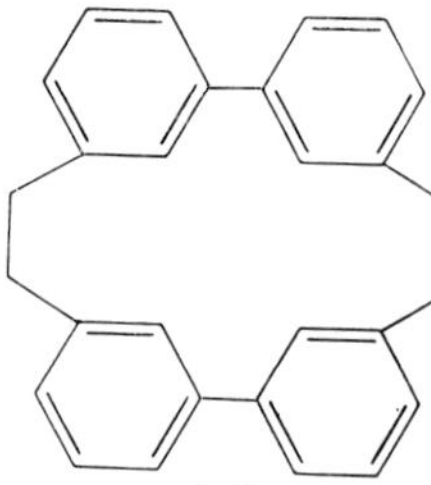

151

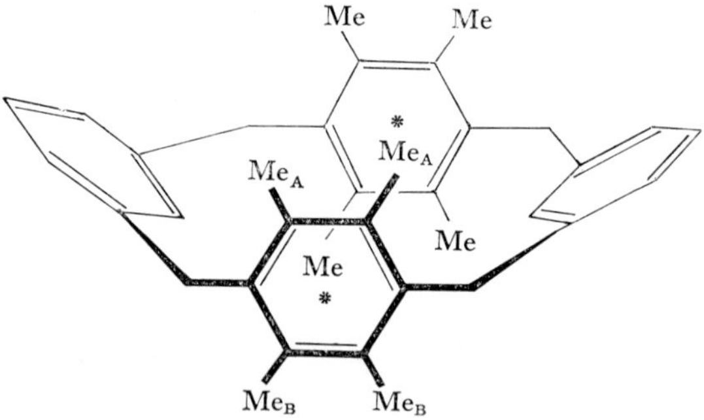

152

E. Annulenes

Three types of change may be detected in annulene systems by NMR spectroscopy, since one of these involves conformational inversion of non-planar annulene systems the annulenes will be included in the section of this review discussing ring inversion processes. The other two types of structural change that may be studied are bond-shift processes in annulenes which have alternating single and double bonds, and bond rotational processes in annulenes with rings larger than twelve-membered.

The first two types of changes are exemplified by the studies which have been made of cyclo-octatetraene ([8]annulene) and its derivatives. Cyclo-octatetraene adopts a non-planar tub-like conformation, and conformational inversion has been successfully examined[201] using the derivative (153) which has a prochiral hydroxyisopropyl substituent. The inversion process (153)⇌(153a) exchanges the methyl groups (Me and Me') between the diastereotopic environments A and B, and the free energy of activation for this process was calculated from the coalescence temperature of the two methyl signals observable in the spectrum at low temperatures ($\Delta G^{\ddagger}$ 14·7 kcal.mole^{-1} at 271°K). The rate of double bond shift (153b)⇌(153c) was obtained for the same compound by a complete line-shape study of the ring proton signals, since the bond-shift process exchanges the ring proton between two non-identical environments (A and B). The free energy of activation for this second process ($\Delta G^{\ddagger}$ 17·1 kcal.mole^{-1} at 271°K) showed that the bond-shift process in a planar cyclo-octatetraene molecule, possibly having a transition state in which all eight ring bonds are of equal length, involved an energy increase of 2·4 kcal.mole^{-1}. This result was of considerable interest in connection with theoretical estimates of the importance of Jahn-Teller distortion in a hypothetical, planar cyclo-octatetraene system. Furthermore, the relatively large value for the inversion barrier indicates that even in the planar molecule the π-electron delocalization energy is rather small. Several other studies have been made of the kinetics of bond-shift in simple

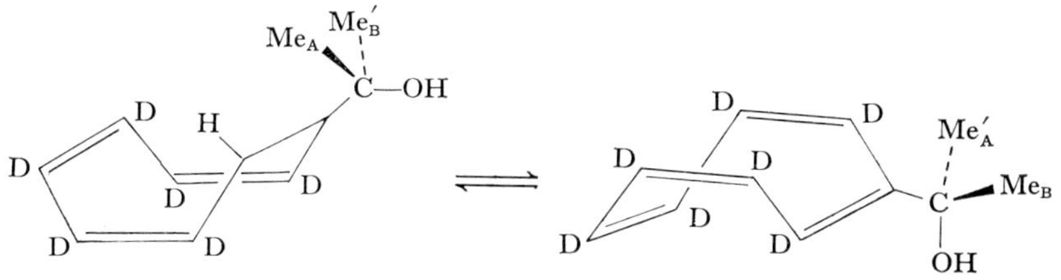

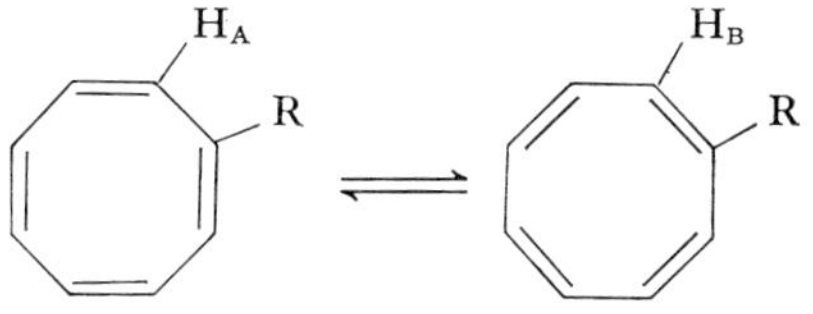

R	$\Delta G^{\ddagger}$ (153b⇌153c) kcal.mole^{-1}	Reference
153 CMe$_2$OH	17·1	201
153d CO$_2$Et	15·3	201
153e H	ca. 13·7	202
153f OMe	16·4	203
153g OCMe$_3$	15·0	203
153h F	ca. 12	204

cyclo-octatetraene derivatives[202 to 204] and the results obtained are summarized below formulae (153). Compounds (153d), (153f) and (153g) were studied by line-shape methods and are analogous to (153). The study of cyclo-octatetraene itself (153e) involved an ingenious use[202] of the temperature dependence of the ^{13}C-satellite signals associated with the proton resonance spectrum, and the monofluoro-derivative (153h) was studied using the temperature dependence of the $^{19}F-^1H$ coupling.[204] The study[205] of the disubstituted cyclo-octatetraene (154) is of particular interest since in this case the interconversion of the isomers (154) and (154a) was studied directly and by line-shape methods, the results obtained by both methods were in excellent agreement [$\Delta G^{\ddagger}$ 19·5 kcal.mole^{-1} for (154 → 154a) by the line-shape method and $\Delta G^{\ddagger}$ 18·8 kcal.mole^{-1} for (154a → 154) by direct observation].

154   154a

The rate processes that result in the interchange of the environments of the "inner" and "outer" protons of annulenes with ring systems of twelve or more atoms are complex. The activation energies associated with these changes, which involve both bond-shift and bond rotation processes, are remarkably low and may be studied by NMR line-shape methods. In most cases the reported data have been based only upon the coalescence temperature method and the results obtained in these cases will be reported only briefly (Table V). A more complete study has been made of [16]annulene, and it shows that the situation in annulenes may be further complicated by equilibria in solution involving different geometrical isomers. The results listed in Table V refer to the activation parameters associated with the exchange of the ring protons between the inner and outer environments in annulenes having the geometry indicated in the structural formulae (155 to 163). The very large chemical shift differences which are observed for these two types of protons are due to the well-known ring current phenomenon; in [4n+2]annulenes the inner protons are observed at high field (often higher than $\delta=0$) and the outer protons at low field in the region of benzenoid proton resonance or lower. This situation is reversed in the [4n]annulenes and these effects have recently become a popular basis for comment upon the aromatic or anti-aromatic character of annulenes. The site exchange processes for the [4n+2]annulenes are difficult to comment upon in general, but clearly involve rotational processes in which at least one pair of adjacent p-orbitals must be arranged in an orthogonal relationship. The low activation energies for these cases therefore suggests that the difference in π-electron delocalization

TABLE V

Activation energies for the exchange of inner and outer proton environments in [4n + 2]annulenes and [4n]annulenes

Annulene	Process	$\Delta G^{\ddagger}$ kcal.mole^{-1}	Reference
[14]Annulene (**155**)	I[a]	10·8	206
[18]Annulene (**156**)	I[a]	13·4	206
Nitro[18]annulene (**157**)	II[b]	12·9	206
Acetyl[18]annulene (**157a**)	II[b]	12·1	206
1,5-Bisdehydro[12]annulene (**158**)	I[c]	7·9	206
[12]Annulene (**159, 159a**)	K	5·5	208
1,9-Bisdehydro[16]annulene (**160**)	I[c]	9·0	206
[16]Annulene (**161 to 161c**)	*85 → 91*[d]	11·1	207
	91 → 85	10·7	207
	K$_{85}$	8·6	207
	V$_{85}$	8·6	207
	V$_{91}$ and K$_{91}$	6·1	207
1,11-Bisdehydro[20]annulene (**162**)	I[c]	9·0	206
[24]Annulene (**163**)	I[c]	11·0	206

[a] [4n + 2]Annulenes do not have localized single and double bonds, process I therefore refers to a general exchange of ring protons between inner and outer environments (A and B, etc.).

[b] The substituents cannot occupy an inner position, the exchange process II does not therefore involve the hydrogens in positions 4, 7, 10, 13 and 16 (see **157**).

[c] The published details refer only to the general exchange of protons between the inner and outer environments as for the [4n + 2]annulenes.

[d] The numbers refer to Isomers *85* and *91* (see **161b** and **161c**).

energy of a [4n + 2]annulene and the corresponding polyene may not be very large. For the [4n]annulenes plausible processes of rotation about single bonds (process K)[207,208] and double bond isomerization (process V)[207,208] may be envisaged, and the detailed scheme that has been suggested for the observable conformational changes of [16]annulene (**161**) is summarized by formulae (**161 to 161c**).

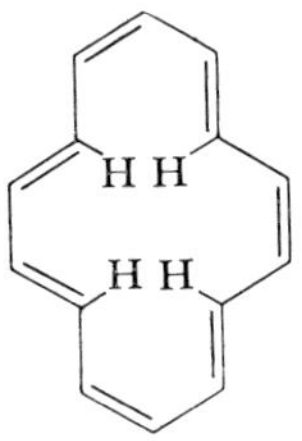

155 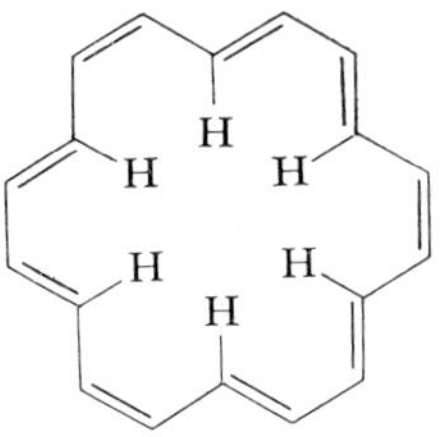   156 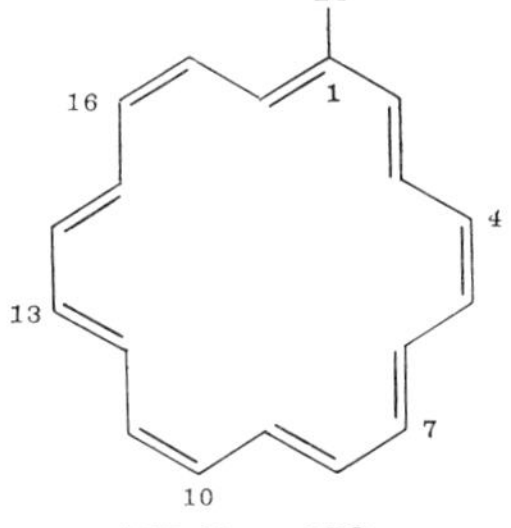   157 R = NO$_2$
                                                  157a R = COCH$_3$

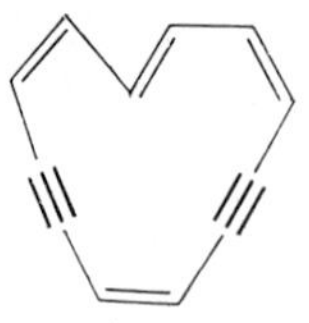

158 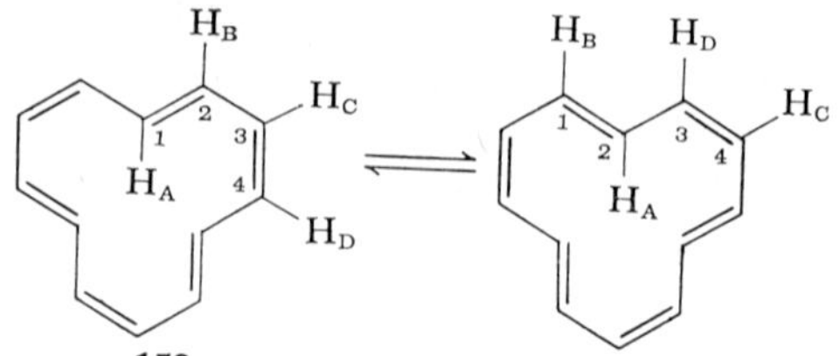   159   159a

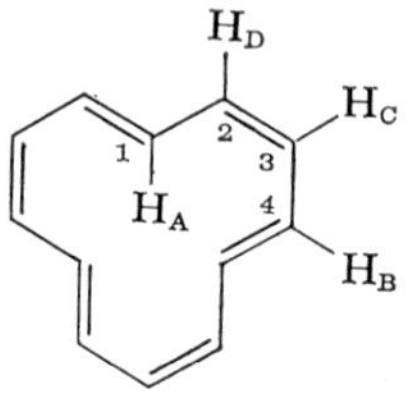

159b

The results listed in Table V refer in most cases to the exchange of the inner and outer proton environments and are based on coalescence data only,[206] but the cases of [12]annulene[208] and [16]annulene[207] have been studied in more detail. Thus, for [12]annulene, the only process detectable in the range 103° to 233°K ([12]annulene undergoes a permanent rearrangement above 233°K) is the process (159) → (159a) which involves rotation about single bonds only,[208] and is rather analogous to the conformational changes of the tri-o-thymotide system. The bond

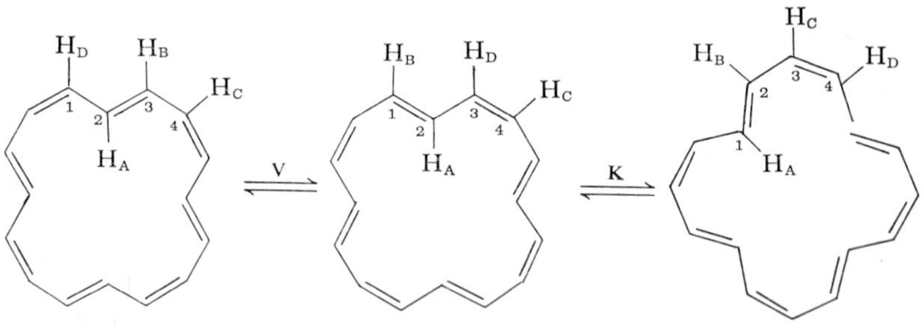

161   161a   161b Isomer 85

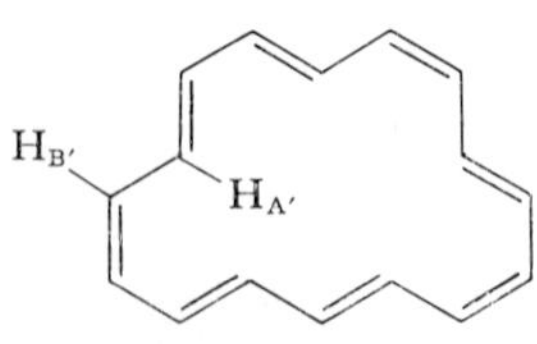

161c Isomer 91 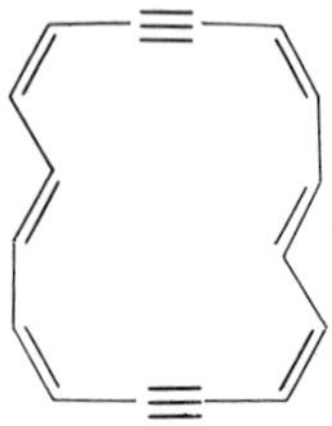   160

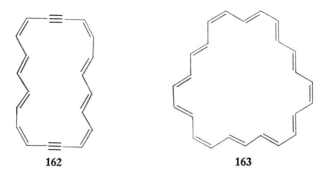

162   163

isomerization process (**159**) → (**159b**) does not occur rapidly on the NMR time-scale within this temperature range, possibly a consequence of the non-planarity of the [12]annulene ring system, and at 233°K two sharp multiplets are observable in the spectrum, corresponding to the averaged pairs of environments A and B, and C and D. The rather small paramagnetic shift of the inner protons (δ 8·07), as compared with the inner protons of [16]annulene (δ 10·56), may indicate that the non-planarity of the conjugated system in [12]annulene also results in a decrease in magnitude of the paramagnetic ring current.

The study of [16]annulene[207] represents the most complete NMR study of any annulene that has been reported. Thus the spectrum of [16]annulene shows temperature dependence which is not only assignable to bond rotation (**161a**)⇌ (**161b**) (process K in the nomenclature used by Oth and Gilles) and bond isomerization (**161a**)⇌(**161**) (process V in the same nomenclature), but also to the process of geometrical isomerization which converts the configuration (**161**) ([16]annulene isomer *85*) into the alternative [16]annulene configuration (**161c**) ([16]annulene isomer *91*). The free energies of activation associated with each of these processes, together with an approximate value for processes K and V in the isomer (**161c**), were obtained from a complete line-shape analysis using Kubo and Sack's method for a multi-site exchange (see Table V). The contrast between the approximately equal bond lengths found by crystal structure studies for [14]- and [18]- annulenes, and the activation energy that is required for double bond isomerization in [12]- and [16]- annulenes shows an interesting and revealing

CO₂Me   CO₂Me

164   164a

difference between the [4n+2] and [4n] systems. The configurational isomerization process [cf. (161)⇌(161c)] has also been detected[209] in methoxycarbonyl[16]annulene (164). In this case the methoxycarbonyl substituent must
occupy an outer position and the process (164)⇌(164a), which is slow on the
NMR time-scale at low temperatures, results in sharp and distinct signals from
the inner and outer protons at ca. 300°K when it is fast on the NMR time-scale,
due to restrictions placed upon the possible rotational processes (K) as a result of
the substituent. The detailed kinetics of the changes have not yet been elucidated.

V. INVERSION OF PYRAMIDAL ATOMIC CONFIGURATIONS AND RELATED ROTATIONAL BARRIERS

The best known inversion processes of this type involve inversion of the pyramidal configuration of trisubstituted nitrogen atoms. Examples of this type of
configurational change at other atoms have also been examined by NMR methods
and these will be included in this section, together with the closely related topic of
rotational barriers associated with N–X (X=N, O, P, B) single bonds. The
pseudo-rotational process that exchanges the environments of the ligands of
penta-coordinated phosphorus and related examples of complex ligand exchange
processes will not be included.

The pioneering examination by Roberts and Bottini[210] of nitrogen inversion in
aziridines was one of the first examples of the application of NMR line-shape
methods to the measurement of the rates of conformational changes. This work
followed earlier suggestions[211] that the resolution of suitably substituted aziridines might be possible, in view of the restriction placed upon nitrogen inversion
by the three-membered ring, because of the increased strain in the trigonal
transition state relative to the pyramidal ground state. Early attempts to resolve
aziridines were unsuccessful,[212] although very recently attempts of this type,
involving the separation of diastereomeric N-halo-aziridines for example, have
met with success.[213 to 216] Following this early NMR study of aziridines a considerable number of substituted aziridines have been examined[217 to 230] and the
energy barriers for nitrogen inversion that have been measured are listed in
Table VI. In most cases the, reasonably reliable, free energies of activation,
based usually upon the coalescence data, are quoted, but in a few cases the
Arrhenius activation parameters are also available. The latter appear to be rather
unreliable in view of the abnormally low (10^5 to 10^9) and abnormally high (10^{17} to
10^{19}) values which have been reported for the frequency factors, and comments
upon the relative magnitudes of inversion barriers are, at the present time, more
suitably based upon the relative free energies of activation. The effects of substituents on the nitrogen atom upon the rates of inversion of its pyramidal configuration may be considered in terms of a number of factors (cf. refs. 219, 229).

(i) *Steric effects.* As originally suggested[210] large substituents on nitrogen tend to lower the inversion barrier, since the steric interaction between the substituent and the adjacent ring methylene groups is less in the transition state for inversion, in which the exocyclic CNC angles are larger, than in the pyramidal ground state. This effect is shown clearly by N-t-butyl- and N-triphenylmethyl- aziridine.

(ii) *Inductive effects.* Strongly electron withdrawing groups on nitrogen, such as CF_3 and CF_2R, apparently cause a marked decrease in the inversion barrier. This effect is not shown by other electronegative substituents such as oxygen and nitrogen which have non-bonded electron pairs, and may therefore be a consequence of a conjugation effect rather than an inductive effect.

(iii) *Conjugation effects.* Nitrogen atoms, in which the lone-pairs are associated with π-bonding, have a tendency towards trigonal geometry[231] to maximize the π-bonding. This effect is clearly reflected in the reduced inversion barriers of aziridines in which the substituents on nitrogen include Ph, $C=CH_2$, and COR. The similar effect due to substituents such as SO_2R, SOR, SR, and POR_2 could be taken as evidence for the importance of p_π–d_π bonding, but could alternatively be a consequence of the electronegativity effect or simply a property of second row substituents associated with the involvement of $3s$ and $3p$ orbitals. Thus low inversion barriers have been predicted for carbanions stabilized by SO_2R, SOR and SR by calculations[232] which do not include the sulphur-d orbitals.

(iv) *Electrostatic effects.* These effects are associated with substituents on the nitrogen atom which have lone-pair electrons, such as NH_2 and halogens, and which cause significant increases in the nitrogen inversion barrier. In some cases this increase is sufficient to permit the isolation of diastereomers related by nitrogen inversion. These effects may be associated with the electronegativity of the substituents, and have also been attributed to increased repulsion between the nitrogen lone-pair electrons and the substituent lone-pair(s) in the transition state for nitrogen inversion. This rationalization may not, however, survive theoretical scrutiny. For substituents with vacant d orbitals, such as sulphur and phosphorus, the conjugative (or second row element) effect seems to be more important than the lone-pair effects.

(v) *Solvent effects.* Hydroxylic solvents such as MeOH and D_2O appear to increase the nitrogen inversion barrier. This effect has been rationalized in terms of more efficient hydrogen bonding between the OH (OD) group of the solvent and pyramidal nitrogen as compared with trigonal nitrogen. This effect should be used with caution as a method for diagnosing nitrogen inversion barriers since examples have recently been recognized in which the effects of hydroxylic solvents cannot be rationalized in this way.

These effects (i to iv) of substituents upon nitrogen inversion barriers in aziridines are probably general effects observable for nitrogen inversion in other

TABLE VI

Inversion barriers for aziridine derivatives

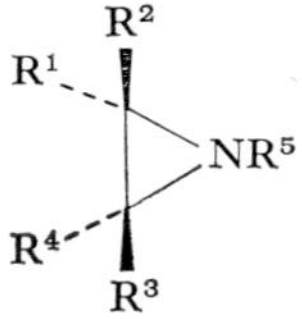

```
        R²         NR⁵
          \       /
  R¹ ···    —————
          /       \
  R⁴ ···           R³
```

165

| Compound[a] | | | | | $\Delta G^{\ddagger}$ | E_a | | | |
R¹	R²	R³	R⁴	R⁵	kcal.mole^{-1}	kcal.mole^{-1}	$\log_{10}A$	Solvent	Ref.
H	H	H	H	Et	19.4			Neat	210
H	H	H	H	CH$_2$Ph	>21.3			D$_2$O	210
H	H	H	H	C$_6$H$_{11}$	19.2			Neat	210
H	H	H	H	CH$_2$CH$_2$Ph	18.8			Neat	210
H	H	H	H		18.6			Neat	210
H	H	H	D	t-Bu	ca. 17.0			C$_6$H$_6$	217
H	H	D	H	t-Bu	ca. 16.0			C$_6$H$_6$	217
H	H	H	H	CPh$_3$	15.9			CDCl$_3$	218
H	H	H	H	Ph	11.8			CS$_2$	219
H	H	H	H	CF$_2$·CHF·CF$_3$	13.5[b]	9.1	9.6	CCl$_4$	220
H	H	H	H	CF$_2$·CH(CF$_3$)$_2$	13.7[b]	6.8	7.8	CCl$_4$	220
Me	Me	H	H	Me	17.9	24.1	17.0	Neat	221
Me	Me	H	H	Me	17.7	23.5	16.7	Neat	221
Me	Me	H	H	Me	18.2	23.4	16.3	C$_6$H$_6$	221
Me	Me	H	H	Me	18.9	32.5	21.7	CDCl$_3$	221
Me	Me	H	H	Me	18.3	24.2	16.6	(CD$_3$)$_2$CO	221
Me	Me	H	H	CH$_2$CH$_2$CH$_2$CO$_2$H	17.8				222
Me	Me	H	H	CH$_2$CH$_2$CH$_2$CO$_2$Et	17.6				222
Me	H	Me	H	Et	17.6				222
Me	Me	H	H	CF$_2$CHF·CF$_3$	13.1[b]	6.9	8.3	CCl$_4$	220
Me	Me	H	H	CF$_2$CH(CF$_3$)$_2$	12.7[b]	5.8	7.8	CCl$_4$	220

R1	R2	R3	R4	R5	$\Delta G^{\ddagger}$	E_a	$\log_{10} A$	Solvent	Ref.
CF3	CF3	H	H	Me	16·2[b]	7·0	6·1		223
F	Me	H	H	CF3	11·1[b]	5·5	8·7		224
Me	Me	Me	Me	H	16·9[e]	11·0		CCl4	225
Me	Me	Me	Me	D	17·9[e]	14·3		CCl4	225
H	H	H	H	NH2	> 22				215
Me	Me	H	Me	NH2	> 22				215
Me	H	H	H	Xf	T_c ca. 403°K			C6H4Cl2	226
Me	Me	Me	H	Cl	27·1[c]				216
H	(CH2)4		H	Cl	23·5				213, 227
Me	Me	H	H	Cl	23·8[d]				214
CF3	CF3	H	H	Br	> 21·3				213, 227
CF3	CF3	H	H	Br	22·4[b]				223
CF3	CF3	H	H	F	T_c > 463°K	22·7	13·0	C6H6	223
Me	Me	H	H	SCCl3	9·1			CDCl3	223
Me	Me	H	H	S-t-Bu	12·2			CDCl3	228
Me	Me	H	H	SPh	12·4			CDCl3	228
Me	Me	H	H	SMe	13·4			CDCl3	228
H	H	H	H	SPh	13·0			CDCl3	228
H	H	H	H	SC6H3(NO2)2	12·6				229
H	H	H	H	SOPh	13·6				229
H	H	H	H	SO2Me	12·8				229
H	H	H	H	SO2Ph	12·4				219
H	H	H	H	SO2C6H4CH3	12·4				229
H	H	H	H	POPh2	8·2				229
H	H	H	H	CONMe2	9·9			CH2Cl2	229
H	H	H	H	CO2Me	7·1			CH2=CHCl	219
H	H	H	H	COMe	T_c < 113°K			CH2=CHCl	219
H	H	H	H	COPh	T_c < 118°K			CH2=CHCl	219
=CH2		H	H	Et	10·3	6·4	9·0	Neat	210
=CH2		H	H	Me	11·6[b]				222

[a] The groups R1 to R5 refer to the formula (165).

[b] Calculated at 300°K from the published data for E_a and $\log_{10} A$.

[c] k (cis → trans) obtained by direct measurement at 353° and 383°K.

[d] k (endo → exo) by direct measurement at 302·5°K.

[e] Some care was taken to exclude the possibility of intramolecular NH and ND exchange, but these must be considered the minimum values for the inversion barriers.

X =

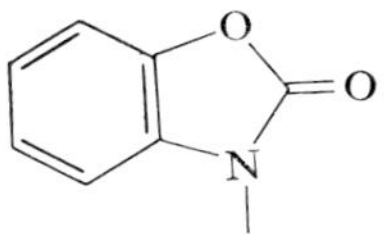

systems. They may therefore be used to distinguish between nitrogen inversion and alternative processes, such as bond rotation, in the rate-determining step of a conformational change. This is discussed further below.

The high nitrogen inversion barriers, found for aziridines having substituents with lone-pair electrons, suggest that nitrogen inversion barriers in oxaziridines and diaziridines should be even higher and this has been found to be so. Thus oxaziridines such as (166) and (166a) have been prepared in optically active form,[233,234] and their racemization rates have been studied in two cases to give the activation parameters listed in Table VII. The very large rate enhancing effect of

TABLE VII

Nitrogen inversion barriers in oxaziridines and diaziridines[a]

Compound	$\Delta G^{\ddagger}$ kcal.mole^{-1}	$\Delta H^{\ddagger}$ kcal.mole^{-1}	$\Delta S^{\ddagger}$ e.u.	References
166	32·5	34·1	+5	233, 234
166a	25·9	27·7	+6	233, 234
167	32·4 (167 → 167a)			235
	31·4 (167a → 167)			
168	> 22			237
169	*ca.* 27·3			237
170	27·1 (170 → 170a)			237
	26·3 (170a → 170)			237

[a] All results, except for (168), based on studies of the equilibration of diastereomers or racemization of enantiomers.

the *t*-butyl substituent in (166a) parallels the effect of this substituent upon the aziridine nitrogen inversion rate (Table VI). The interconversion of the diastereomeric oxaziridines (167) and (167a) has also been studied by direct methods.[235] The free energies of activation ($\Delta G^{\ddagger}$ *ca.* 32 kcal.mole^{-1}) found for nitrogen inversion in these experimental studies of oxaziridines are remarkably close to the calculated value (32·4 kcal.mole^{-1}) predicted by *ab initio* SCF LCAO MO calculations[236] for oxaziridine itself.

The nitrogen inversion barriers in diaziridines are somewhat lower than those found for oxaziridines, but are again sufficiently large to permit the separation of the diastereomeric pairs (169) and (169a), and (170) and (170a), related by nitrogen inversion. Thus an NMR study of the diaziridine (168) showed,[237] from the sharp AB system given by the benzyl methylene group up to 432°K, that the nitrogen inversion barrier was greater than 22 kcal.mole^{-1}. The direct study[237]

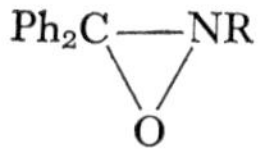

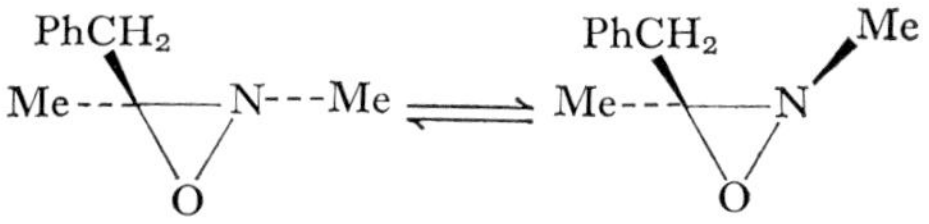

166 R = Me
166a R = t–Bu

167

167a

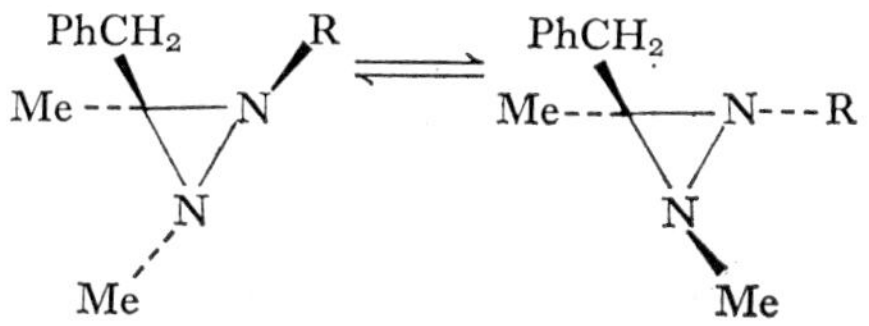

168 R = Me   **168a**
169 R = CH₂Ph   **169a**
170 R = H   **170a**

of the interconversion of the diastereomers (**169**) and (**170**) showed that the nitro-gen inversion barrier in diaziridines (*ca.* 27 kcal.mole^{-1}, see Table VII) lies between those of aziridines and oxaziridines.

TABLE VIII

Nitrogen inversion barriers in tertiary amines

Compound	$\Delta G^{\ddagger a}$ kcal.mole^{-1}	Solvent	Reference
171	8·85	CFCl₃	227
171a	11·5	CFCl₃	227
171a	11·9	CH₂Cl₂	227
171b	11·5	CH₂Cl₂	227
172	*ca.* 8		239
172a	10·2	CF₂Cl₂	238
173	13·3	CH₂Cl₂	238
173a	8·6		240
174	6·4		240
174a	8·4		240
175	8·4		240
175a	10·6		240
176	8·8		240
176a	10·1		240
177	9·7	CDCl₃	241
177	10·9	D₂O-CD₃OD	241
178a	23·5		242
178	*ca.* 14		243
179	6·5		73

[a] At the coalescence temperature.

Nitrogen inversion in systems other than three-membered rings has generally been more difficult to study, but a number of results have now been obtained and a fairly complete picture of nitrogen inversion barriers is emerging from these studies. The inhibition of nitrogen inversion in the four-membered azetidine ring system is surprisingly small. Thus, the only successful study of azetidines reported[227] a nitrogen inversion barrier in the azetidine (171) only a little higher than that found, in acyclic amines (see below). This low inversion barrier is increased, as expected in the N-haloazetidines (171a) and (171b) (see Table VIII). In the analogous five-membered ring systems[238,239] the nitrogen inversion

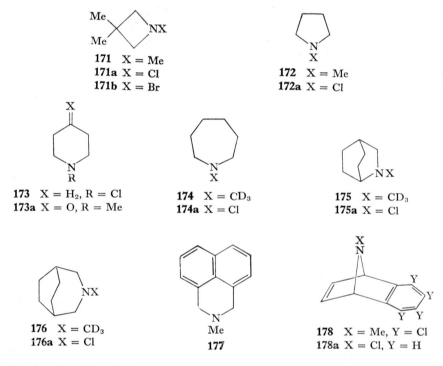

171 X = Me
171a X = Cl
171b X = Br

172 X = Me
172a X = Cl

173 X = H₂, R = Cl
173a X = O, R = Me

174 X = CD₃
174a X = Cl

175 X = CD₃
175a X = Cl

176 X = CD₃
176a X = Cl

177

178 X = Me, Y = Cl
178a X = Cl, Y = H

barriers for N-methyl- and N-chloro- pyrrolidines show a similar relationship to those found for the azetidines. The results obtained in an NMR examination of N-chloropiperidine (173) were ambiguous,[238] and the observed spectral changes were consistent with either hindered ring inversion (cf. N-methylpiperidine) or hindered nitrogen inversion. The situation in the piperidone (173a) is clearer in that the ring inversion barrier, by analogy with cyclohexanone, is expected to be very low and the observed[240] spectral changes may therefore be interpreted in terms of the barrier to nitrogen inversion. The spectral changes in the homopiperidines (174)[239,240] and (174a)[240] have also been interpreted in terms of nitrogen inversion. The results for the bridged ring systems (175) and

(176) may be unambiguously assigned to nitrogen inversion barriers, and in all cases (171) to (176) the relationship between the nitrogen inversion barriers for the N-methyl- and N-chloro- amines is similar. The barriers to nitrogen inversion in the cyclic tertiary amines with four or more atoms in the ring [(171) to (176); $\Delta G^{\ddagger}$ 6·4 to 8·85 kcal.mole^{-1}] are rather similar to that found recently[73] for the acyclic amine N-methyldibenzylamine (179) ($\Delta G^{\ddagger}$ 6·5 kcal.mole^{-1}). The

$$(PhCH_2)_2 \, NMe$$

179

barrier to inversion found in the latter case is in good agreement with the barriers to nitrogen inversion in tertiary amines ($\Delta G^{\ddagger}$ for Me$_3$N 7·5 kcal.mole^{-1}) found by gas-phase infrared measurements,[244] and also with inversion energies calculated by the MINDO method.[72] The ingenious method, used some years ago by Saunders and Yamada[245] to study nitrogen inversion rates at higher temperatures, by slowing down the effective inversion rate through working in aqueous solution at low pH, has been criticized,[246] but in any case it suffers from the disadvantage that inversion barriers are measured in aqueous solution and are therefore subject to an increase due to hydrogen bonding effects. A few other cases of nitrogen inversion have been studied in which the inversion barrier is increased due to restrictions placed upon the inversion process by the cyclic system containing the nitrogen atom. Thus the bridged naphthalene (177) shows an AB system for the methylene protons in the NMR spectrum at low temperatures;[241] from the temperature at which the AB system coalesces to a singlet the free energy barrier to either ring inversion or nitrogen inversion could be obtained (Table VIII). The increase in the barrier, when measurements were made for a deuteriomethanol solution of (177), suggested that nitrogen inversion was the rate-determining step in the conformational change studied. The existence of unusually high barriers to nitrogen inversion in the 7-azabenzonorbornadienes (178)[243] and (178a)[242] has also been recognized. In the case of the N-chloro-derivative (178a) the inversion barrier is sufficiently large to permit the isolation of diastereomers which differ in their solvolytic reactivity, and the inversion barrier in the N-methyl derivative (178) is approximately twice that found in other tertiary amines (Table VIII). The high barriers to nitrogen inversion found in (178) and (178a) are believed to be a consequence of ring strain, but the magnitude of the effect is surprising, in view of the relatively small effects found in the azetidines (171) and (171a), and is related to the known difficulty of forming a planar carbonion at the 7-position in norbornyl derivatives.

The increase in nitrogen inversion barriers in cyclic compounds arising from the presence of substituent atoms with lone-pair electrons has been noted, and the effect is also evident in some acyclic systems. Thus the nitrogen inversion barrier in the hydrazines (180) and (180a) have been measured;[247,248] in both cases the benzyl methylene protons give AB spectra at low temperatures as a result of hindered inversion of the nitrogen atom N_A. The temperature dependence of the NMR spectra in these cases is consistent with hindered nitrogen inversion, and not with hindered rotation about the N–N bond. The measured inversion barriers (Table IX) are a little higher than those found in simple

TABLE IX

Free energy barriers to conformational changes for hydrazine derivatives

Compound	$\Delta G^{\ddagger}$ kcal.mole^{-1}	Solvent	Process	Reference
180	8·5		N_A inversion	247
180a	6·8	CF_2Cl_2	N_A inversion	248
180b	10·7	CS_2	N–N rotation	249
180c	11·2	CS_2	N–N rotation	249
180d	10·8	CS_2	N–N rotation	249
180e	ca. 8	CF_2Cl_2	N inversion	73
180f	14·2	$CDCl_3$	N–N rotation	250
180g	13·5	$CDCl_3$	N–N rotation	250

tertiary amines and are in accord with calculations made by the MINDO MO method.[72] The situation in the tetra-alkylhydrazines (**180b** to **180d**) is less clear cut and the rather higher barriers to conformational change in these compounds, which show a low-temperature AB system for the benzyl methylene groups coalescing to a singlet at higher temperatures, have been assigned to a rotational barrier about the N–N bond[249] rather than to nitrogen inversion barriers (Table IX). This conclusion was based upon the simplest interpretation of the experimental data; thus hindered nitrogen inversion should result in spectral changes consistent with the presence of diastereomeric conformations differing in configuration at N_A and N_B and giving therefore more complex spectral changes than those observed. Furthermore, the methylene group of the benzyl substituent on N_B in (**180d**) does not give an AB system at low temperatures. The observed spectral changes are consistent with the interconversion of conformations in which the nitrogen atoms are both rapidly inverting, and which may be represented by the enantiomeric projection formulae (**180h**) and (**180i**). The assignment of the

PhCH₂ and R² on N_A—N_B, R¹ and R³

180   $R^1 = CH_2Ph, R^2 = R^3 = H$
180a $R^1 = R^2 = R^3 = Me$
180b $R^1 = R^3 = Et, R^2 = CH_2Ph$
180c $R^1 = R^3 = CHMe_2, R^2 = CH_2Ph$
180d $R^1 = R^3 = CH_2Ph, R^2 = Et$
180e $R^1 = R^2 = R^3 = CH_2Ph$
180f $R^1 = R^3 = Ph, R^2 = CH_2Ph$
180g $R^1 = R^3 = p\text{-}C_6H_4Me, R^2 = CH_2Ph$

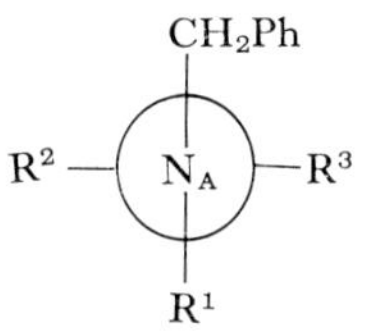

180h 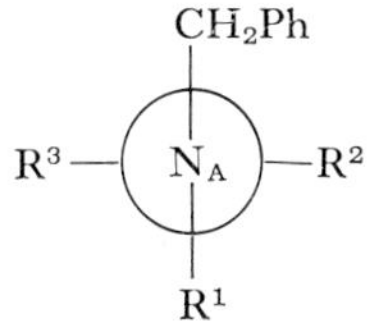   180i 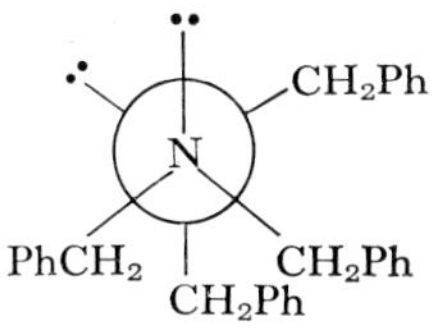   180j

energy barriers in (180b to 180d) to the rotational process is also consistent with the greater magnitude of these barriers as compared with the nitrogen inversion barriers of (180) and (180a). These conclusions have received support[73] from the observation of the NMR spectrum of tetrabenzylhydrazine (180e) at very low temperatures. Thus below 173°K the singlet signal from the methylene protons of (180e) broadens, and at 133°K is observed as two overlapping AB systems corresponding to the "frozen" conformation (180j). The line-shape changes have not been fully analysed, but are reported as being consistent with rotation about the N–N bond in (180) being rather slower than the nitrogen inversion process. The estimated free energy barrier for the nitrogen inversion process is similar to that observed in other acyclic hydrazine derivatives (see Table IX). As would be expected the barriers to rotation[250] about the N–N bonds of the NN'-diaryl-NN'-dialkylhydrazines (180f) and (180g) are considerably larger than those found in the tetra-alkylhydrazines (Table IX).

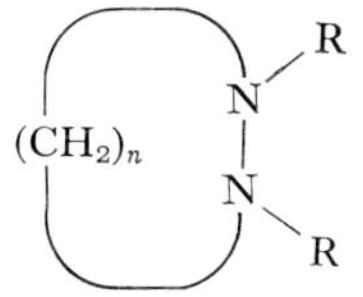

181

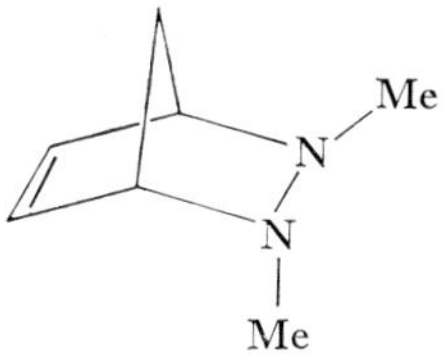

182 $\Delta G^{\ddagger}$ 14·5 kcal.mole^{-1} (CDCl$_3$)
$\Delta G^{\ddagger}$ 16·1 kcal.mole^{-1} (D$_2$O)

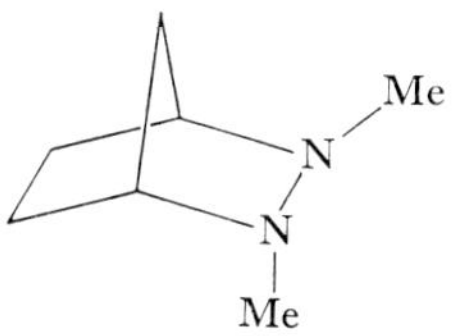

183 $\Delta G^{\ddagger}$ 13·0 kcal.mole^{-1}

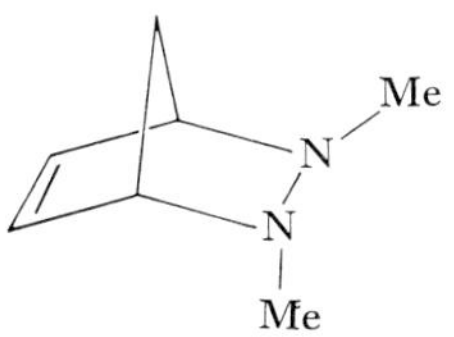

184 $\Delta G^{\ddagger}$ 12·2 kcal.mole^{-1}

Related to the observation of hindered nitrogen inversion and rotation about the N–N bond in tetra-alkylhydrazines it would be expected that cyclic hydrazine derivatives (181) would show temperature dependent NMR spectra associated with both slow ring inversion and slow nitrogen inversion. Effects of this type were first reported some years ago[251] for tetra- and hexa- hydropyridazines, but in these cases the initial examination did not distinguish between hindered ring inversion or hindered nitrogen inversion. The NMR spectra of the bridged cyclic hydrazines (182) to (184) in $CDCl_3$ show two N-methyl signals at low temperature which coalesce to a singlet at higher temperatures.[252,253] This temperature dependence may be unambiguously interpreted in terms of substantial barriers to nitrogen inversion, and the authors reasoned[252] that the observed process involved consecutive inversions at each of the two nitrogen atoms. A more recent examination[254] of the tetra- and hexa- hydropyridazines established that ring inversion probably occurs much more rapidly than nitrogen inversion in the tetrahydropyridazines (185) and (185a). Thus the spectrum of (185) at temperature below 158°K in CF_2Cl_2 shows two N-methyl signals and two AB systems from the ring methylene groups (CH_AH_B and $CH_{A'}H_{B'}$, see 186) consistent with the half-chair conformation (186). At higher temperatures a single N-Me signal is observed and a single AB system for the ring methylene groups, this was interpreted as being consistent with fast ring inversion and slow nitrogen inversion since it was presumed that the ring inversion rate would be comparable with that found in cyclohexene. Finally, at 277°K, the AB quartet collapsed to a singlet owing to both fast ring inversion and fast nitrogen inversion. The alternative explanation involving fast nitrogen inversion and slow ring inversion cannot, however, be ruled out. Ring inversion involves rotation about the N–N bond, which is known to be hindered, and nitrogen inversion would not necessarily be much slower in these cyclic hydrazines (185) than in acyclic hydrazines, in which the ground state conformational situation appears to be rather similar (see 180). The spectral changes observed for (185a)[254] were analogous to those

186

185 $R^1 = R^2 = Me$, $\Delta G^{\ddagger}$ 12·3 kcal.mole^{-1}
                          $\Delta G^{\ddagger}$ 8·2 kcal.mole^{-1}
185a $R^1 = H, R^2 = Me$, $\Delta G^{\ddagger}$ 12·0 kcal.mole^{-1}
                          $\Delta G^{\ddagger}$ 8·5 kcal.mole^{-1}
185b $R^1 = Me, R^2 = CH_2Ph$, $\Delta G^{\ddagger}$ 12·0 kcal.mole^{-1}
185c $R^1 = H, R^2 = CH_2Ph$, $\Delta G^{\ddagger}$ 11·5 kcal.mole^{-1}

for (185) but the other tetrahydropyridazines (185b, c),[255] (187) and (187a),[254] and hexahydropyridazines[251,254] (188) and (188a, b) examined in this and another study showed only the spectral changes associated with the higher energy barrier. In particular the hexahydropyridazine (188) shows an AB system (with additional vicinal coupling) from the N-CH$_2$ groups in the ring down to 123°K consistent with a preferred diequatorial arrangement of the N-Me groups as in (189). The recorded energy barriers for these compounds may therefore be associated either with ring inversion or with nitrogen inversion, although the

187   R = Me, $\Delta G^{\ddagger}$ 12·3 kcal.mole^{-1} (CD$_3$OD)
187a R = Ph, $\Delta G^{\ddagger}$ 13·4 kcal.mole^{-1} (CDCl$_3$)

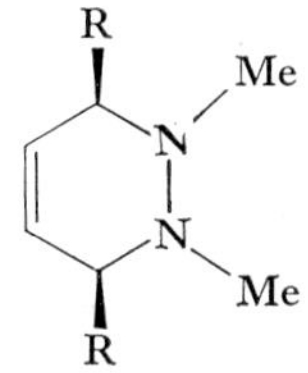

188   R^1 = R^2 = H, $\Delta G^{\ddagger}$ 11·6 kcal.mole^{-1} (CDCl$_3$)
                                $\Delta G^{\ddagger}$ 12·1 kcal.mole^{-1} (CD$_3$OD)
188a R^1 = Me, R^2 = H, $\Delta G^{\ddagger}$ 12·5 kcal.mole^{-1} (CDCl$_3$)
                                $\Delta G^{\ddagger}$ 12·3 kcal.mole^{-1} (CD$_3$OD)
188b R^1 = H, R^2 = Ph, $\Delta G^{\ddagger}$ 11·1 kcal.mole^{-1} (CDCl$_3$)

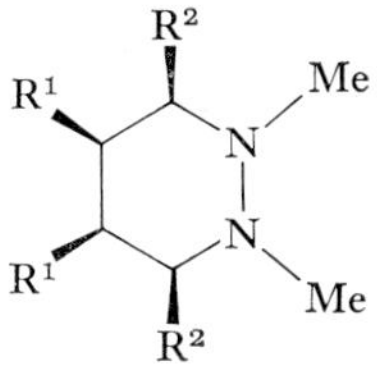

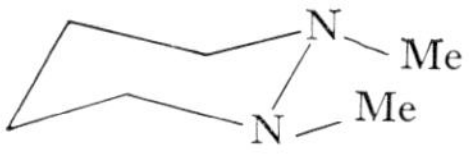

189

latter process was preferred in the publication.[254] The related benzotetrahydropyridazines (190) and (190a) have also been studied,[255] and the similarity between the energy barriers observed for the N-methyl derivative (190) and the N-phenyl derivative (190a) underlines the fact that ring inversion barriers and nitrogen inversion barriers are difficult to distinguish in these compounds; it is presumed that the detectable conformational changes in (190) and (190a) are primarily ring inversion processes and that the inversion barrier is relatively high owing to the large torsional barrier for the N–N bond. The bicyclic system (191) is of interest in that the NMR spectrum at low temperature shows[255] two AB systems for the ring methylene groups consistent with a preferred cis-fused arrangement (192) for this ring system. The energy barrier for both ring and nitrogen inversion (the two AB systems coalesce to a singlet at higher temperatures) is very similar ($\Delta G^{\ddagger}$ 12·4 kcal.mole^{-1}) to the observed nitrogen or ring inversion barriers in the other tetrahydropyridazines (185), (187) and (190). The analogous bicyclic system (193) shows only a single AB system from the ring methylene groups in the spectrum run at 304°K in D$_2$O, which coalesces to a singlet at 331°K; this result may be explained either in terms of the inversion of a *trans*-fused ring system or in terms of slow nitrogen inversion in a pair of rapidly equilibrating *cis*-conformations.[256] The five-membered ring systems of (194) are presumed to be *cis*-fused and the observation of two equally intense methyl singlets and an AB system in the spectrum at 213°K, which coalesce to two singlets at higher temperatures, has been interpreted in terms of the inversion process (195).[256] The hexahydrotetrazine (196) gives rather similar results to the

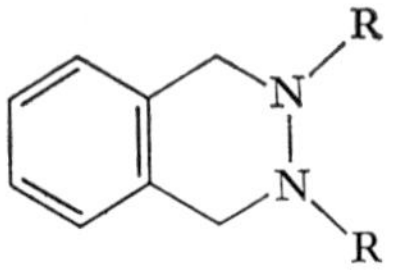

190   R = Me, $\Delta G^{\ddagger}$ 12·0 kcal.mole^{-1}
190a R = Ph, $\Delta G^{\ddagger}$ 12·2 kcal.mole^{-1}

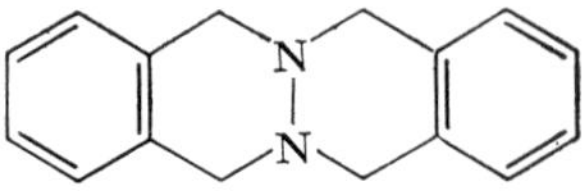

191

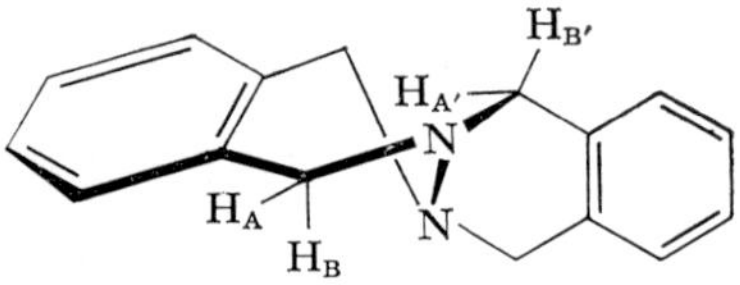

192

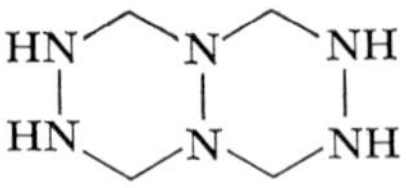

193   $\Delta G^{\ddagger}$ 16·6 kcal.mole^{-1}

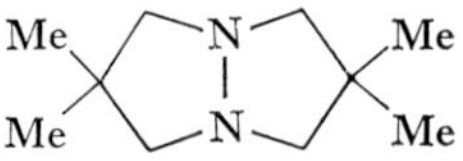

194
$\Delta G^{\ddagger}$ 12·1 kcal.mole^{-1}

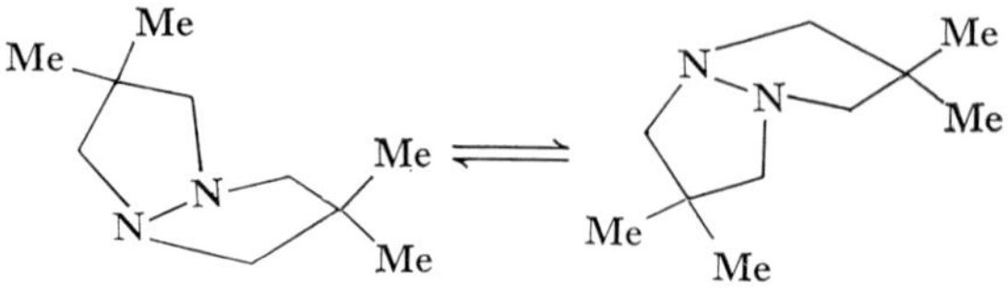

195

pyridazine derivatives.[120] Thus at 186°K the spectrum of (196) shows an AB system from the ring methylene groups and two *N*-methyl signals. This result is consistent with both slow ring inversion and slow nitrogen inversion, and from the dipole moment measurements subsequently reported[257] the preferred conformation of (196) is that shown in (197) with two *N*-methyl groups axial and two equatorial. This conformation minimizes the interactions between the dipoles associated with the hetero-atoms, an effect which has been described as the rabbit ear effect[258] since it may also be thought of, less appropriately, as a repulsion between two axially oriented lone-pairs in a 1,3-relationship. The free energy barrier obtained for the conformational change of (196) may therefore be a barrier for ring inversion or nitrogen inversion, the barrier for the excluded process being higher. Extension of this work to five-membered ring systems, in which nitrogen inversion barriers only would be detectable, shows that for the pyrazolidines (198)[259] and (198a)[260] the barrier to nitrogen inversion is reduced, a result which is comparable with the decrease in the coalescence temperatures of

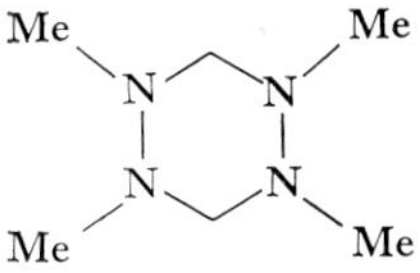

196   $\Delta G^{\ddagger}$ 11·7 kcal.mole^{-1}

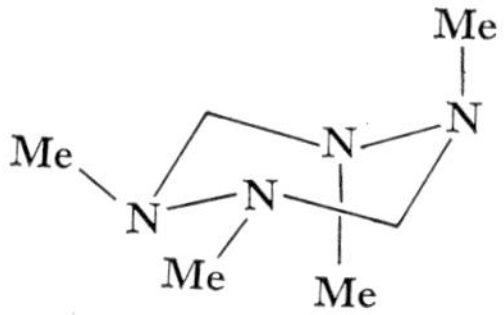

197

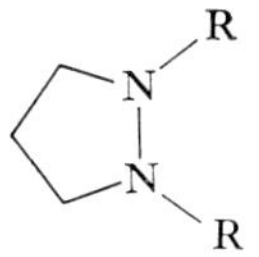

198   R = CH$_2$Ph, $\Delta G^{\ddagger}$ 9·3 kcal.mole^{-1}
198a R = Me, $\Delta G^{\ddagger}$ 11·1 kcal.mole^{-1}

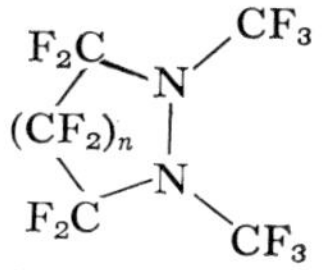

199   $n = 0, 1, 2$

the low temperature AB systems for the N-CF$_2$ group in the perfluoro-compounds (199) as n decreases.[261] The very high nitrogen inversion barriers in diaziridines ($\Delta G^{\ddagger}$ ca. 27 kcal.mole^{-1}) have been discussed and measurements for diazetidines would be of interest, but suitable compounds have not been reported. The nitrogen inversion barriers in the diazetidinones (200) are remarkably high in view of the aryl-substituent on the pyramidal nitrogen atom (N$_B$ see 200), it is assumed that inversion of the amide nitrogen (N$_A$ see 200) would be much too rapid to detect by NMR methods. These inversion barriers for (200) are based[262] upon the coalescence temperature of the AB system observed for the ring methylene group. The barrier for nitrogen inversion in (200) may be enhanced by the

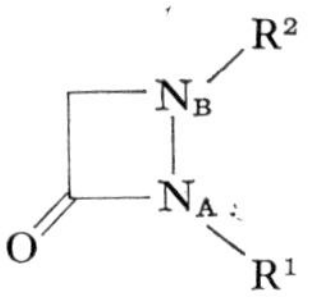

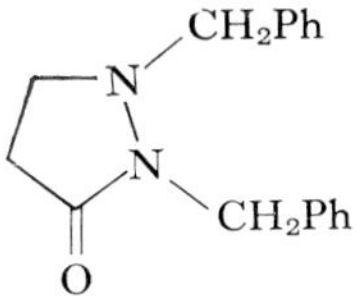

201   $\Delta G^{\ddagger}$ 13·1 kcal.mole^{-1}

	R^1	R^2	$\Delta G^{\ddagger}$ in Me$_2$CO kcal.mole^{-1}
200	m-C$_6$H$_4$CH$_3$	Ph	13
200a	p-C$_6$H$_4$CH$_3$	Ph	12·8
200b	Ph	o-C$_6$H$_4$CH$_3$	16
200c	Ph	m-C$_6$H$_4$CH$_3$	13·4
200d	Ph	p-C$_6$H$_4$CH$_3$	13·7
200e	Ph	Ph	13·3 (in C$_5$D$_5$N)

carbonyl substituent on N_B, since it has been shown[259] that the nitrogen inversion barrier in the pyrazolidinone (201) is considerably larger than that found in the corresponding pyrazolidine (198). Numerous reports have appeared concerning inversion barriers in cyclic diacylhydrazine derivatives,[252,253,263 to 272] and although these have sometimes been described as nitrogen inversion barriers they are more correctly related to the large torsional barriers found in acyclic diacylhydrazines. Since this type of conformational change has been discussed in other reviews it will be dealt with here only briefly. It is first convenient to consider the complex conformational changes, which may be examined by NMR methods, that occur in acyclic NN'-diacylhydrazines.[264] These are exemplified by the compound (202); the spectrum of this compound at 233°K shows four AB systems for the benzyl methylene groups and four ester methyl signals. These signals may be associated with the three diastereomers (203), (203a) and (203b) which differ in the rotational orientation about the N–CO bonds, each of these three conformations is non-planar owing to the preferred torsional situation about the N–N bond described by the projection formula (204). At 313°K the rotation about the N–CO bond is fast on the NMR time scale and a single AB system is observed for the methylene groups and a single signal for the ester methyl groups. The rotational barrier about the N–N bond is large and the AB system only collapses to a singlet at high temperatures (> 465°K). The barriers to rotation about the N–N bond in several diacylhydrazines (202 to 202e) are recorded in Table X. The origin of these large torsional barriers is, at least in part, due to the steric interactions in the planar, or near-planar, transition state for the rotational process, and comparison of the energy barriers for (202c) and (202d) and (202b) and (202e) provides a basis for this opinion. The recognition of these large torsional barriers in the acyclic systems leads to a clearer appreciation of the results found in cyclic systems. The latter may be divided into two structural types, the bridged bicyclic systems and the monocyclic systems. In the first type of cyclic diacylhydrazine, exemplified by compounds (205 to 210), it would be anticipated that the length of the bridge would affect the torsional barrier about the N–N bond. In addition to changes in the NMR spectrum associated with this torsional barrier a second type of change may also be detected associated with hindered rotation about the N–CO bond ($\Delta G^\ddagger$ in the range 13 ± 1 kcal.mole^{-1}) in the three rotational isomers (211), (211a) and (211b), designated[265] S2, DS and S1, and analogous to the isomers (203) for the acyclic systems. Thus compounds (205, 207, 208, 209 and 210) show a maximum of four ester methyl signals at low temperatures for the symmetrical systems (208) and (209) while the asymmetrical systems (205), (207) and (210) could in principle give up to eight methyl signals if both N–CO and N–N rotations are slow; in practice six signals are actually observed for (210). The second conformational change associated with the high torsional barrier about the N–N bond ($\Delta G^\ddagger$ 16 to 19 kcal.mole^{-1}) is, in these bicyclic compounds, a bridge inversion process, e.g.

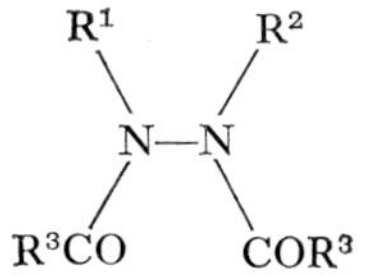

R¹   R²

N—N

R³CO   COR³

202 R¹ = R² = PhCH₂, R³ = OMe
202a R¹ = R² = PhCH₂, R³ = Me
202b R¹ = R² = R³ = PhCH₂
202c R¹ = R² = PhCH₂, R³ = Ph
202d R¹ = R² = CHMe₂, R³ = Ph
202e R¹ = R³ = PhCH₂, R² = H

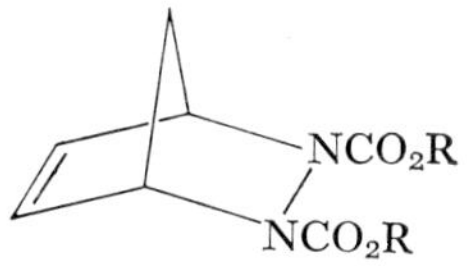

NCO₂R
NCO₂R

205 R = Me
205a R = Et

NCO₂Me
NCO₂Me

206

R¹ — N—N — R²
R³—C   C—R³
   ‖   ‖
   O   O

203

R¹ — N—N — R²
R³—C   C=O
   ‖ |
   O   R³

203a

R¹ — N—N — R²
O=C   C=O
   | |
   R³   R³

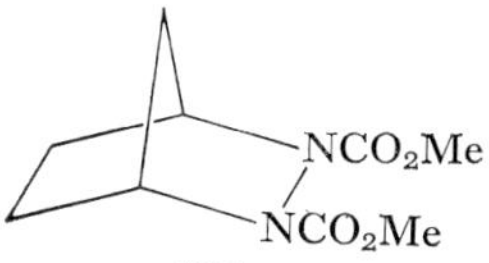

203b

R¹
|
R² — N — COR³
|
COR³

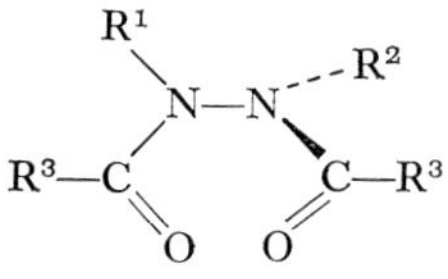

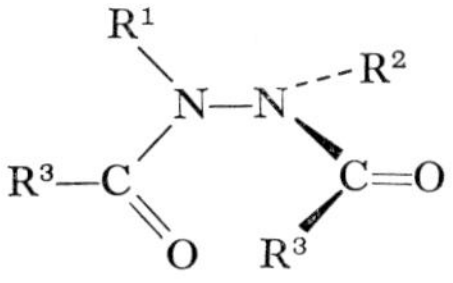

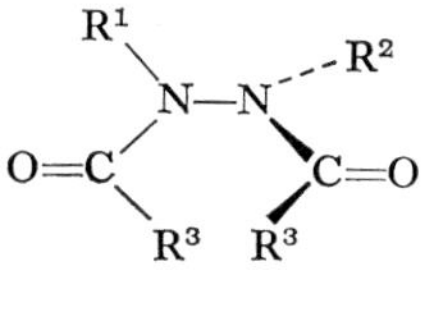

204

NCO₂R
NCO₂R

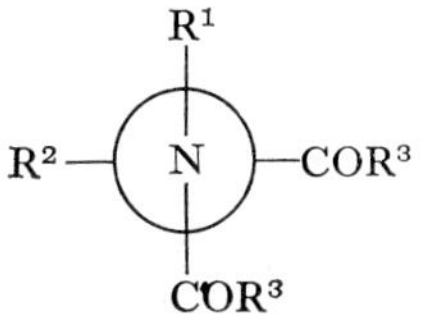

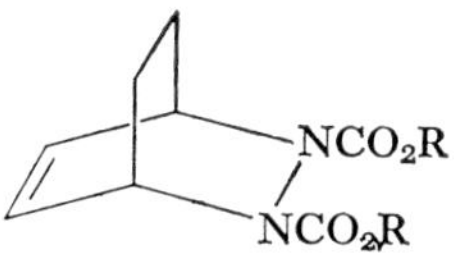

207 R = Me
207a R = Et

NCO₂R
NCO₂R

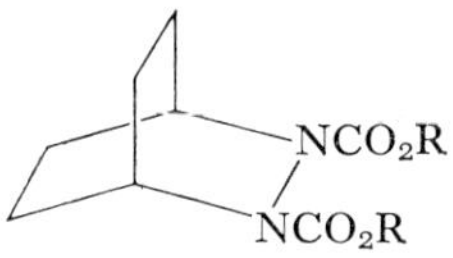

208 R = Me
208a R = Et

CO₂R
N
N
CO₂R

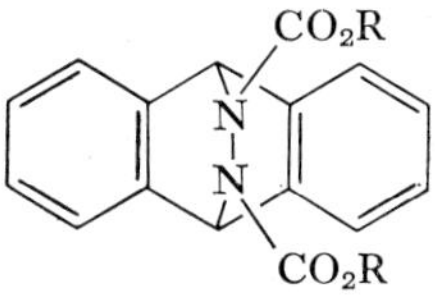

209 R = Me
209a R = Et

CO₂Me
N
N
CO₂Me

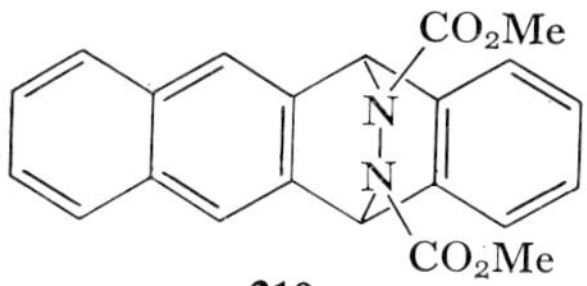

210

TABLE X

Conformational changes in NN'-diacyl hydrazines

Compound	$\Delta G^{\ddagger}$ kcal.mole^{-1}	E_a kcal.mole^{-1}	$\log_{10}A$	Reference
202	23·5			264
202a	23·4			264
202b	23.3			264
202c	19·6			264
202d	23·5			264
202e	14·8			264
205	13·7[a]	16·6	15·3	253, 265
205a	13·9[a]	15·4	14·0	266
206	13·7[a]	14·8	13·6	253
207	16·4 (CDCl$_3$)			265
	16·6 (D$_2$O)			265
207a	17·0			265
208a	19·0			265
209	12·6[a]			265
	13·4[a]			
209a	13·6[a]			267
	18·4	20·6	14·6	267
210	18·5	21·1	14·8	267
213	16·2[a]			268
214	11·8	8·0	10	269
217	14·8[a]			270
	18·5	($\Delta H^{\ddagger}$ 16·4 kcal.mole^{-1}, $\Delta S^{\ddagger}$ -7 e.u.)		270
217a	18·5			270
218	19·7			270
	13·9[a]			270
218a	20·3			270
219	16·7	($\Delta H^{\ddagger}$ 15·6 kcal.mole^{-1}, $\Delta S^{\ddagger}$ $-3·5$ e.u.)		270
220	19·4			270
220a	19·2			270
221	*ca.* 23			270

[a] These energy barriers refer to rotation about the N–CO bonds, the other energy barriers refer to rotation about the N–N bond or ring or bridge inversion processes.

(212)⇌(212a), which probably involves rotation about a twisted N–N bond in a distorted N–N bridge as in (212). This distortion presumably involves both twisting about the N–N bond and some departure from the normal trigonal geometry of the amide nitrogen atoms, and it is more feasible in the less rigid diazabicyclo-octane systems (207 to 210) than in the diazabicyclo-heptane systems (205) and (206). For the latter systems the observed temperature dependence of the NMR spectra may be entirely accounted for in terms of the amide rotational process. The distortion of the bridge depicted in (212) does have some effect on the amide rotational barrier which is generally a little lower in these bridged systems ($\Delta G^{\ddagger}$ *ca.* 13 kcal.mole^{-1})[255,267] than in the analogous acyclic

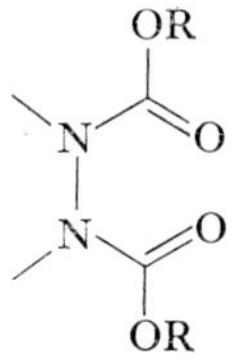

211 S2 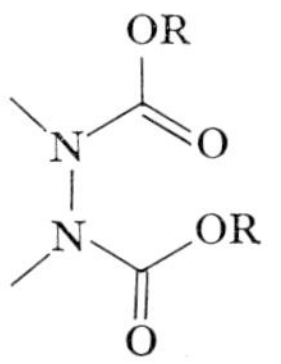   211a DS 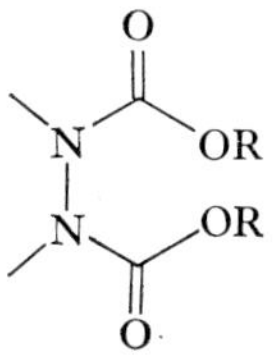   211b S1

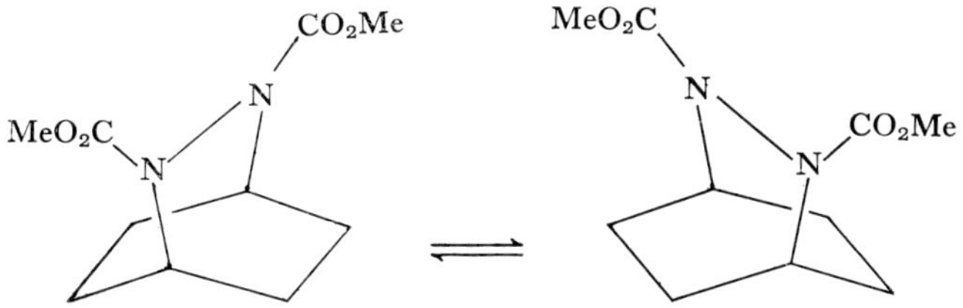

212   212a 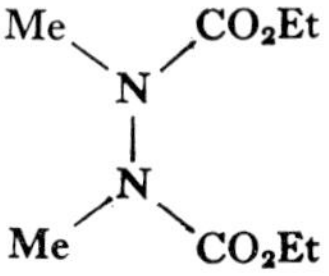   213

dialkoxycarbonyl hydrazine (213) ($\Delta G^{\ddagger}$ 16·2 kcal.mole^{-1}).[268] The temperature dependence of the ^{19}F spectrum of the diazetidine derivative (214), which shows an AA'BB' system for the ring fluorine substituents at low temperatures, was originally interpreted as evidence for a nitrogen inversion process,[269] but analogy with the bridged compounds suggests that the observable process, which averages the environments, A and B, of the fluorine atoms, should be regarded as ring inversion of a buckled four-membered ring with nearly trigonal nitrogen atoms (215). The monocyclic diacylhydrazine derivatives (217 to 220) show similar behaviour[263,266,270,271] but in these cases the barriers for the amide rotation are a little higher ($\Delta G^{\ddagger}$ 14 ± 1 kcal.mole^{-1}) than for the bridged systems, and the higher energy barrier ($\Delta G^{\ddagger}$ 16·7 to 23 kcal.mole^{-1}) must be associated with simultaneous rotation about the N–N bond and ring inversion. For full details of the observed spectral changes the original papers should be consulted;

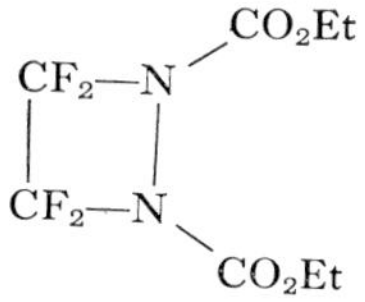

214 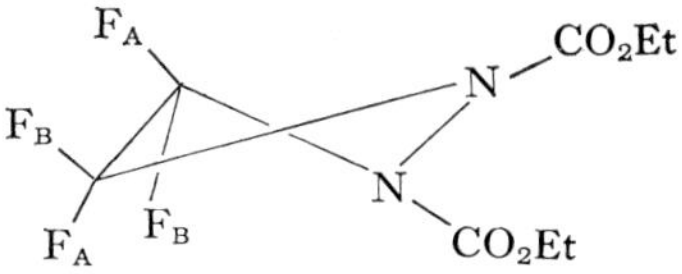   215

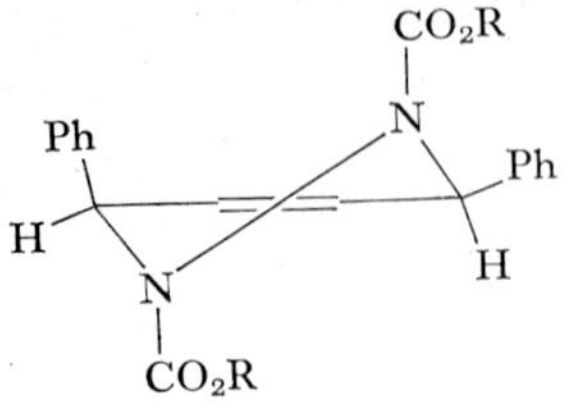

216

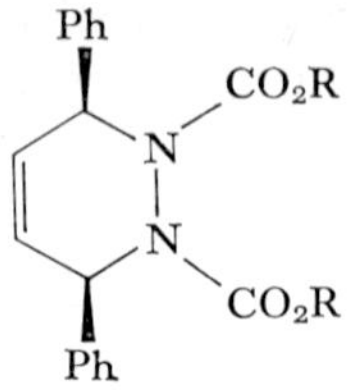

217   R = Me
217a R = Et

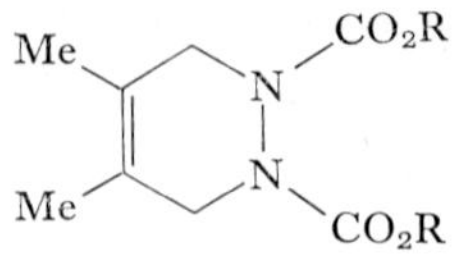

218   R = Me
218a R = Et

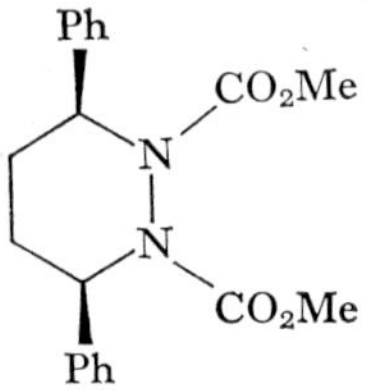

219

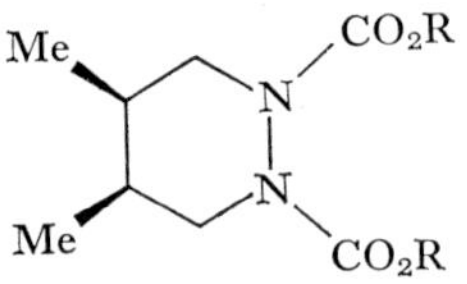

220   R = Me
220a R = Et

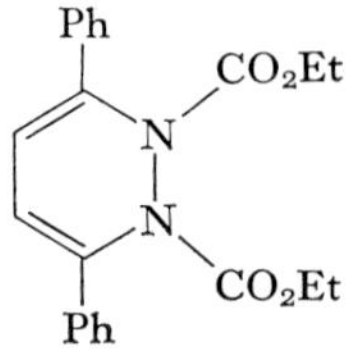

221

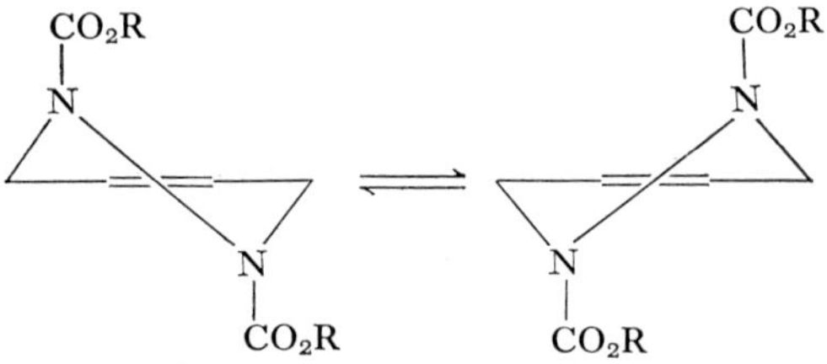

222

222a

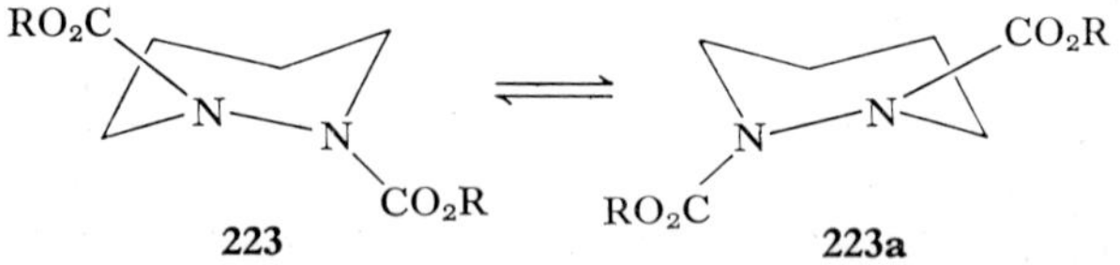

223

223a

the energy barriers[270] for the conformational changes are summarized in Table X. The observed[270] coupling constants for the tetrahydropyridazine (217) are consistent with the half-chair conformation (216), and the inversion process for compounds (217) and (218) must involve simultaneous inversion of the half-chair conformation and the configuration of the diacylhydrazine system (222)⇌(222a). The hexahydropyridazines (219) and (220) probably adopt a chair conformation analogous to that of cyclohexane and the inversion process (223)⇌(223a) again involves simultaneous inversion of the ring and the diacylhydrazine configuration. Inversion barriers in these NN'-diacylpyridazine systems are dominated by the large torsional barrier about the N–N bond of the diacylhydra-zine system, and this is also illustrated by the dihydropyridazine (221).[270] In this case the inversion barrier for the twisted conformation (224) is very high, in spite of the lack of angle strain associated with the planar transition state, and this large activation energy presumably results from the non-bonded interactions between the four vicinal substituents when these are coplanar.

The high conformational rigidity of these ring systems containing a diacylhy-drazine unit may provide a method for investigating conformational possi-bilities[267,270] in otherwise mobile systems. Thus the dibenzodiazocine (225) may adopt both chair (225) and boat (225a) conformations and the NMR spectrum at 308°K shows two AB systems for the ring-methylene protons,[267] consistent with the presence of both conformational types in solution, and with both the inter-conversion (225)⇌(225a) and the ring inversion process being slow on the NMR time-scale. Fresh examples of this phenomenon of conformational rigidity in diacylhydrazine systems continue to be described.[273]

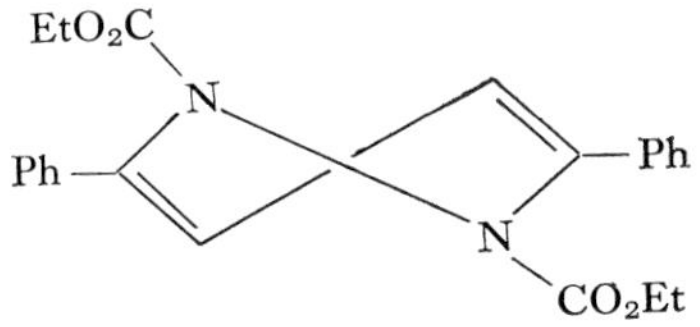

224

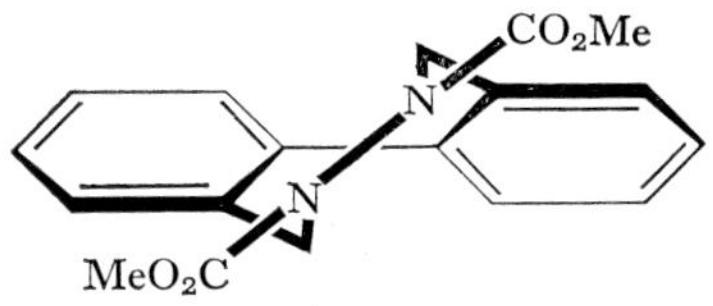

225

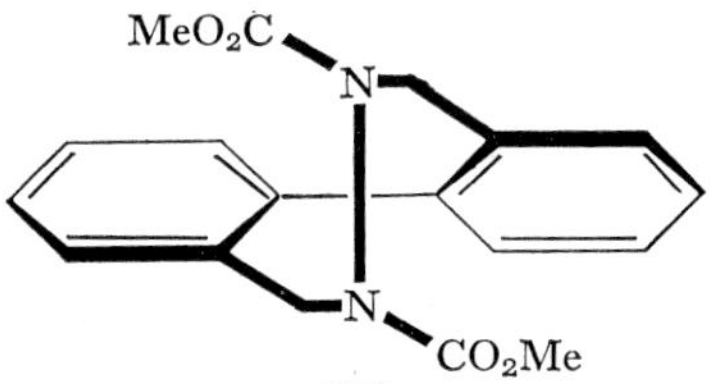

225a

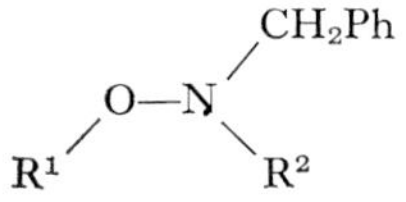

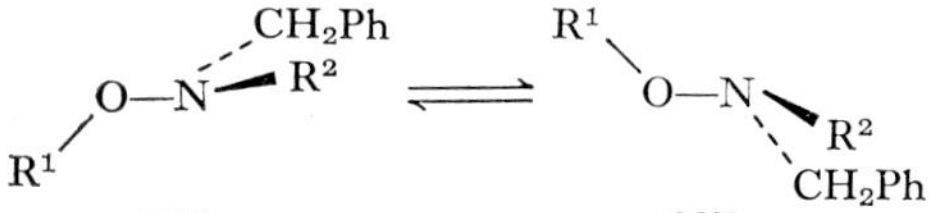

227

227a

226   R¹ = R² = Me
226a R¹ = Me, R² = CHMe₂
226b R¹ = CHMe₂, R² = Me
226c R¹ = H, R² = CH₂Ph
226d R¹ = H, R² = CHMe₂
226e R¹ = Ac, R² = CH₂Ph
226f R¹ = Ac, R² = CHMe₂

Hydroxylamine derivatives might be expected to show similar behaviour to hydrazine derivatives. It was originally suggested[274] that the low-temperature AB system observed for the benzyl methylene group of the hydroxylamine (226) was a consequence of hindered nitrogen inversion, but it was subsequently pointed out[275] that the hindered conformational change (227)⇌(227a), which could account for the low-temperature AB system, is a process in which either nitrogen inversion or rotation about the N–O bond could be the rate-determining step. On the basis of the small increase in the barrier associated with the increased steric demand of the isopropyl substituents in (226a) and (226b) it was argued that the barrier was primarily torsional in origin.[275] This argument is not valid, however, since examination[250] of the hydroxylamines (226c) and (226d) shows that the barrier separating conformations (227) and (227a) in these compounds is very similar to that found for (226a) and (226b) in spite of the replacement of the alkyl substituent on oxygen by a much smaller hydrogen atom. It has therefore been concluded[250] that the energy barriers for the conformational change (227)⇌(227a) are primarily nitrogen inversion barriers. The similarity of the barriers for the O-acetyl derivatives (226e) and (226f) with those for the di- and tri- alkyl hydroxylamines rules out the rather remote possibility that the process (227)⇌(227a) involves oxygen inversion. The effects of the hydroxylic solvent, deuteriomethanol, upon these inversion barriers (Table XI) are not easily

TABLE XI

Nitrogen inversion barriers in hydroxylamine derivatives

Compound	$\Delta G^{\ddagger}$ kcal.mole^{-1}	Solvent	Reference
226	12·3		274, 275
226a	12·8		275
226b	12·8		275
226c	12·8	CDCl$_3$	250
	12·2	MeOH-d_4	250
226d	12·9	CDCl$_3$	250
	12·4	MeOH-d_4	250
226e	12·1	CDCl$_3$	250
	12·3	MeOH-d_4	250
226f	12·0	CDCl$_3$	250
	12·3	MeOH-d_4	250

rationalized and it appears that solvent effects of this type cannot be reliably used to diagnose nitrogen inversion barriers.

The enhanced barrier to nitrogen inversion in acyclic hydroxylamines is reflected in the conformational behaviour of cyclic hydroxylamine derivatives.[276,277,278] The very high nitrogen inversion barriers found in oxaziridines have been discussed; the NMR spectra of the perfluoro-oxazetidine derivatives (228)[278] and (228a)[279] provide evidence for relatively large nitrogen inversion barriers in the four-membered ring systems, but the steric and electronic effects of the fluorine substituents are difficult to assess. The spectrum of the perfluoro-alkylhydroxylamine (299) at room temperature shows geminal non-equivalence of the fluorine atoms in the $-OCF_2-$ and $>NCF_2-$ groups which may be explained[280] in terms of hindered nitrogen inversion, but no quantitative estimate of the barrier height is available.

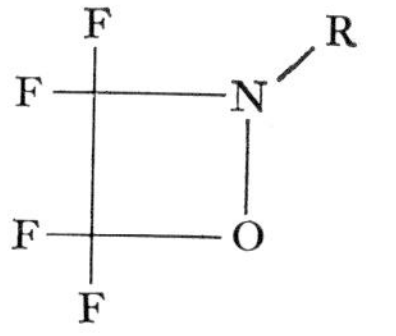

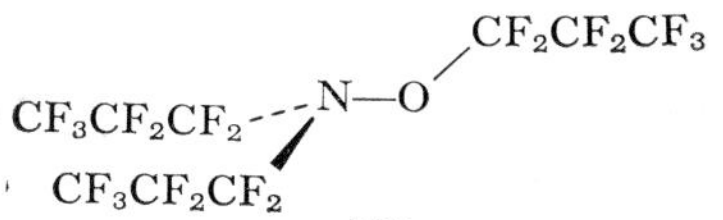

228 R = CF_3, $\Delta G^{\ddagger}$ ca. 10 kcal.mole^{-1}
228a R = CF_2CF_3

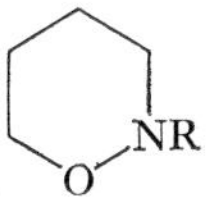

230   R = Me, $\Delta G^{\ddagger}$ 13·7 kcal.mole^{-1} (CH_2Cl_2)
                   $\Delta G^{\ddagger}$ 15·0 kcal.mole^{-1} (D_2O-CD_3OD)
230a R = $MeOCH_2$, $\Delta G^{\ddagger}$ 11·5 kcal.mole^{-1} (CH_2Cl_2)
230b R = $CHMe_2$, $\Delta G^{\ddagger}$ 12·5 kcal.mole^{-1} (CH_2Cl_2)

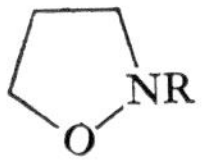

231 R = Me, $\Delta G^{\ddagger}$ 15·6 kcal.mole^{-1} ($CDCl_3$)
                   $\Delta G^{\ddagger}$ 16·9 kcal.mole^{-1} (D_2O)
231a R = $MeOCH_2$, $\Delta G^{\ddagger}$ 10·3 kcal.mole^{-1} (CH_2Cl_2)
231b R = $CHMe_2$, $\Delta G^{\ddagger}$ 14·8 kcal.mole^{-1} (CH_2Cl_2)

The tetrahydro-1,2-oxazines (230) and isoxazolidines (231) have been more fully examined. The energy barriers for (230) and (231) were based upon the coalescence of the geminally non-equivalent protons of the CH_2N group,[276] and are therefore approximate due to the additional coupling from the adjacent ring methylene group protons. The energy barriers for (230a), (231a), (230b) and

(231b) are more accurate, being based upon the coalescence of the simple AB system from the NCH$_2$OR group or of the non-equivalent methyl signals from the CHMe$_2$ group.[277] In the five-membered oxazolidine ring the observed conformational change must be a nitrogen inversion process, but in the six-membered ring either ring or nitrogen inversion could be the rate-determining step. The effects of hydroxylic solvents upon the inversion barriers is similar in both cases suggesting that in fact in both cases the nitrogen inversion process is rate determining.[276] The lowering of the barrier by the isopropyl substituent is consistent with this view, but the apparently much greater effect of the methoxy-methyl substituent in the five-membered ring system is puzzling.[277] Just as rotational barriers in diacylhydrazines are rather greater than those in alkylhydrazines it might be anticipated that the torsional barrier about the N–O bond would be greater in N,O-diacylhydroxylamines (232), with the twisted ground state conformation (233), than in alkylhydroxylamines, and of sufficient magnitude to be measured by NMR methods. This has been found to be the case,[281] and rotational barriers for the N,O-diacylhydroxylamines (232), (232a) and (232b) are listed; in all cases the low-temperature AB system from the benzyl methylene group coalesced to a singlet at higher temperatures. The measured rotational barriers are not very large (9·6 to 9·8 kcal.mole^{-1}) and this is not unexpected from a comparison of the interactions in the planar or near planar transition state for rotation in the hydroxylamines (232) and the NN'-diacylmonoalkylhydrazine (202e) ($\Delta G^{\ddagger}$ 14·8 kcal.mole^{-1} for rotation about the N–N bond). The rotational barriers listed for (232c) and (232d) refer to rotation about the N–CO bond, and the considerable lowering of this barrier, relative to that found in the corresponding NN-dialkylamides, may be a consequence of both the enhanced nitrogen inversion barrier in hydroxylamines as well as the inductive effect of the O-acyl substituent on nitrogen.

232 R^1 = CH$_2$Ph, R^2 = Ph, $\Delta G^{\ddagger}$ *ca.* 9·8 kcal.mole^{-1}
232a R^1 = CH$_2$Ph, R^2 = Me, $\Delta G^{\ddagger}$ 9·6 kcal.mole^{-1}
232b R^1 = R^2 = CH$_2$Ph, $\Delta G^{\ddagger}$ 9·6 kcal.mole^{-1}
232c R^1 = Me, R^2 = Ph, $\Delta G^{\ddagger}$ *ca.* 10·5 kcal.mole^{-1}
232d R^1 = R^2 = Me, $\Delta G^{\ddagger}$ 13·3 kcal.mole^{-1} (minor → major conformer)
                               $\Delta G^{\ddagger}$ 14·2 kcal.mole^{-1} (major → minor conformer)

The torsional and inversion barriers in hydrazines and hydroxylamines apply for situations in which neither atom has a vacant orbital for potential π-bonding involving the lone-pair electrons on the other atom. This is not necessarily the case for P–N and S–N bonds in which $3d$ orbitals are potentially available for

π-bonding, and the conformational changes reported for P–N and S–N derivatives show interesting differences to those reported for N–N and O–N. It is quite clear, from the study of aziridines, that nitrogen inversion barriers are lowered by bonding to sulphur and phosphorus[219,229] and it would be anticipated that conformational changes, detectable by line-shape methods, in substituted P–N and S–N systems are more likely to be associated with hindered rotation than with hindered nitrogen inversion. Thus, although the conformational changes in sulphenamides were originally erroneously assigned to a nitrogen inversion process, a definitive examination,[228] in which the nitrogen atom was placed in rings of varying size, showed that the observable conformational changes were associated with hindered rotation about the S–N bond being the rate-determining step in the process (234)⇌(234a), the stable conformation of sulphenamides being

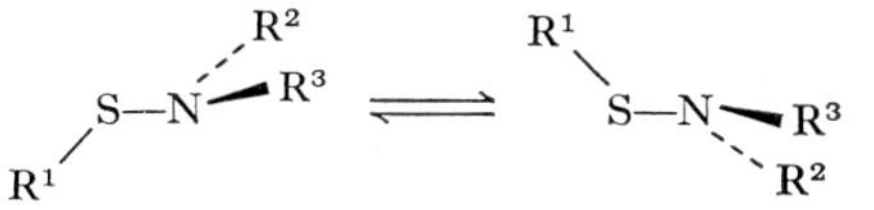

TABLE XII

Energy barriers for conformational changes in sulphenamides

Compound	$\Delta G^{\ddagger}$ kcal.mole^{-1}		Reference
235		9·1	228
235a		12·2	228
235b		13·4	228
235c		12·4	228
236		12·1	228
236a	<9	$(T_c < 173°K)$	228
237	>23	$(T_c > 433°K)$	228
237a		15·8	228
237b		18·1	228
238		14·9	228, 282
238a		14·4	282
238b		15·6	282
238c		16·0	228, 282
238d		16·9	282
239		17·8	282
239a		16·5	282
239b		11·8	282
239c		13·4	282
240		11·8	282

analogous to that of hydroxylamines. The conformational changes detectable in the *N*-sulphenylaziridines (235 to 235c) (Table XII) are assignable to hindered nitrogen inversion,[228] the effect of the substituents on the sulphur atom being quite different to the effects found for the same series of substituents in the *N*-sulphenylazetidines (236 to 236a), and the *N*-sulphenylpiperidones (237 to 237b). In the latter two series the observed conformational changes were therefore assigned to rotation about the N–S bond. As in the hydroxylamines either rotation or inversion may be the rate-determining step in the process (234)⇌ (234a) and the distinction has to be made by an examination of substituent effects. The increase in the energy barrier as the size of one of the substituents on the nitrogen atom is increased in the series of acyclic sulphenamides (238 to 238d)[228,282] confirms that the barrier is primarily rotational in origin in all the sulphenamides examined except the aziridine derivatives (235). The further observations of substantial barriers in the *N*-aryl derivatives (239 and 239a) and the *N*-sulphenylimide (240) confirm that these barriers are correctly assigned to the rotational process. The effects, upon these barriers, of the substituents on the sulphur atom are profound, as illustrated for example by the series of compounds (238c), (239a) and (239c) or the series (236) and (236a), and (237 to 237b). These effects are presumably partly steric in origin since larger substituents tend to increase the torsional barrier but there may also be important electronic effects. Evidence for hindered rotation in the sulphinamide (241) has been reported[283] but no details are available concerning the magnitude of the rotational barrier, the analogous sulphonamide (241a) does not give NMR evidence for hindered rotation, and it has also been reported that other sulphonamides show no evidence for hindered rotation about the N–S bond. The *N*-sulphenylsulphonamides (242), (243), (244) and (245) show temperature dependent NMR spectra which

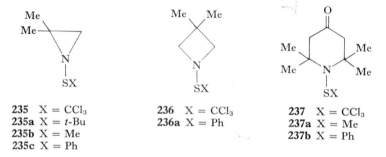

235 X = CCl₃
235a X = *t*-Bu
235b X = Me
235c X = Ph

236 X = CCl₃
236a X = Ph

237 X = CCl₃
237a X = Me
237b X = Ph

may be associated with hindered rotation about the N–S bond of the sulphenamide moiety,[284,285] and an extensive study of substituent effects has been made[285] (see Table XIII). It has been concluded that to some extent the magnitude of the torsional barrier depends upon the electron density at the sulphur atom, electron-withdrawing substituents causing an increase in the barrier, and

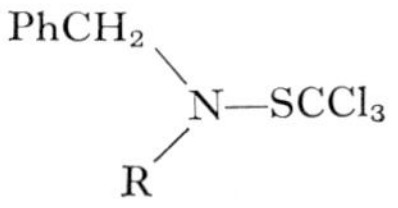

PhCH$_2$
\
    N—SCCl$_3$
/
R

238 R = CH$_2$Ph
238a R = Me
238b R = CH$_3$CH$_2$
238c R = CHMe$_2$
238d R = 1-adamantyl

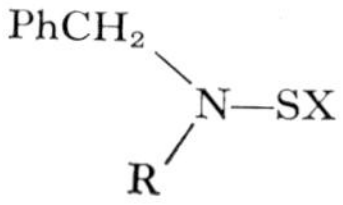

PhCH$_2$
\
    N—SX
/
R

239 X = 2, 4-dinitrophenyl, R = Ph
239a X = 2,4-dinitrophenyl, R = CHMe$_2$
239b X = CF$_3$, R = Me
239c X = CF$_3$, R = CHMe$_2$

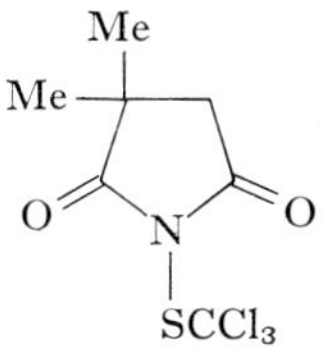

240

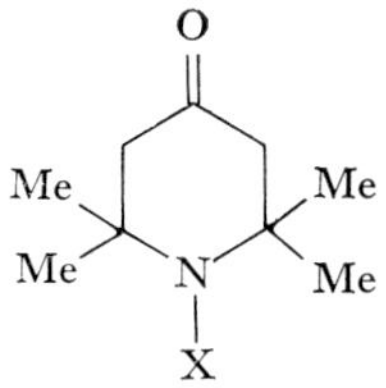

241 X = SOPh
241a X = SO$_2$Ph

that the extent of N to S electron donation is also important. In these studies both chiral (CHMePh) and prochiral (CHMe$_2$) substituents on the nitrogen atoms have been used as probes for the rotational process, in the first case the rotational

TABLE XIII

Rotational barriers in
N-sulphonylsulphena-
mides[284,285]

Compound	$\Delta G^{\ddagger}$ kcal.mole^{-1}
242	17·2
243	13·2
243a	12·9
243b	13·5
243c	13·9
243d	15·6
244	19·3
244a	19·1
244b	15·6
245	13·4
245a	13·5
245b	13·6
245c	13·4

process may be followed by the exchange of proton(s) between different environments in diastereomeric conformations. It is of interest that the sulphinyl carbanion (245), a system which is iso-electronic with the sulphinamide system, also
shows non-equivalence of the aromatic protons which is associated with restricted rotation about the C–S bond.[286] Further studies of the sulphinamides
and the related α-sulphinylcarbanions would be welcome in view of the extensive
discussions which have appeared[232,287] of steric and electronic effects in sulphur-
stabilized carbanions.

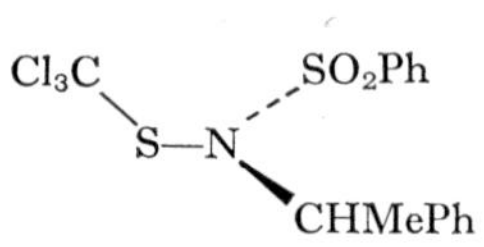

242

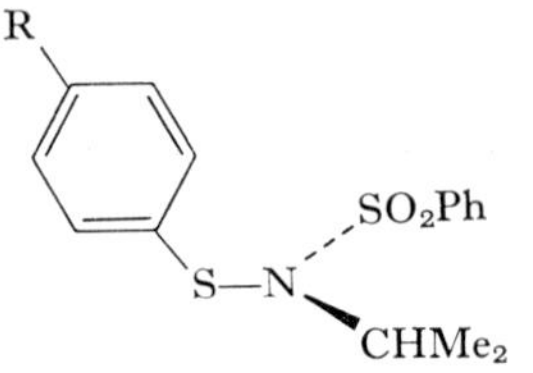

243 R = OMe
243a R = Me
243b R = H
243c R = Cl
243d R = NO$_2$

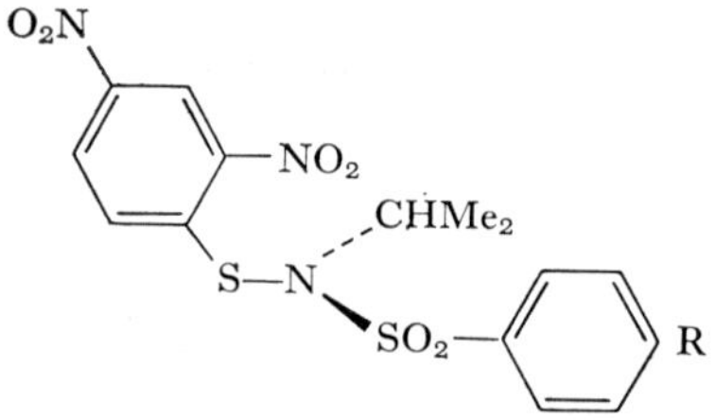

244 R = Me
244a R = H
244b R = NO$_2$

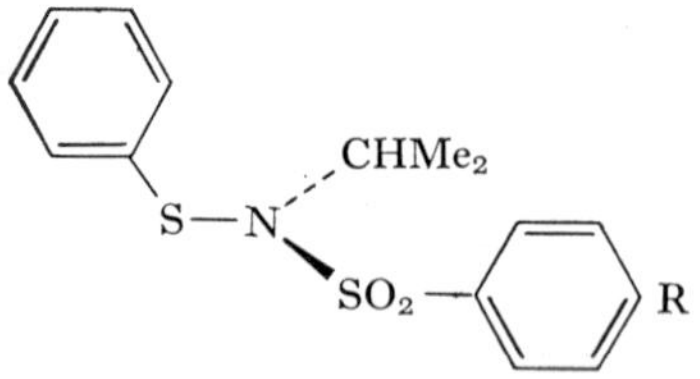

245 R = Me
245a R = H
245b R = Cl
245c R = NO$_2$

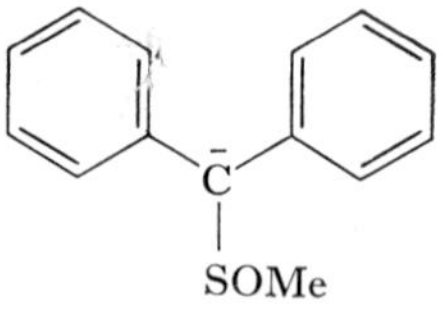

246

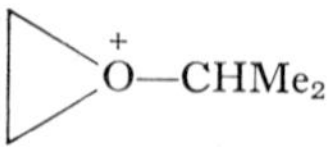

247

Inversion of the pyramidal configuration of tricovalent oxygen in oxonium
salts has also been studied,[288] and the inversion barrier for the salt (247) was
found to be considerably lower ($\Delta G^{\ddagger}$ ca. 10 kcal.mole^{-1}) than the nitrogen inversion barrier found in N-alkylaziridines ($\Delta G^{\ddagger}$ 15 to 20 kcal.mole^{-1}); hindered

inversion could not be detected in the corresponding four-, five- and six- membered cyclic oxonium salts. On the other hand it has been known for some time that inversion of the pyramidal configuration of tri-covalent sulphur,[289] phosphorus[290] and arsenic compounds normally involves an inversion barrier which is too large for measurements by NMR line-shape methods. It was anticipated that the inversion barriers would be lower in the diphosphine (248)[291] and diarsine (249),[292] owing to the effect of the aryl substituents and also to the possibility of p_π–d_π bonding (cf. the effects of P and S substituents on nitrogen inversion barriers). For both (248) and (249) the inversion process was detectable by NMR methods, since hindered inversion at the hetero-atoms resulted in a low-temperature spectrum which could be assigned to a mixture of two diastereomers, but at high temperatures inversion, resulting in the interconversion of these diastereomers, was sufficiently fast for signal coalescence to occur. The inversion barriers for both (248) ($\Delta G^\ddagger$ 24·3 kcal.mole^{-1}) and (249) ($\Delta G^\ddagger$ 25·3 kcal.mole^{-1}) are considerably lower than those found in simple phosphines and arsines. The spectra of these compounds did not show any effects attributable to hindered rotation about the P–P or As–As bonds.

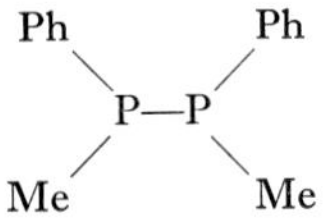

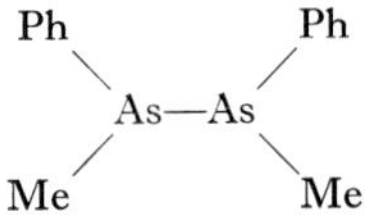

The large barriers to rotation about the S–N bond in sulphenamides have been discussed and similar rotational barriers have also been observed for aminophosphines.[293 to 296] Thus compounds of the general type $R^1PCl \cdot NR^2$ (250) show two sets of signals for the R^2 groups at low temperatures which coalesce at higher temperatures, and these changes are associated with the interconversion of the conformations (251) and (251a). The increase in the energy barriers,[294] as the size of the group R^2 increases, is consistent with a rotational barrier about the

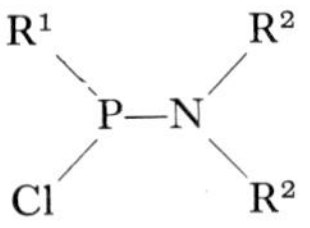

250 R^1 = Ph, R^2 = Me,
     $\Delta G^\ddagger$ 10·5 kcal.mole^{-1}
250a R^1 = Ph, R^2 = CH$_2$Ph
250b R^1 = Ph, R^2 = CHMe$_2$
250c R^1 = CH$_2$Cl, R^2 = Me
250d R^1 = CF$_2$CHCl$_2$, R^2 = Me
250e R^1 = CHMe$_2$, R^2 = Me

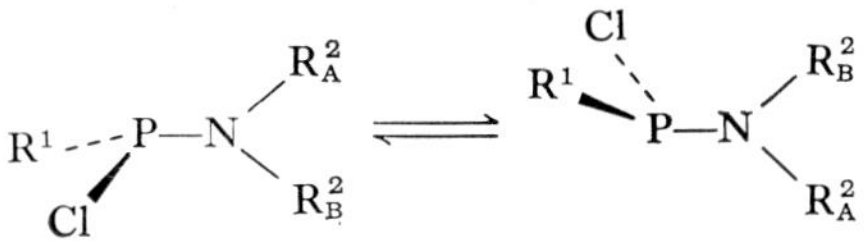

P–N bond, and it is also apparent from the non-equivalence of the prochiral ligands in the group R^1 in (250c), (250d) and (250e)[295] that the conformational change does not involve phosphorus inversion. The aminophosphines (252) and

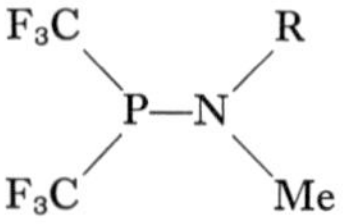

F$_3$C, R — P—N — F$_3$C, Me

Cl, Me — P—N — Cl, Me

252 R = D, $\Delta G^{\ddagger}$ 8·5 kcal.mole^{-1}
252a R = Me, $\Delta G^{\ddagger}$ 9·0 kcal.mole^{-1}

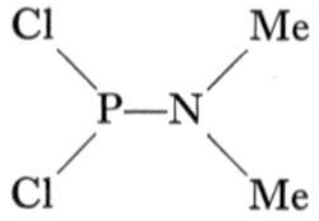

253 $\Delta G^{\ddagger}$ 8·4 kcal.mole^{-1}

(253) show changes in the spectra associated with rather lower rotational barriers,[296] but the symmetry of these compounds requires that the conformational change is that depicted in (251)⇌(251a) rather than an alternative process which had been considered involving P–N p_π–p_π bonding in the ground state. The conformation (251)≡(251a) is also consistent with the known crystal structure o Me$_2$N·PF$_2$.[297] It appears that the situation in the aminophosphines is rather similar to that found in the sulphenamides, and it is tempting to conclude that p_π–d_π bonding is involved. It has been noted[298] that although the phosphine sulphide (254) shows a temperature-dependent spectrum, which might at first sight be associated with an exchange process, the observed changes are in fact merely due to a temperature-dependent chemical shift difference between the diastereotopic methyl groups of the isopropyl-substituents. This observation underlines the importance of carrying out line-shape comparisons rather than restricting the examination to a qualitative detection of signal coalescence.

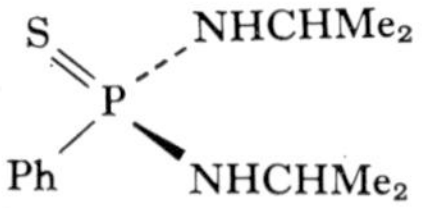

S, NHCHMe$_2$ — P — Ph, NHCHMe$_2$

254

R_2B—$\overset{..}{N}R_2$ ⟷ $R\overset{-}{B}$=$\overset{+}{N}R_2$

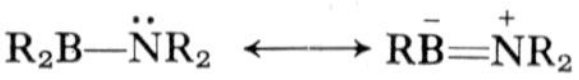

255

The B–N bond in aminoboranes has considerable double bond character, as emphasized by the canonical forms (255), and a number of studies have been made of rotational isomerism using NMR techniques.[299] The magnitudes of the rotational barriers have generally been expressed as the Arrhenius activation energy (E_a 10 to 25 kcal.mole^{-1}), and a considerable range of structural variation (256) has been examined. In view of the uncertainties concerning the significance of the Arrhenius parameter these results will not be discussed here. An interesting comparison has recently been made[300] of the rotational barriers about the B–N bonds in aminoboranes (257 to 259) and the C–N bond in the di-cation (260). The low barrier to rotation for the B–N bonds is said to reflect the higher polarization of the π-electrons in these as compared with the C–N bonds in (260).

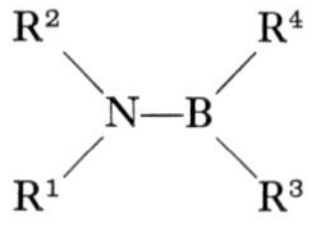

256 R^1, R^2 = alkyl or phenyl
R^3, R^4 = alkyl, phenyl, halogen
or alkoxy

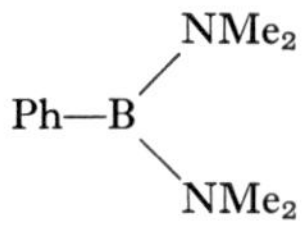

257 $\Delta G^{\ddagger}$ 9·9 kcal.mole^{-1}

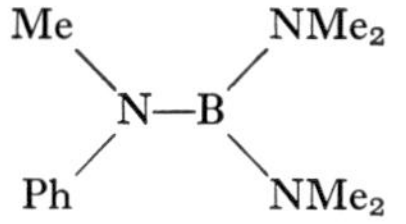

258 $\Delta G^{\ddagger}$ 12·7 kcal.mole^{-1}

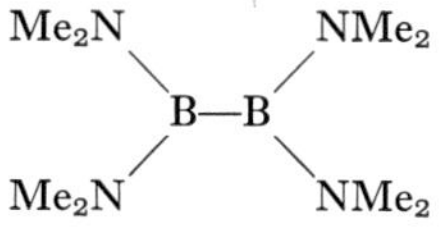

259 $\Delta G^{\ddagger}$ 10·5 kcal.mole^{-1}

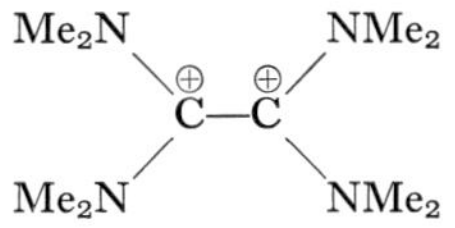

260 $\Delta G^{\ddagger}$ 19·6 kcal.mole^{-1}

The inversion of the configuration of non-planar carbanions is of interest from both theoretical and practical considerations. The inversion process in isolated carbanions cannot be studied, but a number of examinations have been reported of inversion at the primary carbon atom of various metal alkyls of the general type RCH_2M.[39,42,301,302] Much of the work,[39,41,42,301] has been concerned with the Grignard reagents $Me_3C \cdot CH_2 \cdot CH_2 \cdot MgCl$, $Et \cdot CHMe \cdot CH_2MgBr$ and $Me_2CH \cdot CHPh \cdot CH_2MgCl$, and it is evident from the results obtained that carbon inversion rates show a complex dependence upon solvent, concentration and the effects of added ions. They also suggest that the inversion process may involve bimolecular electrophilic displacement at the carbon atom attached to magnesium by the magnesium atom of a second molecule of Grignard reagent.[39,301] It is apparent that little or no information concerning carbanion inversion rates is available from these studies but the results for other metal alkyls may be more informative.[40,302] Typical results in these cases are shown below the structure (261). The inversion rates show a complex dependence upon the conditions used, but there is evidence that at least in some cases a unimolecular mechanism is involved, with probably metal–carbon bond cleavage as the rate-determining step and inversion of the solvated anion a relatively rapid process. The results therefore represent maximum values for carbanion inversion barriers in solution.[302] This work is also of interest because of the complexity of some of the spectral systems undergoing intramolecular site-exchange modification. Thus inversion in the $Me_3C \cdot CH_2 \cdot CH_2M$ case involves a change[40 to 42] from a low-temperature AA'XX' system to a high-temperature A_2X_2 system and the cases $Et \cdot CHMe \cdot CH_2M$[39] and $Me_2CH \cdot CHPh \cdot CH_2M$[42] are treated as low-temperature ABX systems changing to high-temperature A_2X systems. The approximations made in the generation of suitable line-shape equations give good agreement between observed and computed spectra and are apparently justified.

$$(Me_3C \cdot CH_2 \cdot CH_2)_nX$$

261

X	n	Solvent	E_a kcal.mole^{-1}	$Log_{10}A$	ΔG_{300} kcal.mole^{-1}
MgBr	1	Et_2O	11 ± 2	$9 \cdot 5 \pm 1 \cdot 5$	15·5
Mg	2	Et_2O	20 ± 2	$13 \pm 1 \cdot 5$	19·7
Li	1	Et_2O	15 ± 2	$13 \pm 1 \cdot 5$	14·7
Zn	2	Et_2O	26 ± 2	$16 \pm 1 \cdot 5$	21·6
Al	3	Et_2O ⎱ inversion rate too slow			
Hg	2	Et_2O ⎰ to be measured			
$Al(CH_2CHMeCH_2CH_2Me)_3$		$C_6H_5CH_3$	23·1	$(\Delta S^{\ddagger} + 2 \cdot 8$ e.u.$)$	23·3

A series of sulphonyl-stabilized alkali metal cyclopropyls (**262**) have also been studied[303] but again it is difficult to judge the effect of metal–carbon bonding upon the apparent inversion barriers. It was noted that a cyclopropyl Grignard reagent was configurationally stable on the NMR time-scale up to 448°K, and the inversion rates measured for these alkali metal derivatives are likely to approach the true inversion rates. The results suggest that inversion of tricovalent carbon in the benzenesulphonyl cyclopropylanion is rather slower than nitrogen inversion in N-benzenesulphonylaziridine ($\Delta G^{\ddagger}$ 12·4 kcal.mole^{-1}).[229]

$M^{\oplus}$	$\Delta G^{\ddagger}$ kcal.mole^{-1}	Solvent
Li	18·0	DMSO-THF (1:1)
Na	17·4	DMSO-THF (1:1)
Na	18·5	DMSO-THF (1:2)
K	16·6	DMSO-THF (1:2)

262

VI. INVERSION BARRIERS IN SYSTEM CONTAINING C=N

Syn-anti isomerism in oximes, phenylhydrazones, and other imines in which the nitrogen atom bears a hetero-atom substituent, has been recognized for many years, but geometrical isomers of simple imines were not isolated until 1961.[304] For compounds of the general type Ar_2C=NX the rate of isomerization (**263**)$\rightleftharpoons$ (**263a**) depends markedly upon the nature of the group X, and is[305] for example 10^{14} times faster for X=Ph than for X=OMe. It is therefore possible to study *syn-anti* isomerism both by direct equilibration of diastereoisomers and by NMR line-shape methods. The isomerization process **(263)**⇌**(263a)** may involve either inversion of the sp^2 hybridized nitrogen atom by way of a transition state

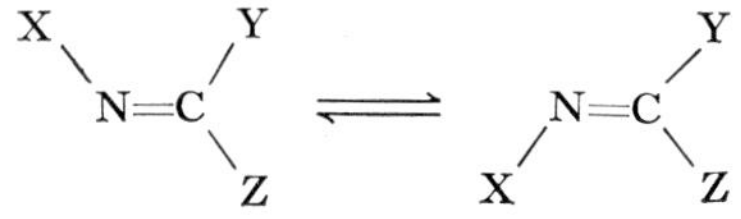

263   **263a**

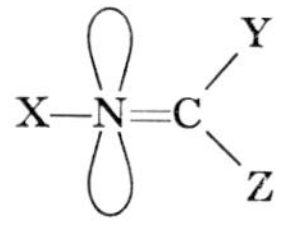

264 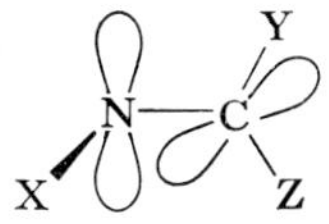   **265**

(264) with an sp hybridized nitrogen atom (the lateral shift mechanism), or may involve rotation about the C–N double bond with a dipolar or diradical transition state **(265)** in which the NX group lies in a plane orthogonal to the Y–C–Z plane (bond rotation mechanism). The distinction between these two mechanisms has been the subject of much discussion, but from the general effects of the substituents X, Y and Z (Table XIV) it now appears that most, if not all, cases involve the lateral shift mechanism. Early investigations[305] showed that *syn-anti* isomerism could be studied in the triarylimines **(266)** by NMR line-shape methods and that in general the magnitude of the isomerization barrier was sensitive to the effects of the *p*-substituents in the *N*-aryl unit (Table XIV). This result, combined with the high configurational stability of the imines **(267)** and the relatively high configurational stability of the imines **(268)**, strongly suggests a lateral shift mechanism. The effects of the substituents upon the inversion rate of sp^2 hybridized nitrogen are thus parallel to the effects of similar substituents upon the inversion rate of sp^3 hybridized nitrogen (see Section V).

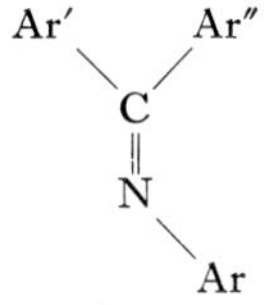

266 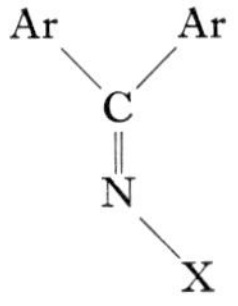   **267** X = OR, Cl, Br   **269**
                 268 X = Me

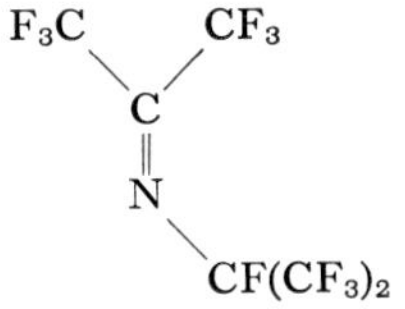

It has also been shown[306] that electron attracting perfluoroalkyl substituents on the nitrogen atom, as in compound **(269)**, lower the isomerization barrier, an effect which is consistent with a process involving primarily nitrogen inversion, and similar results have been reported for another perfluoroimine.[307] The steric effects of substituted aryl-substituents on the nitrogen atom tend to decrease the isomerization barrier[308] (Table XIV), a result which is again more consistent with an inversion rather than a rotation mechanism. The general lowering of the

TABLE XIV

Nitrogen inversion barriers in amines, iminocarbonates, iminothiocarbonates and guanidines

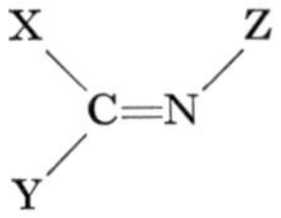

$$\begin{array}{c} X \qquad\qquad Z \\ \diagdown\qquad\diagup \\ C{=}N \\ \diagup \\ Y \end{array}$$

X	Y	Z	$\Delta G^{\ddagger}$ kcal.mole^{-1}	Reference
Ar	Ar	Me	25–27	305
p–C$_6$H$_4$OMe	p–C$_6$H$_4$OMe	p–C$_6$H$_4$NMe$_2$	19·5	305
p–C$_6$H$_4$OMe	p–C$_6$H$_4$OMe	p–C$_6$H$_4$Me	18·7	305
p–C$_6$H$_4$OMe	p–C$_6$H$_4$OMe	Ph	18·1	305
p–C$_6$H$_4$OMe	p–C$_6$H$_4$OMe	p–C$_6$H$_4$CO$_2$Et	16·2	305
p–C$_6$H$_4$OMe	Ph	p–C$_6$H$_4$Cl	19·7	305
Me	Me	CH$_2$Ph	> 23	310
Me	Me	CN	18·9	311
Me	Me	Ph	21, 20·3	310, 308
Me	Me	2,6–C$_6$H$_3$Me$_2$	19·2	308
Me	Me	2,5–C$_6$H$_3$(t-Bu)$_2$	19·4	308
Me	Me	2,4,6–C$_6$H$_2$(i-Pr)$_3$	18·8	308
Me	Me	2,4,6–C$_6$H$_2$(t-Bu)$_3$	18·4	308
CF$_3$	CF$_3$	CF(CF$_3$)$_2$	$ca.$ 13	305
MeCO	MeCO	Ph	19·4	308
MeO	MeO	Cl	> 24	309, 312
MeO	MeO	CH$_2$Ph	19·3	310
MeO	MeO	CN	14·1	311
MeO	MeO	Ph	14·3, 14·4	309, 310, 312
MeO	MeO	p–C$_6$H$_4$Me	14·6	309
MeO	MeO	p–C$_6$H$_4$Cl	14·4	309, 312
MeS	MeS	Me	18·6	312
MeS	MeS	CN	14·0, 14·5	311, 312
MeS	MeS	Ph	13·7, 13·8	310, 312
Me$_2$N	Me$_2$N	CN	< 10	311
Me$_2$N	Me$_2$N	Ph	12·1 (12·9)^a	310, 313
Me$_2$N	Me$_2$N	p–C$_6$H$_4$NMe$_2$	13·7 (13·7)^a	313
Me$_2$N	Me$_2$N	p–C$_6$H$_4$OMe	13·5 (13·8)^a	313
Me$_2$N	Me$_2$N	p–C$_6$H$_4$Me	12·6 (13·1)^a	313
Me$_2$N	Me$_2$N	p–C$_6$H$_4$F	12·6 (13·1)^a	313
Me$_2$N	Me$_2$N	p–C$_6$H$_4$Cl	11·8 (12·4)^a	313

TABLE XIV (*continued*)

X	Y	Z	$\Delta G^{\ddagger}$ kcal.mole^{-1}	Reference
Me$_2$N	Me$_2$N	p–C$_6$H$_4$Br	11·7 (12·3)^a	313
Me$_2$N	Me$_2$N	p–C$_6$H$_4$CO$_2$Me	9·9 (10·8)^a	313
Me$_2$N	Me$_2$N	p–C$_6$H$_4$COMe	9·4 (10·2)^a	313
Me$_2$N	Me$_2$N	p–C$_6$H$_4$CN	9·4 (10·6)^a	313
Me$_2$N	Me$_2$N	p–C$_6$H$_4$NO$_2$	7·6 (9·5)^a	313
Me$_2$N	Me$_2$N	o–C$_6$H$_4$Me	11·9 (12·7)^a	313
Me$_2$N	Me$_2$N	2,4–C$_6$H$_3$Me$_2$	12·3 (13·3)^a	313
Me$_2$N	Me$_2$N	2,6–C$_6$H$_3$Me$_2$	11·9 (13·1)^a	313
Me$_2$N	Me$_2$N	2,4,6–C$_6$H$_2$Me$_3$	12·6 (13·7)^a	313
Me$_2$N	Me$_2$N	2,6–C$_6$H$_3$Et$_2$	11·5 (13·5)^a	313
Me$_2$N	Me$_2$N	2,4,6–C$_6$H$_2$Et$_3$	11·9 (13·3)^a	313
Me$_2$N	Me$_2$N	2,4,6–C$_6$H$_2$(i-Pr)$_3$	11·4 (13·0)^a	313
MeN·CH$_2$·CH$_2$NMe		CH$_2$Ph	< 12	310
MeN·CH$_2$·CH$_2$NMe		Ph	< 12	310

^{a} The first value refers to a solution in CS$_2$-CDCl$_3$ and the value in brackets to solution in CD$_3$OD.

barrier by conjugating substituents on both the nitrogen atom (see Table XIV, Z=Ar,CN) and the carbon atom (see Table XIV, X and Y=COR, Ar, OMe, NMe$_2$, SMe) has been examined in a number of publications[305,309 to 313] and the observed effects have been rationalized in terms of either a rotation mechanism[309,310] or a lateral shift (inversion) mechanism.[311 to 313] The arguments used will not be detailed here since it is evident that either transition state (264) or (265) would be stabilized by the conjugating effects of the substituents X, Y and Z. The recent comparison[313] of substituent effects upon the isomerization barriers in a series of *N*-arylguanidines (270, and see Table XIV) and *N*-aryl-guanidinium trifluoroacetates (271, and see Table XV) is more definitive and provides strong evidence for a lateral shift mechanism for isomerization in the compounds (270). Thus, in a series of *para*-substituted *N*-aryltetramethyl-guanidines (270), there is a roughly linear relationship[313] between the free energy barrier for *syn-anti* isomerism and the Hammett constant (σ_p) for the

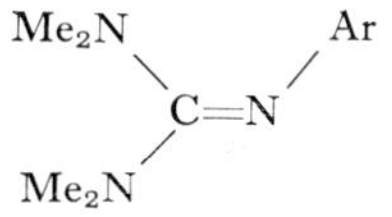

270

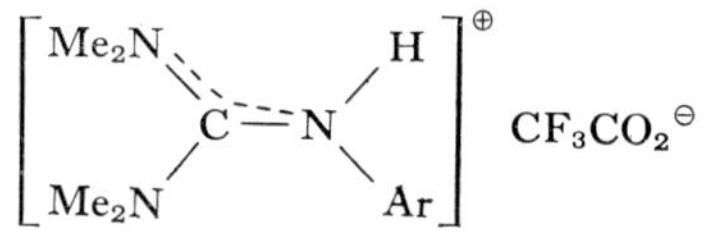

271

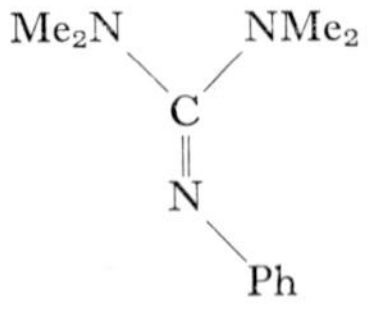

$$Me_2N \diagdown \diagup NMe_2$$
$$C$$
$$\|$$
$$N$$
$$\diagdown Ph$$

272

Solvent	Dielectric Constant	$\Delta G^{\ddagger}$ kcal.mole^{-1}
CS$_2$	2·6	12·1
CDCl$_3$	4·7	11·9
(CD$_3$)$_2$CO	20·7	12·0
CD$_3$CN	37·5	12·0
CD$_3$OD	34·0	12·6

substituent. This is the anticipated result for a transition state involving *sp* hybridized nitrogen and contrasts with the results found for the ArN–C rotational barrier (Table XV, bond *a*) in the analogous series of *N*-arylguanidinium

TABLE XV

Rotational barriers about the C–N bonds of *N*-aryl-*N'N''*-dimethylguanidinium salts in trifluoroacetic acid[313]

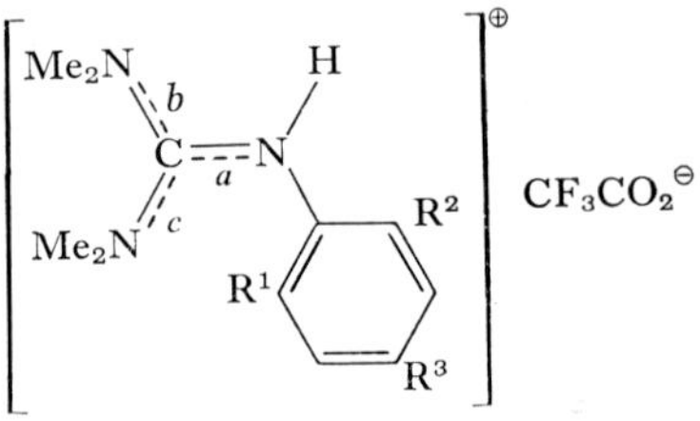

R^1	R^2	R^3	$\Delta G^{\ddagger}$ (kcal.mole^{-1}) for rotation		
			Bond *a*	Bond *b*	Bond *c*
H	H	NMe$_2$	12·9	12·6	10·5
H	H	OMe	13·0	12·6	10·4
H	H	Me	12·7	12·7	11·0
H	H	H	12·5	12·9	11·2
H	H	F	12·6	12·9	10·6
H	H	Cl	12·4	12·8	11·2
H	H	Br	12·2	12·6	11·1
H	H	CO$_2$Me	12·0	12·0	11·4
H	H	COMe	11·9	12·3	11·7
H	H	CN	11·9	12·0	
H	H	NO$_2$	11·6	12·1	
Me	H	H	12·7	12·3	
Me	H	Me	13·1	12·0	
Me	Me	H	13·0	11·8	
Me	Me	Me	15·4	11·3	10·8
Et	Et	H	15·5	11·0	10·3
Et	Et	Et	15·6	10·8	10·2
i-Pr	*i*-Pr	*i*-Pr	16·5	11·0	10·3

salts (271). Furthermore[313] the steric effects of highly substituted N-aryl substituents differ in the two series, whereas the rotational barrier in the guanidinium salts is increased by large *ortho*-substituents the isomerization barrier in the guanidines is, if anything, slightly decreased. The examination of solvent effects[313] also supports the inversion mechanism, thus barriers are generally increased by deuteriomethanol (Table XIV) but are not affected by changes in the solvent dielectric constant (results listed by formula 272). In view of this excellent evidence for a lateral shift mechanism for guanidine isomerization it seems reasonable to suppose that imines in general isomerize by the same mechanism unless evidence to the contrary is available.

As might be expected, similar *syn-anti* isomerism is observed for quinone anils,[314] for example (273), where isomerization is detectable by the averaging of the A and B environments of the quinonoid protons. This process presumably also involves nitrogen inversion ($\Delta G^{\ddagger}$ *ca.* 20 kcal.mole^{-1}), but the much lower barrier[314] to *syn-anti* isomerism for the bis-N-oxide (274) ($\Delta G^{\ddagger}$ *ca.* 12 kcal.mole^{-1}) must involve rotation about the C–N double bonds and reflects the stabilization of a bis-nitroxide diradical transition state for the rotational process.

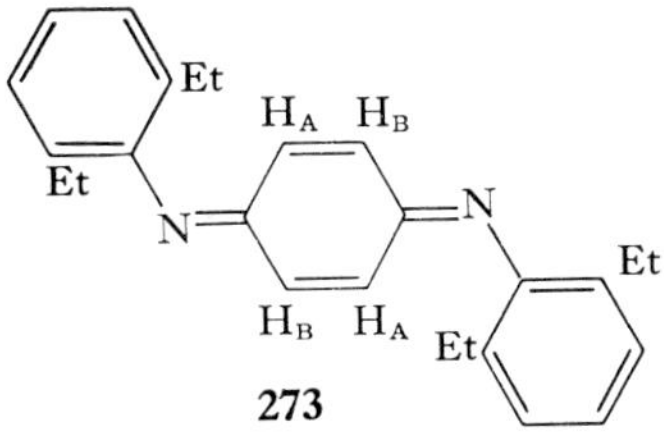

273

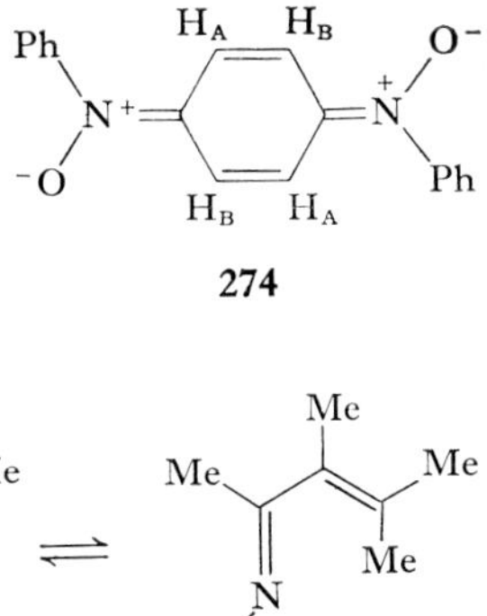

274

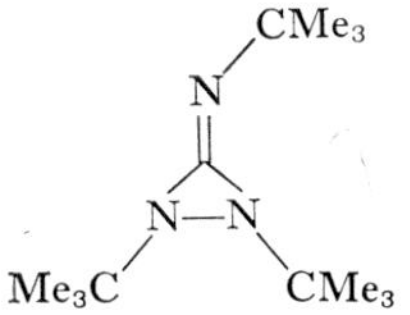

275

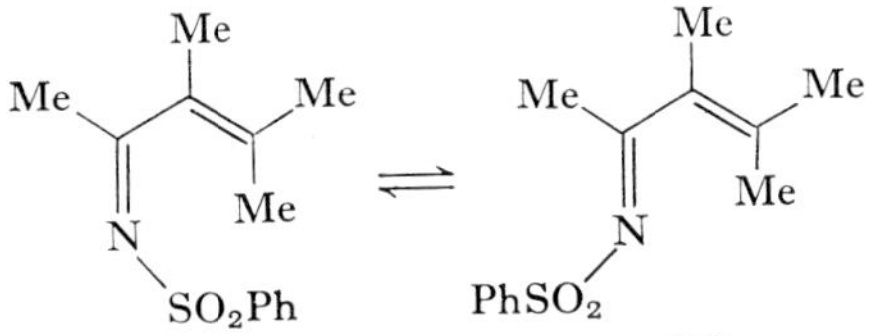

276

276a

The diaziridine derivative (275) has also been studied[315] and the barrier to *syn-anti* isomerism ($\Delta G^{\ddagger}$ 17·4 kcal.mole^{-1}) demonstrates the decreased conjugative ability of the nitrogen atoms of the three-membered ring as compared with the nitrogen atoms of the acyclic guanidines (270). The N-benzenesulphonylimine (276) is of interest[316] in that a single diastereomer (276 or 276a) crystallizes from solution, and *syn-anti* isomerism may be studied by NMR spectroscopy over the temperature range 215·5 to 220·5°K using a solution prepared at 203°K and observing the rate of appearance of the second diastereomer (276a or 276). At higher temperatures the energy barrier may be examined by

NMR line-shape methods, and using $\Delta G^{\ddagger}$ obtained by the two different methods rather accurate values of $\Delta H^{\ddagger}$ and $\Delta S^{\ddagger}$ are obtainable ($\Delta G^{\ddagger}_{324}$ 16·3 kcal.mole^{-1}, $\Delta H^{\ddagger}$ 15·7 kcal.mole^{-1}, $\Delta S^{\ddagger}$ −2 e.u.). The authors suggest[316] that the interconversion is primarily a torsional process in view of the rather slower isomerization of acetone anil ($\Delta G^{\ddagger}$ 20·3 kcal.mole^{-1}) since the inversion rates of N-phenylaziridine and N-benzenesulphonylaziridine are similar. This conclusion ignores the conjugative effect of the double bond in the side chain of (**276**), and in any case it is not clear whether substituent effects in systems as widely different as aziridines and imines may be compared in this way.

VII. ROTATIONAL BARRIERS ABOUT SINGLE AND DOUBLE BONDS

A large number of rotational barriers have been studied by NMR methods and a review has appeared[5] describing some of the results. Rotational barriers may be conveniently divided into four types. The first type involving bonds between atoms having non-bonded electron pairs has been discussed in Section V. The second type concerns rotation about single bonds in unconjugated systems where the rotational barrier is primarily steric in origin. The third type involves rotational barriers about formal single bonds in conjugated systems, the best known example of this type of rotational barrier being that for the C–N bond of amides. The fourth type of rotational barrier is for rotation about double bonds, normally this is too slow for study by NMR line-shape methods but in a number of conjugated systems the barrier is sufficiently lowered to come within the range accessible to NMR techniques.

A. C–C and C–X single bonds

The origin of the torsional barrier in ethane is difficult to explain within the normal terminology of organic chemistry, although explanations have been offered based upon the results of quantum mechanical calculations. The magnitudes of rotational barriers of this type are usually too small to be studied by NMR techniques unless increased by the presence of bulky substituents. A number of such cases have been recognized, but in general the spectral changes associated with the hindered rotation are rather complex and the first detailed kinetic study[43] was carried out shortly after the development of line-shape equations for intramolecular exchange in coupled systems.[32] This work[43] is of particular interest in that exchange rates were obtained by the comparison of observed and computed spectra for the most complex systems studied at that time. The various rotational barriers found for a variety of halogenated ethanes are recorded in Table XVI, the value of $\Delta G^{\ddagger}$ in this Table is given relative to the minimum energy conformation of the ethane derivative. The rotational barrier in FCCl$_2$—CHCl$_2$ has been studied[62] by both steady-state and spin-echo methods and good agreement was obtained for activation parameters measured by both techniques, a similar study of $BrCF_2-CBrCl_2$ by spin-echo methods[63] also gave satisfactory agreement with the earlier,[43] and less complete, study by the steady-state technique. Two further papers on halogenated ethanes have appeared recently. The first[48] discusses a complete examination of $CHBr_2-CFBr_2$ by total line-shape comparison, and the second[317] an approximate study of rotational barriers about the CF_3-C bonds in both the *trans* and *gauche* conformations of $CF_3CCl_2-CCl_2CF_3$. The results of these various studies, listed in Table XVI,

TABLE XVI

Rotational barriers in ethane derivatives

Compound	$\Delta G^{\ddagger a}$ kcal.mole^{-1}	Eclipsed pairs of substituents in transition state	Method	Reference
$CF_2Br-CHBrCl$	$\geqslant 7\cdot8$	Br, Cl; Br, F; H, F	TLS	43
	$\geqslant 7\cdot8$	Br, Br; Cl, F; F, H		
	$6\cdot9$	Br, F; Br, H; Cl, F		
$(CF_3-CCl_2)_2$	*ca.* 6^b	F, Cl; F, Cl; F, $CCl_2\cdot CF_3$	Approximate	317
	ca. 8^c			
$CF_2Br-CFBr_2$	$7\cdot7$	Br, F; Br, F; F, Br	TLS	43
	$9\cdot9$	Br, Br; Br, F; F, F		
$CF_2Br-CFClBr$	$7\cdot9$	Br, F; Br, F; Cl, F	TLS	43
	$\geqslant 8\cdot8^d$	Br, Br; Cl, F; F, F		
	$\geqslant 8\cdot8^d$	Br, Cl; Br, F; F, F		
$CFCl_2-CFCl_2$	$9\cdot65$	Cl, Cl; Cl, F; Cl, F	TLS	43
$CFClBr-CFClBr$	$10\cdot1$	Br, Cl; Br, F; Cl, F	TLS	43
	$\geqslant 12\cdot0^d$	Br, Br; F, F; Cl, Cl		
	$9\cdot9$	Br, F; Br, F; Cl, Cl		
	$\geqslant 10\cdot6^d$	Cl, F; Cl, F; Br, Br		
	$\geqslant 10\cdot6^d$	Cl, Br; Cl, Br; F, F		
$CFCl_2-CHCl_2$	$9\cdot1$	F, Cl; H, Cl; Cl, Cl	TLS and spin echo	43, 63
$CFBr_2-CHBr_2$	$10\cdot0^g$	F, Br; H, Br; Br, Br	TLS	48
$CF_2Br-CCl_2Br$	$11\cdot0^e$	Cl, F; Br, F; Br, Cl	TLS and spin echo	62, 43
	$12\cdot0^f$	Cl, F; Cl, F; Br, Br		

^{a} For the bond indicated in the formula and between the conformers indicated by the listed transition-state interactions.

^{b} For the *gauche* conformation (**277**).

^{c} For the *trans* conformation (**277a**).

^{d} No definite value assignable.

^{e} For *trans* → *gauche*.

^{f} For *gauche* → *gauche*.

^{g} Shown to be solvent dependent, the value stated refers to a $CFCl_3$ solution.

show that the ethane rotational barrier is increased, as expected, as the size of the halogen substituents is increased. Although transition-state interactions may be recognized in terms of eclipsed pairs of substituents (see Table XVI) the magnitudes of these interactions apparently vary from molecule to molecule and it is not possible to assign a magnitude to the interaction of any particular pair of eclipsed substituents.[43]

Hindered rotation of t-butyl groups attached to sp^3 hybridized carbon has been observed in a number of situations. The NMR spectra of the t-butyl substituents in the cycloalkanes (278) gave 2:1 doublet signals at low temperatures,[318] due to hindered rotation about the $Me_3C–C(1)$ bond associated with the conformational situation (279). Rotational barriers of this type, which are based upon coalescence temperatures and must therefore be regarded as approximate, seem to be rather smaller in the cyclopentane and cyclohexane derivatives than for the larger ring systems. The di-t-butylcyclohexadienones (280) show two

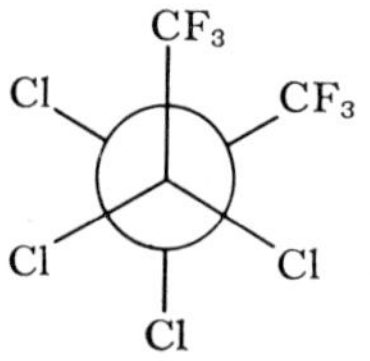

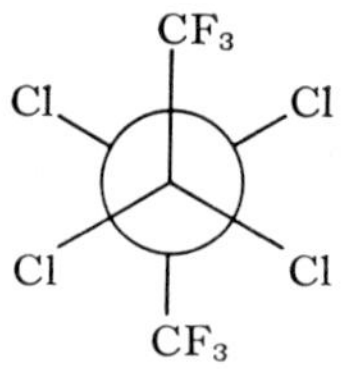

n	$\Delta G^{\ddagger}$ kcal.mole^{-1}
4	ca. 6·0
5	ca. 6·3
6	7·4
7	7·8
8	7·3
9	7·3

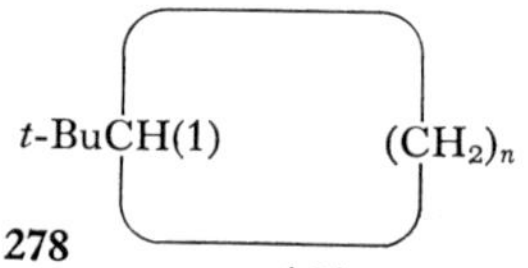

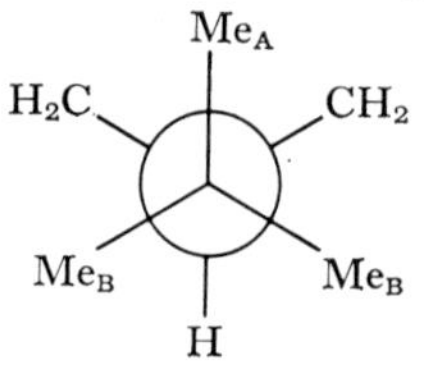

types of structural change which may be detected by the temperature dependence of the NMR spectra.[319] The first is associated with the migration of the bromine substituent from position 2 to position 6 (280)⇌(280a) and the weak paramagnetism shown by solutions of (280) suggests[319] that the mechanism of bromine migration involves homolytic fission of the C–Br bond, although such a suprafacial [1,5] sigmatropic rearrangement is allowed as a concerted process. A second process is detectable at lower temperatures (<183°K) which causes the low field t-butyl signal to split into two signals with a 2:1 ratio of intensities. This second change is probably due to hindered rotation of the t-butyl substituent at C-2 (see 280), resulting in slow exchange of the three methyl groups between the A and B environments indicated in the Newman projection formula (281). The magnitudes of these rotational barriers could not be measured for the *o*-dienones (**280**) owing to overlapping signals, but are probably similar to the rotational barriers found for the C(4)–CMe$_3$ bond by a similar study[319] of the low-temperature spectra of the *p*-dienones (**282**). The rotational barriers for the

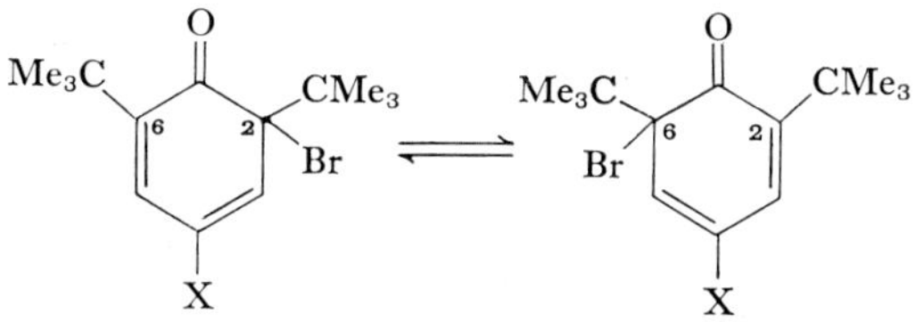

X	$\Delta G^{\ddagger}$ kcal.mole^{-1}
CN	16·5
NO$_2$	17·2

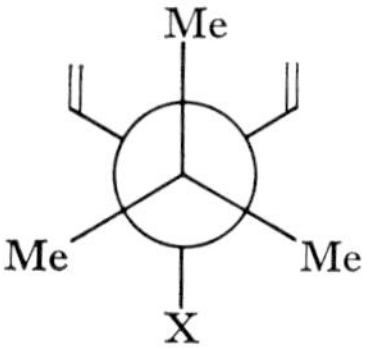

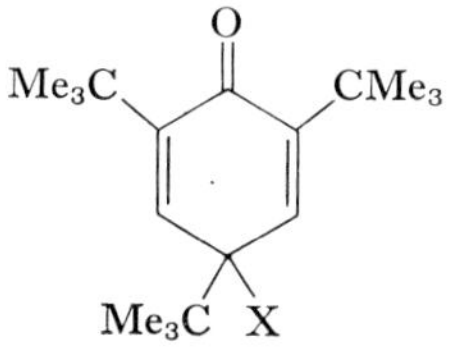

	X	$\Delta G^{\ddagger}$ kcal.mole^{-1}
282	Br	9·0
282a	OMe	8·9

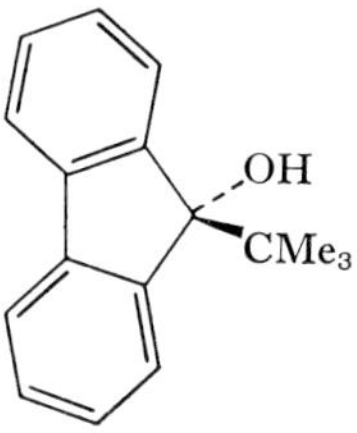

compounds (**282**) are rather similar to that found in the 9-*t*-butylfluorenol (**283**) ($\Delta G^{\ddagger}$ 9·4 kcal.mole^{-1})[320] and a little lower than the rotational barrier found for the Me$_3$C–C bond in the ethane derivative (**284**) ($\Delta G^{\ddagger}$ 11·1 kcal.mole^{-1}).[320] The stereochemical situation for the *t*-butyl substituent in the tetrafluoro-benzyne-*t*-butylbenzene adduct (**285**) is exceptional[321] and leads to an extremely high rotational barrier about the C–CMe$_3$ bond in the conformation shown. The signals associated with the methyl groups in the A and B environments (see **285**) coalesce only in the temperature range 393 to 453°K.

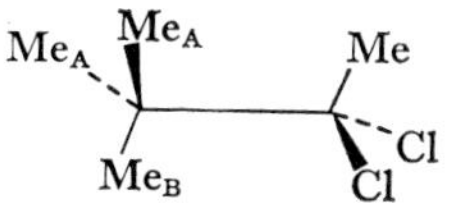

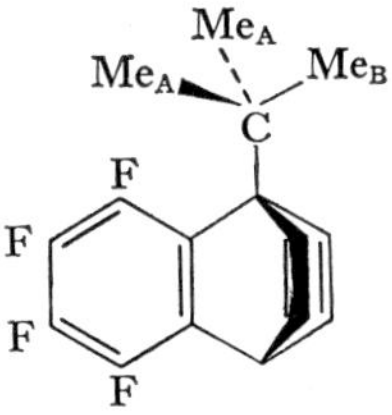

Rotational barriers about single bonds joining sp^2 and sp^3 hybridized carbon atoms are sufficiently large to be observed using NMR line-shape methods in a number of examples. The first report[322] of this type of rotational barrier was for tetramethyl-1,2-di-neopentyl-benzene (286) in which the neopentyl methylene groups are observed as AB systems up to 323°K. The activation parameters for the concerted rotational process, by which H and H' of both methylene groups are exchanged between environments A and B (see 286), were obtained by comparison of computed and observed spectral line shapes ($\Delta G^\ddagger$ ca. 16·5 kcal.mole^{-1}).

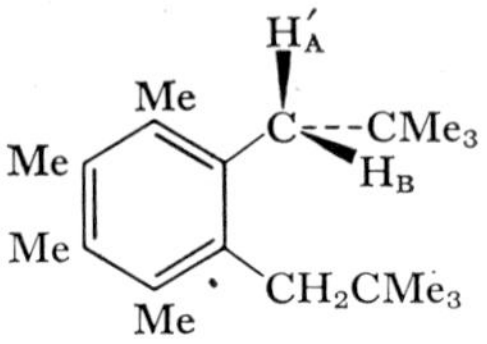

	X	kcal.mole^{-1} (250°K)
287	Cl	12·1
287a	Br	13·5
287b	I	15·0

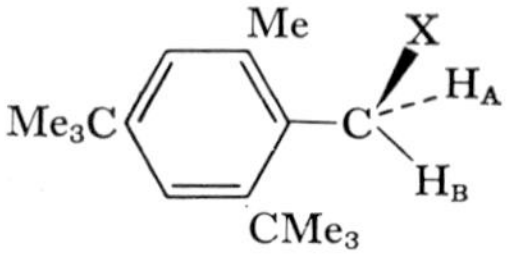

A rather similar rotational barrier was observed[323] for the substituted benzyl halides (287), in which the methylene groups also give AB systems at low temperature which coalesce to singlets at higher temperatures. The increase in the barriers as the size of the halogen substituent is increased supports the interpretation in terms of hindered rotation about the Ar–CH$_2$X bond. Other substituted benzenes have similar rotational barriers about Ar–C bonds which may be detected by the non-equivalence of methyl or methoxyl substituents at the 2 and 6 positions of the benzene ring as in (288) and (289).

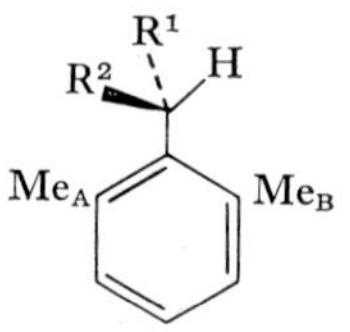

	R^1	R^2	$\Delta G^\ddagger$ kcal.mole^{-1}
288	Ph	Cl	11·3
288a	Ph	Me	11·2
288b	Me	Me	12·8
288c	–(CH$_2$)$_5$–		14·4

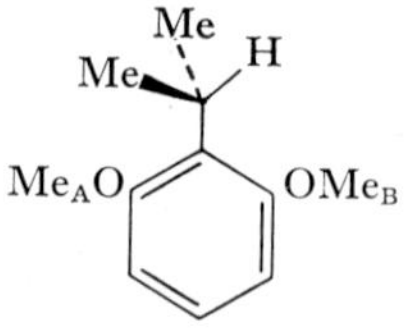

289 $\Delta G^\ddagger$ 9·6 kcal.mole^{-1}

Thus the series of alkyl benzenes (288 to 288c) and 2,6-dimethoxyisopropyl-benzene (289) have been studied[324] by the coalescence temperature method and rotational barriers about the indicated Ar–C bond measured. Hindered rotation was also observed[324] for the Ar–N bond of the 2,6-dimethyl-NN-dimethylani-

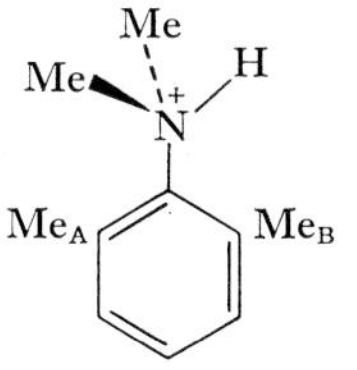

290 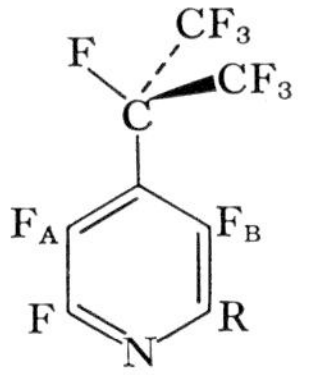   **291** R = F, OMe, CF(CF$_3$)$_2$ 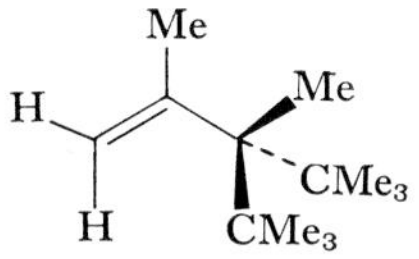   **292**

linium cation (**290**) ($\Delta G^{\ddagger}$ 15·9 kcal.mole^{-1} in CF$_3$CO$_2$H). Evidence for hindered rotation about Ar–C bonds has also been reported for a number of perfluoropyridine derivatives (**291**) but barrier heights have not been estimated.[325] The olefin (**292**) shows[326] two allylic methyl signals in the spectrum at low temperatures; this is believed to be a consequence of hindered rotation about the C(2)–C(3) bond (see **292**) with the minimum energy conformation shown ($\Delta G^{\ddagger}$ ca. 15 kcal.mole^{-1}). A number of cases have been reported[320,327 to 329] of hindered rota-

294

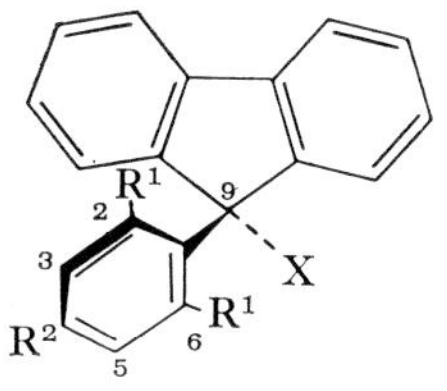

	X	R^1	R^2	$\Delta G^{\ddagger}$ kcal.mole^{-1}
293	H	Me	Me	> 25
293a	OH	Me	Me	20·2
293b	Cl	Me	Me	16·2
293c	H	OMe	H	20·6
293d	OH	OMe	H	14·4
293e	Cl	OMe	H	9·2

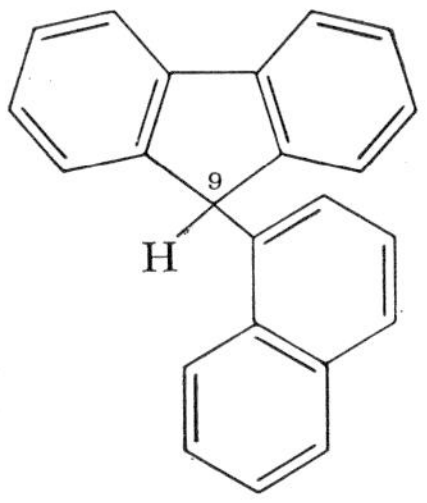

295

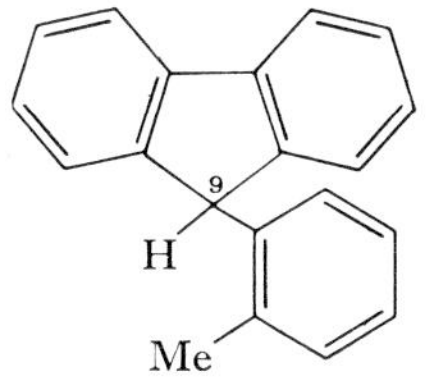

tion about the C(9)–Ar bond of 9-arylfluorenes such as (**293 to 295**). Hindered rotation may be detected by the non-equivalence of groups, in the 2 and 6 positions, or 3 and 5 positions, of the aryl substituent (see **293**). The observed rotational barrier is markedly dependent upon the 9-fluorenyl substituent in the cases (**293 to 293e**)[320] in which the effect of changing this substituent has been systematically examined. The substitution of the 9-aryl group is also of importance as expected, as is illustrated both in the series (**293 to 293e**) and 9-naphthylfluorene (**294**) ($\Delta G^{\ddagger}_{333}$ 17·8 kcal.mole^{-1} in DMSO,[328] $\Delta G^{\ddagger}_{333}$ 18.0 kcal.mole^{-1} in C$_2$Cl$_4$[329]) and 9-o-tolyfluorene (**295**) ($\Delta G^{\ddagger}_{333}$ 16·5 kcal.mole^{-1}).[329] These results are of interest in that they represent an extension of earlier work which was carried out using more conventional techniques of rate measurement.[330] The rotational barriers about the C–Ar bonds in suitably substituted tri-arylmethanes may also be sufficiently large to be measurable by NMR line-shape methods. This has been found to be the case[320,331] for the triarylmethanes (296) ($\Delta G^{\ddagger}$ 11·1 kcal.mole^{-1}) and (297) ($\Delta G^{\ddagger}$ 8·8 kcal.mole^{-1} for the C-mesityl bond), although the rotational barriers in both the alcohol (296a) and the chloride (296b) are too low to be measured ($\Delta G^{\ddagger} < 8·2$ kcal.mole^{-1}). It would be anticipated that the two-fold rotational barriers for single bonds joining two sp^2 hybridized carbon atoms would tend to be larger, and therefore more likely to fall within the range

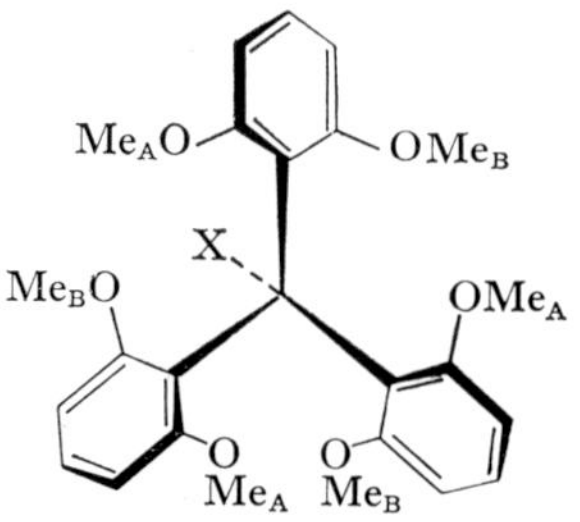

296   X = H
296a X = OH
296b X = Cl

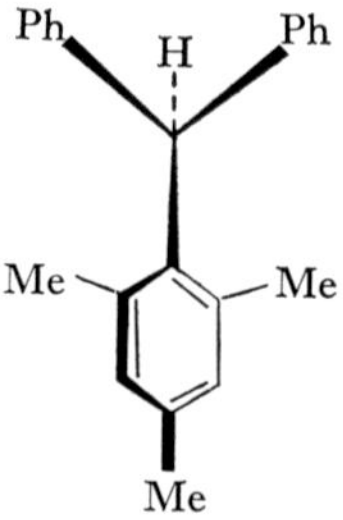

297

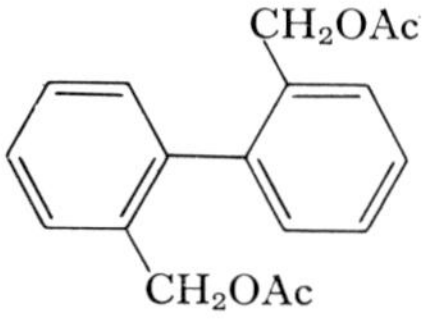

298

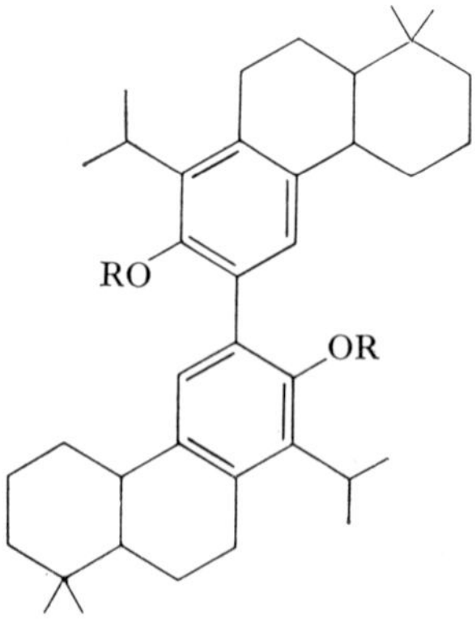

299   R = Me
299a R = Ac

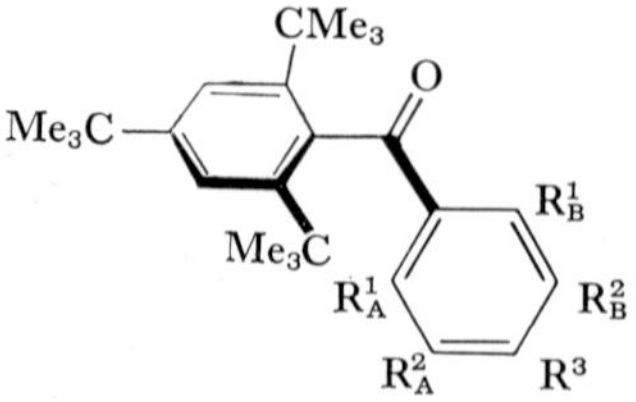

	R^1	R^2	R^3	$\Delta G^{\ddagger}$ kcal.mole^{-1}
300	H	Me	H	17·7
300a	H	OMe	OMe	18·5
300b	Me	Me	Me	17·3

studied by NMR line-shape methods, than those between sp^2 and sp^3 hybridized carbon atoms.

One of the simplest examples of this phenomenon is the well-known hindered rotation observable in many biphenyl systems, and observations of this type may be extended to lower energy barriers by NMR methods. Thus the diacetoxy-methylbiphenyl (298) gives an AB system at room temperature, which provides evidence for restricted rotation about the C(1)–C(1)' bond although the magnitude of the rotational barrier was not measured.[332] Similar restricted rotation in the podototarin derivatives (299) results in diastereoisomerism, and the rates of diastereomer interconversion were obtained by line-shape methods[333] [$\Delta G^{\ddagger}_{248}$ 13·7 and 13·8 kcal.mole^{-1} for (299) and $\Delta G^{\ddagger}_{319}$ 18·4 and 18·7 kcal.mole^{-1} for (299a)]. Hindered rotation about the thickened Ar–CO bond of the highly substituted benzophenones (300 to 300b) results in the indicated non-equivalence of the pairs of groups R^1 and R^2 and rotational rates may readily be studied.[334] The benzil (301) shows non-equivalence of the o-t-butyl substituents in the spectrum recorded at low temperatures, presumably owing to hindered rotation about the Ar–CO bond; these signals coalesce at higher temperatures when rotation becomes fast on the NMR time-scale ($\Delta G^{\ddagger}$ 16·7 kcal.mole^{-1}).[335] These Ar–CO rotational barriers are enhanced by the 2,4,6-tri-t-butylphenyl substituent in much the same way as the N–CO rotational barriers in amides such as (302) ($\Delta G^{\ddagger}$ $ca.$ 23 kcal.mole^{-1}).[335] Restricted rotation about the Ar–N bond of certain

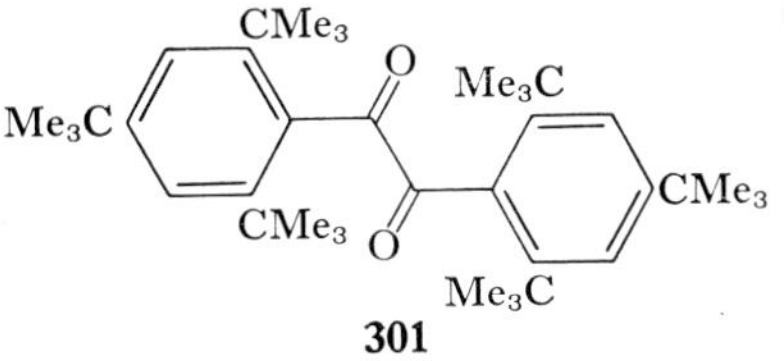

301

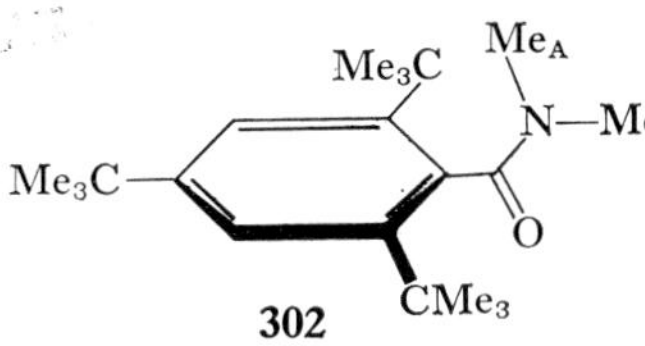

302

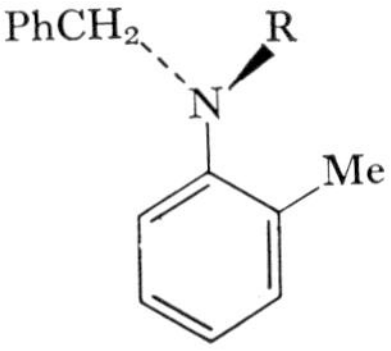

	$\Delta G^{\ddagger}$
R	kcal.mole^{-1}
303 COMe	19·3
303a COPh	18·1
303b SO$_2$C$_6$H$_4$Me	15·3
303c SO$_2$Me	14·8
303d CMe$_3$	15·6

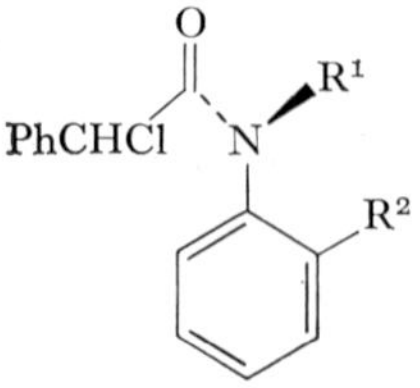

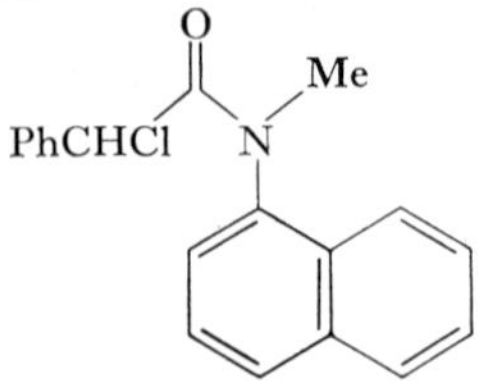

	R^1	R^2	$\Delta G^{\ddagger}_{298}$ kcal.mole^{-1}	E_a kcal.mole^{-1}	$\mathrm{Log}_{10}A$ kcal.mole^{-1}
304	Me	Me	20·3	19·2	11·9
304a	Me	CHMe$_2$	22·3	22·1	12·7
304b	PhCH$_2$	Me	20·5	18·9	11·5
304c	Et	Me	21·3	21·1	12·6
304d	CHMe$_2$	Me	25·4	23·8	11·6
305			21·7	22·6	13·5

aniline derivatives had been recognized long before the availability of NMR spectrometers and had been extensively studied.[336] These classical investigations have been extended by NMR line-shape methods in a number of investigations. Rotational barriers of sufficient magnitude about the Ar–N bond of o-toluidine derivatives, (**303**) and (**304**), which have the non-planar ground state conformations shown, may be recognized either by the non-equivalence of the prochiral methylene protons of the N-benzyl group in (**303**) or by spectral evidence for the presence of diastereomers of the α-chlorophenylacetamides (**304**). Both situations have been examined,[337 to 339] and rotational barriers about the Ar–N bonds have been measured. The examination of the compounds (**303 to 303d**) was made using line-shape methods only,[337] but the examination of the series of amides (**304 to 304d**) and (**305**) is of particular significance in that the interconversion rates were obtained[339] by a combination of equilibration studies, using isolated diastereomers, at low temperatures and line-shape methods at high temperatures. The kinetics were therefore studied over a very wide temperature range and it is of interest that frequency factors do not deviate very far from 10^{13}. Restricted

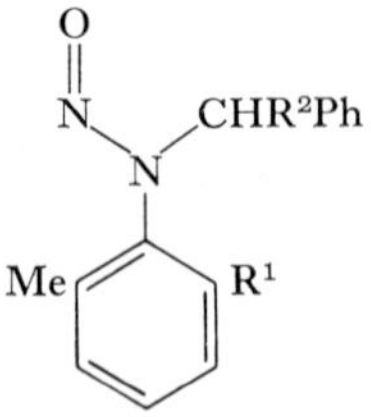

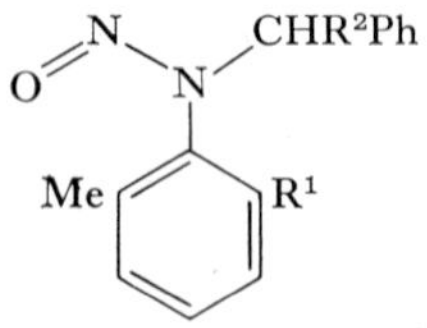

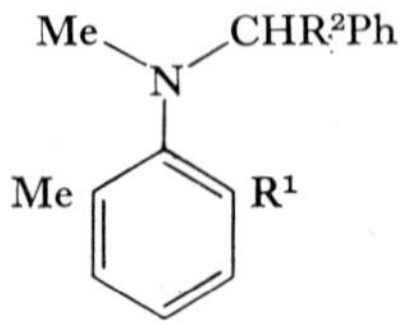

R^1	R^2	$\Delta G^{\ddagger}$ kcal.mole^{-1}
Cl	H	16·5
Br	H	17·9
Me	Me	19·8

R^1	R^2	$\Delta G^{\ddagger}$ kcal.mole^{-1}
Cl	H	> 20
Br	H	21·8
Me	Me	> 21

R^1	R^2	$\Delta G^{\ddagger}$ kcal.mole^{-1}
Cl	H	15·1
Br	H	15·8
Me	Me	17·6

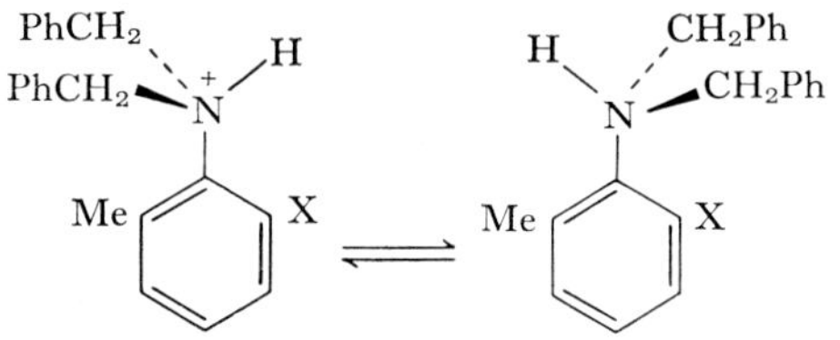

rotation about the Ar–N bond of other aniline derivatives has also been studied,[340] these include the nitrosoamines (306), both geometrical isomers (306) and (306a) being examined in this case, the amines (307) and the anilinium cations (308). The latter give rise to the diastereomeric conformations (308) and (308a) which are separated by a substantial torsional barrier ($\Delta G^{\ddagger} \geqslant 15$ kcal.mole^{-1} for X = Cl, Br). NMR evidence for hindered rotation about the Ar–N bond has also been reported for the amine (309).[341] Further examples of this type of restricted rotation involve the Ar–O and Ar–S bonds of the aromatic ethers and sulphides (310) and the disulphides (311), the conformational change may be studied[342] by the coalescence of the two low-temperature signals of the groups X which are rendered geminally non-equivalent by the restricted rotation.

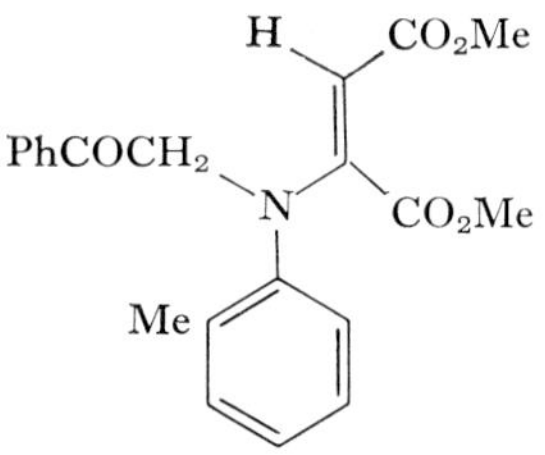

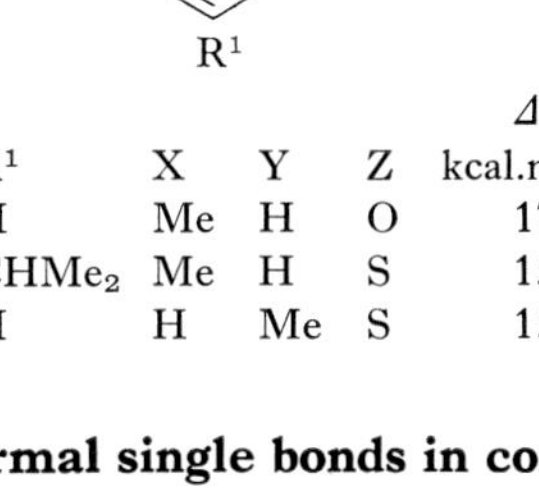

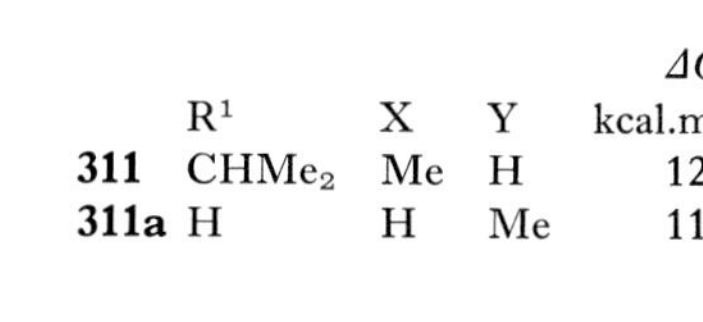

R^1	X	Y	Z	$\Delta G^{\ddagger}$ kcal.mole^{-1}
310	H	Me	H	O	17·8
310a	CHMe$_2$	Me	H	S	15·0
310b	H	H	Me	S	15·1

R^1	X	Y	$\Delta G^{\ddagger}$ kcal.mole^{-1}
311	CHMe$_2$	Me	H	12·8
311a	H	H	Me	11·7

B. Formal single bonds in conjugated systems

The representation of amides by the resonance notation (312) has the value of suggesting that the N–CO bond should have partial double bond character,[343] and that rotation about this bond should be rather more hindered than for a simple C–N bond in, for example, an amine. The same conclusion also follows from the rather more satisfactory MO representation of the π-bonding system present in the N–C–O portion of the amide structure. The predictions were first confirmed[344] experimentally in 1955 when the NMR spectrum of dimethyl-formamide was found to show separate signals for the N-methyl groups in the environments A and B (see **313**). The methyl groups Me and Me' are exchanged between these environments by rotation about the N–CO bond, and in 1956 the classical paper of Gutowsky and Holm[11] described the temperature dependence of the N-methyl signals of dimethylformamide and dimethylacetamide. The line-shape equation derived in the same paper[11] was used to derive the equation relating peak separation to exchange rate, and this approach, or the equally unreliable method of intensity ratios,[13] were used in several subsequent examinations of the amide system, both methods resulting in large systematic errors in the exchange rates. The early papers on amide rotational barriers[13,345] therefore, although providing reasonably accurate measure of the coalescence temperatures, give unacceptable values for the Arrhenius activation parameters and many of the discussions based on these parameters are not valid. An attempt was made to correct these errors by allowing for temperature dependent changes in chemical

$$R_2N-C\overset{O}{\diagup} \longleftrightarrow R_2\overset{+}{N}=C\overset{O^-}{\diagup}$$

312

$$\begin{matrix} Me'_A \\ Me_B \end{matrix} N-C\overset{O}{\diagup}$$

313

shifts independent of the exchange process,[346] but only recently have reliable activation parameters been obtained for amide rotational barriers by using total line-shape comparison methods and by treating T_2 and $(\nu_A - \nu_B)$ as variable input parameters in addition to the rate constant k. The discussion here will therefore be limited to these recent results, although free energies of activation derivable from the earlier studies may also be used to comment upon the substituent effects.

Allerhand and Gutowsky[54] examined the use of the spin-echo technique to determine amide rotational barriers and compared their results, for NN-dimethyl-trichloroacetamide and NN-dimethylcarbamoylchloride, with those obtained in earlier work using steady-state methods. The agreement with Arrhenius parameters based upon the high-temperature line-narrowing approximation was quite good, but it was clear that results obtained using the peak separation or intensity ratio approximations were inaccurate. In the latter studies the frequency factors were in most cases much lower than the expected value of ca. 10^{13} for a unimolecular process, but the spin-echo method gave frequency factors encouragingly close to 10^{13} in both this[54] and a later[68] examination of the rotational barriers in NN-dimethyltrifluoroacetamide and N-nitrosodimethylamine. The discrepancies between the results obtained by spin-echo and steady-state methods arose from the use of unreliable approximations in the latter method and are not found when the total line-shape method is used. Recent studies using the total line-shape method have been reported for NN-dimethylacetamide,[21] NN-dimethylformamide,[22,347] aliphatic NN-dimethylamides,[348] and a series of substituted NN-dimethylbenzamides.[69] A further study of NN-dimethylformamide using closed form expressions has also been reported,[349] and in this case the results agree quite well with the more rigorous total line-shape analysis.[22,347] Full details of the results of these careful and detailed studies are reported in

CONMe₂

	X	Y		X	Y
314	NO₂	H	**314g**	Cl	H
314a	H	NO₂	**314h**	H	OMe
314b	CN	H	**314i**	F	H
314c	H	Br	**314j**	H	H
314d	H	Cl	**314k**	H	Me
314e	I	H	**314l**	Me	H
314f	Br	H	**314m**	MeO	H

TABLE XVII

Rotational barriers for the N–CO bond of amides

Compound	E_a kcal.mole^{-1}	$\log_{10}A$	$\Delta G_{298}^{\ddagger}$	Solvent	Method	Reference
HCONMe₂	20.5 ± 0.2	12.7	21.0	none	TLS	22, 347
HCONMe₂	22.0	13.0	21.7	none	closed form equations	349
CD₃CONMe₂	19.6 ± 0.3	13.8 ± 0.2	18.2	none	TLS	21
CD₃CONMe₂	20.6 ± 0.3	14.3 ± 0.3	18.6	DMSO-d_6	TLS	21
Me₃CCONMe₂	11.5	12.3	12.2		TLS	348
CF₃CONMe₂	20.6 ± 1.4	14.3	18.6	none	spin echo[a]	68
	18.5 ± 2.7	12.8			spin echo[a]	68
CCl₃CONMe₂	14.6 ± 0.6	12.5 ± 0.5	15.0	none	spin echo	54
ClCONMe₂	14.0 ± 0.9	10.9 ± 0.6		none	spin echo	54
314	18.07	14.02	16.40	MeCN	TLS	69
314a	18.20	14.46	15.93	MeCN	TLS	69
314b	18.02	14.11	16.22	MeCN	TLS	69
314c	17.04	13.77	15.71	MeCN	TLS	69
314d	19.00	15.18	15.75	MeCN	TLS	69
314e	18.04	14.60	15.58	MeCN	TLS	69
314f	16.00	13.14	15.53	MeCN	TLS	69
314g	17.75	14.47	15.46	MeCN	TLS	69
314h	17.81	14.44	15.57	MeCN	TLS	69
314i	16.45	13.71	15.20	MeCN	TLS	69
314j	17.40	14.18	15.50	MeCN	TLS	69
314k	18.39	14.99	15.40	MeCN	TLS	69
314l	17.18	14.41	14.97	MeCN	TLS	69
314m	15.61	13.54	14.59	MeCN	TLS	69

[a] Two slightly different methods were used.

Table XVII. Comparison of the results listed in Table XVII for the series RCONMe$_2$, where R$=$H, CD$_3$, CF$_3$, CCl$_3$, CMe$_3$ and Ph, suggests that steric effects may well be of greater importance than electronic effects and that in general the free energy barrier for N–CO rotation decreases as the size of R increases. When R is an aryl substituent the electronic effects of the substituents on the aryl moiety do influence the rotational barrier (compounds **314** to **314m**),[69] and a reasonably good linear relationship is found between $\Delta G^{\ddagger}$ and the σ or σ^{+} parameter for the substituent. Steric effects are also important in o-substituted benzamides as is illustrated by the very high rotational barrier ($\Delta G^{\ddagger}_{433}$ 22·5 kcal.mole^{-1}) found[350] for NN-dimethylmesitamide (**315**); other mesitamides (**315a**) may be isolated in diastereomeric forms and interconversion rates measured by direct methods ($\Delta G^{\ddagger}$ 23 to 24 kcal.mole^{-1} at 311 to 314°K).

These high N–CO rotational barriers, found in the mesitamides, are presumably a consequence of the interaction between the 2- and 6- methyl substituents and the N-alkyl groups in the transition state (**316**) for the rotational

315 R^1 = R^2 = Me
315a R^1 ≠ R^2

316

process. A number of other amides have been studied including N-acyltetrahydroquinolines[351] and N-acyltetrahydroisoquinolines,[352,353] in the latter case a total line-shape examination has been made[353] and reliable entropies and enthalpies of activation have been determined. It might have been thought that amide rotational barriers would be very sensitive to changes in the substituents on the nitrogen atom, a number of such cases have been investigated and the effects will be briefly reviewed here. Rotational barriers in the N-vinylamides (**317**) and (**318**) are rather lower than those in the corresponding N-alkylamides (**317a**) and (**318a**), the study[345d] of the vinylamides was based upon approximate methods of rate evaluation and a more accurate study by the total line-shape method would be desirable. The N–CO rotational barriers in diacylhydrazines are apparently not significantly different from those found in the corresponding NN-dialkylamides, thus the dibenzoyl hydrazine (**319**) ($\Delta G^{\ddagger}_{290}$ 14·9 kcal.mole^{-1})[266] has a rotational barrier only slightly lower than that of NN-dimethylbenzamide ($\Delta G^{\ddagger}_{298}$ 15·5 kcal.mole^{-1}).[69] The rotational barrier in N-acylhydroxylamines is, however, significantly lowered[281] and this is exemplified by (320) ($\Delta G_{198}^{\ddagger}$ ca. 10·5 kcal.mole^{-1}) and (320a) ($\Delta G_{257}^{\ddagger}$ 14·2 kcal.mole^{-1} as compared with $\Delta G_{298}^{\ddagger}$ 18·2 kcal.mole^{-1} for NN-dimethylacetamide). This considerable lowering of the

RN(Me)CHO

317 R = CH=CH$_2$, $\Delta G_{300}^{\ddagger}$ 17·6 kcal.mole^{-1}
317a R = Me, $\Delta G_{300}^{\ddagger}$ 21·0 kcal.mole^{-1}

RN(Me)COMe

318 R = CH=CH$_2$, $\Delta G_{300}^{\ddagger}$ 13·4 kcal.mole^{-1}
318a R = Me, $\Delta G_{300}^{\ddagger}$ 18·2 kcal.mole^{-1}

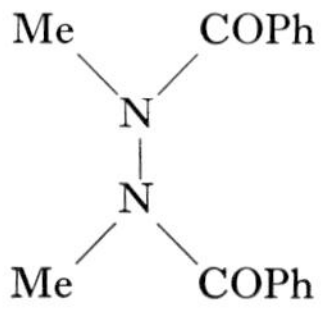

319 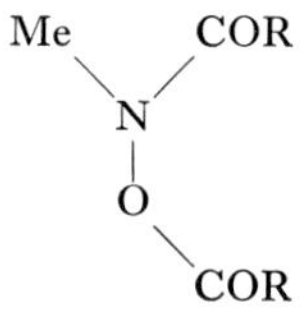   **320** R = Ph   **321**
         320a R = Me

amide rotational barrier in the acylhydroxylamines (320) and (320a) is probably a consequence of the enhanced nitrogen inversion barrier in hydroxylamine derivatives (see Section IV), and an extreme example of this effect is provided by N-acetylaziridine (321) in which less the N–CO rotational barrier is probably than 7 kcal.mole^{-1}. Amide rotational barriers are also rather low in N-acylpy-roles[354] (322) in which the nitrogen lone-pair forms part of the aromatic sextet of the pyrrole ring. The degree to which the rotational barrier is lowered is perhaps less than might have been anticipated indicating that, although the nitrogen lone-pair electrons in pyrrole are not readily available for σ-bond formation in salts, they can participate effectively in further π-electron conjugation.

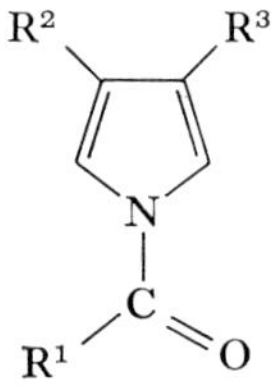

	R^1	R^2	$\Delta G^{\ddagger}$ kcal.mole^{-1}
322	H	H	14·1
322a	Me	H	12·2
322b	Me	Me	13·5

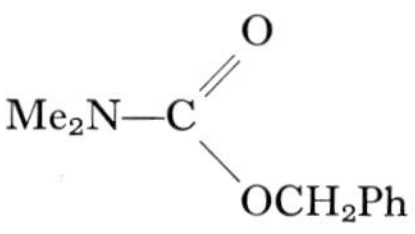

323 $\Delta G_{270}^{\ddagger}$ 15·9 kcal.mole^{-1}

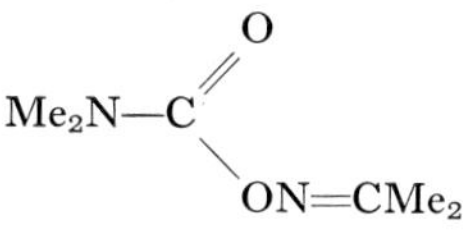

324 $\Delta G_{264}^{\ddagger}$ 14·4 kcal.mole^{-1}

$$\underset{\substack{\text{MeC}_6\text{H}_4\text{SO}_2\text{CH}_2}}{\overset{\text{Me}}{\diagdown}}\text{N}-\text{C}\underset{\text{OMe}}{\overset{\text{O}}{\diagup}}$$

325 $\Delta G^{\ddagger}_{200}$ 16·7 kcal.mole^{-1}

$$\text{Me}_2\text{N}-\text{C}\underset{\text{Cl}}{\overset{\text{X}}{\diagup}}$$

326 X = O
326a X = S

As has been pointed out above substituents on the carbonyl carbon atom of amides tend to influence the magnitude of the barrier more by their steric effects than their electronic effects, and the rotational barriers in both NN-dimethylacrylamide ($\Delta G^{\ddagger}_{298}$ 16·1 kcal.mole^{-1})[345a] and NN-dimethylbenzamide ($\Delta G^{\ddagger}_{298}$ 15·5 kcal.mole^{-1})[69] are not very different from that found in NN-dimethylpropionamide ($\Delta G^{\ddagger}_{298}$ 16·7 kcal.mole^{-1}).[13] Even the cross conjugated system in urethanes (e.g. **323**) does not lower the amide rotational barrier to a very marked degree,[268] and rather similar N–CO rotational barriers have been observed in more complex urethane systems such as (**324**)[355] and (**325**);[356] the latter compound being examined by total line-shape comparison.

The replacement of the carbonyl oxygen atom of the amides by a sulphur atom in the thioamides results in a significant increase in the amide rotational barrier. This effect is shown clearly by NN-dimethylcarbamoyl chloride (**326**) ($\Delta G^{\ddagger}_{298}$ 16·8 kcal.mole^{-1} by steady-state techniques[357] and $\Delta G^{\ddagger}_{298}$ 16·6 kcal.mole^{-1} by spin-echo methods[54]) and NN-dimethylthiocarbamoyl chloride ($\Delta G^{\ddagger}_{298}$ 18·1 kcal.mole^{-1} by steady-state methods[357]), and also by a comparison of the rather less reliable results[358] found for the thioamide (**327**) ($\Delta G^{\ddagger}_{356}$ 17·8 kcal.mole^{-1}), the selenoamide (**327a**) ($\Delta G^{\ddagger}_{380}$ 19·0 kcal.mole^{-1}) and NN-dimethylbenzamide (**327b**) ($\Delta G^{\ddagger}_{298}$ 15·5 kcal.mole^{-1}).[69] Other thioamide derivatives which have been examined include the thioureas (**328**),[359] the acylthioureas (**329**)[359] and the thioformamides (**330**).[360] Some direct studies of the equilibration of isolated diastereomeric thioamides have also been reported, examples being the thioformamide (**331**)[361] and the thioformylhydrazide (**332**),[362] the reported energy barriers being for the change major conformer → minor conformer. A number of studies have also been made of the vinylogues of simple amides (**333** to **335**), these are of interest in that the magnitudes of the C–N rotational barriers may be influenced by the electronic effects of remote substituents. The most extensive examination reported was based upon coalescence data only[363] and the free energies of acti-

$$\text{Ph}-\text{C}\underset{\text{NMe}_2}{\overset{\text{X}}{\diagup}}$$

327 X = S
327a X = Se
327b X = O

$$\text{RNHC}-\text{N}\underset{\text{CH}_2\text{Ph}}{\overset{\text{CH}_2\text{Ph}}{\diagup}}\quad(\text{S})$$

328 R = Me, $\Delta G^{\ddagger}$ 10·8 kcal.mole^{-1}
328a R = Ph, $\Delta G^{\ddagger}$ 11·3 kcal.mole^{-1}

$$\underset{\text{329}}{\text{RCONH}-\overset{\overset{\text{S}}{\|}}{\text{C}}-\text{N}\overset{\text{CH}_2\text{Ph}}{\underset{\text{CH}_2\text{Ph}}{}}}$$

329   R = MeCH$_2$, $\Delta G^{\ddagger}$ 15·0 kcal.mole^{-1}
329a R = Ph, $\Delta G^{\ddagger}$ 15·5 kcal.mole^{-1}

$$\overset{\text{S}}{\underset{\text{H}}{\|}}\text{C}-\text{NR}_2$$

330   R = Me, $\Delta G^{\ddagger}_{300}$ 26·7 kcal.mole^{-1}
330a R = CHMe$_2$,
$\Delta G^{\ddagger}_{300}$ 28·8 kcal.mole^{-1}

$$\underset{\text{PhCH}_2}{\overset{\text{Me}}{}}\text{N}-\text{C}\overset{\text{S}}{\underset{\text{H}}{}}$$

331   $\Delta G^{\ddagger}_{300}$ 22·7 kcal.mole^{-1}

$$\underset{\text{PhMeN}}{\overset{\text{H}}{}}\text{N}-\text{C}\overset{\text{}}{\underset{\text{H}}{}}$$

332   $\Delta G^{\ddagger}$ 22·4 kcal.mole^{-1}

vation found for a number of vinylogous amides, in CHCl$_3$ or CH$_2$Br$_2$, are re-ported below formula (333), the recorded energy barriers can be seen to be very little influenced by the nature of the substituent R on the carbonyl carbon atom. The vinylogous thioamides, for example (334), have larger C–N rotational barriers[363] than the corresponding vinylogous amides, just as is found in the comparison of amides and thioamides. Extension of the conjugated systems, by interposing an additional CH=CH group between the nitrogen atom and the carbonyl group, as in (335) and (335a), lowers the C–N rotational barrier,[364] as might be expected. The C–CO and C–C double bonds of vinylogous amides may also, in some cases, have rotational barriers within the range accessible to NMR line-shape study, and a number of examinations of this type are reported in Section VIC.

The squaramides (336) may also be considered as vinylogous amides, and quite substantial C–N rotational barriers may be observed by NMR methods in the series (336 to 336b).[365] Extended conjugation is also present in the benzaldehyde derivatives (337 to 337b)[366] and the acetophenones (337c) and (337d),[367]

$$\underset{\text{Me}}{\overset{\text{Me}}{}}\text{N}-\text{CH}=\text{CH}-\text{C}\overset{\text{O}}{\underset{\text{R}}{}}$$

	R	$\Delta G^{\ddagger}$ kcal.mole^{-1}
333	H	15·8
333a	Me	14·3
333b	CHMe$_2$	14·5
333c	CH=CHMe	14·3
333d	Ph	14·4

$$\underset{\text{Me}}{\overset{\text{Me}}{}}\text{N}-\text{CH}=\text{CH}-\text{C}\overset{\text{S}}{\underset{\text{Ph}}{}}$$

334   $\Delta G^{\ddagger}$ 16·5 kcal.mole^{-1}

$$\underset{\text{Me}}{\overset{\text{Me}}{}}\text{N}-\text{CH}=\text{CH}-\text{CH}=\text{CR}-\text{C}\overset{\text{O}}{\underset{\text{H}}{}}$$

335   R = H, $\Delta G^{\ddagger}$ 13·0 kcal.mole^{-1}
335a R = Me, $\Delta G^{\ddagger}$ 12·5 kcal.mole^{-1}

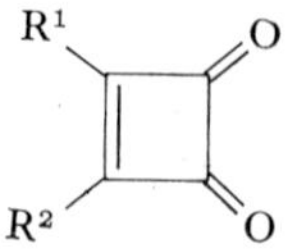

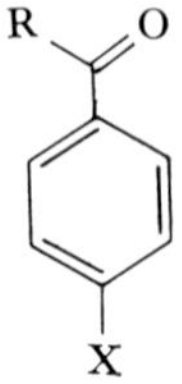

	R¹	R²	$\Delta G^{\ddagger}$ kcal.mole^{-1}
336	OEt	NMe$_2$	16·9
336a	OEt	NEt$_2$	17·3
336b	OEt	N(CH$_2$Ph)$_2$	16·7

	R	X	$\Delta G^{\ddagger}$ kcal.mole^{-1}
337	H	H	7·9
337a	H	OMe	9·2
337b	H	NMe$_2$	10·8
337c	Me	OMe	<7·3
337d	Me	NMe$_2$	8·5

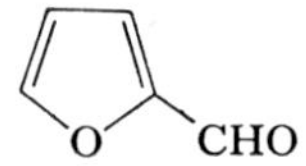

338

and in these compounds the Ar–CO rotational barrier have been examined. The enhancement of the barrier by the p-methoxy and p-dimethylamino substituents is in accord with earlier estimates made[368] for similar resonance interactions in p-disubstituted benzenes on the basis of chemical reactivity. The C–CHO rotational barrier in furfuraldehyde (**328**) is similarly enhanced ($\Delta G^{\ddagger}$ 10·9 kcal. mole^{-1} for major conformer $\rightarrow$ minor conformer)[369] by π-electron donation from the ring oxygen atom; the C–CHO rotational barriers in the compounds (**337a**), (**337b**) and (**338**) should be compared with the rather lower rotational barriers ($\Delta G^{\ddagger}$ 5–8 kcal.mole^{-1}) observed by ultrasonic techniques for other α, β-unsaturated aldehydes.[370]

A number of other systems, in which conjugation involving the nitrogen lone pair is important, also show substantial barriers to rotation about formal single bonds between carbon and nitrogen, a few examples which are associated with reduced rotational barriers about C=C double bonds will be discussed in Section VIC, the others will be discussed here. The importance of π-electron conjugation in the amidines (**339**) is demonstrated by the large C–N rotational barriers found in a fairly wide variety of acyclic amidine systems.[371,372] These observations have been extended by other groups of workers to a variety of heterocyclic systems with a dimethylamino-substituent which constitutes part of an amidine system. These include the thiazole (**340**),[373] the dimethylaminopyridines

(341),[374,375] and 4-dimethylaminopyrimidine (342).[375] The free energy barrier for C–N rotation[373] in the thiazole (340) is, as expected, rather similar to that for the analogous acyclic amidine (339c). As expected, from simple resonance considerations, the rotational barriers in 2-dimethylaminopyridines are raised by a 5-nitro-substituent (341a and 341b),[375] and the additional ring nitrogen atom in

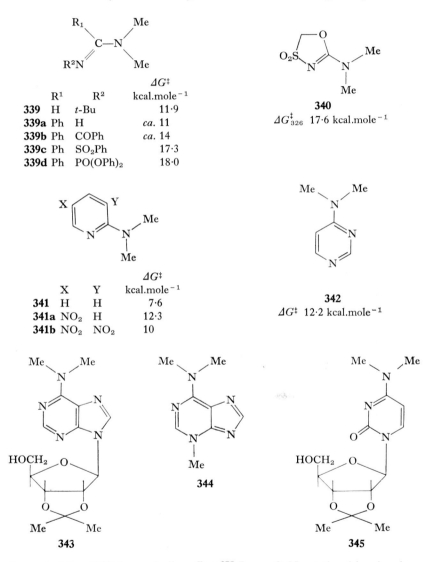

	R^1	R^2	$\Delta G^{\ddagger}$ kcal.mole^{-1}
339	H	t-Bu	11·9
339a	Ph	H	ca. 11
339b	Ph	COPh	ca. 14
339c	Ph	SO$_2$Ph	17·3
339d	Ph	PO(OPh)$_2$	18·0

340
$\Delta G^{\ddagger}_{326}$ 17·6 kcal.mole^{-1}

	X	Y	$\Delta G^{\ddagger}$ kcal.mole^{-1}
341	H	H	7·6
341a	NO$_2$	H	12·3
341b	NO$_2$	NO$_2$	10

342
$\Delta G^{\ddagger}$ 12·2 kcal.mole^{-1}

343

344

345

the pyrimidine (342) has a similar effect.[375] Large C–N rotational barriers have also been recorded in the adenosine derivative (343) ($\Delta G^{\ddagger}_{273}$ 13·4 kcal.mole^{-1}),[376] the adenine derivative **(344)** ($\Delta G^{\ddagger}_{303}$ 15·3 kcal.mole$^{-1)377}$ and the cytidine derivative **(345)** ($\Delta G^{\ddagger}_{303}$ 15·5 kcal.mole^{-1}).[376]

The determination[378] of the magnitude of the rotational barrier about the N–N bond of dimethylnitrosamine (E_a 23 kcal.mole^{-1}, $\log_{10}A$ 12·8) provided one of the first examples of the application of NMR line-shape methods to the measurement of the rates of hindered internal rotation. Although only an approximate method was used in this examination[378] (the peak separation method) the results obtained compare very well with those obtained[68] in a later examination using the spin-echo technique (E_a 21·9 ± 1·6 kcal.mole^{-1}, $\log_{10}A$ 12·0). It is also apparent that *N*-nitrosohydroxylamines[379] have lower N–N rotational barriers than *N*-nitrosoamines, but kinetic measurements for the former have not yet been made (*cf.* amides and hydroxamic acids). *p*-Nitrosodimethylaniline **(346)** may be regarded as a vinylogue of dimethylnitrosamine and, as indicated by the canonical forms **(346)** and **(346a)**, both the Ar–NMe$_2$ and Ar–NO bonds would

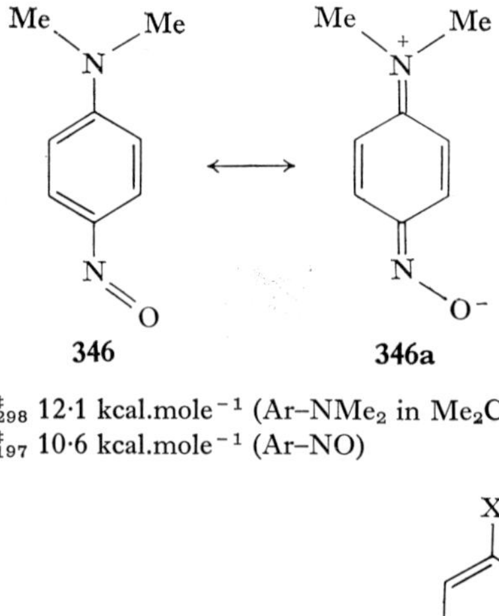

346   **346a**

$\Delta G^{\ddagger}_{298}$ 12·1 kcal.mole^{-1} (Ar–NMe$_2$ in Me$_2$CO)
$\Delta G^{\ddagger}_{197}$ 10·6 kcal.mole^{-1} (Ar–NO)

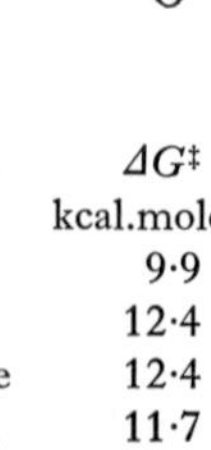

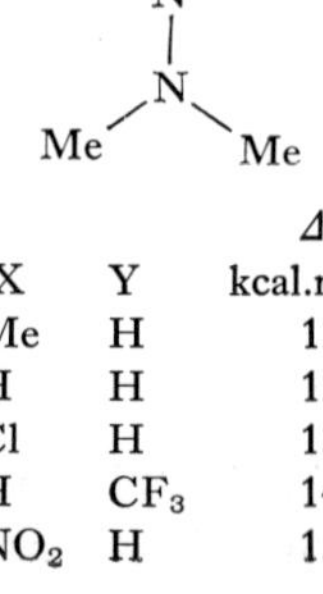

	R	$\Delta G^{\ddagger}$ kcal.mole^{-1}	σ_R
347	OMe	9·9	−0·268
347a	NMe$_2$	12·4	−0·600
347b	NHMe	12·4	−0·592
347c	NHPh	11·7	
347d	NH$_2$	12·4	−0·660

	X	Y	$\Delta G^{\ddagger}$ kcal.mole^{-1}
348	Me	H	12·1
348a	H	H	12·7
348b	Cl	H	13·3
348c	H	CF$_3$	14·2
348d	NO$_2$	H	15·7

be expected to have some double bond character. Rotational barriers for both of these bonds have been measured[52,380,381] and the examination of the Ar–NO rotational barrier has been extended to a series of *p*-substituted nitrosobenzenes. The expected relationship is observed between these rotational barriers and the σ value for the substituent, the relevant data are listed below formula (347).

Restricted rotation about N–N single bonds has also been observed[382] for the N–NMe$_2$ bond of the aryltriazenes (348), where again the σ value of the aryl substituents shows an approximately linear correlation with the free energy barrier for rotation. It is also evident from the published NMR data[383] that there is a considerable barrier to rotation about the N–NR$_2$ bond in the 1-tosyltriazenes (349), but kinetic measurements have not been reported.

349 R = Me, CH$_2$Ph

350   **350a**

R	E_a	$T_c(°K)$	ratio **350/350a**
Me	9·0	230	0·3
Et	9·0	227	2
Pr	9·0	227	2

Hindered rotation about the N–O bond of alkylnitrites (350)⇌(350a) was also observed in a very early[384] kinetic study by NMR line-shape methods. The rotational barriers were originally based[384] on the Gutowsky and Holm coalescence expression [$\Delta G^{\ddagger}$ *ca.* 10 kcal.mole^{-1} for (350), R = CH$_2$CHMe$_2$]. A subsequent examination,[25] using the equation relating line-width to exchange time, gave the Arrhenius activation energies for the cases listed below formula (350). It has been assumed in these cases that inversion at the sp^2 hybridized nitrogen atom is slower than the rotational process, this is probably correct but in the absence of proof the measured rotational barriers must be regarded as giving minimum values for the activation energy associated with the rotational process. This reservation applies in the cases of rotation about the N–N bond in the nitrosoamines and the triazenes (348) and (349), the C–N bond in the nitrosobenzene derivatives (346) and (347), and the O–N bond of the nitrites (350).

It would be expected that ylids of nitrogen (351), sulphur (352) and phosphorus (353), in which the carbanion centre is stabilized by an adjacent carbonyl group, would have a substantial degree of double bond character in the C–CO bond and that the *cis-trans* isomerization process (351)⇌(351a), etc., could be studied by NMR line-shape methods. The first report of a study of this phenomenon[385] was for the phosphonium ylid (354) which showed two methoxyl signals at low temperature coalescing to a singlet above 328°K in CDCl$_3$. Similar phenomena were reported by other groups[386] and it was recognized[387,388] that the rate of rotation about the C–CO bond (353)⇌(353a) was considerably en-

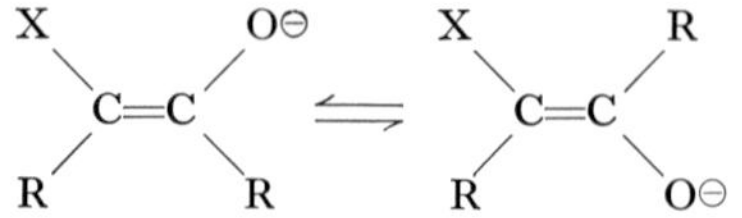

$$351 \quad X = \overset{+}{N}R_3 \qquad 351a$$
$$352 \quad X = \overset{+}{S}R_2 \qquad 352a$$
$$353 \quad X = \overset{+}{P}R_3 \qquad 353a$$

hanced by a transylidation reaction if traces of the corresponding phosphonium salt (355) were present, or by protonation if traces of a prostic solvent such as water or methanol were present.

354

355

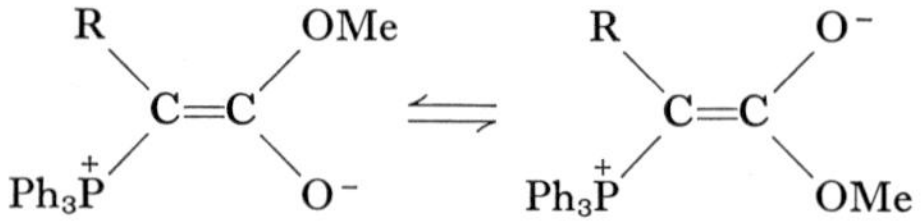

356   356a

Errors arising from these factors could be eliminated[388] by examining carefully purified ylids in deuteriochloroform containing a small quantity of alkaline alumina and using this procedure, which is probably also suitable for the examination of analogous rotational barriers in ylids of other types, reliable coalescence temperatures have been obtained[389] for a number of triphenylphosphonium ylids (356) (see Table XVIII); the results indicate that $\Delta G^{\ddagger}$ for the rotational process (356)⇌(356a) usually lies between 15 and 18 kcal.mole^{-1}. The rotational barrier is generally decreased by the increasing size of the substituent R and by factors which tend to favour the localization of the negative charge on carbon. It has been reported[390] that the spectra of sulphonium ylids may also be affected by transylidation or other proton exchange phenomena. Although such ylids do show signal broadening[391] and even separate signals due to *cis* and *trans* diastereomers at low temperatures,[392] there are to the author's knowledge no reliable measurements of rotational barriers for sulphonium ylids. The suggestion[393] that the spectrum of the ylid (357) provides evidence for hindered rotation about the $\overset{\ominus}{C}$–$\overset{\oplus}{S}$ bond requires further investigation. The reported temperature dependence of the NMR spectrum is more likely to be a consequence of hindered rotation about the $\overset{\ominus}{C}$–COMe bonds.

TABLE XVIII

Rotational barriers for the C–CO bond of triphenylphosphonium ylids (356)[389]

R	T_c (°K)	$\nu_A - \nu_B$ H_z	$\varDelta G$ (356$\rightleftharpoons$356a) kcal.mole^{-1}
H	308	15	−0·93
Me	341	27	0·00
Et	335	30	0·09
n-C$_3$H$_7$	331	29	0·19
n-C$_5$H$_{11}$	333	30	0·19
CH$_2$CHMe$_2$	338	29	0·38
CHMe$_2$	309	31	0·58
p-Me$_2$NC$_6$H$_4$	256	25	−0·64
p-MeOC$_6$H$_4$	254	23	−0·73
C$_6$H$_5$	225	25	−0·59
p-BrC$_6$H$_4$	214	23	−0·59
p-NO$_2$C$_6$H$_4$	< 208		

$\overset{\oplus}{Me_2S}$—$\overset{\ominus}{C}$(COMe)$_2$

357

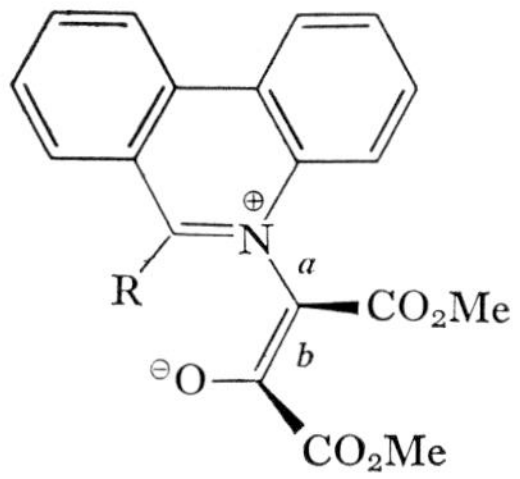

358

R = PhCH$_2$, PhCHMe

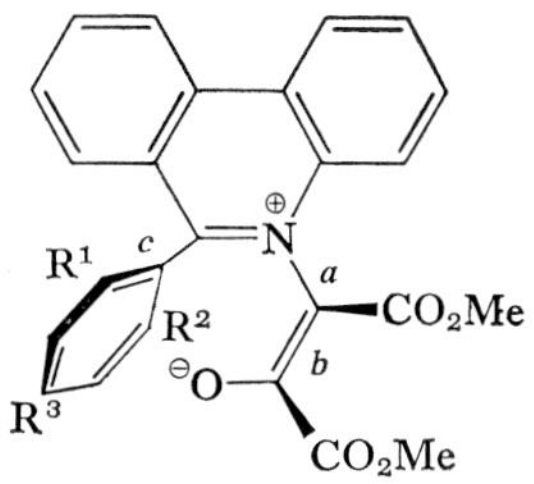

359 R^1 = R^2 = H
359a R^1 = Me, R^2 = H
359b R^1 = R^2 = Me

Hindered rotation in the complex nitrogen ylids (**358**) and (**359 to 359b**) about the bonds labelled *a*, *b* and *c* gives rise to complex spectra at low temperatures which show changes at higher temperatures as the rotational processes become fast on the NMR time-scale. The resulting spectroscopic changes are complex and the various rotational barriers have yet to be measured.[394] Diazoketones (**360**) are structurally analogous to ylids in that they have a structure in which a carbanion is stabilized by an adjacent carbonyl group, with resulting partial double bond character in the $\overset{\ominus}{C}$–CO bond (see **360, 360a** and **360b**). Rotation about this bond in a series of diazoketones (361) has been studied by NMR line-shape methods,[395] and the rates for the rotational process (361⇌361a) determined by the total line-shape comparison method. The rotational barriers in $CDCl_3$ are a

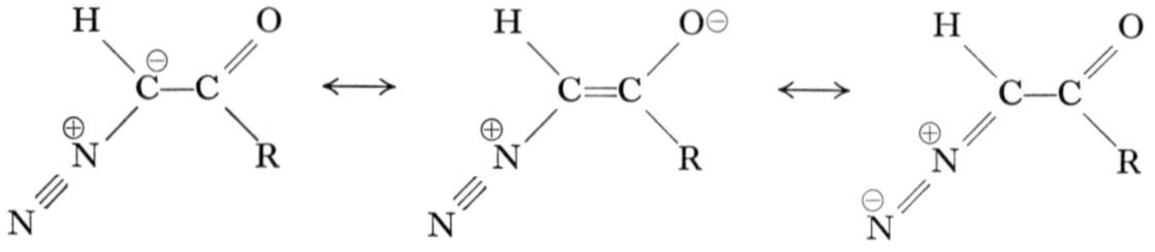

360   360a   360b

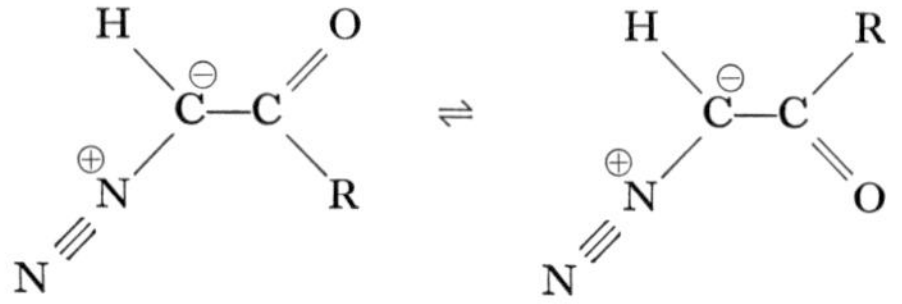

361   361a

R	$\Delta G^{\ddagger}_{298}$ (361a→361) kcal.mole^{-1}	$\Delta G^{\ddagger}_{298}$ (361→361a) kcal.mole^{-1}
Me	15·4	13·9
Et	15·3	13·5
PhCH$_2$	15·3	13·4
OMe	12·8	12·7
OEt	13·3	13·2

little lower than those observed for phosphonium ylids, and qualitatively this may be due to the additional delocalization of negative charge suggested by the canonical form (360b). The observed rotational barrier for diazoacetone (361, R=Me) (15·4 kcal.mole^{-1}) is in reasonably good agreement with the value calculated[396] by extended Huckel theory (ca. 14 kcal.mole^{-1}), although such calculations ignore the effect of the solvent.

C. C–C double bonds

In general uncatalysed rotation about C–C double bonds involves high energy diradical or dipolar transition states,[397] and the activation energy involved is too high for kinetic studies to be made by NMR line-shape methods. There are a number of ways in which the energy barrier may be significantly lowered. These include stabilization of the diradical (362) or dipolar (363) transition states, or

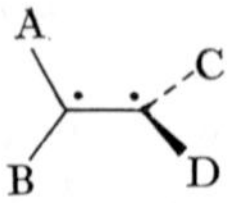

362 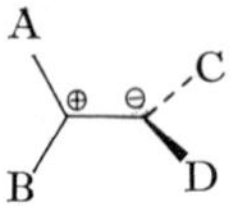   363 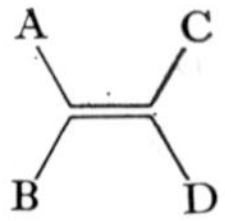   364

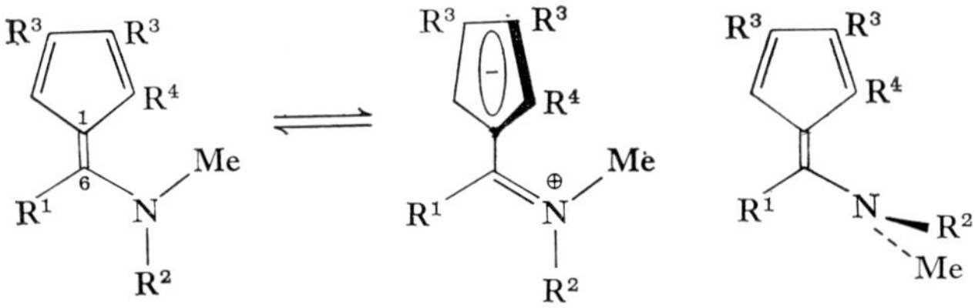

destabilization of the planar ground state (364); the latter effect usually resulting from large non-bonded interactions between the groups A and C, and B and D. Most of the examples which have been reported involve stabilization of a dipolar transition state analogous to (363). Thus rotation about the C(1)–C(6) double bond in the fulvenes (365) and (367)[398,399] and the fulvalene (366)[400] might be expected to involve the dipolar transition states (365a) and (366a); the carbanion centre in these transition states is stabilized by incorporation into a cyclopentadienyl system, and the cationic centre involves either positively charged nitrogen (365a) or the cyclopropenyl cation (366a). The rotational barriers found in these compounds by NMR methods are listed in Table XIX and are based upon the temperature dependence of the ring proton signals [for compounds (365) and (367) ABCD system at low temperatures, AA'BB' system at high temperatures] which in some cases were simplified by partial deuteration.[398] The rotational barrier for compound (366) is based upon the coalescence of the signals from the two different n-propyl substituents.[400] The rather low activation energies for the bond rotation process ($\Delta G^{\ddagger}$ 11 to 22 kcal.mole^{-1}) demonstrate the ease of polarization in these compounds, rather than a low bond order for the C(1)–C(6) bond, and are therefore not inconsistent with coupling constant measurements[398,399] and dipole moment data which indicate a high degree of double bond localization in both types of compound, as required by the representations (365) and (366). The effects of solvent changes upon these C(1)–C(6) rotational barriers are completely in accord[398 to 400] with the dipolar transition states (365a) and (366a). The 6-dialkylaminofulvenes (365) also show moderately high barriers to rotation about the C(6)–N bonds (Table XIX)[398,401] as do the related compounds (368) and (369);[401] these rotational barriers, as might be expected, are less sensitive to solvent changes than the C(1)–C(6) rotational

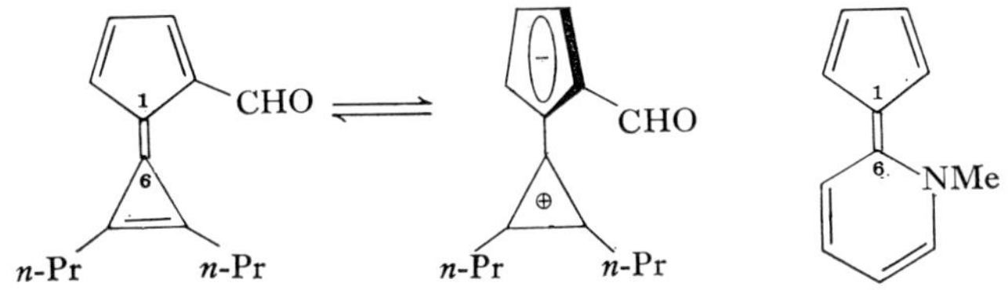

TABLE XIX

Rotational barriers for fulvenes (365) and the fulvalene (366)

Compound	R^{1a}	R^{2a}	R^{3a}	R^{4a}	$\Delta G^{\ddagger}_{C=C}$ kcal.mole^{-1}	Solvent	$\Delta G^{\ddagger}_{C-N}$ kcal.mole^{-1}	Reference
365	H	Me	H	H	22·1	DMSO	13·5	398, 399
365	Me	Me	H	H	15·5	DMSO–D$_2$O		398
					16·4	DMSO		398
					17·5	(CD$_3$)$_2$CO		398
					17·5	CDCl$_3$	10·7	398
365	Ph	Me	H	H	19·2	DMSO	11·8	398
365	p-C$_6$H$_4$OMe	Me	H	H	18·8	DMSO	12·1	398
365	—(CH$_2$)$_3$—		H	H	18·3	MeCN		399
					19·1	MeCONMe$_2$		399
					19·6	Me$_2$CO		399
366					18·0	DMF		400
					18·4	PhCN		400
					19·2	o-C$_6$H$_4$Cl$_2$		400
					19·4	Ph$_2$O		400
367					11·4	Me$_2$CO		399
365	H	Me	H	CHO			17·9	398
365	H	Me	CHO	H			21·5	398
365	H	Me	CHO	Me			20·3	398, 401
368							10·4	398, 401
368a							14·7	401
368b							12·6	398
369							<11·0	401
369a							11·8	401

^{a} These substituents refer only to the formula (365).

barriers. The moderately high energy barriers for the C(6)–N rotational process are due to loss of conjugation energy in going from the planar situation (e.g. **365**) to the non-planar transition state (e.g. **365b**) which has isolated fulvene and amine systems. Barriers of this type are lowered by benzene annelation (compounds **368** to **368b**), and by the replacement of CH by N at position-6 (compounds **369** and **369a**). These C(6)–N rotational barriers are analogous to those observed in amides and a number of other conjugated systems in which a C–N bond has partial double bond character. Barriers of this type have been discussed in Section VIB but, for convenience, a number are also discussed in this section.

368 R¹ = R² = H
368a R¹ = H, R² = CHO
368b R¹ = R² = CHO

369 R = H
369a R = CHO

The magnitudes of the rotational barriers about the C–C double bond for a variety of systems (**370** to **377**) are listed in Table XX,[402 to 408] together with C–N rotational barriers for appropriate cases.[403 to 405,408] A number of generalizations may be made about the relative magnitudes of the observed C–C rotational barriers in these systems, all of which are consistent with a dipolar transition state (**363**) for the rotational process. Thus the negative pole of the transition state may be stabilized by CO_2R, COR, CN, NO_2 and even p-$NO_2C_6H_4$ substituents, and in all cases, except the nitroketenemercaptal (**375**),[407] two of these stabilizing substituents are present at the potential negative pole. The positive pole is stabilized by NR_2, OMe and SMe substituents with decreasing effectiveness, and either one or two of such substituents may be present. Surprisingly it appears that a single NMe_2 substituent (**372**) is more effective than two NMe_2 substituents (**373**), but predictably the sequence of increasing effectiveness for a single NR_2 substituent is $NMe_2 > MeNC_6H_4OMe(p) > MeNPh > MeNC_6H_4NO_2(p)$. Alkyl substituents lower the C–C rotational barrier by a combination of steric and electronic effects, as is well exemplified by the series of enol ethers (**374** to **374d**).[406] Compounds (**373a**) and (**373b**) show barriers to rotation about the C–COPh bond [(**373a**), $\Delta G^{\ddagger}$ ca. 13 kcal.mole^{-1}] and the C–$C_6H_4NO_2$ bond [(**373b**), $\Delta G^{\ddagger}$ 11·6 kcal.mole^{-1}] in addition to the rotational barriers listed in Table XIX, further demonstrating the extent and importance of π-electron delocalization in these compounds.[407] In addition to the compounds listed in Table XIX a number of cyclic systems (**379**) have also been examined[404,405] and

TABLE XX

Rotational Barriers in enamines and related compounds

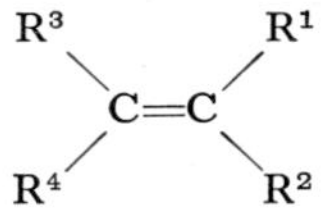

$$R^3R^1C=CR^4R^2$$

378

Com-pound	R^{1a}	R^{2a}	R^{3a}	R^{4a}	C=C rotation $\Delta G^{\ddagger}$ kcal.mole^{-1}	C=C rotation Solvent	C–N rotation Solvent	C–N rotation $\Delta G^{\ddagger}$ kcal.mole^{-1}	Reference
370	CO_2Me	CO_2Me	H	NMe_2	15·6	CH_2Cl_2	CH_2Cl_2	13·3	402, 404
370a	CO_2Me	CO_2Me	Me	NMe_2	<9·1	CH_2Cl_2	CH_2Cl_2	ca. 8·7	404
370b	CO_2Me	CO_2Me	H	NMePh	19·4	CH_2Cl_2			402, 404
370c	CO_2Me	CO_2Me	Me	NMePh	10·0	$(CD_3)_2CO$			404
370d	CO_2Me	CO_2Me	H	$MeNC_6H_4OMe(p)$	18·5	$CHBr_3$			402
370e	CO_2Me	CO_2Me	H	$MeNC_6H_4NO_2(p)$	22·1	$CHBr_3$			402
371	CO_2Me	CN	Me	NMe_2	14·9^b 14·8^c	CH_2Cl_2	CH_2Cl_2	12·1^b 14·8^c	405
371a	CO_2Me	CN	Me	NMePh	18·3^b 17·8^c	C_6H_5Br			405
371b	CO_2Me	CN	H	NMe_2	<12	CH_2Cl_2			405
372	COMe	COMe	H	NMe_2	<13	CH_2Cl_2	C_6H_5Br	17·6	402
372a	COMe	COMe	H	$MeNC_6H_4OMe(p)$	13·9	CH_2Cl_2			402
372b	COMe	COMe	H	NMePh	16·9	CH_2Cl_2			402
372c	COMe	COMe	H	$MeNC_6H_4NO_2(p)$	15·0	CS_2-CH_2Cl_2			402
373	COMe	COMe	NMe_2	NMe_2	15·3	$CHCl_2F \cdot CHF_2Cl$			403
373a	COPh	CN	NMe_2	NMe_2		$CHCl_2F \cdot CHF_2Cl$	$CHCl_2F \cdot CHF_2Cl$	10·8^b 13·7^c	403

	R1	R2	R3	R4	Solvent		CS_2-$CDCl_3$		
					CS_2-$CDCl_3$			13·1	
373b	$C_6H_4NO_2(p)$	CN	NMe_2	NMe_2	CS_2-$CDCl_3$	15·0		13·1	403
374	CO_2Me	CO_2Me	OMe	H	C_4Cl_6	ca. 27·7			406
374a	CO_2Me	CO_2Me	OMe	Me	C_4Cl_6	25·7			406
374b	CO_2Me	CO_2Me	OMe	Et	C_4Cl_6	24·7			406
374c	CO_2Me	CO_2Me	OMe	i-Pr	C_4Cl_6	23·3			406
374d	CO_2Me	CO_2Me	OMe	t-Bu	C_6H_5Br	18·3			406
375	NO_2	H	SMe	SMe	C_5H_5N	14·8			407
375a	CN	CO_2Me	SMe	SMe	o-$C_6H_4Cl_2$	24·6			407
376	CO_2Me	CO_2Me	Me	NMe_2		>27·5			408
377	CO_2Me	CO_2Me	SMe	NMe_2	various	<9·4	$(CD_3)_2CO$	8·9	408
377a	CO_2Me	CO_2Me	SMe	NHPh	CH_2Cl_2	12·0			408
377b	CO_2Me	CO_2Me	SMe	NMePh	$(CD_3)_2CO$	<8·5			408
377c	CO_2Me	CO_2Me	SMe	$MeNC_6H_4NO_2(p)$	$(CD_3)_2CO$	9·9			408

[a] The substituents R^1, R^2, R^3, and R^4 listed in the Table refer to the general formula (378).
[b] For major conformer.
[c] For minor conformer.

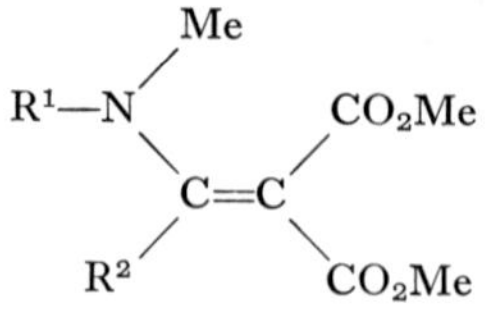

$$R^1-N \overset{Me}{\underset{R^2}{\diagup}} C=C \overset{CO_2Me}{\underset{CO_2Me}{\diagdown}}$$

370 $R^1 = Me, R^2 = H$
370a $R^1 = R^2 = Me$
370b $R^1 = Ph, R^2 = H$
370c $R^1 = Ph, R^2 = Me$
370d $R^1 = p\text{-}C_6H_4OMe, R^2 = H$
370e $R^1 = p\text{-}C_6H_4NO_2, R^2 = H$

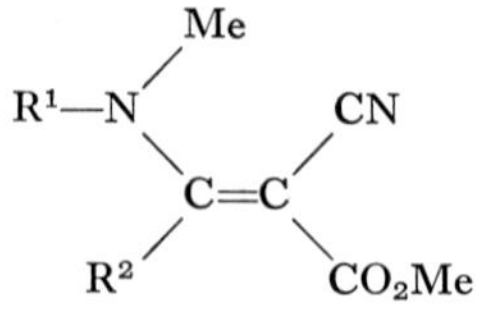

$$R^1-N \overset{Me}{\underset{R^2}{\diagup}} C=C \overset{CN}{\underset{CO_2Me}{\diagdown}}$$

371 $R^1 = R^2 = Me$
371a $R^1 = Ph, R^2 = Me$
371b $R^1 = Me, R^2 = H$

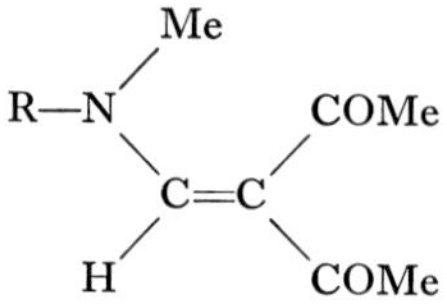

$$R-N \overset{Me}{\underset{H}{\diagup}} C=C \overset{COMe}{\underset{COMe}{\diagdown}}$$

372 $R = Me$
372a $R = p\text{-}C_6H_4OMe$
372b $R = Ph$
372c $R = p\text{-}C_6H_4NO_2$

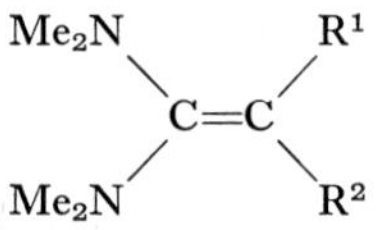

$$\overset{Me_2N}{\underset{Me_2N}{\diagdown}} C=C \overset{R^1}{\underset{R^2}{\diagup}}$$

373 $R^1 = R^2 = COMe$
373a $R^1 = COPh, R^2 = CN$
373b $R^1 = p\text{-}C_6H_4NO_2, R^2 = CN$

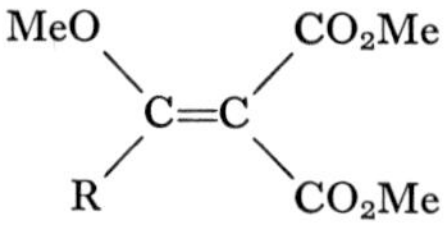

$$\overset{MeO}{\underset{R}{\diagdown}} C=C \overset{CO_2Me}{\underset{CO_2Me}{\diagup}}$$

374 $R = H$
374a $R = Me$
374b $R = Et$
374c $R = CHMe_2$
374d $R = CMe_3$

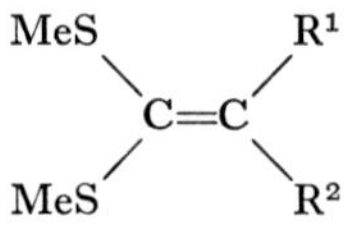

$$\overset{MeS}{\underset{MeS}{\diagdown}} C=C \overset{R^1}{\underset{R^2}{\diagup}}$$

375 $R^1 = H, R^2 = NO_2$
375a $R^1 = CN, R^2 = CO_2Me$

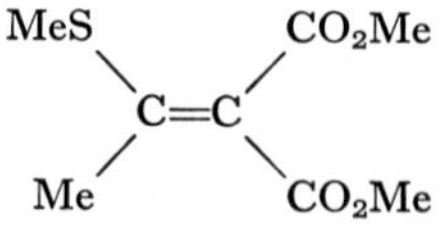

$$\overset{MeS}{\underset{Me}{\diagup}} C=C \overset{CO_2Me}{\underset{CO_2Me}{\diagdown}}$$

376

$$\overset{MeS}{\underset{R^1-N}{\diagdown}} C=C \overset{CO_2Me}{\underset{CO_2Me}{\diagup}} \quad R^2$$

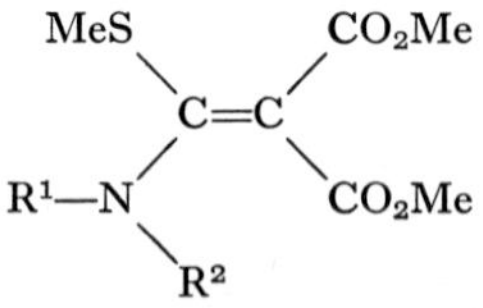

377 $R^1 = R^2 = Me$
377a $R^1 = H, R^2 = Ph$
377b $R^1 = Me, R^2 = Ph$
377c $R^1 = Me, R^2 = p\text{-}C_6H_4NO_2$

the results show the same general trends. Rotation about the interannular double bond of the extended quinone (**380**) may also be detected by the temperature dependence of the NMR spectrum[409] ($\Delta G^\ddagger$ 21·0 kcal.mole^{-1} in *trans*-decalin), but in this case the transition state for the rotational process is probably the diradical (**380a**), best represented as a biphenoxy radical. The low rotational

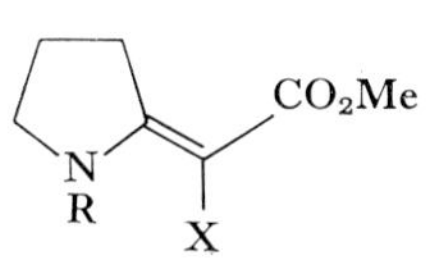

379 R = alkyl or aryl
X = CN or CO₂Me

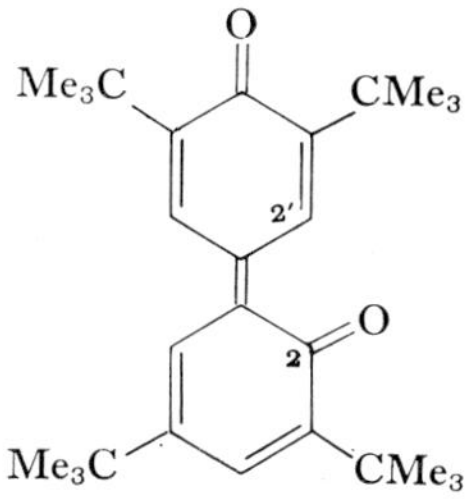

380

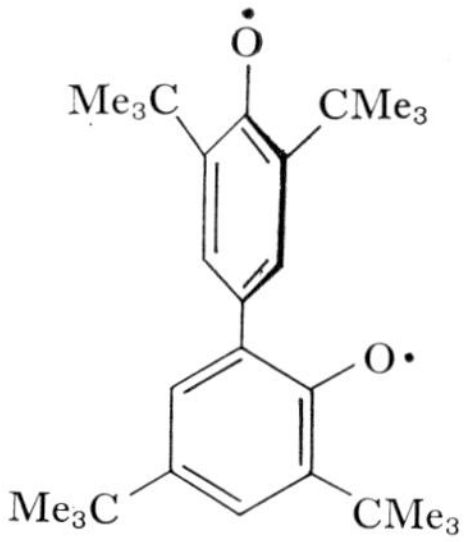

380a

barrier for the quinone (**380**) may result to some extent from the steric inter-actions between the 2-carbonyl group and the C(2′) hydrogen substituent in the planar ground state (see **380**), but this effect is probably unimportant compared with the delocalization of the unpaired electrons in the phenoxy systems of the transition state (**380**). Relatively low rotational barriers have also been found by NMR methods[410] for the diphenoquinone (**381**) [$\Delta G^{\ddagger}_{424}$ 24·2 kcal.mole^{-1} from coalescence data, $\Delta G^{\ddagger}_{310}$ 23·2 kcal.mole^{-1} by direct equilibration of isolated diastereomers (**381**) and (**381a**)].

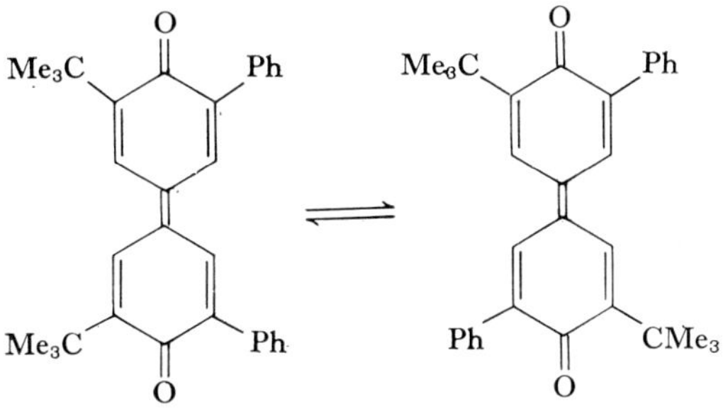

381

381a

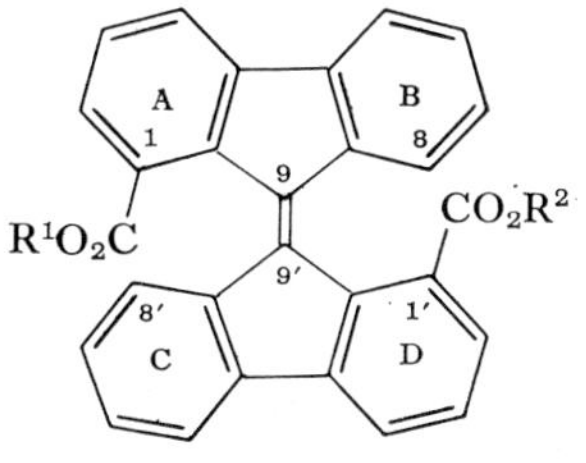

382 R¹ = R² = Me
382a R¹ = R² = CHMe₂
382b R¹ = Me, R² = CHMe₂

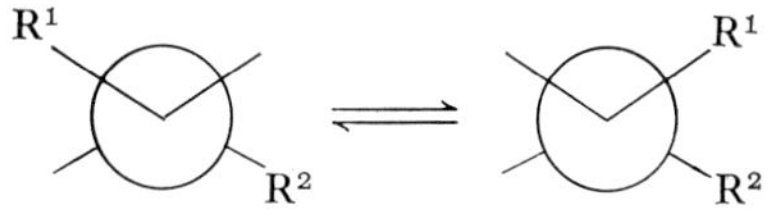

383

383a

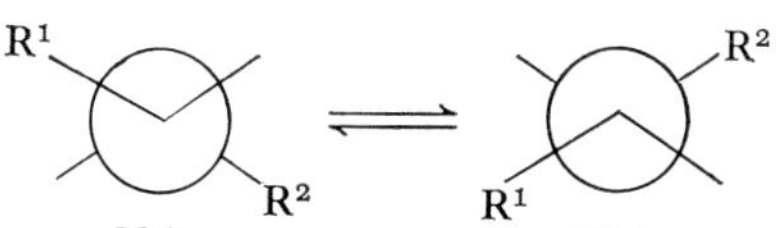

384

384a

The rather low rotational barrier about the C(9)–C(9′) double bond of the bisfluorenylidenes ($\Delta G^{\ddagger}$ 20 to 21 kcal.mole^{-1} for *cis-trans* isomerization)[411] is probably to a considerable extent a consequence of ground-state destabilization rather than stabilization of a diradical transition state. A further consequence of this ground-state strain, due to obvious non-bonded interactions between the pairs of substituents at positions 1 and 8′, and 1′ and 8 (see **382**), is the non-planarity of the bisfluorenylidene molecule, which in the ground state probably adopts a conformation with a folding deformation of each of the five-membered rings so that aromatic rings A and B are above the mean molecular plane and rings C and D are folded below it (see **382** and the projectional formulae along the C(9)–(9′) bonds, **383** and **384**). This non-planar conformation is chiral (for $R^1 \neq R^2$) and at low temperatures the prochiral isopropyl groups of (**382a**) and (**382b**) exhibit geminal non-equivalence of the methyl groups in the NMR spectra. The two doublet signals observed at low temperature coalesce to a single doublet at higher temperatures when the isomerization process (**384**)⇌(**384a**) becomes fast on the NMR time-scale. The free energy of activation for this inversion process [$\Delta G^{\ddagger}_{363}$ 21·0 kcal.mole^{-1} for (**382a**) and $\Delta G^{\ddagger}_{363}$ 20·8 kcal.mole^{-1} for (**382b**)] is similar to that for the *trans* → *cis* isomerization process (**383** → **383a**); the transition state is apparently the same for both processes and must therefore be associated with the geometry shown in (**385**) in which the thickened bonds are coplanar. The relationship between the free energy of the transition state (**385**) and that of the diradical system, in which the two fluorenyl units are arranged in orthogonal planes, is not known. *Cis-trans* isomerism in the 1,1′-dioxygenated bianthrones (e.g. **386**) and 1,1′,3,3′-tetraoxygenated bixanthylenes (e.g. **387**) is too slow, up to 473°K, to be studied by line-shape methods although the kinetics of equilibration may be studied directly using isolated diastereomers.[412]

386   $R^1 = OCHMe_2, R^2 = H, X = CO$
387   $R^1 = R^2 = OCHMe_2, X = 0$

385

The inversion of the folded conformations of the *trans*-isopropoxy compounds (**386**) and (**387**) may, however, be studied by line-shape methods and the measured energy barriers to configurational inversion [$\Delta G^{\ddagger}_{467}$ 25·8 kcal.mole^{-1} for (**386**), and $\Delta G^{\ddagger}_{440}$ 24·1 kcal.mole^{-1} for (**387**)][412] are rather larger than the inversion barriers for the 1-alkoxycarbonyl-bisfluorenylidenes (**382**). The 2,2′-dioxygenated bixanthylenes (**388**) and bianthrones (**389**) are predictably much more mobile with respect to configurational inversion and surprisingly also much more mobile with respect to *cis-trans* isomerization [$\Delta G^{\ddagger}_{388}$ 21·0 kcal.mole^{-1} for (**389**), and $\Delta G^{\ddagger}$ 18·4 kcal.mole^{-1} for (**388**)].[412] These rather low rotational barriers suggest that the diradical transition states (390) are stabilized, since the ground-state conformations of (388) and (389) are probably relatively strain free.

388 X = O, R = Me
389 X = CO, R = CHMe$_2$

390

Ph   Ph
 \   /
  C=C=C=C=C=C
 /   \
Me$_3$C   CMe$_3$
                391

Rotation about the double bonds in cumulenes also involves, in some cases, unusually low free energies of activation, and the activation energy for *cis-trans* isomerism of the hexapentaene (391) is sufficiently low ($\Delta G^\ddagger$ *ca.* 20 kcal.mole^{-1}) to be studied by line-shape methods.[413] The rotational barrier in the corresponding butatriene ($\Delta G^\ddagger$ *ca.* 30 kcal.mole^{-1}) is, however, much larger and can only be measured by direct equilibration of isolated diastereomers.[413]

REFERENCES

1. L. W. Reeves, *Advances in Phys. Org. Chem.*, 1965, **3**, 187.
2. G. Binsch, *Topics in Stereochemistry*, 1968, **3**, 97.
3. C. S. Johnson, *Advances in Magnetic Resonance*, 1965, **1**, 33.
4. J. E. Anderson, *Quart. Rev.*, 1965, **19**, 426.
5. H. Kessler, *Angew. Chem. Internat. Edn.*, 1970, **9**, 219.
6. F. Bloch, *Phys. Rev.*, 1946, **70**, 460.
7. A. Carrington and A. D. McLachlan, "Introduction to Magnetic Resonance", Harper, New York, 1967, Ch. 11.
8. E. L. Hahn and D. E. Maxwell, *Phys. Rev.*, 1952, **88**, 1070.
9. H. M. McConnell, *J. Chem. Phys.*, 1958, **28**, 430.
10. H. S. Gutowsky, D. W. McCall and C. P. Slichter, *J. Chem. Phys.*, 1953, **21**, 279; H. S. Gutowsky and A. Saika, *J. Chem. Phys.*, 1953, **21**, 1688.
11. H. S. Gutowsky and C. H. Holm, *J. Chem. Phys.*, 1956, **25**, 1228.
12. R. Kubo, *J. Phys. Soc. Japan*, 1954, **9**, 935; R. Kubo and K. Tomita, *J. Phys. Soc. Japan*, 1954, **9**, 888; R. A. Sack, *Mol. Phys.*, 1958, **1**, 163.
13. M. T. Rogers and J. C. Woodbrey, *J. Phys. Chem.*, 1962, **66**, 540.
14. For a general account of some of these see J. A. Pople, W. G. Schneider and H. J. Bernstein, "High Resolution Nuclear Magnetic Resonance", McGraw-Hill, New York, 1959, Ch. 10.
15. A. Allerhand, H. S. Gutowsky, J. Jonas and R. A. Meinzer, *J. Amer. Chem. Soc.*, 1966, **88**, 3185.

16. H. G. Schmid, H. Friebolin, S. Kabuss and R. Mecke, *Spectrochim. Acta*, 1966, **22**, 623.
17. G. Binsch and J. D. Roberts, *J. Amer. Chem. Soc.*, 1965, **87**, 5157.
18. J. M. Lehn, B. J. Price, F. G. Riddell and I. O. Sutherland, *J. Chem. Soc.(B)*, 1967, 387.
19. J. Jonas, A. Allerhand and H. S. Gutowsky, *J. Chem. Phys.*, 1965, **42**, 396.
20. H. S. Gutowsky, J. Jonas and T. H. Siddall, *J. Amer. Chem. Soc.*, 1967, **89**, 4300.
21. R. C. Neuman, jun. and V. Jonas, *J. Amer. Chem. Soc.*, 1968, **90**, 1970.
22. M. Rabinovitz and A. Pines, *J. Amer. Chem. Soc.*, 1969, **91**, 1585.
23. L. M. Jackman, T. E. Kavanagh and R. C. Haddon, *Org. Magn. Resonance*, 1969, **1**, 109.
24. F. A. L. Anet and A. J. R. Bourn, *J. Amer. Chem. Soc.*, 1967, **89**, 760.
25. L. H. Piette and W. A. Anderson, *J. Chem. Phys.*, 1959, **30**, 899.
26. M. Takeda and E. O. Stejskal, *J. Amer. Chem. Soc.*, 1960, **82**, 25.
27. G. Binsch, *J. Amer. Chem. Soc.*, 1969, **91**, 1304.
28. A. Abragam, "The Principles of Nuclear Magnetism", Oxford Univ. Press, London and New York, 1961; C. P. Slichter, "Principles of Magnetic Resonance", Harper, New York, 1963.
29. R. M. Lynden-Bell, *Progress in Nuclear Magnetic Resonance Spectroscopy*, 1967, **2**, 163.
30. I. I. Rabi, N. F. Ramsey and J. Schwinger, *Rev. Mod. Phys.*, 1954, **26**, 167.
31. J. I. Kaplan, *J. Chem. Phys.*, 1958, **28**, 278; 1958, **29**, 462.
32. S. Alexander, *J. Chem. Phys.*, 1962, **37**, 967, 974; 1963, **38**, 1787; 1964, **40**, 2741.
33. C. S. Johnson, *J. Chem. Phys.*, 1964, **41**, 3277.
34. J. Heidberg, J. A. Weil, G. A. Janusonis and J. K. Anderson, *J. Chem. Phys.*, 1964, **41**, 1033.
35. F. B. Mallory, S. L. Manatt and C. S. Wood, *J. Amer. Chem. Soc.*, 1965, 87, 5433.
36. M. Oki, H. Iwamura and N. Hayakawa, *Bull. Chem. Soc. Japan*, 1963, **36**, 1542.
37. R. J. Kurland, M. B. Rubin and W. B. Wyse, *J. Chem. Phys.*, 1964, **40**, 2426.
38. C. Ganter, S. M. Pokras and J. D. Roberts, *J. Amer. Chem. Soc.*, 1966, **88**, 4235.
39. G. Fraenkel and D. T. Dix, *J. Amer. Chem. Soc.*, 1966, **88**, 979.
40. M. Witanowski and J. D. Roberts, *J. Amer. Chem. Soc.*, 1966, **88**, 737.
41. G. M. Whitesides, F. Kaplan and J. D. Roberts, *J. Amer. Chem. Soc.*, 1963, **85**, 2167.
42. G. M. Whitesides, M. Witanowski and J. D. Roberts, *J. Amer. Chem. Soc.*, 1965, **87**, 4878.
43. R. A. Newmark and C. H. Sederholm, *J. Chem. Phys.*, 1965, **43**, 602.
44. J. T. C. Gerig and J. D. Roberts, *J. Amer. Chem. Soc.*, 1966, **88**, 2791.
45. R. E. Lack, C. Ganter and J. D. Roberts, *J. Amer. Chem. Soc.*, 1968, **90**, 7001.
46. S. L. Spassov, D. L. Griffith, E. S. Glazer, K. Nagarajan and J. D. Roberts, *J. Amer. Chem. Soc.*, 1967, **89**, 88.
47. J. B. Lambert and R. G. Keske, *J. Org. Chem.*, 1966, **31**, 3429.
48. G. Govil and H. J. Bernstein, *J. Chem. Phys.*, 1968, **48**, 285.
49. S. Forsén and R. A. Hoffman, *J. Chem. Phys.*, 1963, **39**, 2892.
50. S. Forsén and R. A. Hoffman, *J. Chem. Phys.*, 1964, **40**, 1189.
51. S. Forsén and R. A. Hoffman, *Progress in NMR Spectroscopy*, 1966, **1**, 89.
52. I. C. Calder, P. J. Garratt and F. Sondheimer, *Chem. Comm.*, 1967, 41.
53. J. Feeney and A. Heinrich, *Chem. Comm.*, 1966, 295.
54. A. Allerhand and H. S. Gutowsky, *J. Chem. Phys.*, 1964, **41**, 2115.
55. A. Allerhand and H. S. Gutowsky, *J. Chem. Phys.*, 1965, **42**, 1587.

56. A. Allerhand, F. Chen and H. S. Gutowsky, *J. Chem. Phys.*, 1965, **42**, 3040.
57. J. Jonas, A. Allerhand and H. S. Gutowsky, *J. Chem. Phys.*, 1965, **42**, 4203.
58. H. S. Gutowsky and F. M. Chem, *J. Phys. Chem.*, 1965, **69**, 3216.
59. A. Allerhand and H. S. Gutowsky, *J. Amer. Chem. Soc.*, 1965, **87**, 4092.
60. H. S. Gutowsky, R. L. Vold and E. J. Wells, *J. Chem. Phys.*, 1965, **43**, 4107.
61. H. S. Gutowsky and P. A. Temussi, *J. Amer. Chem. Soc.*, 1967, **89**, 4358.
62. R. L. Vold and H. S. Gutowsky, *J. Chem. Phys.*, 1967, **47**, 2495.
63. T. D. Alger, H. S. Gutowsky and R. L. Vold, *J. Chem. Phys.*, 1967, **47**, 3130.
64. H. Y. Carr and E. M. Purcell, *Phys. Rev.*, 1954, **94**, 630.
65. A. Allerhand and E. Thiele, *J. Chem. Phys.*, 1966, **45**, 902.
66. C. S. Johnson and M. Saunders, *J. Chem. Phys.*, 1965, **43**, 4170.
67. M. Bloom, L. W. Reeves and E. J. Wells, *J. Chem. Phys.*, 1965, **42**, 1615.
68. K. H. Abrahamson, P. T. Inglefield, E. Karkower and L. W. Reeves, *Can. J. Chem.*, 1966, **44**, 1685.
69. L. M. Jackman, T. E. Kavanagh and R. C. Haddon, *Org. Magn. Resonance*, 1969, **1**, 109.
70. S. Glasstone, K. J. Laidler and H. Eyring, "Theory of rate Processes", McGraw-Hill, New York, 1941; I. Amdur and G. Hammes, "Chemical Kinetics. Principles and Selected Topics", McGraw-Hill, New York, 1966; M. Boudart, "Kinetics of Chemical Processes", Prentice-Hall, New Jersey, 1968.
71. L. P. Hammett, "Physical Organic Chemistry", McGraw-Hill, New York, 1940; P. R. Wells, *Chem. Rev.*, 1963, **63**, 171; J. E. Leffler and E. Grunwald, "Rates and Equilibria of Organic Reactions", Wiley, New York, 1963; S. Ehrenson, *Progress in Phys. Org. Chem.*, 1964, **2**, 195.
72. M. J. S. Dewar and M. Shanshal, *J. Amer. Chem. Soc.*, 1969, **91**, 3654.
73. M. J. S. Dewar and W. B. Jennings, *Tetrahedron Letters*, 1970, 339.
74. R. K. Harris and R. A. Spragg, *J. Chem. Soc.(B)*, 1968, 684.
75. F. G. Riddell, *Quart. Rev.*, 1967, 364.
76. F. R. Jensen, D. S. Noyce, C. H. Sederholm and A. J. Berlin, *J. Amer. Chem. Soc.*, 1960, **82**, 1256.
77. R. K. Harris and N. Sheppard, *Proc. Chem. Soc.*, 1961, 419.
78. S. Meiboom, Symposium on NMR, Boulder, Colorado, 1962, quoted in ref. 24.
79. F. A. L. Anet, M. Ahmad and L. D. Hall, *Proc. Chem. Soc.*, 1964, 145.
80. F. A. Bovey, F. P. Hood, E. W. Anderson and R. L. Kornegay, *Proc. Chem. Soc.*, 1964, 146; *J. Chem. Phys.*, 1964, **41**, 2041.
81. J. B. Hendrickson, *J. Amer. Chem. Soc.*, 1961, **83**, 4537; K. B. Wiberg, *J. Amer. Chem. Soc.*, 1965, **87**, 1070; M. Bixon and S. Lifson, *Tetrahedron*, 1967, **23**, 769; N. L. Allinger, J. A. Hirsch, M. A. Miller, I. J. Tyminski and F. A. Van-Catledge, *J. Amer. Chem. Soc.*, 1968, **90**, 1199; C. Altona and M. Sunaralingham, *Tetrahedron*, 1970, **26**, 925.
82. J. B. Hendrickson, *J. Amer. Chem. Soc.*, 1964, **86**, 4854; 1967, **89**, 7047.
83. A. Allerhand and H. S. Gutowsky, *J. Chem. Phys.*, 1965, **42**, 3396.
84. H. Kessler, V. Gusowski and M. Hanack, *Tetrahedron Letters*, 1968, 4665.
85. G. V. D. Tiers, *Proc. Chem. Soc.*, 1960, 389.
86. L. W. Reeves and K. O. Strømme, *Can. J. Chem.*, 1960, **38**, 1241.
87. W. C. Neckham and B. P. Dailey, *J. Chem. Phys.*, 1963, **38**, 445.
88. F. A. Bovey, E. W. Anderson, F. P. Hood and R. L. Kornegay, *J. Chem. Phys.*, 1964, **40**, 3099.
89. L. W. Reeves and K. O. Strømme, *Trans. Faraday Soc.*, 1961, **57**, 390.

90. H. M. van Dort and T. J. Sekuur, *Tetrahedron Letters*, 1963, 1301.
91. S. Brownstein, *Can. J. Chem.*, 1962, **40**, 870.
92. R. K. Harris and N. Sheppard, *Mol. Phys.*, 1964, **7**, 595.
93. S. Wolfe and J. R. Campbell, *Chem. Comm.*, 1967, 874.
94. S. Wolfe and J. R. Campbell, *Chem. Comm.*, 1967, 877.
95. H. Friebolin, H. G. Schmid, S. Kabuss and W. Faisst, *Org. Magn. Resonance*, 1969, **1**, 147.
96. H. G. Schmid, A. Jaeschke, H. Friebolin, S. Kabuss and R. Mecke, *Org. Magn. Resonance*, 1969, **1**, 163.
97. F. R. Jensen and B. H. Beck, *J. Amer. Chem. Soc.*, 1968, **90**, 1066.
98. J. T. Gerig, *J. Amer. Chem. Soc.*, 1968, **90**, 1065.
99. M. St-Jacques and M. Bernard, *Can. J. Chem.*, 1969, **47**, 2911.
100. F. R. Jensen and C. H. Bushweller, *J. Amer. Chem. Soc.*, 1969, **91**, 5774.
101. F. A. L. Anet and M. Z. Haq, *J. Amer. Chem. Soc.*, 1965, **87**, 3147.
102. J. B. Lambert, R. G. Keske, R. E. Cahart and A. P. Johanovich, *J. Amer. Chem. Soc.*, 1967, **89**, 3761.
103. F. G. Riddell, *J. Chem. Soc.(B)*, 1967, 560.
104. R. F. Farmer and J. Hamer, *Tetrahedron*, 1968, **24**, 829.
105. H. Friebolin, S. Kabuss, W. Maier and A. Luttringhaus, *Tetrahedron Letters*, 1962, 683; H. Friebolin, H. G. Schmid, S. Kabuss and W. Faisst, *Org. Magn. Resonance*, 1969, **1**, 67.
106. J. E. Anderson and J. C. D. Brand, *Trans. Faraday Soc.*, 1966, **62**, 39.
107. J. E. Anderson, *Chem. Comm.*, 1969, 669.
108. J. E. Anderson, *Chem. Comm.*, 1970, 417.
109. G. A. Yousif and J. D. Roberts, *J. Amer. Chem. Soc.*, 1968, **90**, 6428.
110. G. Gatti, A. L. Segre and C. Morandi, *J. Chem. Soc.(B)*, 1967, 1203.
111. J. M. Lehn, P. Linschied and F. G. Riddell, *Bull. Soc. chim. France*, 1968, 1172.
112. L. W. Reeves and K. O. Strømme, *J. Chem. Phys.*, 1961, **34**, 1711.
113. G. Claeson, G. M. Androes and M. Calvin, *J. Amer. Chem. Soc.*, 1961, **83**, 4257.
114. G. Claeson, G. M. Androes and M. Calvin, *J. Amer. Chem. Soc.*, 1960, **82**, 4428.
115. A. Lüttringhaus, S. Kabuss, W. Maier and H. Friebolin, *Z. Naturforsch.*, 1961, **16b**, 761.
116. A. Geens, G. Swaelens and M. Anteunis, *Chem. Comm.*, 1969, 439.
117. F. R. Jensen and C. H. Bushweller, *Tetrahedron Letters*, 1968, 2825.
118. C. H. Bushweller, J. Golini, G. U. Rao and J. W. O'Neil, *Chem. Comm.*, 1970, 51; C. H. Bushweller, *J. Amer. Chem. Soc.*, 1967, **89**, 5978; 1968, **90**, 2450; 1969, **91**, 6019.
119. R. W. Murray, P. R. Story and M. L. Kaplan, *J. Amer. Chem. Soc.*, 1966, **88**, 526.
120. J. E. Anderson and J. D. Roberts, *J. Amer. Chem. Soc.*, 1968, **90**, 4186.
121. C. H. Bushweller and J. W. O'Neil, *Tetrahedron Letters*, 1969, 4713.
122. P. W. Rabideau, R. G. Harvey and J. B. Stothers, *Chem. Comm.*, 1969, 1005.
123. M. Oki, H. Iwamura and N. Hayakawa, *Bull. Chem. Soc. Japan*, 1964, **37**, 1865.
124. M. S. Newman and A. S. Hussey, *J. Amer. Chem. Soc.*, 1947, **69**, 3023; F. Bell and D. H. Waring, *J. Chem. Soc.*, 1949, 2689; M. Crawford, R. A. M. Mckinnon and V. R. Supanekar, *J. Chem. Soc.*, 1959, 2807.

125. M. S. Newman and D. J. Lednicer, *J. Amer. Chem. Soc.*, 1956, **78**, 4765; R. H. Martin, N. Defay, H. P. Figeys, M. Flammang-Barbieux, J. P. Cosyn, M. Gelbecke and J. J. Schurter, *Tetrahedron*, 1969, **25**, 4985.
126. D. Y. Curtin, C. G. Carlson and C. G. McCarty, *Can. J. Chem.*, 1964, **42**, 565.
127. Z. M. Holubec and J. Jonas, *J. Amer. Chem. Soc.*, 1968, **90**, 5986.
128. R. Munday and I. O. Sutherland, *J. Chem. Soc.(B)*, 1968, 80.
129. W. B. Moniz and J. A. Dixon, *J. Amer. Chem. Soc.*, 1961, 83, 1671; N. Muller and W. C. Tosch, *J. Chem. Phys.*, 1962, **37**, 1170.
130. F. G. Riddell and M. J. T. Robinson, *Chem. Comm.*, 1965, 227.
131. J. Altman, H. Gilboa, D. Ginsburg and A. Loewenstein, *Tetrahedron Letters*, 1967, 1329.
132. R. E. Lack and J. D. Roberts, *J. Amer. Chem. Soc.*, 1968, **90**, 6997.
133. B. Fuchs, *Tetrahedron Letters*, 1969, 3571.
134. H. Gilboa, J. Altman and A. Loewenstein, *J. Amer. Chem. Soc.*, 1969, **91**, 6062.
135. J. B. Hendrickson, *J. Amer. Chem. Soc.*, 1962, **84**, 3355; *Tetrahedron*, 1963, **19**, 1387.
136. R. Knorr, E. S. Ganter and J. D. Roberts, *Angew. Chem. Internat. Edn.*, 1967, **6**, 556.
137. S. Kabuss, H. Friebolin and H. Schmid, *Tetrahedron Letters*, 1965, 469.
138. H. Friebolin, R. Mecke, S. Kabuss and A. Lüttringhaus, *Tetrahedron Letters*, 1964, 1929.
139. S. Kabuss, A. Lüttringhaus, H. Friebolin, H. G. Schmid and R. Mecke, *Tetrahedron Letters*, 1966, 719.
140. S. Kabuss, H. G. Schmid and H. Friebolin, *Org. Magn. Resonance*, 1969, **1**, 451.
141. R. M. Moriarty, N. Ishibe, M. Kayser, K. C. Ramey and H. J. Gisler, jun., *Tetrahedron Letters*, 1969, 4883.
142. I. O. Sutherland and M. V. J. Ramsay, *Tetrahedron*, 1965, **21**, 3401.
143. M. Oki and H. Iwamura, *Tetrahedron*, 1968, **24**, 2377.
144. K. Mislow, M. A. W. Glass, H. B. Hopps, E. Simon and G. H. Wahl, jun., *J. Amer. Chem. Soc.*, 1964, **86**, 1710.
145. F. A. L. Anet, *J. Amer. Chem. Soc.*, 1964, **86**, 458.
146. F. R. Jensen and L. A. Smith, *J. Amer. Chem. Soc.*, 1964, **86**, 956.
147. K. Conrow, M. E. H. Howden and D. Davis, *J. Amer. Chem. Soc.*, 1963, **85**, 1929.
148. W. E. Heyd and C. A. Cupas, *J. Amer. Chem. Soc.*, 1969, **91**, 1559.
149. J. B. Lambert, L. J. Durham, P. Lepoutre and J. D. Roberts, *J. Amer. Chem. Soc.*, 1965, **87**, 3896.
150. M. Nógrádi, W. D. Ollis and I. O. Sutherland, *Chem. Comm.*, 1970, 158.
151. W. Tochtermann, U. Walter and H. Mannschreck, *Tetrahedron Letters*, 1964, 2981.
152. C. M. Combs, W. G. Lobeck, jun. and Y-H. Wu, *J. Org. Chem.*, 1970, **35**, 275.
153. A. Ebnöther, E. Jucker and A. Stoll, *Helv. Chim. Acta*, 1965, **48**, 1237.
154. F. A. L. Anet, C. H. Bradley, M. A. Brown, W. L. Mock and J. H. McCausland, *J. Amer. Chem. Soc.*, 1969, **91**, 7782.
155. W. Tochtermann, H. Kuppers and C. Franke, *Chem. Ber.*, 1968, **101**, 3808, and preceding papers in the same series.
156. P. T. Lansbury, J. F. Bieron and M. Klein, *J. Amer. Chem. Soc.*, 1966, **88**, 1477.

157. M. E. C. Biffen, L. Crombie, T. M. Connor and J. A. Elvidge, *J. Chem. Soc.* (*B*), 1967, 841.
158. P. T. Lansbury and M. Klein, *Tetrahedron Letters*, 1968, 1981.
159. F. A. L. Anet and M. St. Jacques, *J. Amer. Chem. Soc.*, 1966, **88**, 2585.
160. F. A. L. Anet and J. S. Hartman, *J. Amer. Chem. Soc.*, 1963, **85**, 1204.
161. J. E. Anderson, E. S. Glazer, D. L. Griffith, R. Knorr and J. D. Roberts, *J. Amer. Chem. Soc.*, 1969, **91**, 1386.
162. J. M. Lehn and F. G. Riddell, *Chem. Comm.*, 1966, 803.
163. M. St. Jacques, M. A. Brown and F. A. L. Anet, *Tetrahedron Letters*, 1966, 5947.
164. A. Krebs, *Tetrahedron Letters*, 1968, 4511.
165. J. M. Davies and S. H. Graham, *Chem. Comm.*, 1968, 542.
166. R. Huisgen and G. Boche, *Tetrahedron Letters*, 1965, 1769.
167. J. Dale, *Angew. Chem. Internat. Edn.*, 1966, **6**, 1000.
168. A. T. Blomquist and R. D. Miller, *J. Amer. Chem. Soc.*, 1968, **90**, 3233.
169. A. C. Cope, K. Banholzer, H. Keller, B. A. Pawson, J. J. Whang and H. J. S. Winkler, *J. Amer. Chem. Soc.*, 1965, **87**, 3644.
170. J. Dale, T. Ekeland and J. Schaug, *Chem. Comm.*, 1968, 1477.
171. H. L. Carrell, B. W. Roberts, J. Donohue and J. J. Vollmer, *J. Amer. Chem. Soc.*, 1968, **90**, 5263; B. W. Roberts, J. J. Vollmer and K. L. Servis, *J. Amer. Chem. Soc.*, 1968, **90**, 5264.
172. A. Fiegenbaum and J. M. Lehn, *Bull. Soc. chim. France*, 1969, 3724.
173. S. Dev, J. E. Anderson, V. Cormier, N. P. Damodaran and J. D. Roberts, *J. Amer. Chem. Soc.*, 1968, **90**, 1246.
174. B. Miller and B. D. Gesner, *Tetrahedron Letters*, 1965, 3351; A. Lüttringhaus and K. C. Peters, *Angew. Chem. Internat. Edn.*, 1966, **5**, 593; N. K. Anand, R. C. Cookson, B. Halton and I. D. R. Stevens, *J. Amer. Chem. Soc.*, 1966, **88**, 370.
175. J. D. White and B. D. Gesner, *Tetrahedron Letters*, 1968, 1591.
176. A. P. Downing, W. D. Ollis and I. O. Sutherland, *J. Chem. Soc.*(*B*), 1970, 24.
177. J. Dale and K. Titlestad, *Chem. Comm.*, 1969, 656.
178. F. Vögtle, *Tetrahedron Letters*, 1969, 3193.
179. F. Vögtle, *Chem. Ber.*, 1969, **102**, 1784.
180. F. Vögtle, *Tetrahedron Letters*, 1968, 5221.
181. R. H. Mitchell and V. Boekelheide, *Tetrahedron Letters*, 1969, 2013.
182. H. Nozaki, T. Koyama and T. Mori, *Tetrahedron Letters*, 1968, 2181.
183. A. T. Blomquist and B. H. Smith, *J. Amer. Chem. Soc.*, 1960, **82**, 2073; A. T. Blomquist, R. E. Stahl, Y. C. Meinwald and B. H. Smith, *J. Org. Chem.*, 1961, **26**, 1687.
184. M. Nakazaki, Y. Yamamoto and S. Okamoto, *Tetrahedron Letters*, 1969, 4597.
185. G. M. Whitesides, B. A. Pawson and A. C. Cope, *J. Amer. Chem. Soc.*, 1968, **90**, 639.
186. S. Akabori, S. Hayashi, M. Nawa and K. Shioni, *Tetrahedron Letters*, 1969, 3727.
187. D. T. Hefelfinger and D. J. Cram, *J. Amer. Chem. Soc.*, 1970, **92**, 1073.
188. F. Vögtle, *Chem. Ber.*, 1969, **102**, 3077.
189. F. A. L. Anet and M. Brown, *J. Amer. Chem. Soc.*, 1969, **91**, 2389.
190. C. J. Brown, *J. Chem. Soc.*, 1953, 3278.
191. T. Sato, S. Akabori, M. Kainosho, and K. Hata, *Bull. Chem. Soc. Japan*, 1966, **39**, 856; 1968, **41**, 218.

192. J. R. Fletcher and I. O. Sutherland, *Chem. Comm.*, 1969, 1504.
193. I. Gault, B. J. Price and I. O. Sutherland, *Chem. Comm.*, 1967, 540.
194. F. Vögtle, *Tetrahedron Letters*, 1968, 3623.
195. F. Vögtle and A. H. Effler, *Chem. Ber.*, 1969, **102**, 3071.
196. R. W. Griffin, jun. and C. A. Coburn, *J. Amer. Chem. Soc.*, 1967, **89**, 4638.
197. T. Sato, M. Wakabayashi and M. Hata, *Tetrahedron Letters*, 1968, 4185.
198. F. Vögtle and L. Schunder, *Chem. Ber.*, 1969, **102**, 2677.
199. F. Vögtle, *Annalen*, 1969, **728**, 17.
200. P. A. Temussi, A. Segre and F. Bottino, *Chem. Comm.*, 1968, 1645.
201. F. A. L. Anet, A. J. R. Bourn and Y. S. Lin, *J. Amer. Chem. Soc.*, 1964, **86**, 3576.
202. F. A. L. Anet, *J. Amer. Chem. Soc.*, 1962, **84**, 671.
203. J. F. M. Oth, R. Merényi, Th. Martin, and G. Schröder, *Tetrahedron Letters*, 1966, 3087.
204. D. E. Gwynn, G. M. Whitesides and J. D. Roberts, *J. Amer. Chem. Soc.*, 1965, **87**, 2862.
205. F. A. L. Anet and L. A. Bock, *J. Amer. Chem. Soc.*, 1968, **90**, 7130.
206. F. Sondheimer, I. C. Calder, J. A. Elix, Y. Gaoni, P. J. Garratt, K. Grohmann, G. Di Maio, J. Mayer, M. V. Sargent, and R. Wolovsky, *Chem. Soc. Spec. Pubn.* No. 21, p. 75; I. C. Calder and P. J. Garratt, *J. Chem. Soc.(B)*, 1967, 660.
207. J. F. M. Oth and J. M. Gilles, *Tetrahedron Letters*, 1968, 6259.
208. J. F. M. Oth, J. M. Gilles and G. Schröder, *Tetrahedron Letters*, 1970, 67.
209. G. Schröder, G. Kirsch and J. F. M. Oth, *Tetrahedron Letters*, 1969, 4575.
210. A. T. Bottini and J. D. Roberts, *J. Amer. Chem. Soc.*, 1958, **80**, 5203.
211. R. Adams and T. L. Cairns, *J. Amer. Chem. Soc.*, 1939, **61**, 2464; P. Maitland, *Chem. Soc. Ann. Reports*, 1939, **36**, 239; J. Meisenheimer and L-H. Chou, *Annalen*, 1939, **539**, 70; J. D. C. Mole and E. E. Turner, *Chem. and Ind.*, 1939, **17**, 582.
212. T. L. Cairns, *J. Amer. Chem. Soc.*, 1941, **63**, 871; H. M. Kissman and D. S. Tarbell, *J. Amer. Chem. Soc.*, 1952, **74**, 4317.
213. S. J. Brois, *J. Amer. Chem. Soc.*, 1968, **90**, 508.
214. D. Felix and A. Eschenmoser, *Angew. Chem. Internat. Edn.*, 1968, **7**, 224.
215. S. J. Brois, *Tetrahedron Letters*, 1968, 5997.
216. R. G. Kostyanovsky, Z. E. Samojlova and I. I. Tchervin, *Tetrahedron Letters*, 1969, 719.
217. S. J. Brois, *J. Amer. Chem. Soc.*, 1967, **89**, 4242.
218. W. D. Ollis and I. O. Sutherland, unpublished results; R. Aneja, J. S. Chadha, A. P. Davies, and C. A. Rose, *Chemistry and Physics of Lipids*, 1969, **3**, 286.
219. F. A. L. Anet and J. M. Osyany, *J. Amer. Chem. Soc.*, 1967, **89**, 352.
220. R. G. Kostyanovsky, Z. E. Samojlova and I. I. Tchervin, *Tetrahedron Letters*, 1968, 3025.
221. M. Jautelat and J. D. Roberts, *J. Amer. Chem. Soc.*, 1969, **91**, 642.
222. A. Loewenstein, J. F. Neumer, and J. D. Roberts, *J. Amer. Chem. Soc.*, 1960, **82**, 3599.
223. R. G. Kostyanovsky, I. I. Tchervin, A. A. Fomichov, Z. E. Samojlova, C. N. Makarov, Yu. V. Zeifman, and B. L. Dyatkin, *Tetrahedron Letters*, 1969, 4021.
224. A. L. Logothetis, *J. Org. Chem.*, 1964, **29**, 3049.

225. T. J. Bardos, C. Szantay and C. K. Navada, *J. Amer. Chem. Soc.*, 1965, **87**, 5796.
226. R. S. Atkinson, *Chem. Comm.*, 1968, 676.
227. J. M. Lehn and J. Wagner, *Chem. Comm.*, 1968, 148.
228. J. M. Lehn and J. Wagner, *Chem. Comm.*, 1968, 1298.
229. F. A. L. Anet, R. D. Trepka and D. J. Cram, *J. Amer. Chem. Soc.*, 1967, **89**, 357.
230. G. R. Boggs and J. T. Gerig, *J. Org. Chem.*, 1969, **34**, 1484.
231. For a discussion of this point see M. J. S. Dewar, "The Molecular Orbital Theory of Organic Chemistry", McGraw-Hill, New York, 1969, p. 406.
232. S. Wolfe, A. Rauk and I. G. Csizmadia, *J. Amer. Chem. Soc.*, 1969, **91**, 1567; S. Wolfe, A. Rauk, L. M. Tel and I. G. Csizmadia, *Chem. Comm.*, 1970, 96.
233. F. Montanari, I. Moretti and G. Torre, *Chem. Comm.*, 1968, 1694; *Chem. Comm.*, 1969, 1086.
234. D. R. Boyd, *Tetrahedron Letters*, 1968, 4561.
235. A. Mannschreck, J. Linss and W. Seitz, *Annalen*, 1969, **727**, 224.
236. J. M. Lehn, B. Munsch, P. Millie and A. Veillard, *Theoret. Chim. Acta*, 1969, **13**, 313.
237. A. Mannschreck, R. Radeglia, E. Grundemann and R. Ohme, *Chem. Ber.*, 1967, **100**, 1778; A. Mannschreck and W. Seitz, *Angew. Chem. Internat. Edn.*, 1969, **8**, 212.
238. J. B. Lambert and W. L. Oliver, *Tetrahedron Letters*, 1968, 6187.
239. J. B. Lambert and W. L. Oliver, *J. Amer. Chem. Soc.*, 1969, **91**, 7775.
240. J. M. Lehn and J. Wagner, *Chem. Comm.*, 1970, 414.
241. J. E. Anderson and A. C. Oehlschlager, *Chem. Comm.*, 1968, 284.
242. V. Rautenstrauch, *Chem. Comm.*, 1969, 1122.
243. G. W. Gribble, N. R. Easton, jun. and J. T. Eaton, *Tetrahedron Letters*, 1970, 1075.
244. G. W. Koeppl, D. S. Sagatys, G. S. Krishnamurthy and S. I. Miller, *J. Amer. Chem. Soc.*, 1967, **89**, 3396.
245. M. Saunders and F. Yamada, *J. Amer. Chem. Soc.*, 1963, **85**, 1882.
246. D. E. Leyden and W. R. Morgan, *Chem. Comm.*, 1969, 598.
247. M. J. S. Dewar and W. B. Jennings, *J. Amer. Chem. Soc.*, 1969, **91**, 3655.
248. J. E. Anderson, D. L. Griffith and J. D. Roberts, *J. Amer. Chem. Soc.*, 1969, **91**, 6371.
249. J. R. Fletcher and I. O. Sutherland, *Chem. Comm.*, 1969, 706.
250. J. R. Fletcher and I. O. Sutherland, *Chem. Comm.*, 1970, 687.
251. J. E. Anderson and J. M. Lehn, *Bull. Soc. chim. France*, 1966, 2402.
252. J. E. Anderson and J. M. Lehn, *J. Amer. Chem. Soc.*, 1967, **89**, 81.
253. E. L. Allred, C. L. Anderson, R. L. Miller and A. L. Johnson, *Tetrahedron Letters*, 1967, 525.
254. J. E. Anderson, *J. Amer. Chem. Soc.*, 1969, **91**, 6371.
255. B. Junge and H. A. Staab, *Tetrahedron Letters*, 1967, 709.
256. J. P. Kintzinger, J. M. Lehn and J. Wagner, *Chem. Comm.*, 1967, 206.
257. R. A. Y. Jones, A. R. Katritzky and A. C. Richards, *Chem. Comm.*, 1969, 708.
258. R. O. Hutchins, L. D. Kopp and E. L. Eliel, *J. Amer. Chem. Soc.*, 1968, **90**, 7174; E. L. Eliel and R. O. Hutchins, *J. Amer. Chem. Soc.*, 1969, **91**, 2703 and references therein; P. J. Brignell, K. Brown and A. R. Katritzky, *J. Chem. Soc.(B)*, 1968, 1463 and earlier papers.
259. J. R. Fletcher, Ph.D.Thesis, Sheffield, 1970.

260. B. Dietrich, J. M. Lehn and P. Linschied, unpublished work cited in ref. 276.
261. P. Ogden, *Chem. Comm.*, 1969, 1084.
262. E. Fahr, W. Fischer, A. Jung, L. Sauer and A. Mannschreck, *Tetrahedron Letters*, 1967, 161.
263. J. C. Breliere and J. M. Lehn, *Chem. Comm.*, 1965, 426.
264. G. J. Bishop, B. J. Price and I. O. Sutherland, *Chem. Comm.*, 1967, 672.
265. J. E. Anderson and J. M. Lehn, *Tetrahedron*, 1968, **24**, 123.
266. B. J. Price, I. O. Sutherland and F. G. Williamson, *Tetrahedron*, 1966, **22**, 3477.
267. B. J. Price and I. O. Sutherland, *J. Chem. Soc.(B)*, 1967, 573.
268. B. J. Price, R. V. Smallman and I. O. Sutherland, *Chem. Comm.*, 1966, 319.
269. W. D. Phillips, "Determination of Organic Structures by Physical Methods", F. C. Nachod and W. D. Phillips ed., Academic Press, 1962, Vol. 2, p. 452.
270. J. E. Anderson and J. M. Lehn, *Tetrahedron*, 1968, **24**, 137.
271. R. Daniels and K. A. Roseman, *Tetrahedron Letters*, 1966, 1335.
272. B. M. Korsch and N. V. Riggs, *Tetrahedron Letters*, 1966, 5897.
273. P. C. Arora and D. Mackay, *Chem. Comm.*, 1969, 677.
274. D. L. Griffith and J. D. Roberts, *J. Amer. Chem. Soc.*, 1965, **87**, 4089.
275. M. Raban and G. W. J. Kenney, jun., *Tetrahedron Letters*, 1969, 1295.
276. F. G. Riddell, J. M. Lehn and J. Wagner, *Chem. Comm.*, 1968, 1403.
277. D. L. Griffith and B. L. Olson, *Chem. Comm.*, 1968, 1682.
278. J. Lee and K. G. Orell, *Trans. Faraday Soc.*, 1965, **61**, 2342.
279. S. Andreades, *J. Org. Chem.*, 1962, **27**, 4163.
280. R. E. Banks, M. G. Barlow, R. N. Haszeldine and M. K. McCreath, *J. Chem. Soc.*, 1965, 7203.
281. B. J. Price and I. O. Sutherland, *Chem. Comm.*, 1967, 1070.
282. M. Raban, F. B. Jones, jun. and G. W. J. Kenney, jun., *Tetrahedron Letters*, 1968, 5055; M. Raban, G. W. J. Kenney, jun. and F. B. Jones, jun., *J. Amer. Chem. Soc.*, 1969, **91**, 6677.
283. K. Murayama and T. Yoshioka, *Tetrahedron Letters*, 1968, 1363.
284. M. Raban, G. W. J. Kenney, jun., J. M. Moldowan and F. B. Jones, jun., *J. Amer. Chem. Soc.*, 1968, **90**, 2985.
285. M. Raban and F. B. Jones, jun., *J. Amer. Chem. Soc.*, 1969, **91**, 2180.
286. H. Kloosterziel, *Chem. Comm.*, 1968, 1330.
287. S. Wolfe, A. Rauk and I. G. Csizmadia, *J. Amer. Chem. Soc.*, 1967, **89**, 5710; idem, *Canad. J. Chem.*, 1969, **47**, 113, and papers cited therein.
288. J. B. Lambert and D. H. Johnson, *J. Amer. Chem. Soc.*, 1968, **90**, 1349.
289. D. Darwish and G. Tovrigny, *J. Amer. Chem. Soc.*, 1966, **88**, 4303; K. Mislow, *Rec. Chem. Progr.*, 1967, **28**, 217.
290. L. Horner and H. Winkler, *Tetrahedron Letters*, 1964, 461; S. E. Cremer, R. J. Chorvat, C. H. Chang and D. W. Davis, *Tetrahedron Letters*, 1968, 5799; J. M. Lehn and B. Munsch, *Chem. Comm.*, 1969, 1327.
291. J. B. Lambert, G. F. Jackson and D. C. Mueller, *J. Amer. Chem. Soc.*, 1968, **90**, 6401.
292. J. B. Lambert and G. F. Jackson, *J. Amer. Chem. Soc.*, 1968, **90**, 1350.
293. M. P. Simonnin, J. J. Basselier and C. Charrier, *Bull. Soc. chim. France*, 1967, 3544; D. Imberry and H. Friebolin, *Z. Naturforsch.*, 1968, **23b**, 759.
294. A. H. Cowley, M. J. S. Dewar and W. R. Jackson, *J. Amer. Chem. Soc.*, 1968, **90**, 4185.
295. H. Goldwhite and D. G. Rowsell, *Chem. Comm.*, 1969, 713.

296. A. H. Cowley, M. J. S. Dewar, W. R. Jackson and W. B. Jennings, *J. Amer. Chem. Soc.*, 1970, **92**, 1085.

297. E. D. Morris, jun. and C. E. Nordman, *Inorg. Chem.*, 1969, **8**, 1673.

298. A. H. Cowley, M. J. S. Dewar, W. B. Jennings and W. R. Jackson, *Chem. Comm.*, 1969, 482.

299. G. E. Ryschkewitsch, W. S. Brey, jun. and A. Saji, *J. Amer. Chem. Soc.*, 1961, **83**, 1010; P. A. Barfield, M. F. Lappert and J. Lee, *Proc. Chem. Soc.*, 1961, 421; H. Baechle, H. J. Becher, H. Beyer, W. G. Brey, jun., J. W. Dawson, M. E. Fuller and K. Niedenzu, *Inorg. Chem.*, 1963, **2**, 1065; H. Watanabe, T. Totani, K. Tori and T. Nakogawa, "NMR and Relaxation in Solids-Proceedings of the XIIIth. Collogue Ampere", L. Van Garven ed., North Holland Publishing Co., Amsterdam, 1965, p. 374; H. J. Becher and H. T. Baechle, *Chem. Ber.*, 1965, **98**, 2159; H. T. Baechle and H. J. Becher, *Spectrochim. Acta*, 1965, **21**, 579; K. Niedenzu, J. W. Dawson, G. A. Neece, W. Sawodny, D. R. Squire and W. Weber, *Inorg. Chem.*, 1966, **5**, 2161.

300. M. J. S. Dewar and P. Rona, *J. Amer. Chem. Soc.*, 1969, **91**, 2259.

301. G. Fraenkel, D. T. Dix and D. G. Adams, *Tetrahedron Letters*, 1964, 3155.

302. G. Fraenkel, D. T. Dix and M. Carlson, *Tetrahedron Letters*, 1968, 579.

303. A. Ratajezak, F. A. L. Anet and D. J. Cram, *J. Amer. Chem. Soc.*, 1967, **89**, 2072.

304. D. Y. Curtin and J. W. Hausser, *J. Amer. Chem. Soc.*, 1961, **83**, 3474.

305. D. Y. Curtin, E. J. Grubbs and C. G. McCarty, *J. Amer. Chem. Soc.*, 1966, **88**, 2775.

306. S. Andreades, *J. Org. Chem.*, 1962, **27**, 4163.

307. L. Cavalli and P. Piccardi, *Chem. Comm.*, 1969, 1132.

308. H. A. Staab, F. Vögtle and A. Mannschreck, *Tetrahedron Letters*, 1965, 697.

309. N. P. Marullo and E. H. Wagener, *J. Amer. Chem. Soc.*, 1966, **88**, 5034.

310. N. P. Marullo and E. H. Wagener, *Tetrahedron Letters*, 1969, 2555.

311. C. G. McCarty and D. M. Wieland, *Tetrahedron Letters*, 1969, 1787.

312. F. Vögtle, A. Mannschreck and H. A. Staab, *Annalen*, 1967, **708**, 51.

313. H. Kessler, *Tetrahedron Letters*, 1968, 2041; H. Kessler and D. Liebfritz, *Tetrahedron*, 1969, **25**, 5127.

314. R. W. Layer and C. J. Carman, *Tetrahedron Letters*, 1968, 1285.

315. H. Quast and E. Schmitt, *Angew. Chem. Internat. Edn.*, 1969, **8**, 449.

316. E. Carlson, F. B. Jones, jun. and M. Raban, *Chem. Comm.*, 1969, 1235.

317. F. J. Weigert and J. D. Roberts, *J. Amer. Chem. Soc.*, 1968, **90**, 3577.

318. F. A. L. Anet, M. St. Jacques and G. N. Chmurny, *J. Amer. Chem. Soc.*, 1968, **90**, 5243.

319. A. Rieker, N. Zeller and H. Kessler, *J. Amer. Chem. Soc.*, 1968, **90**, 6566.

320. A. Rieker and H. Kessler, *Tetrahedron Letters*, 1969, 1227.

321. J. P. N. Brewer, H. Heaney and B. A. Marples, *Chem. Comm.*, 1967, 27.

322. D. T. Dix, G. Fraenkel, H. A. Karnes and M. S. Newman, *Tetrahedron Letters*, 1966, 517.

323. C. Cupas, J. M. Bollinger and M. Haslanger, *J. Amer. Chem. Soc.*, 1968, **90**, 5502.

324. A. Mannschreck and L. Ernst, *Tetrahedron Letters*, 1968, 5939.

325. R. D. Chambers, J. A. Jackson, W. K. R. Musgrave, L. H. Sutcliffe and G. J. T. Tiddy, *Chem. Comm.*, 1969, 178; *idem*, *Tetrahedron*, 1970, **26**, 71.

326. P. D. Bartlett and T. T. Tidwell, *J. Amer. Chem. Soc.*, 1968, **90**, 4421.

327. T. H. Siddall III and W. E. Stewart, *Tetrahedron Letters*, 1968; *idem*, *Chem.*

Comm., 1968, 1116; E. A. Chandross and C. F. Shiley, jun., *J. Amer. Chem. Soc.*, 1968, **90**, 4345.

328. K. D. Bartle, P. M. G. Bavin, D. W. Jones and R. L'amie, *Tetrahedron*, 1970, **26**, 911.
329. T. H. Sidall III and W. E. Stewart, *J. Org. Chem.*, 1969, **34**, 233.
330. R. Adams and J. Campbell, *J. Amer. Chem. Soc.*, 1950, **72**, 153.
331. H. Kessler, A. Moosmayer and A. Rieker, *Tetrahedron*, 1969, **25**, 287.
332. W. L. Meyer and R. B. Meyer, *J. Amer. Chem. Soc.*, 1963, **85**, 2170.
333. L. D. Colebrook and J. A. Jahnke, *J. Amer. Chem. Soc.*, 1968, **90**, 4687.
334. D. Lauer and H. A. Staab, *Tetrahedron Letters*, 1968, 177; *idem*, *Chem. Ber.*, 1969, **102**, 1631.
335. D. Lauer and H. A. Staab, *Chem. Ber.*, 1968, **101**, 864.
336. M. M. Harris, *Progress in Stereochemistry*, 1958, **2**, 157; D. M. Hall and M. M. Harris, *J. Chem. Soc.*, 1960, 490.
337. B. J. Price, J. A. Eggleston and I. O. Sutherland, *J. Chem. Soc.(B)*, 1967, 922.
338. Y. Shvo, E. C. Taylor, K. Mislow, and M. Raban, *J. Amer. Chem. Soc.*, 1967, **89**, 4910.
339. T. H. Siddall III and W. E. Stewart, *J. Phys. Chem.*, 1969, **73**, 40 and earlier papers.
340. A. Mannschreck and H. Muensch, *Tetrahedron Letters*, 1968, 3227.
341. S. H. Khetan and M. V. George, *Tetrahedron*, 1969, **25**, 531.
342. H. Kessler, A. Rieker and W. Rundel, *Chem. Comm.*, 1968, 475.
343. L. Pauling, "The Nature of the Chemical Bond", Cornell University Press, Ithaca, New York, 1948, 2nd. Edn., p. 207.
344. W. D. Phillips, *J. Chem. Phys.*, 1955, **23**, 1363.
345. (a) B. Sunners, L. H. Piette and W. G. Schneider, *Can. J. Chem.*, 1960, **38**, 681; (b) R. M. Hammaker and B. A. Gugler, *J. Mol. Spectroscopy*, 1965, **17**, 356; (c) R. C. Neuman, jun. and L. B. Young, *J. Phys. Chem.*, 1965, **69**, 2570; (d) D. G. Gehring, W. A. Mosher and G. S. Reddy, *J. Org. Chem.*, 1966, **31**, 3436.
346. C. W. Fryer, F. Conti and C. Franconi, *Ricerca sci.*, 1965, **8**, 1788.
347. A. Pines and M. Rabinovitz, *Tetrahedron Letters*, 1968, 3529.
348. L. L. Graham and R. E. Diel, *J. Phys. Chem.*, 1969, **73**, 2696.
349. F. Conti and W. von Philipsborn, *Helv. Chim. Acta*, 1967, **50**, 603.
350. A. Mannschreck, *Tetrahedron Letters*, 1965, 1341.
351. A. M. Monro and M. T. Sewell, *Tetrahedron Letters*, 1969, 595.
352. D. R. Dalton, M. P. Cava and K. T. Buck, *Tetrahedron Letters*, 1965, 2687; G. Fraenkel, M. P. Cava and D. R. Dalton, *J. Amer. Chem. Soc.*, 1967, **89**, 329.
353. D. R. Dalton, K. C. Ramey, H. J. Gisler, jun., L. J. Lendray and A. Abraham, *J. Amer. Chem. Soc.*, 1969, **91**, 6367.
354. T. Matsuo and H. Shosenji, *Chem. Comm.*, 1969, 501.
355. C. H. Bushweller and M. A. Tobias, *Tetrahedron Letters*, 1968, 595.
356. S. van der Werf, T. Olijnsma and J. B. F. N. Engberts, *Tetrahedron Letters*, 1967, 689; S. van der Werf and J. B. F. N. Engberts, *Tetrahedron Letters*, 1968, 3311.
357. R. C. Neuman, jun., D. N. Roark and V. Jonas, *J. Amer. Chem. Soc.*, 1967, **89**, 3412.
358. G. Schwenker and H. Rosswag, *Tetrahedron Letters*, 1967, 4237.
359. B. T. Brown and G. F. Katekar, *Tetrahedron Letters*, 1969, 2343.

360. A. Loewenstein, A. Melera, P. Rigny and W. Walter, *J. Phys. Chem.*, 1964, **68**, 1597.
361. W. Walter, G. Maerten and H. Rose, *Annalen*, 1966, **691**, 25.
362. W. Walter and H. Weiss, *Angew. Chem. Internat. Edn.*, 1969, **8**, 989.
363. M. L. Filleux-Blanchard, F. Clesse, J. Bignebat and G. J. Martin, *Tetrahedron Letters*, 1969, 981.
364. M. L. Filleux-Blanchard, A. Chevallier and G. J. Martin, *Tetrahedron Letters*, 1967, 5057.
365. J. E. Thorpe, *J. Chem. Soc.(B)*, 1968, 435.
366. F. A. L. Anet and M. Ahmad, *J. Amer. Chem. Soc.*, 1968, **90**, 118.
367. R. E. Pinck, D. H. Marr and J. B. Stothers, *Chem. Comm.*, 1967, 409.
368. R. W. Taft, jun., "Steric Effects in Organic Chemistry", ed. M. S. Newman, Wiley and Sons Inc., New York, 1955.
369. K.-I. Dahlquist and S. Forsén, *J. Phys. Chem.*, 1965, **69**, 4062.
370. M. S. de Groot and J. Lamb, *Proc. Roy. Soc.*, 1957, **242A**, 36; J. Lamb, *Z. Elektrochem.*, 1960, **64**, 135.
371. D. L. Harris and K. M. Wellman, *Tetrahedron Letters*, 1968, 5225.
372. G. Schwenker and H. Rosswag, *Tetrahedron Letters*, 1968, 2691.
373. H. H. Jakobsen and A. Senning, *Chem. Comm.*, 1968, 1245.
374. D. D. MacNicol, *Chem. Comm.*, 1969, 933.
375. A. R. Katritzky and G. J. T. Tiddy, *Org. Magn. Resonance*, 1969, **1**, 57.
376. D. M. G. Martin and C. B. Reese, *Chem. Comm.*, 1967, 1275.
377. Z. Neinam and F. Bergmann, *Chem. Comm.*, 1968, 1002.
378. C. E. Looney, W. D. Phillips and E. L. Reilly, *J. Amer. Chem. Soc.*, 1957, **79**, 6136.
379. T. Axenrod, M. J. Wieder and G. W. A. Milne, *Tetrahedron Letters*, 1969, 401.
380. D. D. MacNicol, R. Wallace and J. C. D. Brand, *Trans. Faraday Soc.*, 1965, **61**, 1; P. K. Korver, P. J. van der Haak and T. J. de Boer, *Tetrahedron*, 1966, **22**, 3157; D. D. MacNicol, *Chem. Comm.*, 1969, 1516.
381. I. C. Calder and P. J. Garratt, *Tetrahedron*, 1969, **25**, 4023.
382. N. P. Marullo, C. B. Mayfield and E. H. Wagener, *J. Amer. Chem. Soc.*, 1968, **90**, 510.
383. G. Koga and J.-P. Anselme, *Chem. Comm.*, 1969, 894.
384. W. D. Phillips, C. E. Looney and C. P. Spaeth, *J. Mol. Spectroscopy*, 1957, **1**, 35.
385. H. J. Bestman, G. Joachim, I. Lengyal, J. F. M. Oth, J. Merenyi and J. Weitkamp, *Tetrahedron Letters*, 1966, 3335.
386. D. M. Crouse, A. T. Wehman and E. Schweizer, *Chem. Comm.*, 1968, 866; F. J. Randall and A. W. Johnson, *Tetrahedron Letters*, 1968, 2841.
387. H. Schmidbaur and W. Tronich, *Angew. Chem. Internat. Edn.*, 1967, **6**, 448.
388. P. Crews, *J. Amer. Chem. Soc.*, 1968, **90**, 2961; H. J. Bestmann, H. G. Liberda and J. P. Snyder, *J. Amer. Chem. Soc.*, 1968, **90**, 2963.
389. H. I. Zeliger, J. P. Snyder and H. J. Bestmann, *Tetrahedron Letters*, 1969, 2199.
390. S. H. Smallcombe, R. J. Holland, R. H. Fish and M. C. Caserio, *Tetrahedron Letters*, 1968, 5987.
391. K. W. Ratts and A. N. Yao, *J. Org. Chem.*, 1966, **31**, 1185; B. M. Trost, *J. Amer. Chem. Soc.*, 1967, **89**, 138.
392. J. Casanova, jun. and D. A. Rutolo, jun., *Chem. Comm.*, 1967, 1224.

393. H. Nozaki, D. Tunemoto, Z. Morita, K. Nakamura, K. Watanabe, M. Takaku and K. Kondo, *Tetrahedron*, 1967, **23**, 4279.
394. R. M. Acheson and I. A. Selby, *Chem. Comm.*, 1970, 62.
395. F. Kaplan and G. K. Meloy, *J. Amer. Chem. Soc.*, 1966, **88**, 950.
396. I. G. Csizmadia, S. A. Houlden, O. Meresz and P. Yates, *Tetrahedron*, 1969, **25**, 2121.
397. R. B. Cundall, *Progress in Reaction Kinetics*, 1964, **2**, 165.
398. A. P. Downing, W. D. Ollis and I. O. Sutherland, *Chem. Comm.*, 1967, 143; 1968, 1053; *idem, J. Chem. Soc.(B)*, 1969, 111.
399. J. H. Crabtree and D. J. Bertelli, *J. Amer. Chem. Soc.*, 1967, **89**, 5384.
400. A. S. Kende, P. T. Izzo and W. Fulmor, *Tetrahedron Letters*, 1966, 3697.
401. A. Mannschreck and U. Koelle, *Tetrahedron Letters*, 1967, 863.
402. Y. Shvo, E. C. Taylor and J. Bartulin, *Tetrahedron Letters*, 1967, 3259.
403. J. Sandström and I. Wennerbeck, *Chem. Comm.*, 1969, 306.
404. Y. Shvo and H. Shanan-Atidi, *J. Amer. Chem. Soc.*, 1969, **91**, 6683.
405. Y. Shvo and H. Shanan-Atidi, *J. Amer. Chem. Soc.*, 1969, **91**, 6689.
406. Y. Shvo, *Tetrahedron Letters*, 1968, 5923.
407. G. Isakson, J. Sandström and I. Wennerbeck, *Tetrahedron Letters*, 1967, 2233.
408. Y. Shvo and I. Belsky, *Tetrahedron*, 1969, **25**, 4649.
409. H. Kessler and A. Rieker, *Tetrahedron Letters*, 1966, 5257.
410. A. Rieker and H. Kessler, *Chem. Ber.*, 1969, **102**, 2147.
411. I. R. Gault, W. D. Ollis and I. O. Sutherland, *Chem. Comm.*, 1970, 269.
412. V. J. Downing, I. R. Gault, W. D. Ollis and I. O. Sutherland, to be published.
413. R. Kuhn, B. Schulz and J. C. Jochims, *Angew. Chem. Internat. Edn.*, 1966, **5**, 420.

Nuclear Magnetic Resonance Spectroscopy in Pesticide Chemistry

R. HAQUE AND D. R. BUHLER

*Department of Agricultural Chemistry and Environmental Health Sciences Center,
Oregon State University, Corvallis, Oregon 97331, U.S.A.*

I. INTRODUCTION

NUCLEAR MAGNETIC RESONANCE (NMR) spectroscopy has only recently been employed in studies with insecticides, herbicides and other pesticides in spite of its widespread use in elucidating structure and chemical interactions of other organic compounds. Recent advances in NMR instrumentation has led to the use of high frequency spectrometers and computer averaging techniques, thus allowing a significant reduction in required sample size. In addition, the availability of frequency synthesizers and variable radiofrequency units now permits study of resonance of nuclei other than proton and fluorine. These developments have resulted in an increased application of NMR spectroscopy to the study of pesticides.[1]

The purpose of this review is to summarize recent progress in the application of NMR techniques to the study of various aspects of pesticide chemistry. While this review will not attempt to include all NMR studies on these compounds, it will report the more significant results with pesticides.

II. SPECTRA OF PESTICIDES

A. Organophosphates

Organophosphate insecticides are primarily phosphate or thiphosphate esters and can be represented by the general formula (1), where R_1 and R_2 are usually

$$
\begin{array}{c}
X \\
\parallel \\
R_1O\!-\!P\!-\!Y\!-\!R_3 \\
\mid \\
OR_2
\end{array}
$$

1

methyl or ethyl groups, X is oxygen or sulfur, Y is oxygen, sulfur or nitrogen and R_3 is a bulky organic group attached to Y.

A compilation of the NMR spectra of organophosphate insecticides in chloroform-d has been made by Babad et al.[2] and by Keith et al.[3] The R_1–O–P– region of the spectrum is quite comparable in most of the compounds examined with the alkyl group R_1 always showing a characteristic doublet splitting due to an indirect spin-spin coupling of ^{31}P and ^1H nuclei. For compounds, where R_1 and R_2 are both methyl groups, the methyl peak appears in the region $\delta = 3\cdot9$ to $3\cdot7$ ppm with $J(P\text{–}CH_3) = 11$ to 16 Hz. Organophosphates in which R_1 and R_2 are both ethyl show methyl peaks at δ 1·4 and methylene peaks in the region δ 4·2 to 4·4. In this case, the $J(P\text{–}CH_3)$ and $J(P\text{–}CH_2)$ coupling constants are 0·8 and 10 Hz, respectively. Coupling constants and chemical shifts for some methyl and ethyl substituted organophosphate insecticides are given in Tables I and II. The long-range coupling between ^{31}P and CH_3 in ethoxy type organophosphates is small yet observable. The chemical shifts of methyl and ethyl protons are quite comparable, between oxygen-containing organophosphate insecticides and their sulfur analogs, but the coupling constants are somewhat higher for organophosphates with a P=S bond than with the P=O bond.

Methyl proton peaks in organophosphates where R_1 and R_2 are both methyl and methylene peaks in organophosphates where R_1 and R_2 are both ethyl show further splitting (these compounds are marked with asterisks in Tables I and II). This has been explained by Keith et al.[3] on the basis of magnetic non-equivalence of the methyl protons probably due to hindred rotation around one or more bonds of the phosphorus atom. These splittings are also characteristic of compounds where R_3 contains an assymetric carbon atom.

The Y–R_3 portion of the spectrum of organophosphates with the general

TABLE I
Chemical shifts and coupling constants for methyl groups in various organophosphates (1)

Compound	R_1	R_2	R_3	X	Y	δ CH$_3$	J(P–CH$_3$) Hz
Bidrin	Me	Me	N,N-dimethyl-cis-crotonamide	O	O	3·83	11·0
Ciodrin	Me	Me	α-methylbenzyl-cis-crotonate	O	O	3·8	11·0
DDVP	Me	Me	2,2-dichlorovinyl	O	O	3·86	11·0
Dicapthon	Me	Me	2-chloro-4-nitro-phenyl	S	O	3·92	14·0
Dimethoate	Me	Me	N-methylcarbamoyl-methyl	S	S	3·8	15·0
Dimethoxon	Me	Me	N-methylcarbamoyl-methyl	O	S	3·83	12·5
Guthion	Me	Me	4-oxo-1,2,3-benzo-triazin-3(4H)-yl-methyl	S	S	3·76	15·0
Guthion (oxygen analog)	Me	Me	4-oxo-1,2,3-benzo-triazin-3(4H)-yl-methyl	O	S	3·81	12·0
Imidan	Me	Me	phthalimidomethyl	S	S	3·77	15·0
Malaoxon*	Me	Me	1,2-dicarbethoxyethyl	O	S	3·83, 3·82	13·0
Malathion*	Me	Me	1,2-dicarbethoxyethyl	S	S	3·81, 3·8	15·5
Meta-Systox R	Me	Me	2-(ethylsulfinyl)ethyl	O	S	3·82	13·0
Methyl Parathion	Me	Me	4-nitrophenyl	S	O	3·87	14·0
Methyl Trithion	Me	Me	p-chlorophenylthio-methyl	S	S	3·72	15·0
Naled*	Me	Me	1,2-dibromo-2,2-dichloroethyl	O	O	3·92, 3·91	12·0
Phosdrin	Me	Me	2-carbomethoxy-1-methylvinyl	O	O	3·75	11·0
Phosphamidon*	Me	Me	2-chloro-2-(N,N-di-ethylcarbamoyl)-1-methylvinyl	O	O	3·88, 3·8	12·0
Ronnel	Me	Me	2,4,5-trichlorophenyl	S	O	3·9	14·0
Ruelene	Me	4-t-butyl-2-chloro-phenyl	methyl	O	NH	3·81	11·0
Tiguvon	Me	Me	4-methylthio-m-tolyl	S	O	3·81	14·0
Trichlorofon*	Me	Me	1-hydroxy-2,2,2-tri-chloroethyl	O	—	3·91, 3·9	11·0
Zytron	Me	2,4-di-chloro-phenyl	isopropyl	S	NH	3·8	14·0

TABLE II

Chemical shifts and coupling constants for ethyl groups in various organophosphates (1)

Compound	R_1	R_2	R_3	X	Y	δ CH$_3$	J(P–CH$_3$) Hz	δ CH$_2$	J(P–CH$_2$) Hz
Co-Ral	Et	Et	3-chloro-4-methyl-2-oxo-2H-benzopyran-7-yl	S	O	1·4	0·8	4·25	10·0
Diazinon	Et	Et	2-isopropyl-4-methyl-6-pyridinyl	S	O	1·38	0·8	4·34	9·5
Diazoxon	Et	Et	2-isopropyl-4-methyl-6-pyridinyl	O	O	1·39	1·2	4·33	8·0
Dioxathion	Et(2)	Et(2)	2,3-p-dioxane	S(2)	S(2)	1·36		4·17	10·0
Disulfoton*	Et	Et	2-ethylthioethyl	S	S	1·35	0·7	4·17, 4·15	10·0
EPN	p-nitro-phenyl	Et	phenyl	S	—	1·36	0·5	4·27	10·0
Ethion*	Et(2)	Et(2)	methylene	S(2)	S(2)	1·36	0·8	4·2, 4·18	10·0
Paraoxon	Et	Et	4-nitrophenyl	O	O	1·39	0·9	4·26	8·5
Parathion	Et	Et	4-nitrophenyl	S	O	1·37	0·8	4·25	10·0
Phencapton*	Et	Et	methyl(2,5-dichlorophenylthio)	S	S	1·36	0·8	4·18, 4·16	10·0
Phorate*	Et	Et	methylthioethyl	S	S	1·36	0·8	4·18, 4·17	10·0
Thionazin	Et	Et	2-pyrazinyl	S	O	1·41	0·8	4·35	9·0
Trithion*	Et	Et	4-chlorophenylthiomethyl	S	S	1·33	0·8	4·12, 4·09	10·0

formula (1) show the usual characteristics of the organic ligand R_3. In addition, long-range spin-spin coupling between ^{31}P and the methinyl protons are observable. Some typical values[3] of the chemical shifts and coupling constants for such compounds are given in Table III.

The occurrence of *cis-trans* isomerism in many organophosphates has been detected by NMR. Isomerism is exhibited when phosphorus is attached, by

TABLE III

**Chemical shifts and coupling constants for methinyl groups in
some organophosphates (1)**

Compound	R_1	R_2	R_3	X	Y	δ CH	J(P–CH) Hz
DDVP	Me	Me	2,2-dichlorovinyl	O	O	7·0	5·5
DEF	*n*-butyl	*n*-butyl	*n*-butyl	O	O	2·09	15
Dimethoate	Me	Me	N-methylcarba-moylmethyl	S	S	3·56	18
Dimethoxon	Me	Me	N-methylcarba-moylmethyl	O	S	3·51	17
Dioxathion	Et(2)	Et(2)	2,3-*p*-dioxane	S(2)	S(2)	5·6	16
Disulfoton	Et	Et	2-ethylthioethyl	S	S	3·2 − 2·5	—
Ethion	Et(2)	Et(2)	methylene	S(2)	S(2)	4·26	17
Guthion	Me	Me	4-oxo-1,2,3-ben-zotriazin-3(4H)-yl-methyl	S	S	5·77	16
Guthion (oxygen analog)	Me	Me	4-oxo-1,2,3-ben-zotriazin-3(4H)-yl-methyl	O	S	5·8	15
Imidan	Me	Me	phthalimidomethyl	S	S	5·02	15
Malaoxon	Me	Me	1,2-dicarbethoxy-ethyl	O	S	4·1	—
Malathion	Me	Me	1,2-dicarbethoxy-ethyl	S	S	4·1	13
Meta-systox R	Me	Me	2-(ethylsulfinyl)-ethyl	O	S	3·2	—
Methyl Trithion	Me	Me	*p*-chlorophenyl-thiomethyl	S	S	4·26	14
Naled	Me	Me	1,2-dibromo-2,2-dichloroethyl	O	O	6·7	9·0
Phencapton	Et	Et	methyl(2,5-di-chlorophenyl-thio)	S	S	4·34	14
Phorate	Et	Et	methylthioethyl	S	S	4·03	13
Trithion	Et	Et	4-chlorophenyl-thiomethyl	S	S	4·28	13·5

TABLE IV

Chemical shifts and coupling constants in phosdrin isomers (2 and 3)

Compound	R₁	R₂	R₃	X	Y	H	CH₃–O–P	CH₃O₂C	CH₃	J(CH₃–OP), Hz
							Chemical shift, δ			Coupling constant
cis Phosdrin	Me	Me	2-carbomethoxy-1-methylvinyl	O	O	5·78	3·86	3·70	2·42	10·4
trans Phosdrin	Me	Me	2-carbomethoxy-1-methylvinyl	O	O	5·30	3·88	3·67	2·15	11·2
cis Thionophosdrin	Me	Me	2-carbomethoxy-1-methylvinyl	S	O	5·68	3·88	3·70	2·37	14·6
trans Thionophos-drin	Me	Me	2-carbomethoxy-1-methylvinyl	S	O	5·36	3·82	3·67	2·10	14·6

oxygen or sulfur, to a carbon-carbon double bond. For example, the *cis* and *trans* isomers of phosdrin and the sulfur analogs, represented by the formula (**2**) and (**3**), have the coupling constants and chemical shifts summarized in Table IV.[4,5]

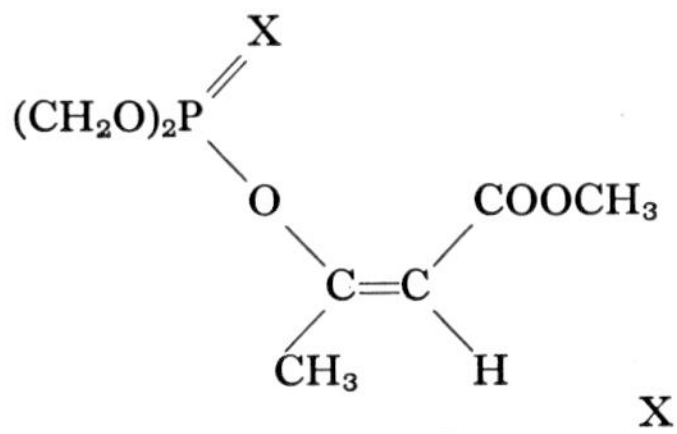

$$X = O \text{ or } S$$

2   **3**

TABLE V

Long-range coupling constants in phosphoramides in $CDCl_3$ at Ambient temperature

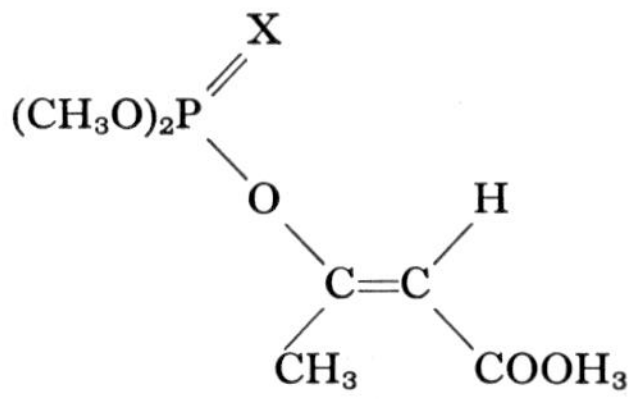

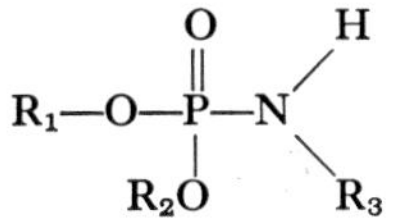

| Substituent | | | Coupling constant $J(P-N-C-C-H)$ |
R_1	R_2	R_3	Hz
$-CH_3$	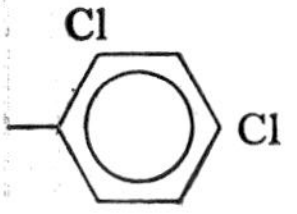 Cl—⟨benzene⟩—Cl (2,4-dichlorophenyl)	$-CH(CH_3)_2$	0·7
$-CH_3$	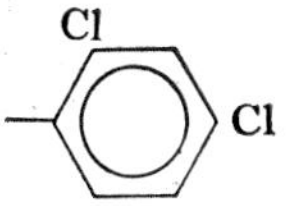 Cl—⟨benzene⟩—Cl	$-C(CH_3)_2CH_3$	0·8
$-CH_3$	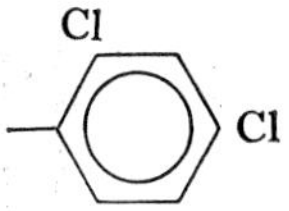 Cl—⟨benzene⟩—Cl (2,6-dichlorophenyl)	$-CH_2-CH_3$	1·0
$-C_2H_5$	$-C_2H_5$	$-CH(CH_3)_2$	0·7
$-C_2H_5$	$-C_2H_5$	$-C(CH_3)_2CH_3$	0·7
$-C_2H_5$	$-C_2H_5$	$-CH_2-CH_3$	1·0

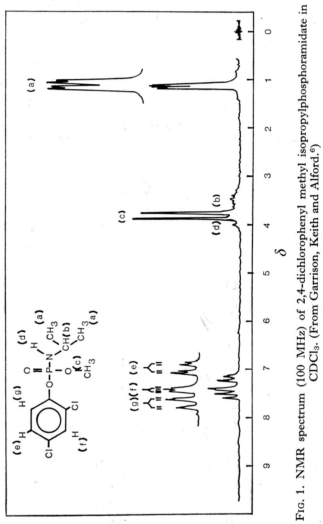

Fig. 1. NMR spectrum (100 MHz) of 2,4-dichlorophenyl methyl isopropylphosphoramidate in CDCl₃. (From Garrison, Keith and Alford.[6])

Some interesting results have been reported for phosphoramidate type compounds in which Y is a nitrogen atom. The NMR spectrum in the methyl region, when two methyl groups are attached to the nitrogen (as in bidrin), exhibits a pattern characteristic of hindered rotation around the partial carbon-nitrogen double bond.[3] The spectrum of 2,4 dichlorophenyl methylisopropylphosphormidate (Fig. 1) shows an enhancement in the isopropyl methyl proton resonance which has been explained on the basis of a difference in the chemical shift of the two methyl groups.[6] This difference arises from steric hindrance to rotation about the N–C bond resulting in enhancement of the non-equivalence because of molecular symmetry. The long-range ^{31}P–^1H coupling constant $J(^{31}P-N-CH_3)$, although less than 1 Hz, is always observable (Table V). A concentration dependent difference between the chemical shift of the two isopropyl methyl doublets is interpreted on the basis of intermolecular hydrogen bonding.[6]

Organophosphate insecticides in which the phosphorus atom is attached to identical alkyl groups, such as merphos (4) and DEF (5), give a characteristic

$$(CH_3CH_2CH_2CH_2S)_3\text{—}P \qquad (CH_3CH_2CH_2CH_2S)_3P\text{=}O$$

$$(4) \qquad\qquad\qquad (5)$$

alkyl group spectrum.[3] The protons of the methylene group attached to sulfur exhibit ^{31}P splitting. Peaks from the other methylene groups, however, show complex multiplets due to the long-range ^{31}P coupling and proton-proton splitting among themselves. The NMR spectra of various organophosphates have been depicted diagrammatically.[2]

While relatively little work has been carried out using ^{31}P resonance for the structural determination of organophosphate pesticides, compilations of the ^{31}P chemical shift data of a large number of phosphorus compounds are available.[7,8,9]

B. Carbamates, thiocarbamates, amides and ureas

Carbamate and thiocarbamate pesticides may be represented by the general formula (6), where R_1 is an alkyl group, R_2 is an alkyl group or a hydrogen, R_3

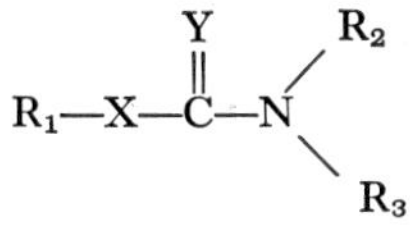

$$R_1\text{—}X\text{—}\overset{\overset{Y}{\|}}{C}\text{—}N\overset{\diagup R_2}{\diagdown R_3}$$

$$(6)$$

may be an alkyl or aryl group and the substituent X and Y are S or O. An important characteristic of carbamate insecticides in which R_2 and R_3 are identical alkyl groups (N,N dialkyl-carbamates) is the occurrence of a partial double bond character of the C–N bond causing a hindered rotation of the alkyl groups.

The NMR spectra of the *N,N*-dialkyl- amides and thioamides indicate separate resonance peaks for the alkyl groups on the NMR time scale as a result of such hindered rotation.[10 to 12] The resolution of separate resonance signals for the *N,N*-dimethyl protons was found to be extremely solvent and temperature dependent.[11,12] In many alkyl or unsubstituted phenyl esters of dimethyl-carbamic and dithiocarbamic acids the protons of the methyl group show only one resonance peak indicating a fast rotation of the alkyl group around the C–N bond.[11] While the NMR spectra of *N*-nitro compounds show rotational isomers in cyclic carbamates,[13] biscarbamates do not exhibit such hindered rotation.[14] Detailed NMR studies of the *N,N*-dimethyl- amides and thioamides have given valuable information about the kinetic parameters of the hindered methyl exchange processes.[15 to 19]

A detailed examination of the NMR spectra from many carbamate pesticides has been made recently by Keith and Alford.[20] These authors divided the carbamates into four sub-groups represented by the general formula (**7**), (**8**), (**9**), and (**10**). With most of the compounds studied in category (**7**), R_1 is H and R_2 is a

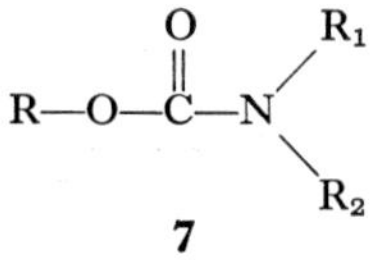

$$R-O-\overset{\overset{O}{\|}}{C}-N\overset{R_1}{\underset{R_2}{<}}$$

7

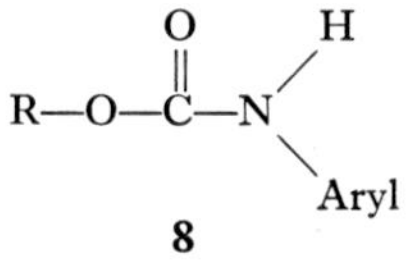

$$R-O-\overset{\overset{O}{\|}}{C}-N\overset{H}{\underset{Aryl}{<}}$$

8

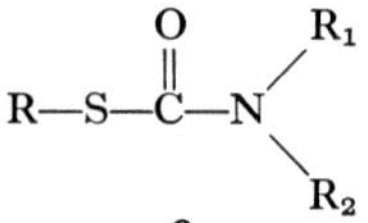

$$R-S-\overset{\overset{O}{\|}}{C}-N\overset{R_1}{\underset{R_2}{<}}$$

9

$$R-S-\overset{\overset{S}{\|}}{C}-N\overset{R_1}{\underset{R_2}{<}}$$

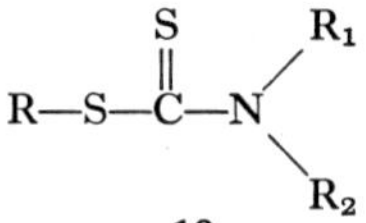

10

methyl group. In such cases, the CH_3 proton signal appears as a doublet with a coupling constant of $J(CH_3–NH)$ of 5 Hz at δ 2·71 to 2·82. Most of the compounds examined failed to show any hindered rotation around the N–CO bond when examined at room temperature. The pesticide Azak, however, contains a bulky *tert*-butyl group substituted on an aromatic ring which apparently interferes with free rotation about the N–CO bond sufficiently at room temperature to produce a methyl proton doublet with chemical shift changes in benzene similar to those observed by Hutton and Richards[21] for the interaction of amides with benzene.

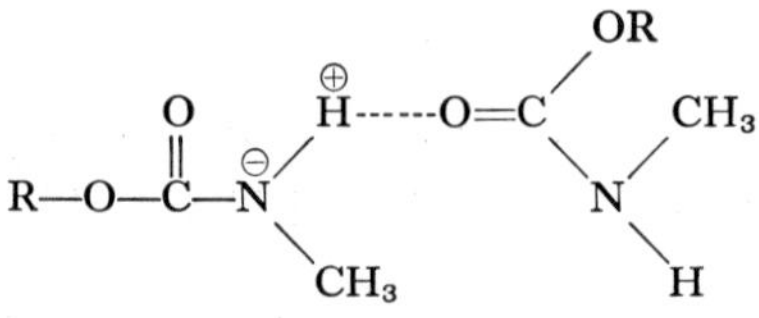

$$R-O-\overset{\overset{O}{\|}}{C}-\overset{\ominus}{N}\overset{\overset{\oplus}{H}-----O=C}{\underset{CH_3}{<}}\overset{OR}{\underset{N}{<}}\overset{CH_3}{\underset{H}{<}}$$

11

Strong hydrogen bonding (11) occurs between molecules of the carbamate insecticide Zectran (4-dimethylamino-3,5-dimethylphenyl-N-carbamate) in CS_2 and $CDCl_3$ and is shown by a high field shift of the N-CH_3 protons and a corresponding low field shift of the N–H proton with increasing carbamate concentration.[20] Similar results were found for the intermolecular association of N-methylvinylcarbamate in CCl_4 solution.[22] The presence of dimethyl sulfoxide (DMSO), however, causes an intermolecular hydrogen bond formation between carbamate and DMSO as shown by a low field shift of the carbamate N–H proton signal with increasing concentration of DMSO.[23] Increasing the ratio of carbamate to DMSO also results in a low field shift of the N–CH_3 and a high field shift of the N–H proton signals.[20]

The spectra of group (8) carbamates, which includes the insecticides IPC, CIPC, and barban, contain complex multiplets at δ 7·0 to 7·6 attributable to the aromatic protons.[20] In most cases the N–H proton signal is not clearly observable but it is hidden under the aromatic proton multiplets.

The thiocarbamate insecticides of group (9) yield spectra in general similar to those found for group (7).[20] Although the effect does not take place at ambient temperatures, separate resonance peaks for the N-alkyl groups of these carbamates occur at low temperature owing to hindered rotation around the N–CO bond as shown by the spectrum of Sutan (Fig. 2).[20]

Hindered rotation around the N–CO bond also occurs at lower temperatures in the dithiocarbamate pesticides assigned to group (10).[20] The N-alkyl proton signal from dithiocarbamate esters[24] is broadened and finally split into a doublet, as the temperature is lowered below ambient, indicating a hindered rotation around the N–CO bond with an activation energy of about 10 to 12 kcal./mole.

In the case of N-substituted aromatic carbamate esters (12, 13), the N–CH_3 and N–CH_2 protons gave sharp absorption peaks.[25] The ester O–CH_3 protons, however, yield a broad peak at room temperature with subsequent splitting as the temperature is lowered. These results suggest that a barrier is formed around the ester group rather than the amide.

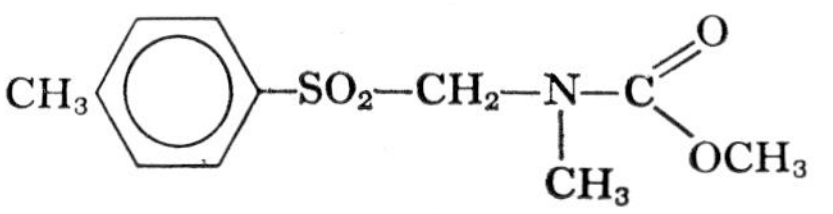

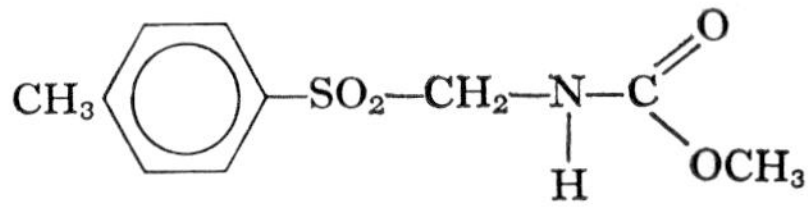

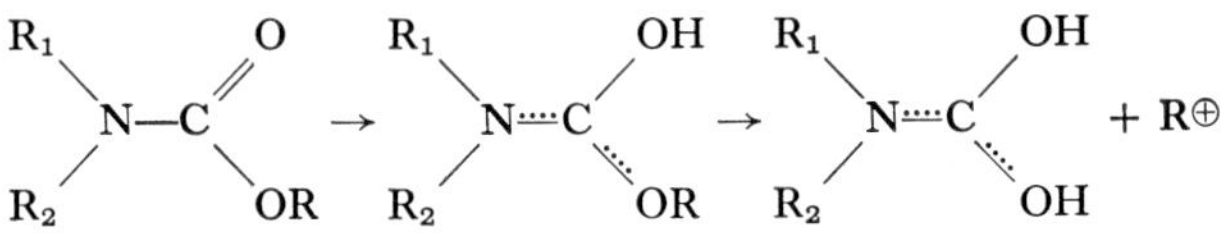

R_1, R_2 are alkyl or hydrogen and R is an alkyl group

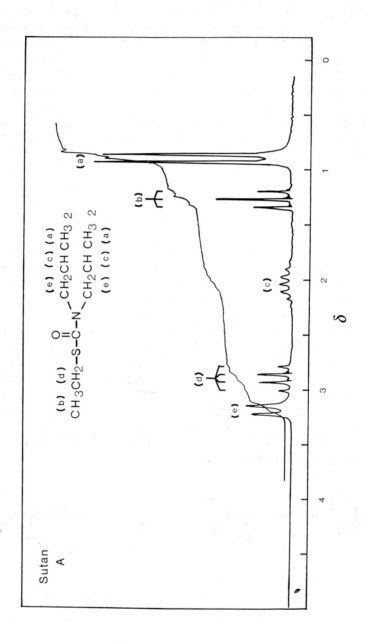

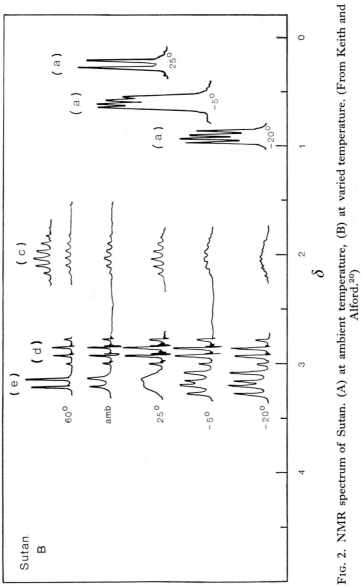

FIG. 2. NMR spectrum of Sutan. (A) at ambient temperature, (B) at varied temperature. (From Keith and Alford.[20])

Formation of protonated species has been detected by Olah and Calin[26] for many carbamates in a solvent mixture of SbF_5, FSO_3H and liquid SO_2 (14). Spectra of carbamates obtained at $-60°C$ in the above solvent give a –COH proton resonance peak with splitting due to the –NH proton indicating that protonation occurs at the carbonyl group.

The spectra of ferric alkyl dithiocarbamates (15) show[27 to 29] large chemical

$$Fe\left(\begin{array}{c} S \\ \diagup \diagdown \\ \diagdown \diagup \\ S \end{array} C-N \begin{array}{c} R \\ \diagup \\ \diagdown \\ R \end{array}\right)_3$$

15

shifts and line broadening because of isotropic hyperfine interaction between the various protons and the unpaired electron of the paramagnetic transition metal.[30] Golding and coworkers,[27,28] assuming that the iron atom has an octahedrally symmetric environment having comparable energies[31] in the two lowest states $^2T_2$ and $^6A_1$, calculated the hyperfine interaction constants A_2 and A_6 corresponding to the above two states from the large temperature-dependent chemical shifts. In each calculation these workers neglected the configurational mixing and spin-orbit coupling from the higher excited states. The value of A_2 and A_6 for the N-methyl protons in ferric dimethyldithiocarbamate were 1·01 and $4·35 \times 10^5$ Hz, respectively.

The hyperfine interaction constants for a number of other ferric dithio-carbamates has also been reported.[27,28] The spectrum of cobalt diethyldithio-carbamate also shows typical paramagnetic transition metal effects.[32]

Hindered rotation around the N–CO bond is evident from the spectra of certain N-alkyl- and N,N-dialkyl- amides. For example, the non-equivalence of the N-methylene protons in a variety of N-substituted aryl amides has been found by Siddell and coworkers.[33 to 36] In a number of N,N-disubstituted amides, containing an *ortho*-substituted aryl group attached to the nitrogen atom, the N-alkyl methylene protons exhibit non-equivalence.[36] The chemical shift is temperature dependent and there is a slow rotation around the aryl-nitrogen bond. Similar slow inversions has also been observed in N-phenylamides.[37]

Amides form hydrogen bond complexes[38,39] with acids as shown by changes in the chemical shift of the acid proton upon addition of increasing amounts of amide. In the presence of very strong acids, the amide carbonyl group becomes protonated resulting in the appearance at low temperatures of a new resonance peak due to the –COH group.[40]

In general the spectra of substituted ureas show characteristics similar to amides and carbamates. The spectra of thiourea compounds of the type (16), where R is either methyl or acetyl, has provided evidence for slow rotation

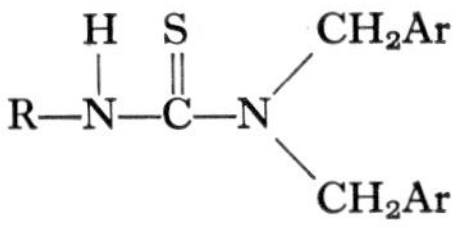

$$\begin{array}{ccc} H & S & CH_2Ar \\ | & \| & / \\ R-N-C-N & & \\ & & \backslash \\ & & CH_2Ar \end{array}$$

16

around the N–C bond.[40] The signal from the benzylic protons is sharp at ambient temperatures, broadens at lower temperature and finally splits into a doublet at even lower temperatures. Activation energies for the rotation around the N–C bond is 10 kcal./mole for N-methylureas and 15 kcal./mole for N-acetyl-ureas.[41] Spectra of a number of urea compounds have been reported by Blood-worth and Davies.[42] The N–H proton resonances in compounds of the general type (**17**) occurred at δ 6.

$$R_1NH-CO-NH-R_2$$

17

The NMR spectrum of the urea (**18**) contains sharp peaks at room tempera-ture, however, at $-40°C$ the methylene and methyl proton signals split as a result of a slow rotation around the aryl-nitrogen bond.[34]

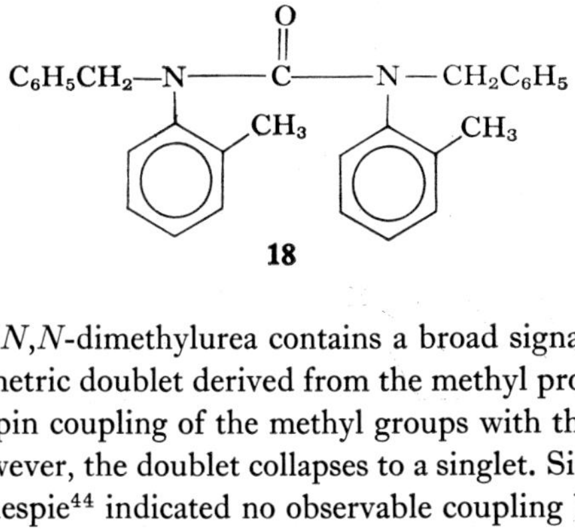

$$C_6H_5CH_2-N-\overset{\overset{\displaystyle O}{\|}}{C}-N-CH_2C_6H_5$$

18

The spectrum of N,N-dimethylurea contains a broad signal for the NH pro-tons and an unsymmetric doublet derived from the methyl protons, apparently[43] as a result of spin-spin coupling of the methyl groups with the –NH proton. In acidic solutions, however, the doublet collapses to a singlet. Similar investigation by Birchall and Gillespie[44] indicated no observable coupling between the –CH$_3$ and –NH protons in N,N-dimethylurea, even in the absence of acid, which was explained on the basis of a rapid proton exchange between the nitrogen protons and the solvent protons. In studies of a large number of substituted ureas in aqueous solution Barker et $al.$[45] found that both N-methylurea and N,N-dimethylurea give doublets in the methyl region of the spectrum and also yield a broad peak for the nitrogen proton. The spectra of two urea pesticides,[46] monuron and fenuron, at room temperature contains no multiplicity of the methyl signal indicating the absence of hindered rotation around the N–C bond (Table VI).

TABLE VI

NMR parameters for monuron and fenuron in dimethyl sulfoxide-d_6

Compound	Chemical shift δ
Monuron	
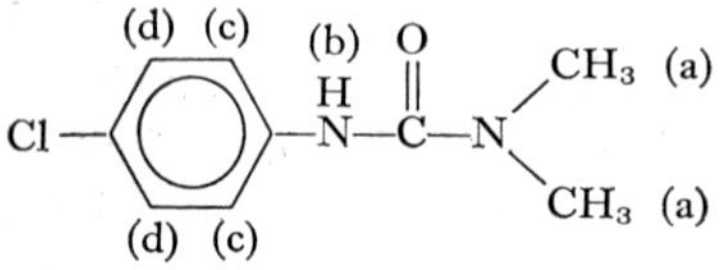	$a = 3 \cdot 22$ $b = 8 \cdot 68$ $c \rbrace\ 7 \cdot 56\ (J = 9 \cdot 0\ \text{Hz})$ $d \rbrace\ 7 \cdot 85\ (J = 9 \cdot 0\ \text{Hz})$
Fenuron	
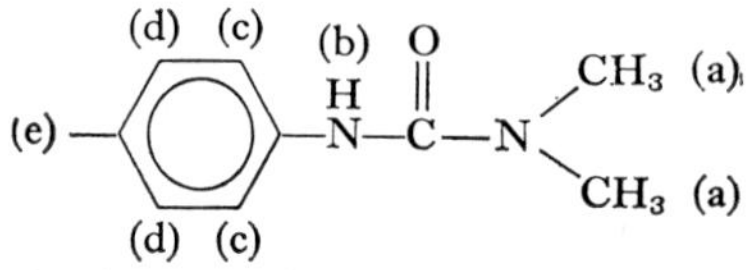	$a = 3 \cdot 21$ $b = 8 \cdot 48$ $c = 5 \cdot 56\quad J_{cd} = 9 \cdot 0\ \text{Hz}$ $d = 5 \cdot 14\quad J_{de} = 7 \cdot 0\ \text{Hz}$ $e = 4 \cdot 84$

C. DDT and related compounds

The basic skeleton of DDT type compounds is diphenylmethane (**19**) in which the phenyl rings are usually substituted with chlorine and R usually represents a CCl_3 or a $CHCl_2$ moiety. The NMR spectra of DDT, [1,1,1-trichloro-2,2-bis(*p*-chlorophenyl)methane] and related compounds have been studied in detail by Sharpless and Bradley[47,48] and Keith *et al.*[49] As expected, from the structure of *p,p'*-DDT (**20**), the NMR spectra show a singlet for the α-benzylic

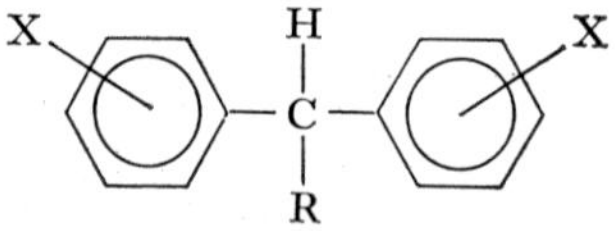

proton and a multiplet for the aromatic protons (Fig. 3). Long-range coupling between the ring protons and the α-benzylic proton is not observable, even when the temperature of the sample is lowered to $-60°C$, indicating that *ortho* proton coupling is stereospecific and that there is a free rotation of the phenyl groups.[47] The chemical shift δ of the α-benzylic proton in compounds of the type

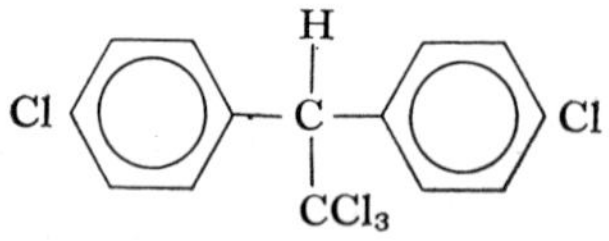

$$\begin{array}{l} R_1 \\ \quad\diagdown \\ \qquad CHCCl_3 \\ \quad\diagup \\ R_2 \end{array}$$

(where R_1 and R_2 represent substituted phenyl rings) correlates[47]

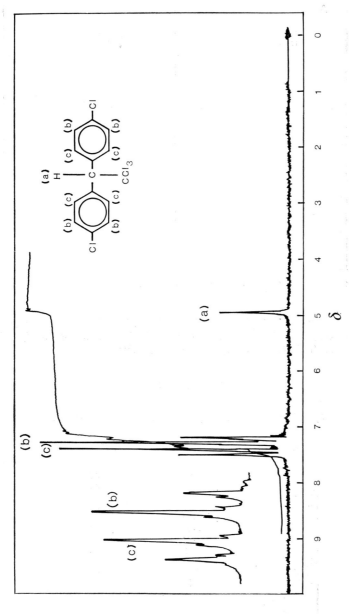

Fig. 3. NMR spectrum of p,p'-DDT. (From Keith, Alford and Garrison.[49])

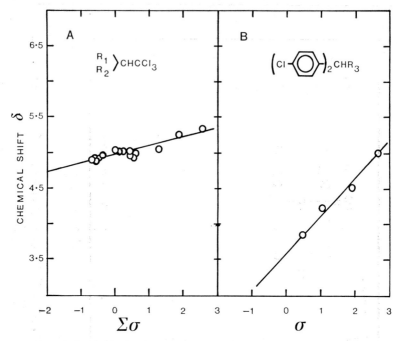

FIG. 4. Hammett and Taft plots of variations in DDT molecules. (A) Ring substituents in $R_1R_2CHCCl_3$– Hammett, (B) Aliphatic substituents in (p-chlorophenyl)$_2$CHR– Taft. (From Sharpless and Bradley.[47])

TABLE VII

Chemical shift of benzylic proton of DDT derivatives of the type (p-chlorophenyl)$_2$-CHR for various R groups

R Group	Chemical shift δ	Reference
H	3·87	47
CHCl$_2$	4·53	47
CH$_2$Cl	4·24	47
CCl$_3$	5·02	47
CBr$_3$	5·17	47
COOH	4·95	47
COOCH$_3$	4·94	49
CH$_3$CHNO$_2$	4·38	49
C$_2$H$_5$CHNO$_2$	4·38	49
CH$_2$OH	4·0	49
(cyclic dioxolane structure) CH—	4·18	49

in a linear manner with the Hammett sigma function[50] and fits a least square curve $\delta = 0.121\sigma + 4.98$. The chemical shift of the α-benzylic proton for DDT-type compounds of the type $(Cl-C_6H_4-)_2CHR$ fits a Taft plot (Fig. 4). Changes in the chemical shift of the α-benzylic proton, as a function of R, are summarized in Table VII.

The stepwise removal of aliphatic chlorine atoms from the DDT molecule results in an upfield shift of the α-benzylic proton resonance signal. Since there is spin-spin coupling between the α-benzylic proton and the protons in the $CHCl_2$ or CH_2Cl groups, the α-benzylic proton signal becomes increasingly more complex.[47]

The aromatic proton pattern of DDT-type compounds is quite complex with a multiplicity depending upon the nature of the ring substituents. Each p,p'-substituted aromatic ring contains four protons which differ magnetically. Analysis of the ring pattern from such compounds has been made by Sharpless and Bradley[48] on an A_2B_2-type spectrum. After numbering the ring proton positions (21), the *ortho* $(J_{3,5}, J_{4,6})$, *meta* $(J_{5,6}, J_{3,5})$ and *para* $(J_{4,5}, J_{3,6})$ coupling

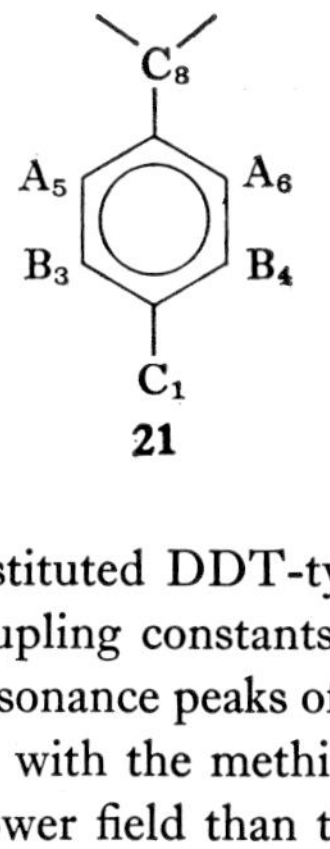

21

constants for a number of substituted DDT-type compounds were calculated. The *ortho, para-* and *meta-* coupling constants were 7·5 to 8·5, 0·2 to 0·5 and 2·0 to 3·0 Hz, respectively. Resonance peaks of the A protons were broadened because of long-range coupling with the methine protons. The peaks from the A protons generally occur at lower field than those of the B protons, although this relationship is reversed for the *p*-nitro- and *p*-iodo- substituted derivatives. The internal chemical shift between the A and B protons gives a linear correlation when plotted against the electronegativity of the substituent R in insecticides of the type $(R-C_6H_4-)_2CHCCl_3$ and $(R-C_6H_4-)_2C{=}CCl_2$ (Fig. 5). Sharpless and Bradley[48] also made molecular orbital calculations of the electron density for the various protons. They found a linear correlation for the electron density at the corresponding carbon versus the chemical shift of the protons *ortho* to the substituent R for compounds of the general formulae $(R-C_6H_4-)_2CHR'$ and $(R-C_6H_4-)_2C{=}CCl_2$ (Fig. 6).

Considerable difficulty was encountered in attempting to synthesize 2,2-*bis*-(*p*-chlorophenyl)acetaldehyde (23), a proposed intermediate in the metabolism

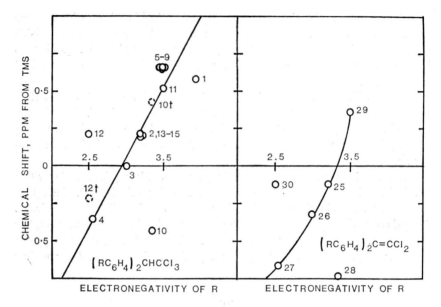

Fig. 5. Internal chemical shifts of ring protons for compounds $(RC_6H_4)_2CHCll_3$ and $(RC_6H_4)_2C = CCl_2$ as a function of the electronegativity of R. (From Sharpless and Bradley.[48])

of DDT. A precursor in the synthesis, 2-(*p,p′*-dichlorobenzhydryl)-1,3-dioxolane (**22**), was characterized[51] by its infrared, mass and NMR spectra. The NMR spectrum was especially useful in the confirmation of structure and showed a pair of doublets ($J=4$ Hz) arising from the coupling of the benzhydryl proton (δ 4·18) and the methinyl proton (δ 5·43) of the dioxolane ring. Hydrolysis of the acetal (**22**), however, gave a mixture of (**23**) and *p,p′*-dichlorobenzophenone. The infrared, mass and NMR spectra of the aldehyde were those expected for the anticipated compound (**23**).

The NMR spectrum of DDT is markedly affected by the nature of the solvent used.[46] Whilst the aromatic proton signal is not appreciably shifted, that of the

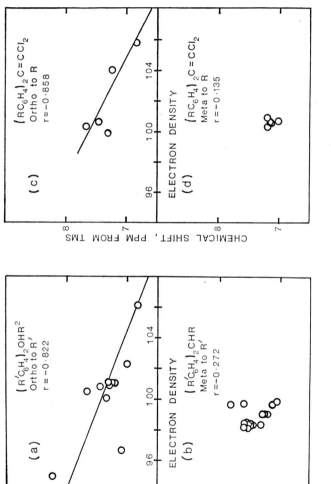

FIG. 6. Observed chemical shift, p.p.m. from TMS, plotted against calculated electron density. (a) Protons *ortho* to ring substituent R^1 for $(R^1C_6H_4)_2CHR^2$, (b) Protons *meta* to ring substituent R^1, (c) Protons *ortho* to ring substituent R for $(RC_6H_4)_2C = CCl_2$, (d) Protons *meta* to R. (From Sharpless and Bradley.[48])

α-benzylic proton shows considerable solvent dependence. The α-benzylic proton at δ 4·94 in CCl_4 is shifted to low field in DMSO or acetone, with a chemical shift of δ 5·60 and 5·39 respectively, indicating intermolecular hydrogen bond formation between the DDT molecule and the electron donor solvents.

Keith and coworkers[49] have analyzed and compiled the 100 MHz NMR spectra of a large number of DDT-type insecticides (p,p'-DDT; o,p'-DDT; o-MDT; methoxychlor; kelthane; p,p'-DDD; perthane; DDE; p,p'-DDMS; o,p'-DDMU; DDNU; DBP; DDA; DDA methyl ester; diphenamid; chlorobenzilate; chloropropylate; prolan; bulan; DDOH; and DDT acetal).

D. Hexachlorocyclohexanes

The hexachlorocyclohexane insecticides can exist in a number of isomeric forms. The cyclohexane ring can assume either a boat or the more stable chair configuration. In addition, a second type of isomerism is possible depending upon whether the substituent chlorine atoms are axial or equatorial. The two types of configuration changes permit the chlorine atoms to exist in several orientations giving rise to a number of isomers. If e denotes the equatorial chlorine and a the axial chlorine, the following five isomeric forms are found in the hexachlorocyclohexanes:

Alpha (α)   a a e e e e
Beta (β)   e e e e e e
Gamma (γ)   a a a e e e
Delta (δ)   a e e e e e
Epsilon (ε)   a e e a e e

The NMR spectra of the hexachlorocyclohexane isomers were first reported by Lemieux et al.[52] with dioxane as internal reference at an operating frequency of 40 MHz. The β-isomer, in which all of the chlorine atoms are equatorial, showed a single resonance peak at 0·63 p.p.m. due to the axial protons. The spectrum of the α isomer gave a multiplet structure with peaks at 1·35 and 0·95 p.p.m., reflecting the presence of two equatorial and four axial protons. Signals at 1·35 and 1·15 p.p.m. were found with the ε isomer in an intensity ratio of 2:4 with the peak at lower field being assigned[52] to the two equatorial hydrogens. The spectrum of the δ isomer contained peaks at 1·2 and 0·17 p.p.m. in the intensity ratio of 1:5 due to the one equatorial and five axial protons, respectively. The γ isomer (lindane), however, yielded only a single peak at 1·3 p.p.m. indicating a rapid exchange of the equatorial and axial protons. Analysis[53] of lindane at −50°C in acetone gave a complex spectrum (Fig. 7), probably of AB_2C_2D type[54] for the molecule in the chair configuration. Similarly, the spectrum of the δ isomer showed[53] fine structure at 36°C at an operating frequency of 60 MHz (Fig. 8). On the basis of first-order perturbation theory, analysis of this spectrum with an AB_2C_2D-type pattern gave the coupling constants $J_{AB} = 2·8$ Hz, $J_{BC} = 10·5$ Hz and $J_{CD} = 10·5$ Hz. As

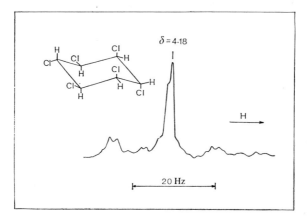

FIG. 7. The proton spectrum at 40 MHz of γ-1,2,3,4,5,6 hexachlorocyclohexane in acetone solution at $-50°C$. (From Harris and Sheppard.[53])

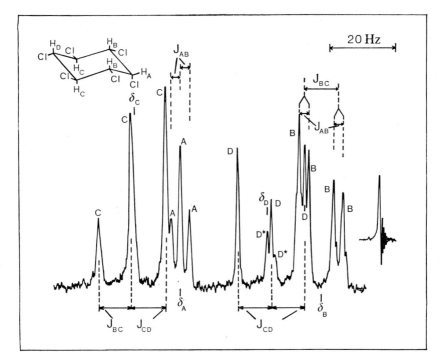

FIG. 8. The proton spectrum at 60 MHz of 1,2,3,4,5,6 hexachlorocyclohexane in solution in benzene at $+36°C$. The sharp peak to the right of the spectrum is that of tetramethyl silane shifted downfield by 165 Hz. (From Harris and Sheppard.[53])

expected, the axial-axial coupling constant was greater than the axial-equatorial coupling constant. The chemical shifts were $\delta_C = 4.01$ and $\delta_D = 3.32$ p.p.m., with reference to tetramethylsilane.

E. Chlorinated cyclodienes

Compounds in this series are chlorinated products of the Diels-Alder reaction involving condensation of a diene group to a double-bonded compound. Some important members of the group are chlordane (**24**), heptachlor (**25**), aldrin (**26**), isodrin (**26**), endrin (**27**), dieldrin (**27**), thiodan (**28**) and telodrin (**29**).

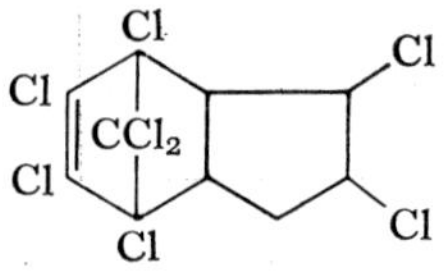

Chlordane
24

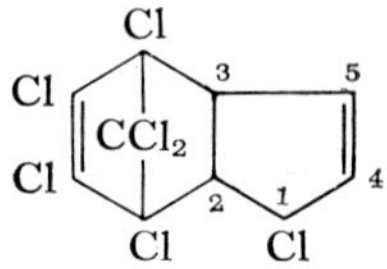

Heptachlor
25

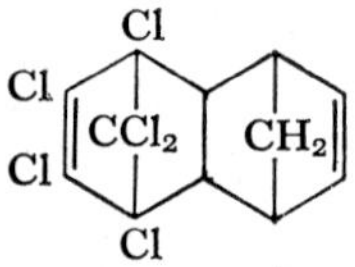

Aldrin and isodrin
26

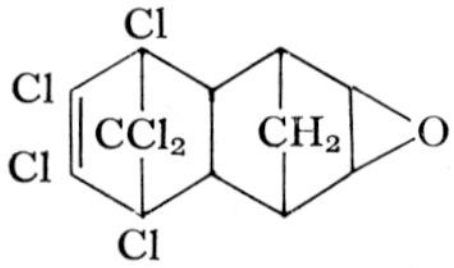

Dieldrin and endrin
27

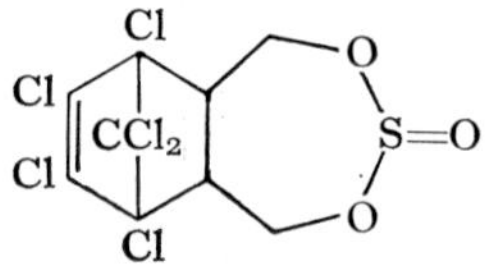

Thiodan (endosulfan)
28

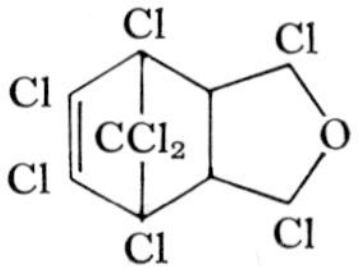

Telodrin
29

These isomeric insecticides are all cyclic, share a fully chlorinated ring and have the chlorinated *endo*-methylene bridge. The unchlorinated precursors of these insecticides, called bicycloalkanes, norbornanes or norborenes have been extensively studied via NMR techniques.[55 to 64]

The spectrum (Fig. 9) of hexachlorbicyclo[2·2·1]heptene, which is common to most of the chlorinated cyclodiene insecticides, was reported by Williamson[65] and a series of compounds of the type (**30**) were analyzed on the basis of an ABX-type pattern. It was observed[65] that the internal chemical shift of the ring protons was dependent on the dihedral angle.[66] Coupling constants and chemical shifts were both dependent on the electronegativity of the substituents adjacent to the coupling protons.

NMR SPECTRUM of DIELS–ALDER ADDUCT

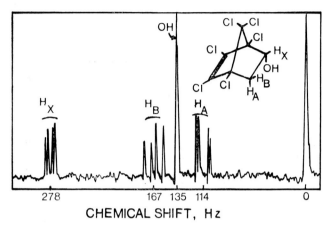

FIG. 9. NMR spectrum of hexachlorobicyclo[2.2.1]heptene at 60 MHz. (From Williamson.[65])

The structures of the six principal products formed upon chlorination of 4,5,6,7,8,8-hexachloro-3a,4,7,7a-tetrahydro-4,7-methanoindane have been assigned by Buechel et al.[67] on the basis of their NMR spectra and by independent

30

(R = —OAc, —OH, —Cl, —C$_6$H$_5$, —CO$_2$H, —CN)

synthesis. Three new compounds, the γ, δ and ϵ isomers of chlordane, were formed in addition to β-dihydroheptachlor, β-chlordane and nonachlor (1,2,3,4, 5,6,7,8,8-nonachloro-3a,4,7,7a-tetrahydro-4,7-methanoindane). The NMR characteristics of the three isomeric chlordane insecticides are summarized in Table VIII.

The spectra of heptachlor (25) and its epoxide have been determined in CCl$_4$ solution.[68] Protons 4 and 5 of heptachlor yield a sharp resonance peak at δ 5·9 while protons 1, 2 and 3 form unresolved multiplets centered at δ 4·75, 4 and 3·5, respectively. The spectrum of heptachlor epoxide is quite similar to that of heptachlor except that the signal from protons 4 and 5 move upfield to δ 3·5 and similar shifts occur in the resonance peaks of the remaining protons.

TABLE VIII
Chemical shift and assignment of chlordane protons[67]

Compound	Number of protons and assignment	Chemical shift δ
γ-Chlordane	2H, tertiary	3·52
	2H, secondary (*endo*)	2·88
	2H, secondary (*exo*)	2·02
δ-Chlordane	2H, tertiary (bridge)	3·65
	2H, tertiary	3·9
	2H, secondary	2·49
ϵ-Chlordane	1H, tertiary (bridge)	3·8
	1H, 3-*exo*	3·0
	3H, 1-*exo*, 1-*endo*, 3-*endo*	2·5
	1H, 2-*endo*	3·8

Addition of HCl to 4,5,6,7,8,8-hexachloro-3a,4,7,7a-tetrahydro-4,7-methano-indene (chlordene) (31), in the presence of light resulted[69] in the formation of three isomeric dihydroheptachlor, (DHC) insecticides, α-DHC (32) (1,4,5,6,7,8,8-heptachloro-3a,4,7,7a-tetra-hydro-4,7-methanoindene), β-DHC (33) (2,4,5,6,7,8,8-heptachloro-3a,4,7,7a-tetrahydro-*exo*-4,7-methanoindene) and γ-DHC (34) (2,4,5,6,7,8,8-heptachloro-3a,4,7,7a-tetrahydro-*endo*-4,7-methano-indene). The configuration of the reaction products has been proved[69] by inde-pendent synthesis and by NMR analysis of the DHC isomers. The principal reaction product, β-DHC (33), exhibited three groups of signals in its NMR spectrum: one proton in the *endo* position at C-2 at δ 4·17, two tertiary protons at 3·57 and the four methylene protons at δ 2·05. The resonance signal from the two *endo* protons at C-1 and C-3 should be shifted downfield by the influence of the chlorine substituted cycloheptene ring. The two *exo* chlorine substituents, however, cause a shift of the two *exo* protons at C-1 and C-3 so that the *exo* and *endo* protons occur as a single peak.

On the other hand, the presence of an *endo*-chlorine substituent at C-2 causes a split of the four methylene protons into two separate band groups as in the case of γ-DHC (34). The NMR spectrum for γ-DHC contains four signals: two C-1 and C-3 *exo* protons at δ 1·43, two C-1 and C-3 *endo* protons at δ 2·48, the C-2 *exo* proton at δ 3·92 and the two tertiary protons at δ 3·15. A split of the resonance signal from the methylene protons also occurs with the chlordanes[67] and is characteristic[69] for the occurrence of an *endo* chlorine substituent in the tetrahydromethanoindane ring system.

The NMR spectrum of α-DHC (32) is comparable to that of β-DHC since both isomers have an *exo* chlorine substituent. The NMR peaks were assigned to the four methylene protons at δ 1·96, the two tertiary protons at 3·87 and the C-1 *endo* proton at 4·16.

The NMR spectra[68] of aldrin (35) and isodrin (36) are shown in Fig. 10. In both cases resonance due to protons 1 and 2 occur at δ 6 and is in the form of a multiplet. Similarly, the peaks due to the 7,8 protons are multiplets because of

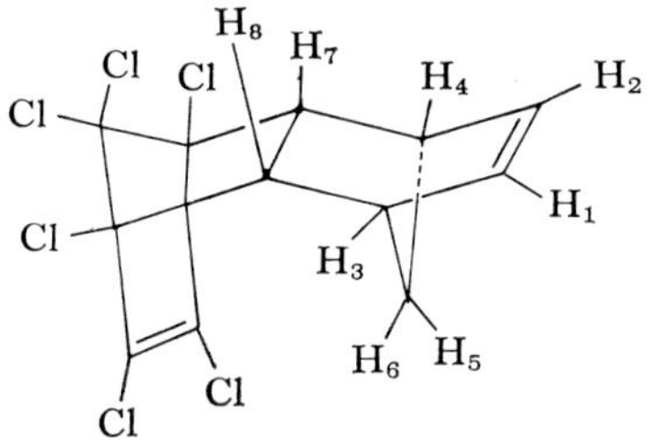

Aldrin
35

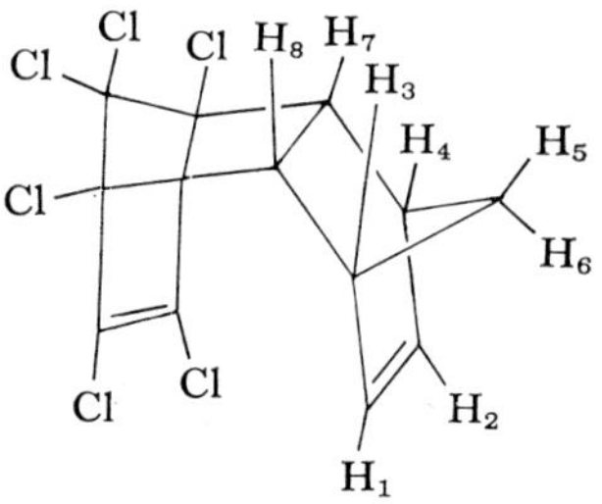

Isodrin
36

spin-spin splitting and are centered at δ 3·3 for isodrin and 2·7 for aldrin. The δ 2·9 and 2·2 signals, for isodrin and aldrin respectively, are assigned to protons 3 and 4. Finally, the methylene protons 5 and 6 give peaks at δ 1·5 having the characteristics of an AB pattern.

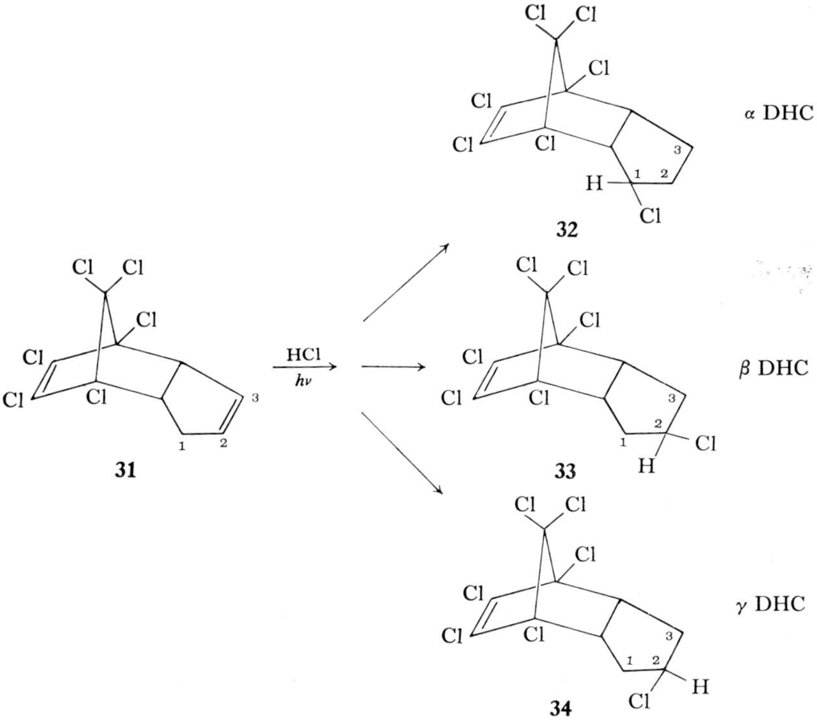

Dieldrin (27) and endrin (27) which are the epoxides of aldrin and isodrin exhibit NMR spectral characteristics similar to those of their parent compounds. The resonance peaks for the olefinic protons 1 and 2 are absent since the unsaturation in dieldrin and endrin is lost by formation of the epoxide bridge. The chemical shift values[70] of these insecticides in $CDCl_3$ solution are given in Table IX.

TABLE IX

Chemical shift of various protons in endrin, isodrin, aldrin and dieldrin

| Compound | Chemical shift, δ | | | | |
	1, 2	3, 4	5	6	7, 8
Isodrin 36	6·01	2·99	1·77	1·55	3·35
Endrin	3·35	2·92	1·81	0·97	3·27
Aldrin 35	6·18	2·26	1·56	1·06	2·72
Dieldrin	3·13	2·68	1·28	1·07	2·72

The relative positions of protons 5 and 6, which are anti-bridge and syn-bridge to each other in the aldrin and isodrin molecules have been assigned by spin-decoupling experiments.[71] The isodrin anti-bridge proton gave a resonance peak which was at higher field than that from the syn-bridge proton. This assignment was made on the basis of the stereospecific long-range coupling, between the anti-bridge proton and one of the vinyl protons, resulting in a broadening of the anti-bridge portion of the AB pattern. This peak broadening disappeared when the vinyl protons 1, 2 were decoupled. Using similar reasoning it was decided that the anti-bridge proton in the aldrin molecule gives a resonance at lower field than the syn-bridge proton. The difference in behavior of aldrin and isodrin is explained by anisotropy and field effects of the vinylic chlorine atoms in the ring adjacent to the norborene ring. Vinylic chlorine atoms in the aldrin molecule usually produce a large paramagnetic shift of the anti-bridge and a large diamagnetic shift of the syn-bridge protons. The chlorine atoms in isodrin thus deshield both the syn- and anti-bridge protons. If the interpretation of Marchand and Rose[71] is correct, the earlier assignment of Parsons and Moore[70] for these protons is in error.

Two stereoisomeric forms of the insecticide thiodan (28) are known, α-thiodan (m.p. 108–110°C) and β-thiodan (m.p. 208–210°C). Although 24 configurational and confirmational isomers are possible, chemical modifications and NMR studies on α- and β- thiodan excluded all but 8 possible structures (Fig. 11).[72] The NMR spectrum (Fig. 12) of α- and β- thiodan shows the presence of only three different protons. Application of the Karplus[66] relationship, between coupling constant and dihedral angle, suggests that the α- and β- isomers of thiodan may be represented by the partial Newman projections (**37, 38**).

Analysis of the NMR spectra of the thiodan isomers yields the chemical shifts and coupling constants for the various protons shown in Table X. Since only

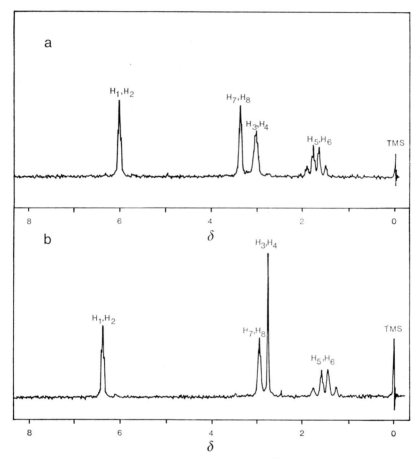

FIG. 10. NMR spectra of (a) Isodrin and (b) Aldrin. (From Selected Nuclear Magnetic Resonance Spectral Data, Texas A. & M. University, Thermodynamic Research Center Data Project.[68])

isomers *a* to *d* (Fig. 11) contained H_1 and H_3 in the *trans* relationship, it was suggested[72] that one of these structures corresponds to α-thiodan. Similarly, NMR evidence indicated that H_1 and H_2 were skew to H_3 in β-thiodan and that

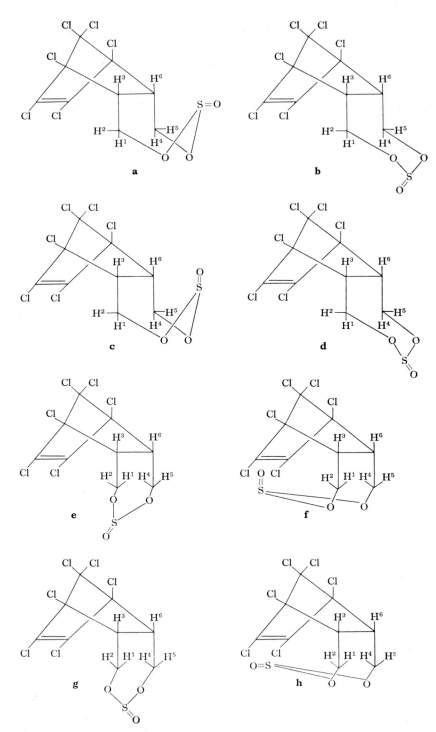

FIG. 11. Possible Thiodan structures. (From Forman *et al.*[72])

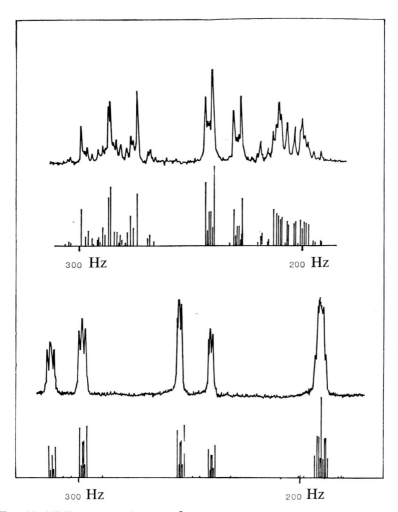

FIG. 12. NMR spectra of α- and β- thiodan. *Top*: α-Thiodan (lower melting point). *Bottom*: β-Thiodan (higher melting point). (From Forman *et al.*[72])

TABLE X

**Chemical shift and coupling constant parameters for
thiodan isomers**

Thiodan	Chemical shift, Hz	(δ)	Coupling constant, Hz
α	$H_1 = H_4 = 285 \cdot 1$ $H_2 = H_5 = 235 \cdot 7$ $H_3 = H_6 = 205 \cdot 6$	(4·75) (3·93) (3·42)	$J_{1,2} = J_{4,5} = -12 \cdot 8$ $J_{1,3} = J_{4,6} = 12 \cdot 1$ $J_{2,3} = J_{5,6} = 3 \cdot 4$ $J_{3,6} = 8 \cdot 7$ All other J values $= 0$
β	$H_1 = H_4 = 302 \cdot 8$ $H_2 = H_5 = 246 \cdot 9$ $H_3 = H_6 = 109 \cdot 5$	(5·05) (4·11) (1·82)	$J_{1,2} = J_{4,5} = -13 \cdot 9$ $J_{1,3} = J_{4,6} = 2 \cdot 5$ $J_{2,3} = J_{5,6} = 2 \cdot 5$ $J_{3,6} = 8 \cdot 5$ All other J values $= 0$

isomers **e** to **h** would represent this form. Forman et al.[72] were unable to differentiate any further the possible structures for α- and β- thiodan on the basis of NMR data alone. Instead, final structural assignments were made on the basis of infrared measurements and ring stability considerations.[72]

The spectrum[68] of the insecticide telodrin (**29**) contains only two peaks of equal intensity, at δ 4 and 6, derived from the bicycloheptene protons and the epoxy ring, respectively.

The miticide tranid (**38a**) [exo-3-chloro-endo-6-cyano-2-norbornanone-o-(methyl-carbamoyl)oxime] was assigned the syn-structural configuration on the basis of NMR evidence.[73] The chemical shift of the proton at C-1 was found to occur at lower field than that of the anti-isomer (**38b**).

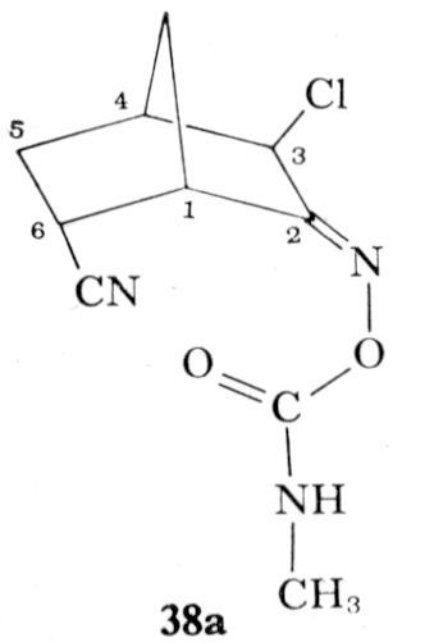

38a

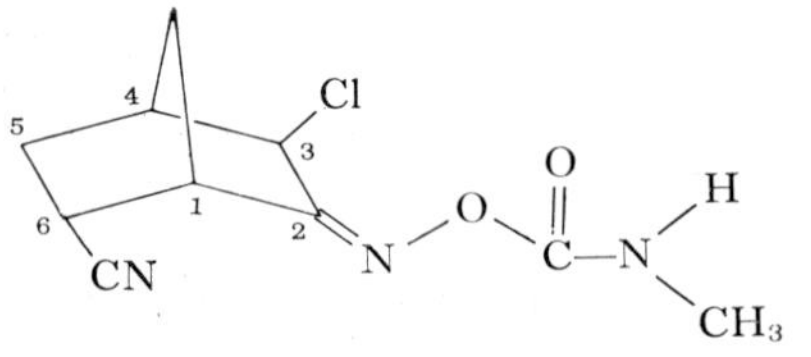

38b

F. Phenols

The structure of simple and substituted phenols and their interaction with various molecules has been studied extensively by NMR spectroscopy.[74 to 80]

Chemical shift and line width of the phenolic proton signal are very dependent on both the acidity of the phenolic proton and the nature of the solvent used. The downfield shift of the phenolic proton signal, for a group of chlorinated phenol fungicides, increases with increasing dissociation of the phenolic proton (Table XI). Solvents with electron donor groups may also interact with the phenols

TABLE XI

Chemical shift of phenolic protons and dissociation constant of chlorinated phenol fungicides

Compound	pK_a[a]	Chemical shift[b], δ
Pentachlorophenol	4·8	6·0
2,3,4,6-Tetrachlorophenol	5·3	5·8
2,4-Dichlorophenol	7·8	5·5

[a] Reference 81.
[b] References 68, 82. In CCl_4 solvent.

forming hydrogen bonds and displacing the OH resonance signals to low field. In a non-polar solvent, such as CCl_4, the phenolic proton of pentachlorophenol absorbs at δ 6·0,[82] while in diethyl ether the proton signal is shifted downfield to δ 8·85.[68] On the other hand, signals from the aromatic protons of 2,3,4,6-tetrachlorophenol and 2,4-dichlorophenol, occurring at about δ 7,[68] are not shifted appreciably when an electron donating solvent is employed.[82]

The NMR spectra of the fungicide hexachlorophene in DMSO -d_6 has been reported by Dietrich and Keller.[83] Proton resonance signals at δ 7·68 and 4·38 were assigned to the aromatic and methylene protons, respectively. The resonance for the phenolic protons was unobservable apparently due to line broadening and chemical exchange resulting from hydrogen bonding between the sulfinyl group of dimethyl sulfoxide and the bisphenol OH groups. Recently, however, the phenolic proton resonance of hexachlorophene has been demonstrated[82] in CCl_4 and the influence of various solvents on line width and chemical shift also examined. Upon addition of DMSO, amides or acetone a broadening and a downfield shift of the phenolic proton peak occurred. These changes have been interpreted in terms of hydrogen bond formation between the bisphenol hydroxyl groups and the carbonyl or sulfinyl group of the solvent. The chemical shift-concentration plot for the hexachlorophene OH group in DMSO and various simple amide solvents shows a minimum followed by an upswing in the chemical shift value at higher concentration of the solvent. This behavior is probably a result of the dissociation of the hydrogen-bonded associated ion-pair complex.

Keith *et al.*[49] have reported the 100 MHz spectrum of the chlorinated bisphe-nol dichlorophen. The chemical shift of the aromatic protons in a large number of phenols have been analyzed semi-emperically in terms of the additive substituent shielding values.[84]

G. Chlorinated phenoxy acetic acids

The 100 MHz spectra of two important members of this class, 2,4-dichloro-phenoxyacetic acid (2,4-D) and 2,4,5-trichlorophenoxyacetic acid (2,4,5-T) in DMSO, gave a single peak for the methylene protons at δ 4·74 and 5·03, respec-tively.[46] The acid proton peak was unobservable apparently due to line broaden-ing caused by hydrogen bonding with the solvent. The ring protons of 2,4-D showed multiple peaks due to the three magnetically non-equivalent protons; analysis of the coupling between these protons resulted in a value of 9 Hz for the *ortho-* and 2·5 Hz for the *meta-* coupling. The two magnetically non-equivalent ring protons of 2,4,5-T gave two singlets at δ 7·5 and 7·8. No *para-* coupling, of the ring protons, in either 2,4-D or 2,4,5-T was observed.

H. Hydrazides and nitriles

Maleic hydrazide may exist in the following tautomeric forms (**39** to **41**). The

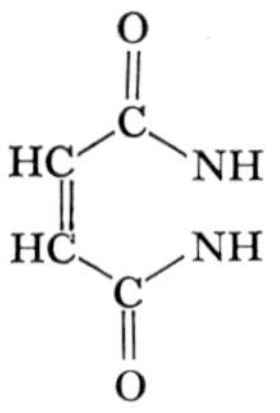

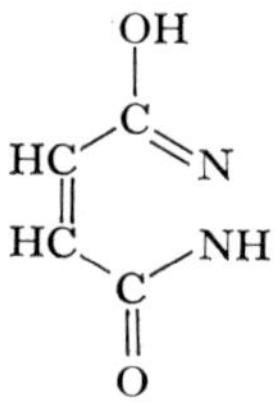

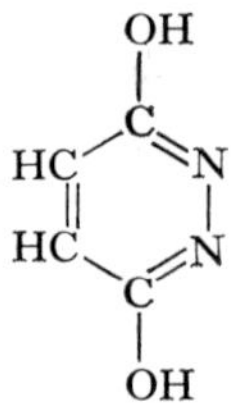

NMR spectrum of this plant growth regulator obtained in DMSO gave[85] a strong peak at δ 7·01 and a broad peak at 11·51. After comparison of the spectrum of this compound with that of maleic methyl hydrazide the peak at 7·01 was assigned to the HC=CH protons and the broad peak at 11·51 was considered to be an average of the C–OH and N–H protons. This assignment lead Ohashi *et al.*[85] to the conclusion that the main species was (**40**) in solution rather than (**39**) as predicted by Gompper and Altreutner.[83]

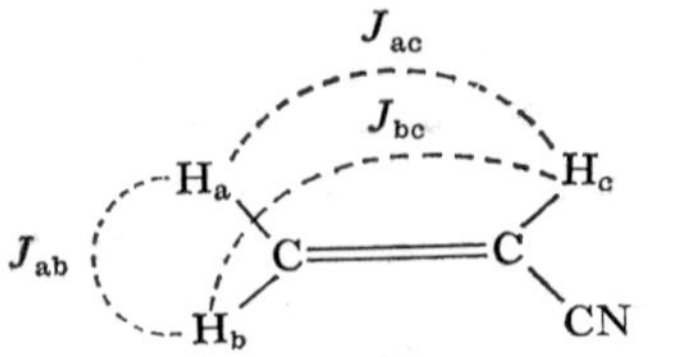

As expected from the formula (**42**) of the fumigant acrylonitrile there are three

magnetically non-equivalent protons in the molecule. The ABX-type spectrum consists of a 12-line pattern due to spin-spin interactions yielding the coupling constant and chemical shift data shown in Table XII.

TABLE XII

Chemical shifts and coupling constants in acrylonitrile

Worker	Chemical shift[a] p.p.m.			Coupling constant Hz		
	ab	bc	ca	J_{ab}	J_{bc}	J_{ca}
Castellano and Waugh[87] (40 MHz)	0·1	0·479	0·379	1·7	18·0	11·0
Reddy, Goldstein and Mandell[88] (60 MHz)	0·175	0·49	0·315	1·0	18·2	11·4
Murayama and Nukada[89] (100 MHz)	0·117	0·45	0·333	1·4	14·7	10·0

[a] These are shift differences between the protons and are *not* related to the usual standards.

I. Substituted pyridines, quaternary bipyridinium salts, uracils and aminotriozoles

The NMR spectrum of the substituted pyridine herbicide picloram (4-amino-3,5,6-trichloropicolinic acid) has been obtained[46] in DMSO-d_6. A sharp peak at δ 7·45 was assigned to the –NH_2 protons while a broader peak occurring at 9·4 was attributed to the carboxylic proton. The broad nature of the latter peak was explained on the basis of hydrogen bond formation between the acidic proton and the sulfinyl group of DMSO-d_6.

The spectra[90] of two quaternary bipyridinium herbicides, diquat (**43**) and paraquat (**44**), have been obtained in D_2O solution (Fig. 13). The methylene and

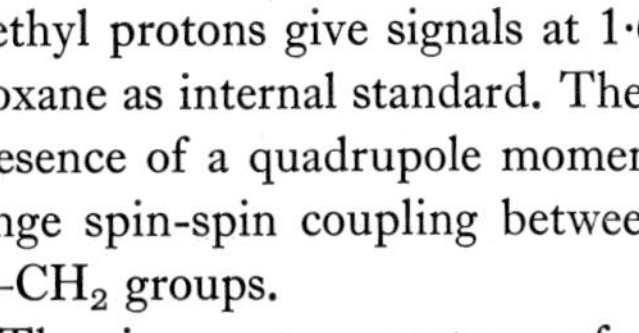

43 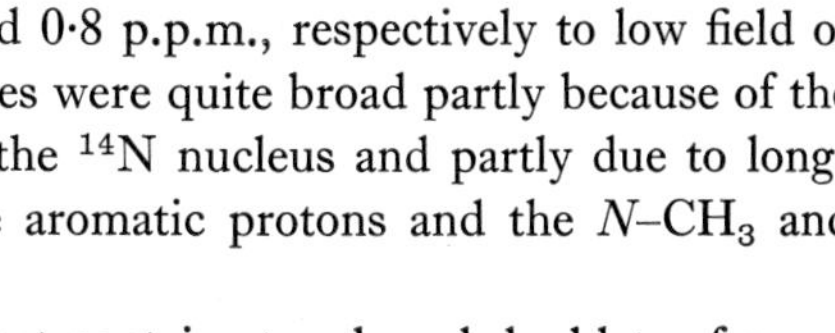   **44**

methyl protons give signals at 1·66 and 0·8 p.p.m., respectively to low field of dioxane as internal standard. These lines were quite broad partly because of the presence of a quadrupole moment of the ^{14}N nucleus and partly due to long-range spin-spin coupling between the aromatic protons and the N–CH_3 and N–CH_2 groups.

The ring proton spectrum of paraquat contains two broad doublets of equal spacing at 4·77 and 5·33 p.p.m. from internal dioxane, reflecting two sets of equivalent protons in the ring (2,6 and 3,5). The presence of an N–CH_3 group and the couplings $J(H–N)$ and $J(CH_3–H)$ causing broadening of the multiplet at 4·77 p.p.m. as compared to the other doublet at 5·33 p.p.m., was used[90] to ascribe the resonance at 4·77 p.p.m. to protons 2 and 6. The presence of a pyridine ring adjacent to protons 3 and 5 served as a basis for the assignment of the lower field resonance at 5·33 p.p.m. to these protons. The coupling constants $J_{2,3}$ and $J_{5,6}$ were 6·5 Hz.

The pyridine ring portion of the spectrum of diquat at 60 MHz shows a doublet centered at 5·46 p.p.m., a sextet at 4·6 p.p.m. and a complex pattern between these two signals. The resonance peaks at 4·6 and 5·46 p.p.m. were assigned to protons 5 and 6, respectively by analogy with the spectrum of 2,2'-bipyridine.[91,92] Due to considerable overlap between the resonance peaks of protons 3 and 4, a 220-MHz spectrum (Fig. 13) was employed[90] to obtain the resonance parameters for these protons. Relating this spectrum to that of 2-2'-bipyridine,[91,92] and using double resonance techniques, the ring portion of diquat spectrum gave the following chemical shifts and coupling constants: $[|J_{3,4}| = 8 \cdot 0$ Hz; $|J_{5,6}| = 6 \cdot 0$ Hz; $|J_{4,5}| = 7 \cdot 5$ Hz; $|J_{3,5}| = 1 \cdot 5$ Hz; $|J_{4,6}| = 1 \cdot 25$ Hz; $\delta_3 = 5 \cdot 22$; $\delta_4 = 5 \cdot 13$; $\delta_5 = 4 \cdot 61$ and $\delta_6 = 5 \cdot 46]$.

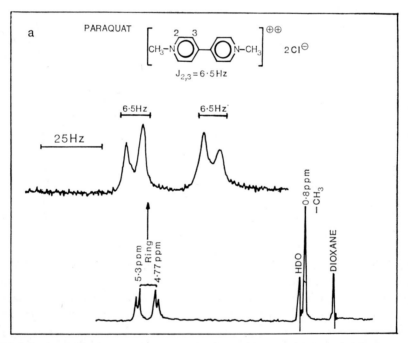

FIG. 13. (a) NMR spectrum of Paraquat, (b) NMR spectrum of Diquat and (c) NMR spectrum of aromatic region of Diquat at 220 MHz. (From Haque, Coshow and Johnson.[90])

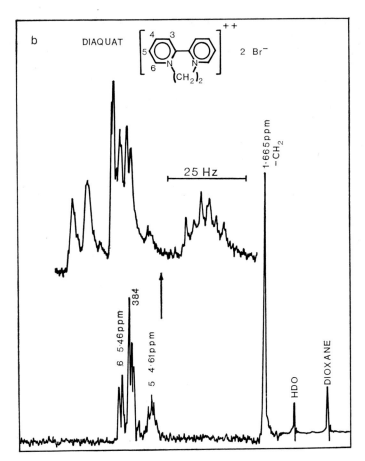

b   DIAQUAT   [structure]   2 Br⁻

25 Hz

1·665 ppm –CH₂

6 5·46 ppm
384
5 4·61 ppm

HDO

DIOXANE

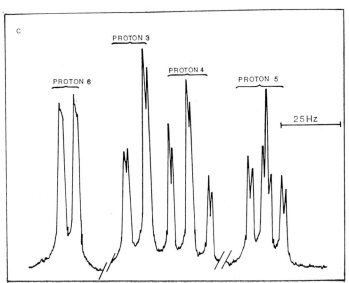

c

PROTON 6   PROTON 3   PROTON 4   PROTON 5

25 Hz

Diquat and paraquat both show[90] chemical shift changes when the anion associated with these cations is replaced. Diamagnetic iodide and ferrocyanide ions shift the $-CH_2$ peaks in diquat and the $-CH_3$ peak in paraquat, as well as the ring protons in both compounds, to low field, while the paramagnetic ferricyanide ion shifts them to high field. These displacements are explained[90] on the basis of charge transfer through ion-association complex formation between the anion and the organic cation.

The NMR spectra of a number of substituted uracils were reported by Kokko, Mandell and Goldstein[93] and the results have been interpreted in terms of tautomerism and hydrogen bonding. The spectrum of the herbicide isocil (5-bromo-6-methyl-3-isopropyl-uracil) has been used to distinguish between the keto (45) and enol (46) form of this compound.[94] The spectrum contained a doublet from the isopropyl-methyl protons, a singlet associated with the N-methyl protons, a multiplet for the isopropyl CH proton and a singlet occurring at δ 11·2 for the remaining proton. This latter resonance signal could be assigned either to the C–OH or N–H protons. Since the N–H proton resonance in pyrimidines[95] and also occurs at δ 11·2, it was concluded[94] that the peak was due to the NH proton and that, consequently, isocil exists completely in the keto form.

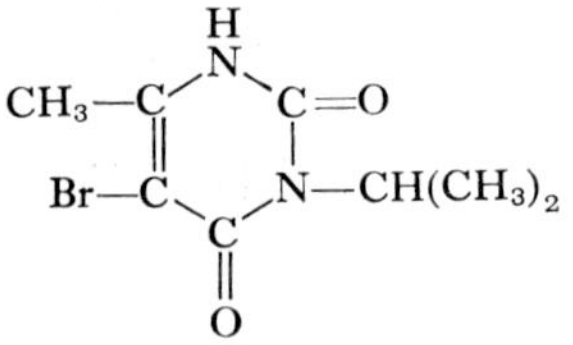

45

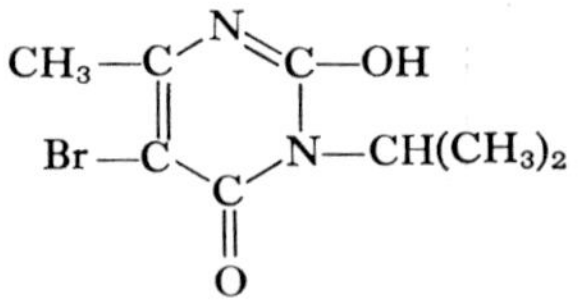

46

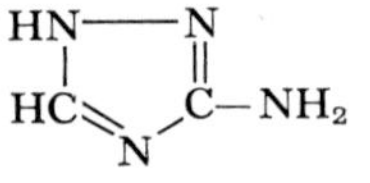

47

The NMR spectra of 1,2,4-triazoles have been recorded by several groups.[96 to 99] The spectrum of the herbicide amitrol (3-amino-1,2,4-triazole) (47) has been reported by Freiberg et al.[100] Only the signal due to the –CH proton at δ 7·47 was observable in acetone-d_6. The $-NH_2$ and –NH peaks were not detected since these protons apparently rapidly exchange with the trace of water which is present in the acetone. These same investigators also determined the spectra of a number of other 3-substituted-1,2,4-triazoles and found that the chemical shift of the –CH proton was very dependent on the nature of the substituent at the 3 position; the proton signal was moved towards low field by electron withdrawing and to higher field by electron donating substituents. The chemical shift of the –CH peak gave a linear correlation with the Hammett's σ_p constant for the substituent.

J. s-Triazines

The spectra of several 2,4-substituted s-triazines were described by Declerck et al.[101] and Tokuhiro and Fraenkel[102] have calculated the ^{13}C and proton chemical shift values for s-triazine. NMR analysis of ten substituted s-triazine herbicides, having the general formula (48), are summarized[46] in Table XIII. The spectra of these compounds in $CDCl_3$ solvent assumed the characteristics of the particular alkyl groups attached to the heterocyclic ring.

TABLE XIII

NMR chemical shifts of substituted s-triazine herbicides

(s = singlet; d = doublet; t = triplet; q = quartet; m = multiplet; b = broad)

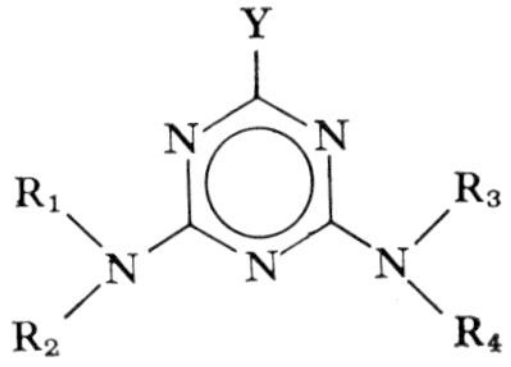

48

Name	Chemical shift, δ	
	in $CDCl_3$	in TFAA
Ametryne		
$Y = SCH_3{}^g\ R_1 = H^e$	a = 1·20 (d, 7)	a, b = 1·38 (m)
$R_2 = CH^d(CH_3)_2{}^a$	b = 1·19 (t, 7)	c = 3·65 (b)
$R_3 = H^f$	c = 3·43 (m, 7)	d = 4·38 (b)
$R_4 = CH_2{}^cCH_3{}^b$	d = 4·17 (m, 7)	e, f = 6·74, 6·92
	e, f = 542, 509 (b)	7·72, 7·95 (b)
	g = 2·42 (s)	g = 2·69 (s)
		TFAA = 12·31
Atratone		
$Y = OCH_3{}^g\ R_1 = H^f$	a = 1·47 (d, 7)	a, b = 1·35 (m)
$R_2 = CH^d(CH_3)_2{}^a$	b = 1·46 (t, 7)	c = 3·63 (b)
$R_3 = H^f$	c = 3·44 (m, 7)	d = 4·22 (b)
$R_4 = CH^dCH_3{}^b$	d = 4·19 (m, 7)	e, f = 6·60, 6·76
	e, f = 5·06, 5·25 (b)	7·91, 8·16 (b)
	g = 3·83 (s)	g = 4·15 (d, 12)
		TFAA = 13·93
Atrazine		
$Y = Cl\ R_1 = H^f$	a = 1·25 (d, 7)	a, b = 1·37 (m)
$R_2 = CH_2{}^cCH_3{}^b\ R_3 = H^e$	b = 1·23 (t, 7)	c = 3·64 (b)
$R_4 = CH^d(CH_3{}^a)_2$	c = 3·47 (m, 6)	d = 4·38 (b)
	d = 4·34 (m, 6)	e, f = 7·44 (m)
	e, f = 5·22, 5·44 (b)	TFAA = 12·31 (s)

Propazine
$Y = Cl$
$R_1 = R_3 = H^c$
$R_2 = R_4 = CH^b(CH_3{}^a)_2$

a = 1·24 (d, 6)
b = 4·16 (m, 7)
c = 5·18 (b)

a = 1·35 (d, 6)
b = 4·25 (b)
c = 7·89, 8·18 (b)
TFAA = 12·15

Simetone
$Y = OCH_{3d}$
$R_1 = R_3 = H^c$
$R_2 = R_4 = CH_2{}^bCH_3{}^a$

a = 1·16 (t, 7)
b = 3·40 (m, 6·5)
c = 5·82 (b)
d = 3·79 (s)

a = 1·35 (d, 6)
b = 3·56 (b)
c = 8·15, 6·72 (b)
d = 4·12 (b)
TFAA = 12·15

Simetryne
$Y = SCH_3{}^d$
$R_1 = R_3 = H^c$
$R_2 = R_4 = CH_2{}^bCH_3$

a = 1·20 (t, 7)
b = 3·44 (m, 7)
c = 6·29 (b)
d = 2·42 (s)

a = 1·35 (t, 7)
b = 3·63 (b)
c = 6·83, 8·37,
    8·09 (b)
d = 2·68 (s)
TFAA = 12·18

Trietrazine
$Y = Cl \; R_1 = H^e$
$R_2 = CH_2{}^dCH_3{}^c$
$R_3 = R_4 = CH_2{}^bCH_3{}^a$

a = 1·20 (t, 7)
b = 3·60 (q, 7)
c = 1·23 (t, 7)
d = 3·49 (m, 7)
e = 5·20 (b)

a, c = 1·35 (m)
b, d = 3·65, 3·79 (m)
e = 7·25 (b)
TFAA = 12·12

Ipazine
$Y = Cl$
$R_1 = R_2 = CH_2{}^cCH_3{}^b$
$R_3 = H^e$
$R_4 = CH^d(CH_3{}^a)_2$

a = 1·18 (d, 6)
b = 1·15 (t, 6)
c = 3·54 (q, 7)
d = 4·08 (m, 7)
e = 5·38 (b)

a, b = 1·34 (m, 6)
c = 3·98 (q, 7)
d = 4·31 (b)
e = 6·83, 7·14 (b)
TFAA = 12·26

Prometone
$Y = OCH_3{}^d$
$R_1 = R_3 = H^c$
$R_2 = R_4 = CH^b(CH_3{}^a)_2$

a = 1·12 (d, 6)
b = 4·12 (q, 6)
c = 5·20 (b)
d = 3·80 (s)

a = 1·34 (d, 6)
b = 4·28 (b)
c = 6·58, 7·92,
    8·16 (b)
d = 4·16 (d, 13)
TFAA = 12·03

Prometryne
$Y = SCH_3{}^d$
$R_1 = R_3 = H^c$
$R_2 = R_4 = CH^b(CH_3{}^a)_2$

a = 1·21 (d, 6·5)
b = 4·18 (m, 6·5)
c = 5·21 (d, 6)
d = 2·42 (s)

a = 1·17 (d, 6·5)
b = 4·20 (b)
c = 6·58, 7·38 (b)
d = 2·48 (s)
TFAA = 12·34

The spectra of the s-triazines undergoes a characteristic change in chemical shift and line width when trifluoroacetic acid (TFAA) is used as a solvent.[46] Large changes in chemical shift of the N–H and TFAA proton signals occur as a function of the TFAA concentration. The s-triazine multiplets also usually collapse to a single broad peak in TFAA. Such changes in the line shape are probably caused by the increased quadrupolar relaxation time of the nitrogen nucleus in the protonated state.

Interesting results are also obtained with methoxy substituted s-triazine derivatives.[46] The methoxy resonance signal, which is a singlet in $CDCl_3$, becomes a doublet in TFAA apparently as a result of protonation of the methoxy atom.

K. Miscellaneous

1. Mercury compounds

The principal feature of the spectra[103 to 107] of organomercury fungicides is the observation of spin-spin splitting due to isotopes of mercury. Mercury possesses two magnetic isotopes, ^{199}Hg which has 16·86% abundance with spin $\frac{1}{2}$ and ^{201}Hg having spin $\frac{3}{2}$ in 13·25% natural abundance. The large quadrupole moment of the ^{201}Hg isotope often prevents the observation of ^{201}Hg–^1H couplings but the ^{199}Hg isotope generally causes a doublet satellite around the centerband of the proton resonance peak. With methylmercury compounds,[105] for example, spin coupling between ^{199}Hg and ^1H produces a doublet situated symmetrically around the central methyl resonance. The spectrum[103] of methylmercury nitrile in pyridine contains a central band at 0·65 p.p.m. (reference to cyclohexane) and satellites with a coupling of 178 Hz. In compounds of general formula CH_3HgX there is a linear correlation between the coupling constant ^{199}Hg–^1H and the proton chemical shift (Fig. 14). The resonance of the ^{199}Hg nucleus in many organomercury compounds also have been reported.[103,107]

2. Fluorine compounds

Simple fluorides, fluoranions and fluoroacetates are used as insecticides or rodenticides. The large natural abundance of the ^{19}F nucleus with a spin of $\frac{1}{2}$ permits the observation of ^{19}F resonance. The ^{19}F spectrum of simple fluorides,[108 to 113] in aqueous solution, usually gives a single peak but the chemical shift of the resonance peak exhibits a strong solvent and concentration dependence. In most cases, the results are interpreted in terms of ion-pair formation and hydrogen bonding. The spectra of fluoroanions $(MF_n)^{-x}$ (where M is the central atom, n the number of fluorines in the fluoroanion and x its valency) exhibits an additional feature. If the central atom has a magnetic moment with nuclear spin of I, then the ^{19}F resonance shows multiplet structure with a multiplicity of $(2I+1)$. When the central atom processes a large quadrupole

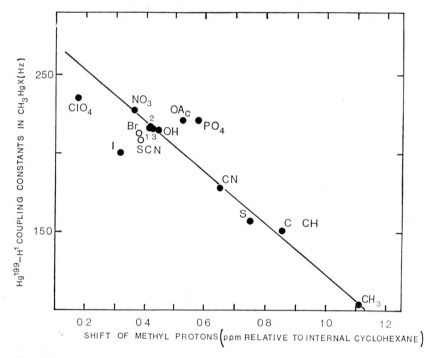

FIG. 14. Plot of chemical shifts of the methyl group vs. the ^{199}Hg–^{1}H coupling constants of CH₃HgX compounds in pyridine. (From Hatton, Schneider and Siebrand.[105])

moment, however, the spin-spin splitting collapses and broad peak(s) in the ^{19}F spectrum is observed.

The ^{19}F spectra of simple fluorides[108 to 113] and fluoroanions, such as fluoroaluminate[114] and fluorosilicate,[112,115,116] in aqueous solution have been reported by many workers.

3. Selenium and thallium compounds

The use of ^{77}Se and ^{205}Tl NMR spectroscopy[117,118] offers the opportunity for studying the behavior of selenium and thallium compounds of pesticidal interest.

III. ANALYSIS OF PESTICIDES

Although NMR spectroscopy has not been extensively applied to the quantitative analysis of pesticides, it offers considerable advantage since the sample is not destroyed by the analytical procedure and structural information is also provided. The most serious limitation for the application of NMR to pesticide analysis is the requirement for a large number of nuclei for a detectable signal. The minimum concentration of a sample necessary for analysis depends upon the signal-to-noise ratio, the strength of the magnetic field, the relaxation time of the nucleus, the sweep rate and the natural abundance of the magnetic isotope in the substance under analysis. While other nuclei can be observed, proton magnetic resonance provides the greatest sensitivity because of the large magnetic moment of hydrogen. With a signal-to-noise ratio of 2 at 14 kgauss one may observe proton signals with 1 mg. of sample (average molecular weight 250) contained in 0·4 ml. sample volume.[119] Computer averaging can further reduce the minimum sample requirements.

Muller and Goldenson[120] have employed ^{31}P resonance to measure the concentrations of pesticides in a mixture. A solution of the insecticide dematon contains an equilibrium mixture of O,O-diethyl-O-2-(ethylthio)ethylphosphorothioate (49) and O,O-diethyl-S-2-(ethylthio)ethylphosphorothioate (50). The

$$
\begin{array}{ccc}
\mathrm{C_2H_5O} \diagdown \ \ \mathrm{S} & & \mathrm{C_2H_5O} \diagdown \ \ \mathrm{O} \\
\ \ \ \ \mathrm{P} & & \ \ \ \ \mathrm{P} \\
\mathrm{C_2H_5O} \diagup \ \ \diagdown \mathrm{OC_2H_4SC_2H_5} \rightleftharpoons \mathrm{C_2H_5O} \diagup \ \ \diagdown \mathrm{SC_2H_4SC_2H_5} \\
\mathbf{49} & & \mathbf{50}
\end{array}
$$

$$
\begin{array}{cc}
\mathrm{C_2H_5O} \diagdown \ \ \mathrm{O} \ \ \mathrm{O} \ \ \diagup \mathrm{OC_2H_5} \\
\ \ \ \ \mathrm{P\text{---}O\text{---}P} \\
\mathrm{C_2H_5O} \diagup \ \ \ \ \ \ \diagdown \mathrm{OC_2H_5} \\
\mathbf{51}
\end{array}
$$

thiono isomer (49) shows a peak at $-67\cdot7$ p.p.m. while the thiol isomer (50) absorbed at $-25\cdot9$ p.p.m. from the phosphoric acid reference standard. Comparison of the areas under the two peaks was used[120] to calculate the amount of each isomer in the dematon mixture.

In addition to compounds (49) and (50) commercial dematon was shown by Babad and Taylor[121] to contain a third phosphorous compound O,O,O,O-tetraethyldithiopyrophosphate (sulfotepp) (51). The proton spectrum of dematon, thus, contained three sets of multiplets which were assigned to the methyl protons (1·1 to 1·5 p.p.m.), the thio ether protons (2·3 to 3·1 p.p.m.) and the oxy-ether protons (3·8 to 4·3 p.p.m.). The mole fraction of each component in a mixture may be determined[121] from the NMR spectrum by setting up a series of simultaneous equations in terms of the concentration and the area under each of the three proton peaks. If A_{OH} is the area of the peak due to protons near a normal ether linkage, A_{SH} is the area of the peak due to protons near a thioether linkage and A_{CH} is the area of the peak due to normal aliphatic protons; X_A, X_B

and X_C are the mole fraction of compounds (49), (50) and (51); n_{AO}, n_{BO} and n_{CO} are the number of normal ether linkage protons in compounds (49), (50) and (51), respectively; n_{AS}, n_{BS} and n_{CS} are number of thioether protons in compounds (49), (50) and (51), respectively; and n_{AC}, n_{BC} and n_{CC} are the numbers of normal alkyl protons in compounds (49), (50) and (51), respectively; then:

$$A_{OH} = n_{AO}X_A + n_{BO}X_B + n_{CO}X_C$$
$$A_{SH} = n_{AS}X_A + n_{BS}X_B + n_{CS}X_C$$
$$A_{CH} = n_{AC}X_A + n_{BC}X_B + n_{CC}X_C$$

Substituting the number of protons for dematon (49), (50) and sulfotepp (51) and solving for X_A, X_B and X_C, one obtains:

$$X_A = \tfrac{3}{8}A_{OH} + \tfrac{1}{8}A_{SH} - \tfrac{1}{4}A_{CH}$$
$$X_B = \tfrac{1}{6}A_{CH} - \tfrac{1}{4}A_{OH}$$
$$X_C = \tfrac{5}{48}A_{CH} - \tfrac{3}{32}A_{SH} - \tfrac{3}{32}A_{OH}$$

The NMR spectrum, thus, yields the mole fraction for each of the three components (49), (50) and (51) in a mixture.

The thermal isomerization of O,O-diethyl-O-2-(ethylthio)ethylphosphorothioate (49) to its thiol isomer (50) also has been studied by ^{31}P resonance.[120] These investigations indicate that the rate of equilibrium between (49) and (50) is between zero and first order rather than first order as reported previously.[122]

Fukato et al.[123] have determined the effect of heat on the insecticide baytex (O,O-dimethyl-O-[4-(methylthio)-3-tolyl]phosphorothioate) (52) by observing changes in the NMR spectra of protons and phosphorus. The ^{31}P spectrum of baytex contained a single multiplet structure at 65·8 p.p.m. downfield from the phosphoric acid reference. After heating for 5 hours at 140°C a second peak appeared at −25·9 p.p.m. accompanied by a corresponding decrease in the intensity of the original peak. Comparison of the chemical shifts with reported values[120,124] led Fukato et al.[123] to conclude that the new signal was due to isomerization of the phosphorothionate (52) to the phosphorothiolate (53) isomer.

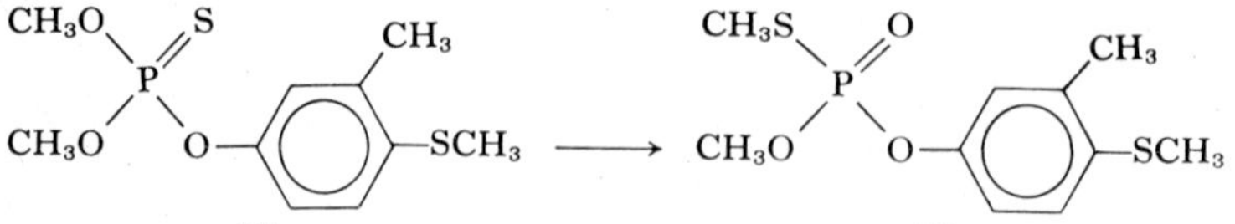

52   53

The proton spectrum of unheated baytex contained[123] three signals. The three aromatic protons formed a singlet at δ 6·95, the six methyl protons, spin coupled with the phosphorus nucleus, appeared as a doublet at 3·64 and 3·82 and the SCH_3 and CH_3 groups attached to the aromatic ring resonated at δ 2·23 and 2·29. Since the peak at δ 2·23 remained constant on heating while the peak at

2·29 increased in size, the latter was assigned to the more labile SCH$_3$ moiety while the signal at δ 2·23 was attributed to the more stable CH$_3$ group. Increase of the δ 2·29 peak on heating was probably due to an intramolecular reaction in which a sulfonium ion was formed. A new peak attributed to the P–SCH$_3$ group appeared at δ 2·11 after baytex was converted to the S-methyl isomer (53) by heating for 4½ hours at 135°C.

The rate of acid or alkaline hydrolysis of the organophosphate insecticides bidrin, dimethoate, disulfoton, malathion, phosdrin and trichlorofon have been examined by NMR spectroscopy.[124] Reference spectra were first obtained on the various reaction products isolated after hydrolysis of large quantities of pesticide in the presence of excess water. An attempt to employ NMR to measure the hydrolysis rates of these organophosphate insecticides in stoichiometric quantities of water, acid or base was unsuccessful because less than 3% of the organophosphates underwent hydrolysis under these conditions.

Biros[125] has recently reported the analysis of mixtures of p,p'-DDT and p,p'-DDE insecticides in various tissues.

IV. PHOTOCHEMICAL REACTIONS OF PESTICIDES

The products, formed by photolysis of the insecticide DDT and its metabolite DDE in methanol, have been isolated and characterized by Plimmer and co-workers.[126] While NMR spectroscopy was used to help identify various photoconversion products, no spectral data has been presented.

When dieldrin (27) is exposed to ultraviolet light, a photoisomerization product is formed which has been tentatively identified (54) by Robinson et al.[127] and Rosen et al.[128] The photo-oxidation product had the same molecular weight and mass spectrum as the parent dieldrin. The 60 MHz spectrum of this material (54) in acetone-d$_6$ showed the absence of a methane bridge across the non-chlorinated ring and the formation of a new carbon-to-carbon bond (δ = 5·33).

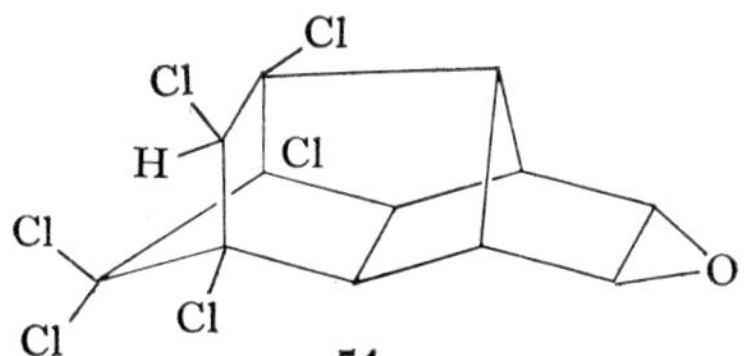

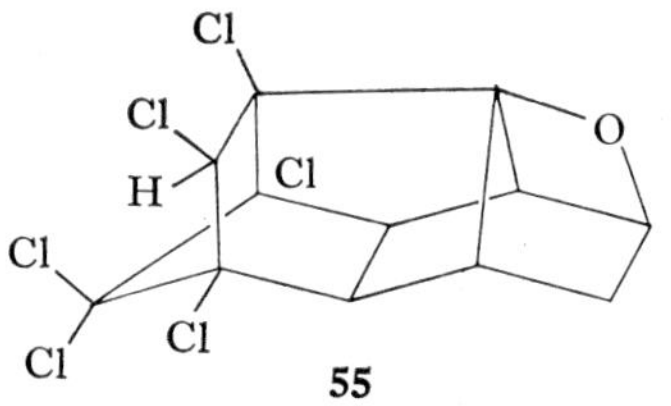

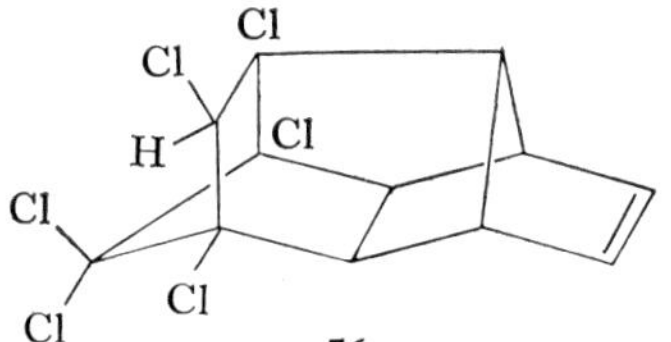

Harrison and coworkers[129] also characterized the irradiation product of dieldrin and on the basis of its NMR and infrared spectrum proposed structure (55) for the compound. The 100 MHz spectrum confirmed[130] the intramolecular rearrangement product of dieldrin to be structure (54). The proton which shares a carbon atom with chlorine, had a chemical shift of δ 4·87 in $CDCl_3$ which is consistent with a skew-bridged structure rather than a straight-bridged compound. A consideration of coupling constants for the C-4 and C-6 protons helped to eliminate other possible structures. The proton chemical shifts and coupling constants for photodieldrin (54) are summarized[130] in Table XIV.

TABLE XIV

Chemical shift and coupling constants of the dieldrin irradiation product

Proton number	Chemical shift, δ	Coupling constant Hz					
		J_3	J_4	J_5	J_6	J_7	J_8
2	2·55	2·7	0	0	2·7	2·7	2·7
3	3·19		1·6	0	0	~1	1·2
4	3·49			3·5	0	0	0
5	3·27				1·6	0	0
6	3·08					0	0·2
7	2·64						
8	3·15						

Irradiation of aldrin (26) resulted[131] in the formation of a similar rearrangement product (56). The spectrum of this compound in acetone-d_6 contained a new singlet at δ 5·12, reflecting addition of a methylene hydrogen to a carbon bearing a chlorine atom in a manner analogous to dieldrin.[130] A multiplet at δ 5·9, with twice the intensity of the singlet, was thus assigned to the olefinic protons. Two other multiplets centered at δ 2·25 and 3·53 were ascribed to the tertiary hydrogens in the compound (56).

Irradiation of dieldrin and aldrin at lower wavelengths produced two additional compounds.[132] The new dieldrin photo-decomposition product (57) exhibited a spectrum with a multiplet centered at δ 1·2, a doublet at 2·7 and singlets at 3·05 and 6·0, with an intensity ratio of 2:4:2:1. Comparisons of these results with the spectrum of dieldrin confirmed that the irradiation product had undergone the net addition of one vinyl proton, the loss of one vinyl chlorine atom and a retention of the same *endo-exo* configuration as dieldrin. These data are consistent with the proposed structure (57).

The mass spectrum of the aldrin photo-product suggested that aldrin had also been dechlorinated as in the case of dieldrin. The spectrum of the new compound was similar to that of the parent aldrin with the exception of one olefinic proton

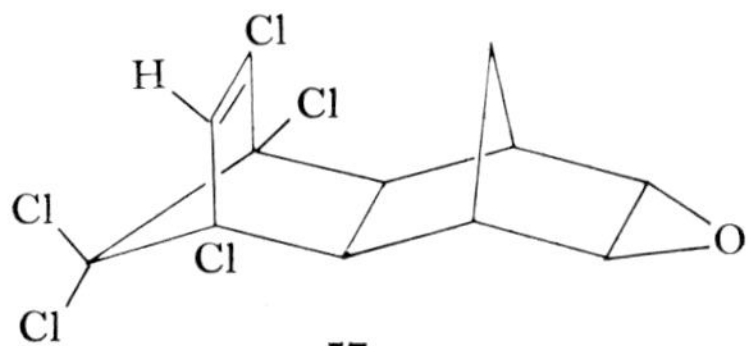

57

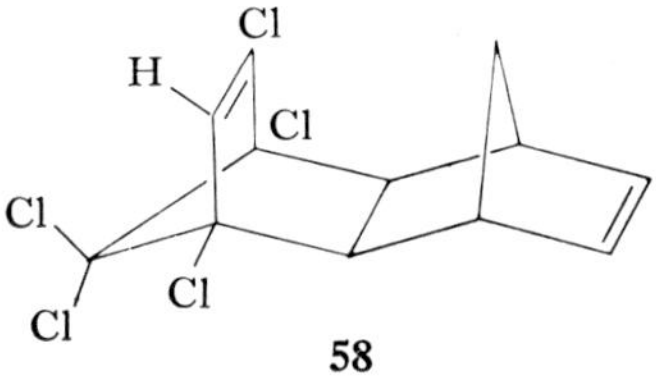

58

absorbing at δ 5·93. Like aldrin, the *exo-endo* configuration had been retained and this compound was then proposed[132] to have structure (**58**); this same structure had also been suggested by Rosen.[133]

The photolysis of the cyclodiene insecticide 1,4,5,6,7,8,8-heptachloro-3a,4,7,7a-tetrahydro-4,7-methanoindene (heptachlor) (**59**) results in the formation of several modification products depending upon the experimental conditions employed.[134,135] The structure of these irradiation products (**60** to **63**) was determined from NMR (Table XV), infrared and mass spectral data.[135]

Two isomeric monodechlorination products (**60**) and (**61**) were obtained when a very dilute solution (10^{-4}M) of heptachlor in hexane or cyclohexane was irradiated.[135] Photolysis of an acetone solution of heptachlor gave the cage compound (**62**) while a solvent adduct, compound (**63**), was formed when heptachlor was irradiated in a mixture of cyclohexane-acetone.[135]

TABLE XV

NMR parameters for heptachlor and its photolysis products

	Chemical shift, δ				
Proton	Heptachlor (59)	Compound (60)	Compound (61)	Compound (62)	Compound (63)
H_3	5·9 (2H)s	5·75 (2H)s	5·70 (2H)s	3·4 (2H)m	5·27 (1H)s
H_2	5·9 (2H)s	5·75 (2H)s	5·70 (2H)s	3·4 (2H)m	5·72 (1H)m
H_1	4·8 (1H)m	4·58 (1H)m	4·5 (1H)m	4·55 (1H)m	2·45 (1H)m
H_7	3·5 (1H)m	3·5 (1H)m	3·5 (1H)m	3·4 (2H)m	3·1 (1H)m
H_{3a}	4·1 (1H)m	3·93 (1H)m	3·91 (1H)m	3·4 (2H)m	3·8 (1H)m
$H_{5/6}$		5·8 (1H)s	5·8 (1H)s		

In the case of photoconversion products, the observed upfield shift in the H_1 proton resonance (Table XV) may be explained on the basis of an increased shielding of H_1, by the enhanced electron cloud associated with the 5,6 double bond, when a chlorine on carbons 5 and 6 of heptachlor (**59**) is replaced with a hydrogen atom ($H_{5,6}$).[135] Although the replacement of the chlorine atom on carbon 6 increases the shielding due to the olefinic bond, it simultaneously eliminates the shielding due to the replaced chlorine. Replacement of the chlorine on carbon 6 would, thus, have less overall effect on the shielding of H_1 than the replacement of chlorine on carbon 5 and would, therefore, result in a smaller upfield shift of the H_1 signal (Table XV). This criterion was used to assign[135] the structures of the two isomeric photolysis products 1,4,5,7,8,8-hexachloro-3a,4,7,7a-tetrohydro-4,7-methanoindene (**60**) and 1,4,6,7,8,8-hexachloro-3a,4,7,7a-tetrahydro-4,7-methanoindene (**61**).

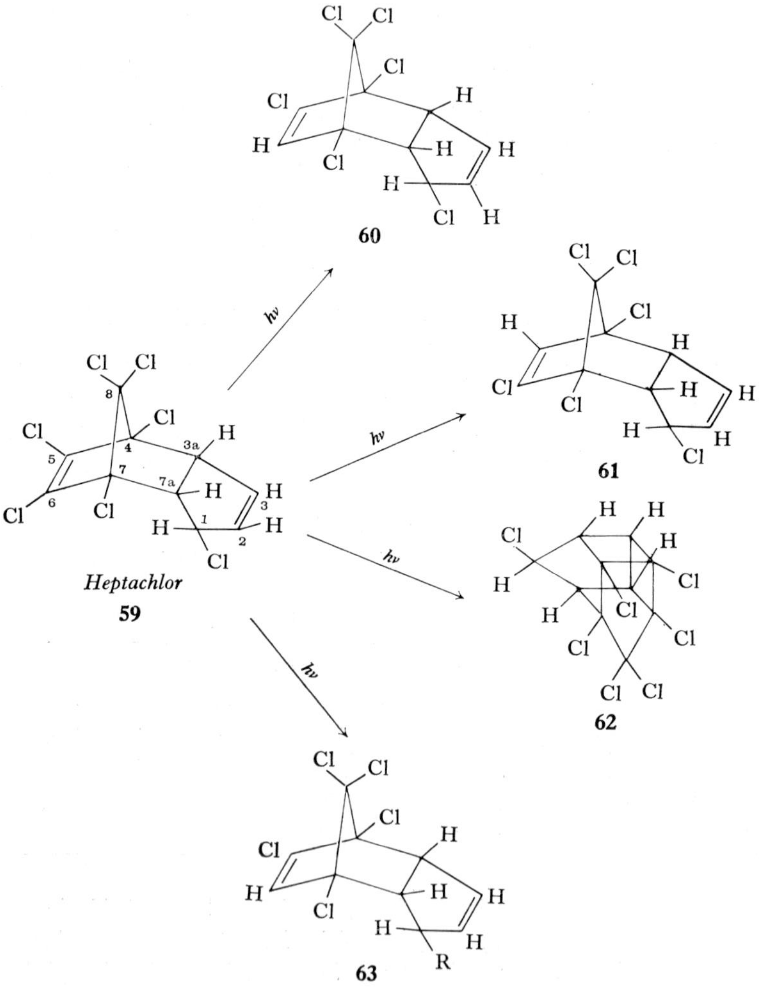

The rearrangement product (**62**) had the same molecular weight as the parent heptachlor (**59**) but showed[134] the loss of the olefinic infrared absorption band at 1618 cm^{-1}. Analysis of this material by NMR confirmed the loss of the olefinic structure by a disappearance of the proton signal at δ 5·9. Ill-defined multiplets also were found centered at δ 4·55 (1H) and 3·40 (4H). On the basis of these data the cage structure 2,3,4,4,5,6,10-heptachloro-pentacyclo[5.3.0.0.^{2,3}.0^{3,4}.0^{3,7}] decane (62) was assigned[134,135] to this heptachlor photo-product.

The photolysis product (63) exhibited a mass and infrared spectrum which was consistent with a structure involving replacement of two chlorine atoms in heptachlor with a cyclohexyl group and a hydrogen atom, respectively.[135] The NMR spectrum (Table XV) of this derivative showed a non-equivalence of H_2 and H_3 and an up-field shift of all resonance peaks especially that due to H_1. This significant up-field shift of the H_1 proton was interpreted as evidence for the replacement of the allyl chlorine on carbon-1 with the cyclohexyl group. In addition to these resonance peaks, a broad multiplet at δ 1·45 was derived from the cyclohexyl ring protons. These results are consistent with the structure (63) proposed.[135]

The irradiation products of several substituted s-triazine herbicides have been characterized with the use of NMR spectroscopy.[136] After photolysis of three chloro-s-triazines (atrizine, propazine and simazine in methanol, a new resonance peak appeared at δ 3·7 to 3·75, which was absent in the spectrum of the parent compound. The new signal was associated with the addition of a methoxy group to the C–2 position according to the following reaction:

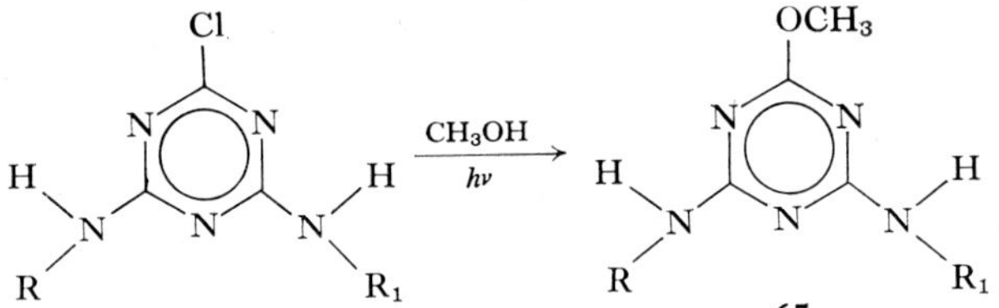

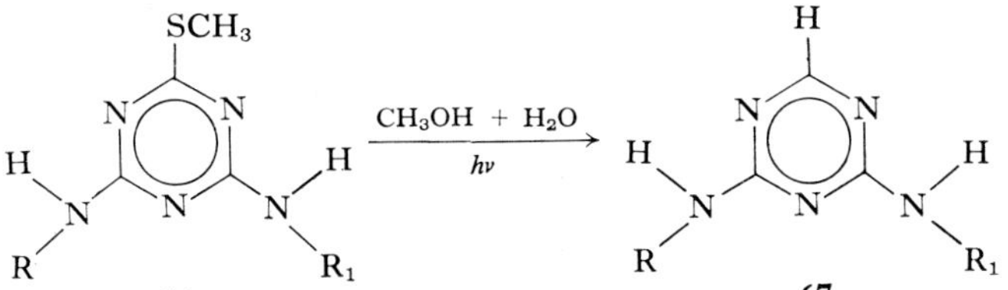

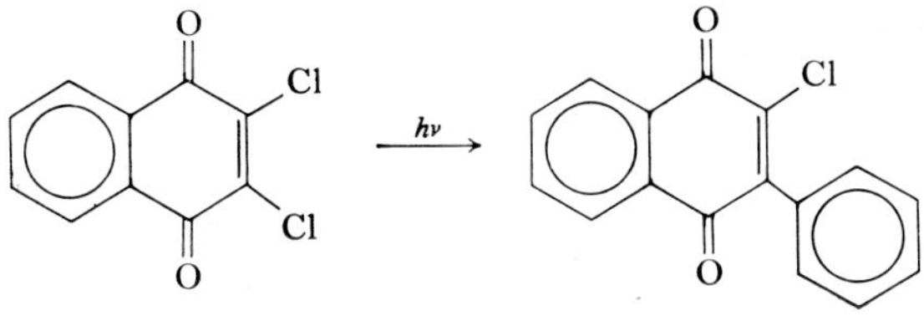

Photolysis of methylthio-s-triazines (66) in aqueous methanol solution resulted in the formation of a degradation product (67).[136] The NMR spectrum of this product indicated hydrogen substitution at C-2 as evidenced by a new single proton peak at δ 7·8 with the simultaneous disappearance of the S–CH$_3$ methyl resonance signal at δ 2·3 to 2·5.

Irradiation of the fungicide phygon (**68**) caused the formation of two photochemical modification products.[137] The minor photolysis product was readily identified as phthalic anhydride on the basis of its infrared spectrum. Infrared and mass spectral analysis of the major irradiation product (**69**) showed it to contain two non-equivalent carbonyl groups, an additional phenyl group and only one chlorine atom. The NMR spectrum of the unknown derivative gave three aromatic signals at about δ 8, with relative intensities of 2:2:5. Comparison of the properties of the chemically synthesized compound with those of the photoconversion product (**69**) confirmed the identity of the latter as 2-chloro-3-phenyl-1,4-naphthoquinone.

V. BIOLOGICAL AND METABOLISM STUDIES

Although NMR spectroscopy has been used extensively in biochemistry[138] and pharmacology,[139] this useful tool has only recently been employed for similar investigations involving pesticides. Functioning biological systems can, in general, only be exposed to low concentrations of pesticides because of the toxic nature of these chemicals. Consequently, it has proven difficult to isolate sufficient quantities of the pesticide or its metabolites to permit characterization using NMR techniques. Recently, however, there has been an increase in the use of NMR for the study of biological problems involving pesticides.

While the principal metabolite of malathion (**70**) in mammals is known[140,141] to be a monoacid, two isomeric monoacid derivatives (**71, 72**) of malathion are

$$
\begin{array}{c}
\quad\quad\quad\quad\quad\quad\quad\quad \overset{\displaystyle S}{\overset{\displaystyle \|}{\longrightarrow (CH_3O)_2-PSCHCO_2H}} \\
\quad\quad\quad\quad\quad\quad\quad\quad\quad\quad | \\
\quad\quad\quad\quad\quad\quad\quad\quad\quad\quad CH_2CO_2C_2H_5 \\
\quad\quad\quad\quad\quad\quad\quad\quad\quad\quad \mathbf{71}
\end{array}
$$

$$
\overset{\displaystyle S}{\overset{\displaystyle \|}{(CH_3O)_2-PSCHCO_2C_2H_5-}}
$$
$$
CH_2CO_2C_2H_5
$$

$$
\begin{array}{c}
\overset{\displaystyle S}{\overset{\displaystyle \|}{\longrightarrow (CH_3O)_2-PSCHCO_2C_2H_5}} \\
| \\
CH_2CO_2H \\
\mathbf{72}
\end{array}
$$

70

equally possible. Chen and coworkers[142] have recently synthesized the two possible malathion monoacid derivatives and demonstrated by infrared and NMR spectroscopy that the biologically formed monoacids, isolated from rat urine or produced *in vitro* by enzymatic hydrolysis of malathion, were identical to the synthetic monoacid (71), O,O-dimethyl-S-(1-carboxy-2-carbethoxy)ethyl phosphorodithioate.

Structural assignment of the synthetic monoacids was based primarily upon their NMR properties, especially the difference in chemical shifts between methylene and methine protons in the two forms (71) and (72). The methine or methylene protons adjacent to a carboxyl group are slightly more deshielded than protons next to an ester group and the methylene absorption in structure (72), thus, should occur at lower field than in structure (71) while the methine resonance should occur at slightly higher field in (72) than in (71).

The NMR spectra of the two isomers synthesized by Chen *et al.*[142] were quite similar (Fig. 15) containing multiplets at about δ 3·0 from the AB portions of an ABX system composed of the non-equivalent methylene protons of the succinate chain and the methine proton (the X proton of the ABX system) resonating at about δ 4·0. Chemical shifts for the AB part were δ 2·96 and 3·02 (Fig. 15) for the two isomers, but the pattern for the methine proton was complicated by additional coupling to phosphorus and was partially obscured by the ethyl ester proton pattern. The spectra were simplified, however, by frequency-sweep experiments using double or triple resonance techniques to collapse the ester methylene multiplet to a singlet. The methine absorption for the two synthetic compounds was then determined to be δ 4·03 and 4·20, respectively, and the chemical shift differences were $4·03 - 3·02 = 1·01$ p.p.m. and $4·20 - 2·96 = 1·24$ p.p.m. (Fig. 15). The larger chemical shift difference, 1·24 p.p.m., was assigned to structure (71) on the basis of the previous considerations.

In investigating an extensive fish kill, Teasley[144] isolated an unknown cholinesterase inhibitor from the effluent of a chemical plant manufacturing S,S,S-tributylphosphorotrithioite (73). Although the NMR spectrum of the unknown substance was similar to that of pure defolient (73), appreciable differences existed in the low field multiplet patterns derived from the three methylene groups which are bonded directly to phosphorus. The phosphorotrithioite compound (73) exhibited a quartet pattern centered at δ 2·8, in which one of the center peaks showed further splitting, while the unknown yielded an equally spaced quartet centered at δ 3·0. Teasley[143] suggested that the paramagnetic shift in the unknown arose from the presence of an electronegative group which was absent in compound (73). The mass spectrum of the unknown was also found to have a parent ion peak 16 mass units greater than that of compound (73). These data helped establish that the unknown cholinesterase inhibitor was S,S,S-tributylphosphorotrithioate (74) formed naturally in waste effluent by oxidation of S,S,S-tributylphosphorotrithioite (73).

The two geometric isomers of the organic phosphate insecticide bomyl (dimethyl-1,3-dicarbomethoxy-1-propene-2-yl phosphate) have been separated and tested for insect toxicity and anticholinesterase activity.[144] The configura-

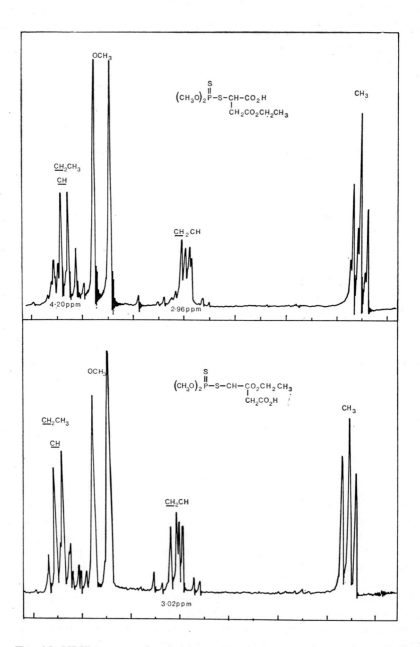

FIG. 15. NMR spectra of malathion monoacid isomers. (From Chen, Tucker and Dauterman.[142])

tion of the *cis-* (**75**) and *trans-* (**76**) isomers was deduced by comparison of the NMR spectra of the two forms with those of previous studies.[4,5] The *cis*-isomer showed a doublet, centered at δ 5·95 for the vinyl proton, while the *trans*-isomer exhibited a singlet vinyl proton peak at 5·50. These values and assignments are consistent with results obtained for other vinyl phosphates.[4,5]

$$(C_4H_9S)_3P + \tfrac{1}{2}O_2 \longrightarrow (C_4H_9S)_3P{=}O$$

$$\textbf{73} \qquad\qquad\qquad \textbf{74}$$

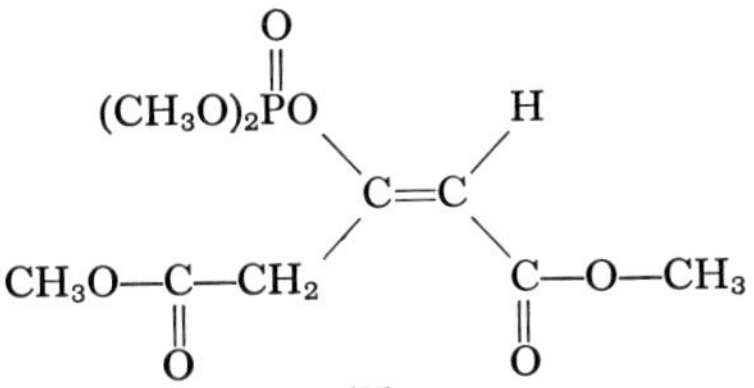

75

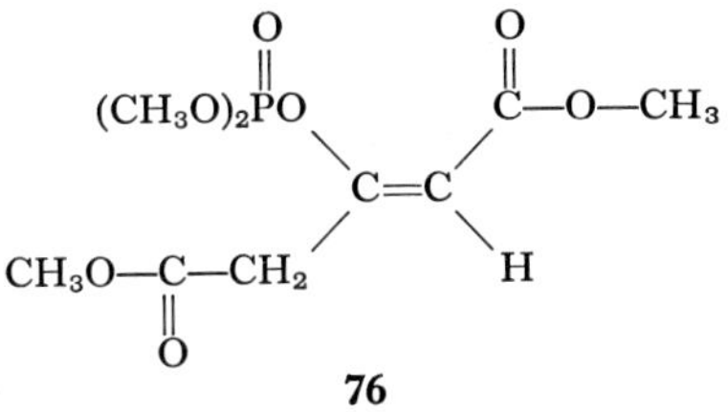

76

Metcalf and coworkers[145] have identified the 3-hydroxy and 3-keto metabolites of the insecticide Furadan (**77**), 2,2-dimethyl-2,3-dihydrobenzofuranyl-7-*N*-methylcarbamate, and their respective 7-hydroxy hydrolysis products in plants and animals. A number of probable metabolites of Furadan were synthesized and the NMR spectra determined.

Gardiner *et al.*[146] identified a major metabolite of the fungicide methyl-1-(butylcarbomyl)-2-benzimidazole-carbamate (**78**) in the urine of rats as methyl-5-hydroxy-2-benzimidazole-carbamate. NMR was used to verify the structure of the chemically synthesized compound (**79**) and this material, in turn, was found to exhibit infrared and mass spectra which were identical to those of the metabolite.

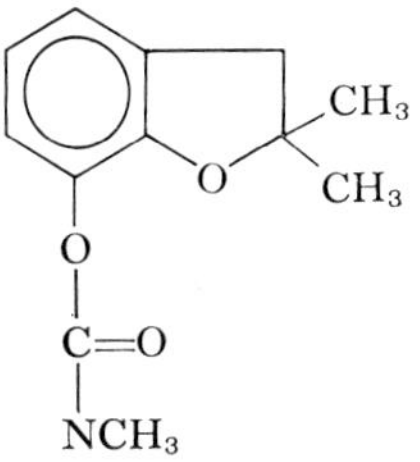

77

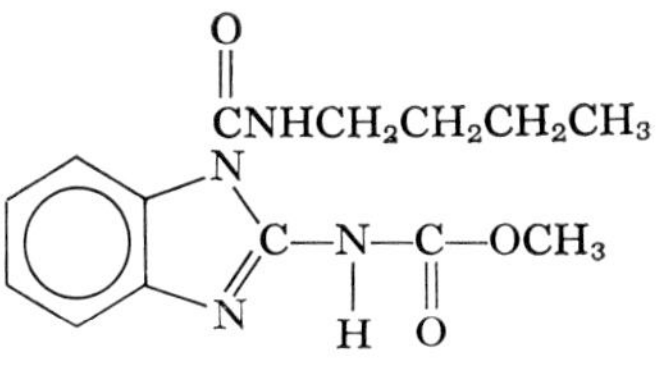

78

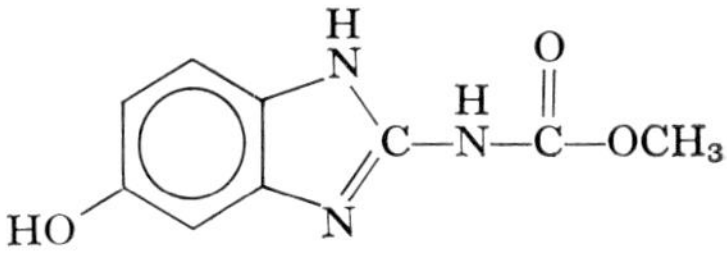

79

Baron *et al.*[147] have isolated and characterized the major organic extractable metabolite of carbaryl (**80**), 1-naphthyl-*N*-methylcarbamate, from the urine and

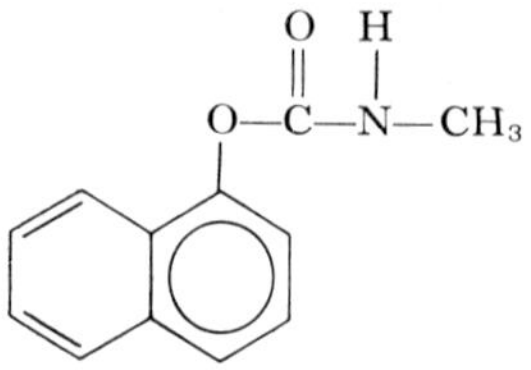

80

milk of cows. The unknown biotransformation product was isolated by chromatography on Florisil and identified with the aid of ultraviolet, infrared, mass and NMR spectroscopy as 5,6-dihydro-5,6-dihydroxycarbaryl (**81**). The NMR spectrum of the metabolite was similar to that reported by Holtzman *et al.*[148] for

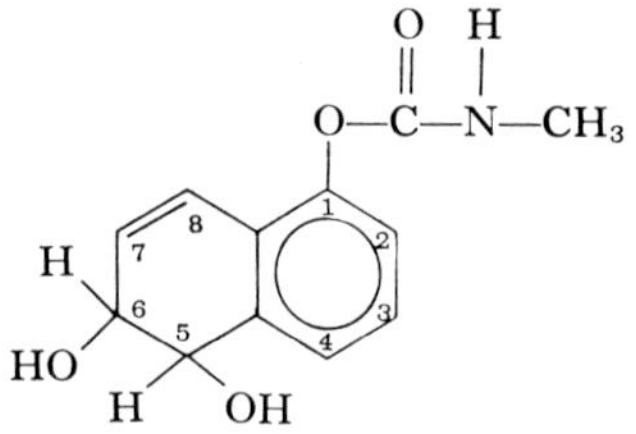

81

1,2-dihydro-1,2-dihydroxynaphthalene with a complex pattern, between δ 6·9 to 7·7, in the metabolite being associated with the aromatic protons at positions 2, 3 and 4. The protons on the alicyclic ring at positions 5, 6, 7 and 8 each formed a doublet with chemical shift values of δ 4·7, 4·4, 6·0 and 6·5, respectively. Assignment of these latter peaks was made on the basis that the couplings between protons 5,8 and 5,7 were nearly zero; the couplings $J_{7,8}$ and $J_{5,6}$ were of the order of 10 Hz; and the remaining couplings $J_{6,7}$ and $J_{6,8}$ were 2 Hz. Partial analysis of the ring proton spectrum confirmed that the *N*-methylcarbamate group was still attached to position 1 on the aromatic ring.

To obtain additional information on the role of the *N*-methyl group in determining biological activity, Fahmy *et al.*[149] investigated the anticholinesterase and insecticidal activities of a series of substituted phenyl and phenyl *N*-trimethylsilyl carbamate pesticides. NMR was used to verify the structure of the deuterated analog, 3-isopropylphenyl-*N*-methyl-d_3-carbamate. The spectrum of the deuturated compound was reported to be identical to that of 3-isopropyl-phenyl-*N*-methylcarbamate except for the absence of the doublet at δ 2·7

(*N*-methyl protons). Other assignments were δ 1·1 to 1·3 (methyl protons of isopropyl group), 3·3 to 3·5 (CH proton of isopropyl group) and 2·05 (NH proton). The chemical shift values, however, and assignments by Fahmy *et al.*[149] for the isopropyl CH and NH protons do not agree with those recently reported by Keith and Alford[20] who listed values of δ 2·88 (CH) and 5·4 (NH), respectively, for 3-isopropylphenyl-*N*-methylcarbamate.

NMR has been employed by Bartley and Heywood[150] to verify the synthesis of a suspected metabolite (3,4-dichlorohippuric acid) of the herbicide UC 22463 (3,4-dichlorobenzyl methylcarbamate).

Three of the major metabolites of siduron (**82**), 1-(2-methylcyclohexyl)-3-phenylurea have been isolated from the urine of dogs fed the herbicide in their diet.[151] Preparative thin layer chromatography of urine extracts was employed to yield the principal metabolites. Three of the siduron metabolites (**83**), (**84**) and (**85**) were characterized by infrared and mass spectral analysis. A molecular

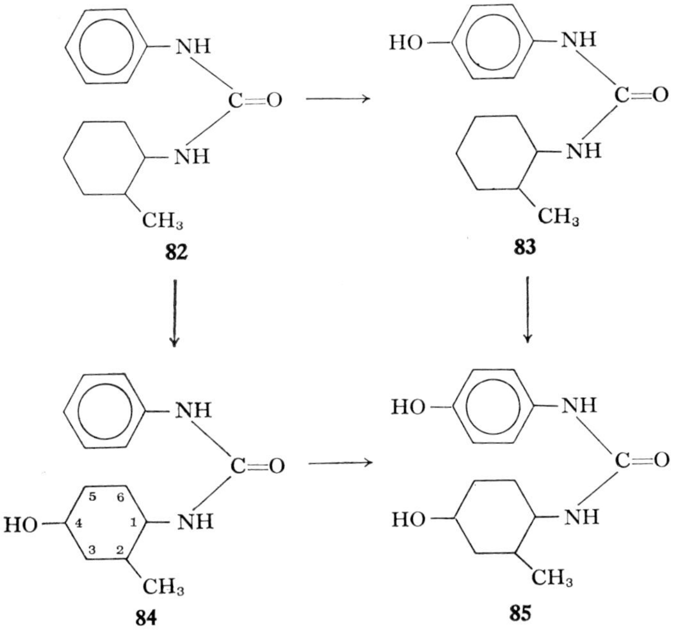

weight difference of 16 between metabolites (**83**) and (**84**) and siduron suggested that one additional oxygen atom was present in both metabolites. The mass spectral fragmentation pattern further revealed that the added oxygen atom was located in the aromatic ring in the case of metabolite (**83**) and in the cyclohexane ring with metabolite (**84**). A third metabolite (**85**) appeared to contain oxygen in both the aromatic and cyclohexyl rings.

Sufficient quantities of metabolites (83) and (84) were obtained to permit examination using NMR. The spectrum of metabolite (83) proved to be identical to that of 1-(*p*-hydroxyphenyl)-3-(2-methylcyclohexyl)urea prepared synthetically (Fig. 16). Comparison of the spectrum of metabolite (84) with that of the parent siduron indicated that the methyl group (doublet, δ 0·85) attached to the cyclohexane ring was still present and attached to a carbon bearing one hydrogen.

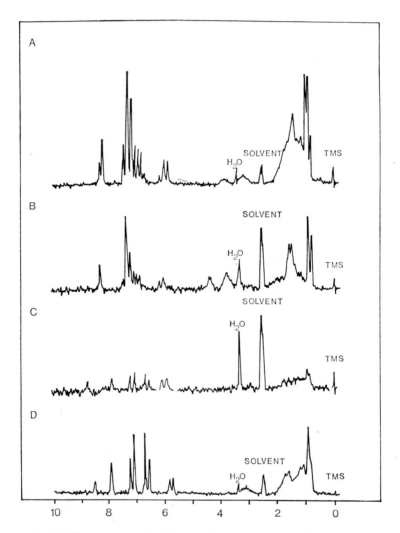

FIG. 16. NMR spectra of (A) Siduron, (B) metabolite **84**, (C) metabolite **83** and (D) 1-(*p*-hydroxyphenyl)-3-(2-methylcyclohexyl)urea. (From Belasco and Reiser.[151])

Because of the occurrence of the doublet at δ 4·35 in metabolite (84) and the absence of a shift in the methyl hydrogen pattern it was deduced that hydroxylation had not taken place at either the C_1, C_3 or C_6 positions on the cyclohexyl ring. The amide nitrogen also was unhydroxylated as revealed by the doublet at δ 6·10, which is typical of an amide linked to a saturated cyclohexane ring. The general shift of the absorption of the cyclohexyl methylene groups in relation to that of siduron, and the lack of changes in the remaining portions of the spectrum, led Belasco and Reiser[151] to deduce that hydroxylation had occurred at the C_4 position of the cyclohexyl ring. Metabolite (84) was, consequently, identified as 1-(4-hydroxy-2-methylcyclohexyl)-3-phenylurea.

Belasco and Reiser[151] also assumed that metabolite (85) was derived from both metabolites (83) and (84) and was, thus, presumed to be 1-(4-hydroxy-2-methylcyclohexyl)-3-(p-hydroxylphenyl)urea.

The metabolism of dieldrin has been investigated in a number of biological systems. Richardson and coworkers[152] have isolated and characterized a metabolite from the faeces of rats fed for six months on a diet containing dieldrin. The unknown metabolite was proposed to be a monohydroxylation product of dieldrin substituted in either the 2 or 3 position (86) on the basis of NMR, mass and infrared evidence.

86   87

Two metabolites of dieldrin extracted from the urine of sheep have recently been identified by Feil et al.[153] One metabolite, trans-6,7-dihydroxydihydroaldrin, had mass and infrared spectra identical to those of the synthetic compound. The infrared and mass spectral properties of the second metabolite were very similar to those of the monohydroxylated rat faecal metabolite previously described by Richardson et al.[152] However, the absence of significant NMR absorption around δ 1, as in dieldrin,[132] provided evidence that the bridge methylene was no longer intact. The spectrum of the unknown in carbon tetrachloride was consistent with an unaltered dieldrin ring system suggesting to Feil et al.[153] that the hydroxyl group must have entered one of the positions in the methylene bridge. Further proof for this postulate was obtained by oxidation of the unknown metabolite to a ketone derivative. The NMR spectrum of the oxidation product contained only three proton peaks in a ratio of 1:1:1 as expected for an intact dieldrin ring system with a bridge ketone group. The ease of acetylation of the unknown metabolite and the infrared evidence for intramolecular hydrogen bonding led Feil *et al.*[153] to conclude that the methylene hydroxyl group was *syn* to the epoxide (**87**) and that the previous assignment[152] of structure (**86**) for the dieldrin metabolite was incorrect.

Seven metabolites have been found in the urine of rats being fed the herbicide bromacil (**88**), 5-bromo-3-*sec*-butyl-6-methyluracil, in their diet.[154] Four of the metabolites have been isolated by preparative TLC in sufficient quantities to permit characterization by mass, infrared and NMR spectroscopy. The mass spectrum of the principal urinary metabolite (**89**) suggested that it contained one more oxygen atom than the parent compound and that the oxygen was probably not attached to the secondary butyl group. The presence of an attached *sec*-butyl group in the metabolite was confirmed by the NMR spectrum (Fig. 17) with a triplet at δ 0·9 and a doublet at 1·5. The singlet at δ 2·35, characteristic of a methyl group at the 6 position of bromacil, was, however, missing from the isolated metabolite. Instead, a new singlet at δ 4·7, integrating for two protons, was observed. These results are consistent with presence of a hydroxylmethyl group at the 6 position in the metabolite. Structural assignment of this metabolite was confirmed following a comparison of the spectral properties of the unknown with those of an authentic synthetic sample of 5-bromo-3-*sec*-butyl-6-hydroxymethyluracil (**89**). A second metabolite (**90**) also was found, from mass spectral data, to contain one more oxygen atom than the parent bromacil. The fragmentation pattern for this unknown, however, suggested that the extra oxygen was associated with the *sec*-butyl group. The NMR spectrum (Fig. 17) of this metabolite no longer contained the characteristic pattern for a *sec*-butyl group but showed two new doublets at δ 1·1 and 1·6, derived from two methyl groups each adjacent to a carbon atom bearing a single proton. The 6-methyl substituent was unaltered since a peak at δ 2·4 was still present. Comparison of the mass, infrared and NMR spectra with those of a synthetic reference standard, verified the structural assignment of the metabolite as 5-bromo-3-(2-hydroxy-1-methypropyl)-6-methyluracil (**90**). Slight differences in the intensities of certain mass and NMR spectral peaks, however, suggested that there were differences in the stereo-chemical configuration between the compounds formed chemically and biologically.

Mass spectral analysis of the third metabolite (**91**) indicated the addition of two atoms of oxygen to bromacil. Based on the fragmentation pattern it was found that one of the oxygen atoms was substituted onto carbon 2 of the *sec*-butyl group. The second oxygen atom was attached to the 6-methyl group as evidenced by the presence of a singlet in the NMR spectrum at δ 4·7 analogous to that found for metabolite (**89**). These results support the structural assignment of 5-bromo-3-(2-hydroxy-1-methylpropyl)-6-hydroxymethyluracil for metabolite (**91**). The mass and NMR spectra of the fourth metabolite (**92**) indicated that it was 3-*sec*-butyl-6-hydroxymethyluracil.

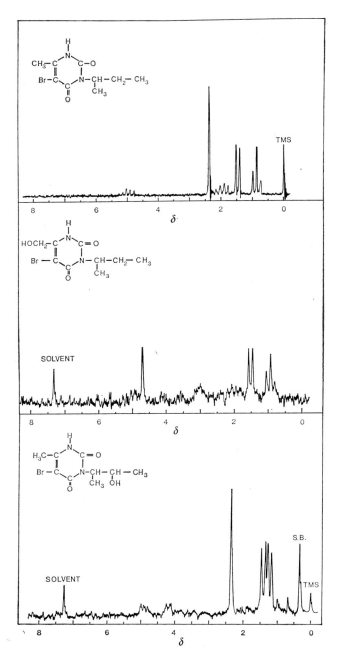

Fig. 17. NMR spectra of Bromacil and its metabolites. *Top*: Bromacil. *Middle*:
Metabolite **89**. *Bottom*: Metabolite **90**. (From Gardiner, Reiser and Sherman.[154])

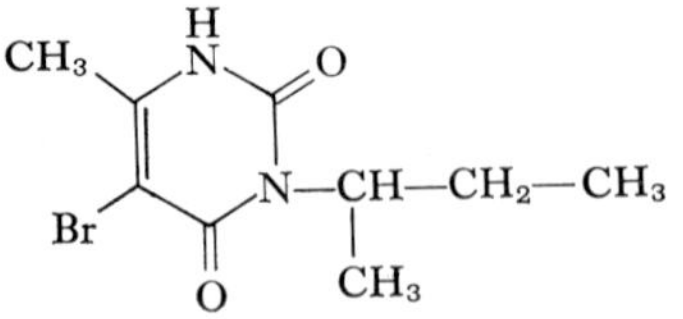

Rhodes et al.[155] have identified two metabolites of terbacil (**93**), 3-*tert*-butyl-5-chloro-6-methyluracil, isolated from the urine of a dog kept for 9 months on diets containing the herbicide.

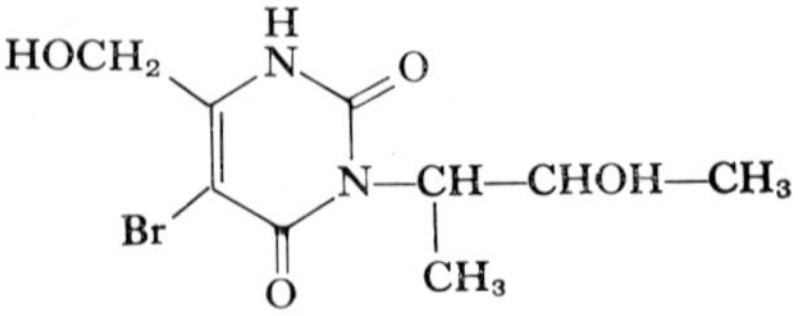

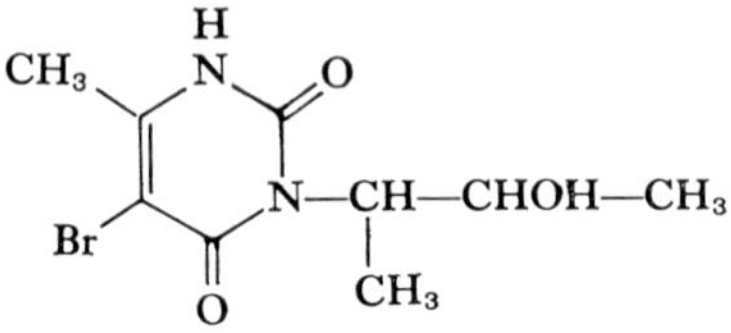

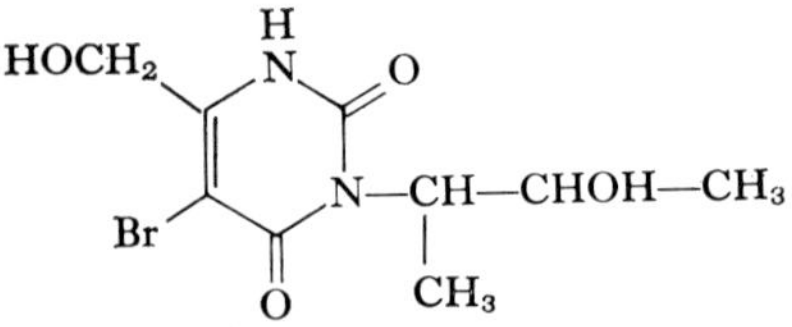

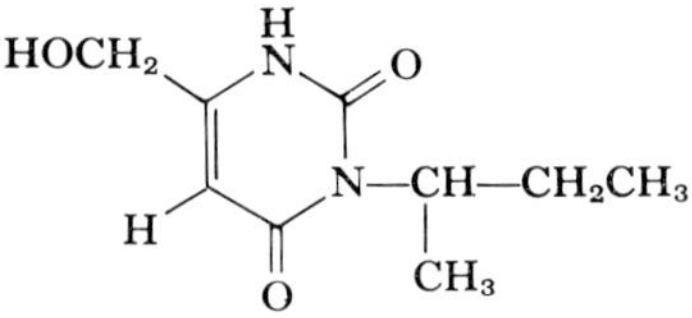

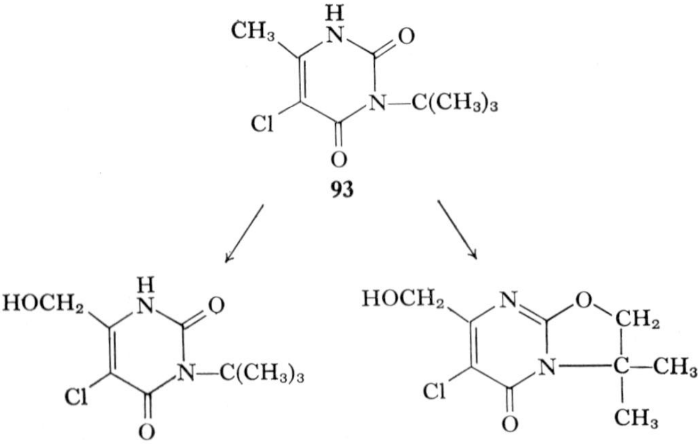

The mass spectrum of the major urinary metabolite showed its molecular weight to be 232, indicating that an oxygen atom had been added to the parent compound. The NMR spectrum (Fig. 18) contained a singlet at δ 1·34 (nine *tert*-butyl methyl protons), a doublet at 4·27 (two methylene protons on a carbon atom which also bears an oxygen or nitrogen atom and which is coupled with one adjacent proton) and a poorly resolved triplet at 4·7 (one hydroxylic proton coupled to an adjacent methylene group). These results, coupled with the mass and infra-red spectra, identify this metabolite (94) as 3-*tert*-butyl-5-chloro-6-hydroxy-methyluracil.

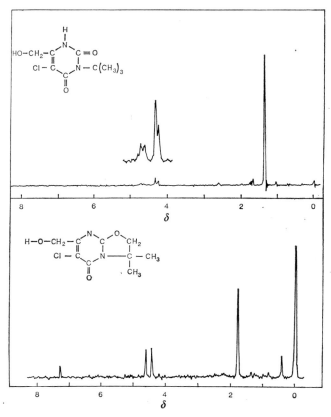

FIG. 18. NMR spectra of Terbacil metabolites. *Top*: Metabolite 94. *Bottom*: Metabolite 95. (From Rhodes *et al.*[155])

Evidence for an alteration of the *tert*-butyl group and a molecular weight 14 greater than that of terbacil was obtained following mass spectral analysis of the second urinary metabolite. The infrared spectrum of the unknown derivative also showed a strong absorption at 3500 cm^{-1} characteristic of an aliphatic hydroxyl group. The NMR spectrum (Fig. 18) contained a peak at δ 1·37, integrating for six protons, in the region expected for methyl groups attached to a tertiary carbon atom, two singlets at 4·43 and 4·62, each integrating for two protons, characteristic of methylene groups which are connected to an oxygen or nitrogen atom, and a broad band at about 1·9 to 3 assigned to the aliphatic OH group. This metabolite (95) was, therefore, identified as 6-chloro-2,3-dihydroxy-7-(hydroxymethyl)-3,3-dimethyl-5H-oxazolo-(3,2,a) pyrimidin-5-one and apparently was formed by abstraction of a molecule of water following oxidation of terbicil in the 3- and 6- positions.

The soil fungicide chloroneb (96), 1,4-dichloro-2,5-dimethoxybenzene, is

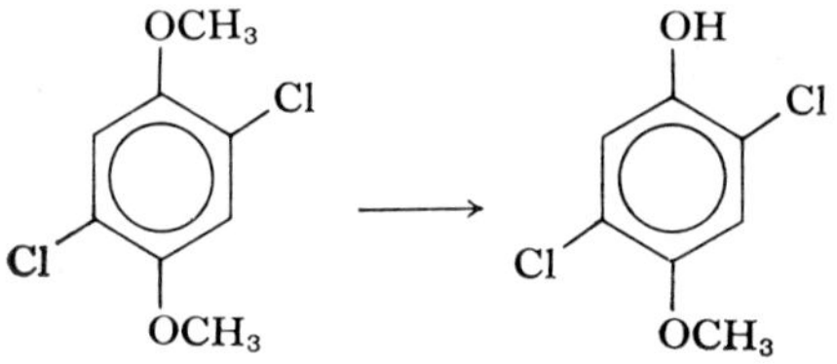

slowly converted to a non-toxic metabolite in the presence of the fungus *R. solani*.[156] Structural identification of the metabolite (97) was based on its mass, infrared and NMR spectra. While the NMR spectrum of the parent chloroneb contained a six-proton singlet at δ 3·84 (two O–CH$_3$ groups) and a two-proton peak at 6·9 associated with two equivalent aromatic protons, the metabolite showed only one O-methyl signal at 3·9, two peaks at 7·18 and 7·35 (two nonequivalent aromatic protons) and a hydroxyl signal in the region 4·25 to 5·0. The metabolite (97) was tentatively identified as 2,5-dichloro-4-methoxyphenol.

VI. INTERACTIONS WITH SURFACES AND PROTEINS

NMR spectroscopy has also been employed to study the interactions of chemicals with various surfaces.[157] Such reactions are usually followed by measurement of spin-spin and spin-lattice relaxation times of nuclei in the adsorbed state with spin-echo or broad-line NMR techniques.[157] Since relaxation times of adsorbed nuclei are affected by the molecular motion of the adsorbate, as well as the intermolecular interactions between the adsorbate and the surface, changes in relaxation time with temperature and surface coverage can be used to calculate activation energies and to help determine the mechanism of adsorption. In spite of the widespread use of NMR to study the adsorption of various chemicals to surface materials, this valuable method has not yet been extended to investigate the adsorption characteristics of pesticides. Such NMR relaxation studies could provide considerable insight into the mechanisms of binding, the diffusion and molecular motion of adsorbed pesticide molecules.

Although pesticides still adsorbed onto surfaces have not been examined by NMR spectroscopy, this technique has been employed to characterize the degradation products of pesticides formed on a clay surface. Chloro-*s*-triazines, such as propazine [2-chloro-4,6-bis(isopropylamino)-*s*-triazine], form protonated hydroxy derivatives following chemical hydrolysis on colloidal silicate or clay surfaces.[158] NMR has been used[158] to verify the formation of a protonated derivative and to locate the site of protonation following acid-catalyzed hydrolysis of propazine on a clay surface. The spectrum of the hydroxy hydrolysis product of propazine, 2-hydroxy-4,6-bis(isopropylamino)-*s*-triazine, extracted from the soil surface exhibited a doublet for the CH_3 protons, a multiplet for the –CH protons and a poorly resolved doublet for the –NH protons. Double irradiation at the –CH protons caused the CH_3 protons to collapse to a singlet and the poorly resolved –NH doublet to become a singlet. After double irradiation of the –CH_3 protons, the –CH multiplet changed to a doublet. These results suggest that protonation had occurred on the ring nitrogens rather than the side chain nitrogens forming the two tautomeric and resonance forms (**98**) and (**99**).

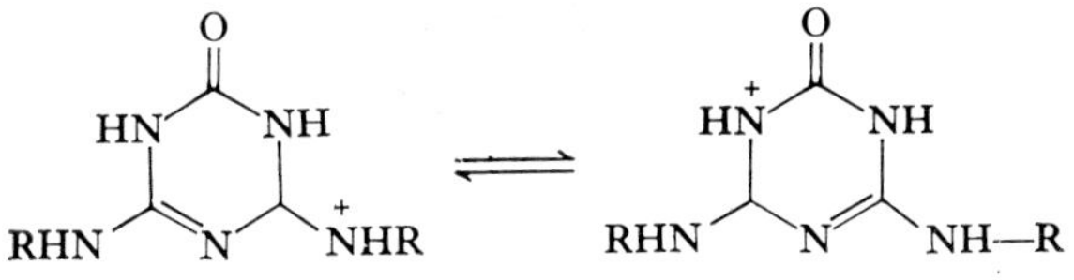

R = CH(CH₃)₂

Extensive use of NMR has been made to study the interactions of organic molecules and metal ions with proteins in solution.[159 to 167] Such associations are normally monitored by observing changes in the chemical shift or the relaxation time of resonating nuclei in the interacting system. While NMR measurements could be readily extended to include pesticide-macromolecular systems, very little work has as yet been accomplished in this area. However, NMR has recently been employed to investigate the interactions of the fungicide hexachlorophene with synthetic polypeptides.[82] Binding of hexachlorophene to the peptides caused significant changes in the chemical shift and line width of the phenolic proton peak. These results were interpreted in terms of formation of associated ion-pair hydrogen bonded complexes between the phenol and the amide linkage of the peptide.

Matsumura and O'Brien[168] have proposed that the mode of action of DDT in biological systems may be explained by formation of a charge transfer complex between the insecticide and protein components of the nerve axon. NMR spectroscopy has recently been employed to demonstrate the formation of charge transfer complexes of DDT with a number of simple aromatic electron donors.[169] This work presumably will be extended to investigate DDT interactions with biologically important macromolecules.

VII. CONCLUSIONS

If one examines the information on pesticides now rapidly accumulating from NMR studies, one must conclude that a majority of the work is confined to the determination of structural configuration especially as it is applied to the synthesis, photochemistry and metabolism of pesticides. These areas have received substantial contributions from NMR spectroscopy, indeed in many cases gaining new knowledge that is unattainable by other means. However, in spite of the rapid acceptance of NMR for structural studies with pesticides, this useful technique has only slowly been extended to other areas of pesticide research. NMR is a uniquely suited technique, having now reached the proper state of development, which permits its application to many other problems of importance in pesticide research. Accordingly, we can expect in the next few years the rapid extension of high-resolution and broad-line NMR techniques to the study of: the molecular interactions of pesticides with surfaces in soils or in biological systems; the association of pesticides with chemicals and macromolecules in solution; the kinetics of reactions involving pesticides; the mode of action of pesticides in biological systems; the transport of pesticides through the environment; and the analysis of pesticides in a variety of materials.

Acknowledgement. This work was supported by the U.S. Public Health Service, National Institutes of Health through research grants ES-00040 and ES-00210. The authors are indebted to Dr. L. H. Keith for kindly sending us a preprint of his paper[1] prior to its publication.

APPENDIX: PESTICIDE INDEX

Common name	Chemical name
Abate®	O,O,O',O'-Tetramethyl-O,O'-thiodi-p-phenylene phosphorothioate
Aldrin (HHDN)	1,2,3,4,10,10-Hexachloro-1,4,4a,5,8,8a-hexahydro-1,4-*endo-exo*-5,8-dimethanonaphthalene
Ametryne	2-Methylthio-4-ethylamino-6-isopropylamino-*s*-triazine
Amitrol (Aminotriazole)	3-Amino-1,2,4-triazole
Aspon®	Tetra-*n*-propyl dithiopyrophosphate
Atratone	2-Methoxy-4-ethylamino-6-(isopropylamino)-*s*-triazine
Atrazine	2-Chloro-4-ethylamino-6-isopropylamino-*s*-triazine
Azak®	2,6-Di-*tert*-butyl-*p*-tolyl-methylcarbamate
Azodrin®	Dimethyl phosphate of 3-hydroxy-*N*-methyl-*cis*-crotonamide
Barban (Carbyne®)	4-Chloro-2-butynyl-*m*-chlorocarbanilate

Baytex® (Fenthion)	O,O-Dimethyl-O-[4-(methylthio)-*m*-tolyl] phosphorothioate
Betasan® (bensulide)	N-(*beta*-O,O-Diisopropyl-dithiophosphorylethyl)-benzene sulfonamide
Bidrin®	3-(Dimethoxyphosphinyloxy)-N,N-dimethyl-*cis*-crotonamide
Bomyl®	Dimethyl 3-hydroxyglutaconate dimethylphosphate
Bromacil	5-Bromo-3-*sec*-butyl-6-methyluracil
Bulan®	2-Nitro-1,1-bis(*p*-chlorophenyl)butane
Carbaryl (Sevin®)	1-Naphthyl-N-methylcarbamate
Chlordane	1,2,3,5,6,7,8,8-Octachloro-2,3,3a,4,7,7a-hexahydro-4,7-methanoindene
Chlorobenzilate	Ethyl 4,4'-dichlorobenzilate
Chloroneb	1,4-Dichloro-2,5-dimethoxybenzene
Chloropropylate® (Acaralate®)	Isopropyl 4,4'-dichlorobenzilate
Ciodrin® (Crotoxyphos)	*Alpha*-methylbenzyl-3-(dimethoxyphosphinyloxy)-*cis*-crotonate
CIPC (Chloro-IPC)	Isopropyl N-(3-chlorophenyl)carbamate
Co-Ral® (Coumaphos)	O,O-Diethyl-O-3-chloro-4-methyl-1-oxo-2*H*-1-benzopyran-7-yl-phosphorothioate
2,4-D	2,4-Dichlorophenoxyacetic acid
DBP	Di-*n*-butyl phthalate
p,p'-DDA	Bis(*p*-chlorophenyl)acetic acid
p,p'-DDD	1,1-Dichloro-2,2-bis(*p*-chlorophenyl)ethane
p,p'-DDE	1,1-Dichloro-2,2-bis(*p*-chlorophenyl)ethylene
p,p'-DDMS	1-Chloro-2,2-bis(*p*-chlorophenyl)ethane
o,p'-DDMU	1-Chloro-2-(*o*-chlorophenyl)-2-(*p*-chlorophenyl)-ethylene
DDNU	*asym*-Bis(*p*-chlorophenyl)ethylene
DDOH	2,2-Bis(*p*-chlorophenyl)ethanol
o,p'-DDT	1,1,1-Trichloro-2-(*o*-chlorophenyl)-2-(*p*-chloro-phenyl)ethane
p,p'-DDT	1,1,1-Trichloro-2,2-bis(*p*-chlorophenyl)ethane
DDT acetal	2-Bis(*p*-chlorophenyl)methyl-1,3-dioxolane
DDVP Dichlorvos	O,O-dimethyl 2,2-dichlorovinyl phosphate
DEF®	S,S,S-tributyl phosphorotrithioate
Demeton (Systox®)	Mixture of O,O-diethyl-O-2-(ethylthio)ethyl phosphorothioate and O,O-diethyl-S-2-(ethylthio) ethyl phosphorothioate
Diazinon	O,O-Diethyl-O-(2-isopropyl-4-methyl-6-pyrimidyl)phosphorothioate

Diazoxon   *O,O*-Diethyl-*O*-(2-isopropyl-4-methyl-6-pyrimidyl)phosphate

Dicapthon   *O,O*-Dimethyl-*O*-(2-chloro-4-nitrophenyl) phosphorothioate

Dichlorophen (Preventol GD®)   Bis(5-chloro-2-hydroxyphenyl)methane

Dieldrin (HEOD)   1,2,3,4,10,10-Hexachloro-6,7-epoxy-1,4,4a,5,6,7,8,8a-octahydro-1,4-*endo-exo*-5,8-dimethanonaphthalene

Dimethoate (Cygon®)   *O,O*-Dimethyl-*S*-(*N*-methylcarbamoylmethyl) phosphorodithioate

Dimethoxon   *O,O*-Dimethyl-*S*-(*N*-methylcarbamoylmethyl) phosphorothioate

Dioxathion (Delvan®)   2,3-*p*-Dioxanedithiol-*S,S*-bis(*O,O*-diethylphosphorodithioate)

Diphenamid   *N,N*-Dimethyl-2,2-diphenylacetamide

Diquat   1,1'-Ethylene-2,2'-dipyridinium dibromide

Disulfoton (Di-Syston®)   *O,O*-Diethyl-*S*-2-(ethylthio)ethyl phosphorodithioate

Dursban®   *O,O*-Diethyl-*O*-3,5,6-trichloro-2-pyridyl phosphorothioate

Dyphonate   *O*-Ethyl-*S*-phenylethylphosphonodithioate

Endrin   1,2,3,4,10,10-Hexachloro-6,7-epoxy-1,4,4a,5,6,7,8,8a-octahydro-1,4-*endo-endo*-5,8-dimethanonaphthalene

EPN   Ethyl-*p*-nitrophenyl thionobenzene-phosphonate

Ethion   *O,O,O',O'*-Tetraethyl-*S,S'*-methylene bis-phosphorodithioate

Ethyl Guthion®   *O,O*-Diethyl-*S*-[4-oxo-1,2,3-benzotriazin-3-(4*H*)-ylmethyl] phosphorodithioate

Fenuron (Dybar®)   3-Phenyl-1,1-dimethylurea

Furadan®   2,3-Dihydro-2,2-dimethyl-7-*N*-benzofuranyl methylcarbamate

GS-13,005   *O,O*-Dimethyl-*S*-[2-methoxy-1,3,4-thiadiazol-5-(4*H*)-onyl-(4)-methyl] dithiophosphate

Heptachlor   1,4,5,6,7,8,8-Heptachloro-3a,4,7,7a-tetrahydro-4,7-*endo*-methanoindene

Hexachlorophene   2,2'-Methylene-bis(3,4,6-trichlorophenol)

Imidan®   *O,O*-Dimethyl-*S*-phthalimidomethyl phosphorodithioate

Ipazine   2-Chloro-4-(diethylamino)-6-(isopropylamino)-*s*-triazine

IPC	Isopropyl *N*-phenylcarbamate
Isocil	5-Bromo-3-isopropyl-6-methyluracil
Isodrin	1,2,3,4,10,10-Hexachloro-1,4,4a,5,8,8a-hexahydro-1,4-*endo,endo*-5,8-dimethanonaphthalene
Kelthane® (Dicofol)	1,1-Bis(*p*-chlorophenyl)-2,2,2-trichloroethanol
Lindane	γ-1,2,3,4,5,6-Hexachlorocyclohexane
Malaoxon	*O,O*-Dimethyl-*S*-(1,2-dicarbethoxyethyl) phosphorothioate
Malathion	*O,O*-Dimethyl-*S*-(1,2-dicarbethoxyethyl) phosphorodithioate
o-MDT	1,1,1-Trichloro-2-(*o*-chlorophenyl)-2-(phenyl)ethane
Merphos	Tributyl phosphorotrithioite
Meta-Systox R®	*O,O*-Dimethyl-*S*-[2-(ethylsulfinyl)ethyl] phosphorothioate
Methoxychlor	2,2-Bis-(*p*-methoxyphenyl)-1,1,1-trichloroethane
Methyl Guthion®	*O,O*-Dimethyl-*S*-[4-oxo-1,2,3-benzotriazin-3-(4*H*)-ylmethyl] phosphorodithioate
Methyl parathion	*O,O*-Dimethyl-*O*-*p*-nitrophenyl phosphorothioate
Methyl trithion®	*O,O*-Dimethyl-*S*-(*p*-chlorophenylthio)methyl phosphorodithioate
Monuron (Telvar®)	3-(*p*-Chlorophenyl)-1,1-dimethylurea
Naled (Dibrom®)	1,2-Dibromo-2,2-dichloroethyl dimethyl phosphate
Nellite®	Phenyl-*N,N'*-dimethylphosphorodiamidate
Nonachlor	1,2,3,4,5,6,7,8,8-Nonachloro-3a,4,7,7a-tetrahydro-4,7-methanoindane
Paraoxon	*O,O*-Diethyl-*O*-*p*-nitrophenyl phosphate
Paraquat	1,1'-Dimethyl-4,4'-dipyridylium cation
Parathion	*O,O*-Diethyl-*O*-*p*-nitrophenyl phosphorothioate
Perthane®	1,1-Dichloro-2,2-bis(*p*-ethylphenyl)ethane
Phencapton	*O,O*-Diethyl-*S*-(2,5-dichlorophenylthiomethyl) phosphorodithioate
Phorate (Thimet®)	*O,O*-Diethyl-*S*-(ethylthio) methyl phosphorodithioate
Phosdrin®	2-Carbomethoxy-1-propen-2-yl dimethyl phosphate
Phosphamidon	2-Chloro-2-diethylcarbamoyl-1-methylvinyl dimethyl phosphate
Phygon® (Dichlone)	2,3-Dichloro-1,4-naphthoquinone
Picloram (Tordon®)	4-Amino-3,5,6-trichloropicolinic acid
Prolan®	2-Nitro-1,1-bis(*p*-chlorophenyl)propane
Prometone	2-Methoxy-4,6-bis(isopropylamino)-*s*-triazine

Prometryne   2,4-Bis(isopropylamino)-6-methylmercapto-*s*-
                            triazine
Propazine   2-Chloro-4,6-bis(isopropylamino)-*s*-triazine
Ronnel   *O,O*-Dimethyl-*O*-(2,4,5-trichlorophenyl)
                            phosphorothioate
Ruelene®   4-*tert*-Butyl-2-chlorophenyl methyl
                            methylphosphoramidite
Schradan (OMPA)   Octamethylpyrophosphoramide
Siduron   1-(2-Methylcyclohexyl)-3-phenylurea
Simazine   2-Chloro-4,6-bis(ethylamino)-*s*-triazine
Simetone   2-Methoxy-4,6-bis(ethylamino)-*s*-triazine
Simetryne   2-Methylthio-4,6-bis(monoethylamino)-*s*-triazine
Sulfotepp   *O,O,O,O*-Tetraethyl dithiopyrophosphate
Sutan   *S*-Ethyl-*N,N*-di-isobutyl thiolcarbamate
2,4,5-T   2,4,5-Trichlorophenoxyacetic acid
Telodrin® (Isobenzan)   1,3,4,5,6,7,8,8-Octachloro-1,3,3a,4,7,7a-hexahydro-
                            4,7-methanoisobenzofuran
Terbacil   3-*tert*-Butyl-5-chloro-6-methyluracil
Thiodan® (Endosulfan)   6,7,8,9,10,10-Hexachloro-1,5,5a,6,9,9a-hexahydro-
                            6,9-methano-2,4,3-benzodioxathiepin 3-oxide
Thionazin (Zinophos)®   *O,O*-Diethyl-*O*-2-pyrazinyl phosphorothioate
Tiguvon®   *O,O*-Dimethyl-*O*-[4-(methylthio)-*m*-tolyl]
                            phosphorothioate
Tranid®   *Exo*-3-chloro-*endo*-6-cyano-2-norbornanone-*O*-
                            (methylcarbamoyl) oxime
Trichlorofon (Dipterex®,   *O,O*-Dimethyl-(1-hydroxy-2,2,2-trichloroethyl)
   Neguvon®)   phosphonate
Trietazine   2-Chloro-4-(diethylamino)-6-(ethylamino)-*s*-
                            triazine
Trithion®   *S*-[(*p*-Chlorophenyl)thiomethyl]-*O,O*-diethyl
                            phosphorodithioate
Zectran®   4-Dimethylamino-3,5-xylyl-*N*-methylcarbamate
Zytron®   *O*-(2,4-Dichlorophenyl)-*O*-methyl
                            isopropylphosphoramidothioate

Chemical names were in general taken from D. E. H. Frear, "Pesticide Index",
Fourth Edition, College Science Publishers, 1969.

REFERENCES

1. L. H. Keith and A. L. Alford, *J. Assoc. Offic. Analyt. Chem.*, 1970, **53**, 1018.
2. H. Babad, W. Herbert and M. C. Goldberg, *Analyt. Chim. Acta*, 1968, **41**, 259.
3. L. H. Keith, A. W. Garrison and A. L. Alford, *J. Assoc. Offic. Analyt. Chemists*, 1968, **51**, 1063; L. H. Keith and A. L. Alford, *Analyt. Chim. Acta*, 1969, **44**, 447.
4. J. B. Stothers and E. Y. Spencer, *Canad. J. Chem.*, 1961, **39**, 1389.
5. T. R. Fukuto, E. O. Hornig, R. L. Metcalf and M. Y. Winton, *J. Org. Chem.*, 1961, **26**, 4620.
6. A. W. Garrison, L. H. Keith and A. L. Alford, *Spectrochim. Acta*, 1969, **25A**, 77.
7. R. A. Y. Jones and A. R. Katritzky, *Angew. Chem.*, 1962, **1**, 32.
8. H. Finegold, *Ann. New York Acad. Sci.*, 1958, **70**, 875.
9. D. M. Crutchfield, C. H. Dungan, J. H. Letcher, V. Mark and R. J. Van Wazer, "Topics in Phosphorous Chemistry," (M. Grayson and E. J. Griffith, Eds.), *Int. Sci.*
10. J. D. Roberts, "Nuclear Magnetic Resonance", McGraw-Hill Book Co. Inc., New York, 1959.
11. T. M. Valega, *J. Org. Chem.*, 1966, **31**, 1150.
12. E. Lustig, W. R. Benson and N. Duy, *J. Org. Chem.*, 1967, **32**, 851.
13. E. H. White, M. C. Chen and L. A. Dolak, *J. Org. Chem.*, 1966, **31**, 3038.
14. R. H. Barker, S. L. Vail and G. J. Boudreaux, *J. Phys. Chem.*, 1967, **71**, 2228.
15. A. Loewenstein and T. M. Connor, *Ber. Bunsengesellschaft Phys. Chem.*, 1963, **67**, 280.
16. M. T. Rogers and J. C. Woodbrey, *J. Phys. Chem.*, 1962, **66**, 540.
17. J. Sandström, *J. Phys. Chem.*, 1967, **71**, 2318.
18. R. C. Neuman Jr., D. N. Roark and V. Jonas, *J. Amer. Chem. Soc.*, 1967, **89**, 3412.
19. A. E. Lemire and J. C. Thompson, *Canad. J. Chem.*, 1970, **48**, 824.
20. L. H. Keith and A. L. Alford, *J. Assoc. Offic. Analyt. Chem.*, 1970, **53**, 157.
21. J. V. Hatton and R. E. Richards, *Mol. Phys.*, 1962, **5**, 139; 1960, **3**, 253.
22. W. C. Meyer and J. T. K. Woo, *J. Phys. Chem.*, 1969, **73**, 3485.
23. W. C. Meyer and J. T. K. Woo, *J. Phys. Chem.*, 1969, **73**, 2989.
24. C. E. Holloway and M. H. Gitlitz, *Canad. J. Chem.*, 1967, **45**, 2659.
25. S. Van Der Werf, T. Olijnsma and J. B. F. N. Engberts, *Tetrahedron Letters*, 1967, 689.
26. G. A. Olah and M. Calin, *J. Amer. Chem. Soc.*, 1968, **90**, 401.
27. R. M. Golding, W. C. Tennant, C. R. Kanekar, R. L. Martin and A. H. White, *J. Chem. Phys.*, 1966, **45**, 2688.
28. R. M. Golding, W. C. Tennant, J. P. M. Bailey and A. Hudson, *J. Chem. Phys.*, 1968, **48**, 764.
29. E. E. Zaev, S. V. Larionov and Iu. N. Molin, *Doklady. Acad. Nauk S.S.S.R.*, 1966, **168**, 341.
30. D. R. Eaton, A. D. Josey, W. D. Phillips and R. E. Benson, *Discuss. Faraday Soc.*, 1962, **34**, 77.
31. R. M. Golding, *Mol. Phys.*, 1964, **8**, 561.
32. C. R. Kanekar, M. M. Dhingra, V. R. Marathe and R. Nagarajan, *J. Chem. Phys.*, 1967, **46**, 2009.

33. T. H. Siddall and C. A. Prohaska, *Nature*, 1965, **208**, 582.
34. T. H. Siddall III and C. A. Prohaska, *J. Amer. Chem. Soc.*, 1966, **88**, 1172.
35. T. H. Siddall III, *Tetrahedron Letters*, 1965, 4515.
36. T. H. Siddall III, *J. Org. Chem.*, 1966, **31**, 3719.
37. A. Ribera and M. Rico, *Tetrahedron Letters*, 1968, 535.
38. L. W. Reeves, *Canad. J. Chem.*, 1961, **39**, 1711.
39. W. E. Stewart, L. Mandelkern and R. E. Glick, *Biochemistry*, 1967, **6**, 143.
40. R. J. Gillespie and T. Birchall, *Canad. J. Chem.*, 1963, **41**, 148.
41. B. T. Brown and G. F. Katekar, *Tetrahedron Letters*, 1969, 2343.
42. A. J. Bloodworth and A. G. Davies, *J. Chem. Soc. (B)*, 1966, 125.
43. C. R. Redpath and J. A. S. Smith, *Trans. Faraday Soc.*, 1962, **58**, 462.
44. T. Birchall and R. J. Gillespie, *Canad. J. Chem.*, 1963, **41**, 2642.
45. R. H. Barker, G. J. Boudreaux and S. L. Vail, *Appl. Spectroscopy*, 1966, **20**, 414.
46. R. Haque and S. Lilley, unpublished results.
47. N. E. Sharpless and R. B. Bradley, *Appl. Spectroscopy*, 1965, **19**, 150.
48. N. E. Sharpless and R. B. Bradley, *Appl. Spectroscopy*, 1968, **22**, 506.
49. L. H. Keith, A. L. Alford and A. W. Garrison, *J. Assoc. Offic. Analyt. Chem.*, 1969, **52**, 1074.
50. H. H. Jaffe, *Chem. Rev.*, 1953, **53**, 191.
51. J. D. McKinney, E. L. Boozer, H. P. Hopkins and J. E. Suggs, *Experientia*, 1969, **25**, 897.
52. R. U. Lemieux, R. K. Kullnig, H. J. Bernstein and W. G. Schneider, *J. Amer. Chem. Soc.*, 1958, **80**, 6098.
53. R. K. Harris and N. Sheppard, *Mol. Phys.*, 1963, **7**, 595.
54. J. A. Pople, W. G. Schneider and H. J. Bernstein, "High Resolution Nuclear Magnetic Resonance", McGraw-Hill, New York, 1959.
55. K. Tori, R. Muneyuki and H. Tanida, *Canad. J. Chem.*, 1963, **41**, 3142.
56. K. Tori, Y. Hata, R. Muneyuki, Y. Takano, T. Tsuji and H. Tanida, *Canad. J. Chem.*, 1964, **42**, 926.
57. K. Tori, K. Aono, Y. Hata, R. Muneyuki, T. Tsuji and H. Tanida, *Tetrahedron Letters*, 1966, 9.
58. E. I. Snyder and B. Franzus, *J. Amer. Chem. Soc.*, 1964, **86**, 1166.
59. P. Laszlo and P. von R. Schleyer, *J. Amer. Chem. Soc.*, 1964, **86**, 1171.
60. J. C. Davis Jr. and T. V. Van Auken, *J. Amer. Chem. Soc.*, 1965, **87**, 3900.
61. P. M. Subramanian, M. T. Emerson and N. A. LeBel, *J. Org. Chem.*, 1965, **30**, 2624.
62. B. Franzus, W. C. Baird Jr., N. F. Chamberlain, T. Hines and E. I. Snyder, *J. Amer. Chem. Soc.*, 1968, **90**, 3721.
63. F. A. L. Anet, *Canad. J. Chem.*, 1961, **39**, 789.
64. D. R. Arnold, D. J. Trecker and E. B. Whipple, *J. Amer. Chem. Soc.*, 1965, **87**, 2596.
65. K. L. Williamson, *J. Amer. Chem. Soc.*, 1963, **85**, 516.
66. M. Karplus, *J. Chem. Phys.*, 1959, **30**, 11.
67. K. H. Buchel, A. E. Ginsberg and R. Fischer, *Chem. Ber.*, 1966, **99**, 421.
68. Selected Nuclear Magnetic Resonance Spectra Data, Texas A. & M. University, Thermodynamic Research Center Data Project.
69. K. H. Buchel, A. E. Ginsberg and R. Fischer, *Chem. Ber.*, 1966, **99**, 405.
70. A. M. Parsons and D. J. Moore, *J. Chem. Soc. (C)*, 1966, 2026.
71. A. P. Marchand and J. E. Rose, *J. Amer. Chem. Soc.*, 1968, **90**, 3724.

72. S. E. Forman, A. J. Durbetaki, M. V. Cohen and R. A. Olofson, *J. Org. Chem.*, 1965, **30**, 169.
73. L. K. Payne Jr., H. W. Stollings and C. B. Strow Jr., *J. Agric. Food Chem.*, 1967, **15**, 883.
74. C. M. Huggins, G. C. Pimental and J. N. Shoolery, *J. Phys. Chem.*, 1956, **60**, 1311.
75. S. Forsén, *Svensk kem. Tidskr.*, 1962, **74**, 10.
76. L. W. Reeves, E. A. Allan and K. O. Strømme, *Canad. J. Chem.*, 1960, **38**, 1249.
77. E. A. Allan and L. W. Reeves, *J. Phys. Chem.*, 1962, **66**, 613.
78. E. A. Allan and L. W. Reeves, *J. Phys. Chem.*, 1963, **67**, 591.
79. D. P. Eyman and R. S. Drago, *J. Amer. Chem. Soc.*, 1966, **88**, 1617.
80. G. Socrates, *Trans. Faraday Soc.*, 1967, **63**, 1083.
81. C. Hansch, K. Kiehs and G. L. Lawrence, *J. Amer. Chem. Soc.*, 1965, **87**, 5770.
82. R. Haque and D. R. Buhler, unpublished results.
83. M. W. Dietrich and R. E. Keller, *J. Amer. Oil Chemists Soc.*, 1967,[**44**, 491.
84. J. A. Ballantine and C. T. Pillinger, *Tetrahedron*, 1967, **23**, 1691.
85. O. Ohashi, M. Mashima and M. Kubo, *Canad. J. Chem.*, 1964, **42**, 970.
86. R. Gompper and P. Altreuther, *Z. analyt. Chem.*, 1959, **170**, 205.
87. S. Castellano and J. S. Waugh, *J. Chem. Phys.*, 1961, **34**, 295.
88. G. S. Reddy, J. H. Goldstein and L. Mandell, *J. Amer. Chem. Soc.*, 1961, **83**, 1300.
89. K. Murayama and K. Nukada, *Bull. Chem. Soc. Japan*, 1963, **36**, 1223.
90. R. Haque, W. R. Coshow and L. F. Johnson, *J. Amer. Chem. Soc.*, 1969, **91**, 3822.
91. F. A. Kramer Jr. and R. West, *J. Phys. Chem.*, 1965, **69**, 673.
92. S. Castellano, H. Gunther and S. Ebersole, *J. Phys. Chem.*, 1965, **69**, 4166.
93. J. P. Kokko, L. Mandell and J. H. Goldstein, *J. Amer. Chem. Soc.*, 1962, **84**, 1042.
94. M. Merkle, A. Danti and R. Hall, *Weed Res.*, 1965, **5**, 27.
95. J. P. Kokko, J. H. Goldstein and L. Mandell, *J. Amer. Chem. Soc.*, 1961, **83**, 2909.
96. N. Joop and H. Zimmermann, *Z. Elektrochem.*, 1962, **66**, 440.
97. K. T. Potts and T. H. Crawford, *J. Org. Chem.*, 1962, **27**, 2631.
98. A. Mannschreck, W. Seitz and H. A. Staab, *Z. Elektrochem.*, 1963, **67**, 470.
99. B. G. Van Den Bos, A. Schipperheyn and F. W. Van Deursen, *Rec. Trav. chim.*, 1966, **85**, 429.
100. W. Freiberg, C. F. Kroger and R. Radeglia, *Tetrahedron Letters*, 1967, 2109.
101. F. Declerck, R. Degroote, J. de Lannoy, R. Nasielski-Hinkens and J. Nasielski, *Bull. Soc. chim. belges*, 1965, **74**, 119.
102. T. Tokuhiro and G. Fraenkel, *J. Amer. Chem. Soc.*, 1969, **91**, 5005.
103. R. E. Dessy, T. J. Flautt, H. H. Jaffe and G. F. Reynolds, *J. Chem. Phys.*, 1959, **30**, 1422.
104. E. F. Kiefer and W. L. Waters, *J. Amer. Chem. Soc.*, 1965, **87**, 4401.
105. J. V. Hatton, W. G. Schneider and W. Siebrand, *J. Chem. Phys.*, 1963, **39**, 1330.
106. E. F. Kiefer, W. L. Waters and D. A. Carlson, *J. Amer. Chem. Soc.*, 1968, **90**, 5127.

107. P. D. Godfrey, M. L. Hefferman and D. F. Kerr, *Austral. J. Chem.*, 1964, **17**, 701.
108. J. N. Shoolery and B. J. Alder, *J. Chem. Phys.*, 1955, **23**, 805.
109. A. Carrington and T. Hines, *J. Chem. Phys.*, 1958, **28**, 727.
110. A. Carrington, F. Dravnicks and M. C. R. Symons, *Mol. Phys.*, 1960, **3**, 174.
111. R. E. Connick and R. E. Poulson, *J. Phys. Chem.*, 1958, **62**, 1002.
112. R. Haque and L. W. Reeves, *Canad. J. Chem.*, 1966, **44**, 2769.
113. R. Haque and L. W. Reeves, *J. Amer. Chem. Soc.*, 1967, **89**, 250.
114. R. E. Connick and R. E. Poulson, *J. Amer. Chem. Soc.*, 1957, **79**, 5153.
115. E. L. Muetterties and W. D. Phillips, *J. Amer. Chem. Soc.*, 1959, **81**, 1084.
116. R. Haque and N. Cyr, *Trans. Faraday Soc.*, 1970, **66**, 1848.
117. T. Birchall, R. J. Gillespie and S. L. Vekris, *Canad. J. Chem.*, 1965, **43**, 1672.
118. R. Freeman, R. P. H. Gasser, R. E. Richards and D. H. Wheeler, *Mol. Phys.*, 1959, **2**, 75.
119. G. E. Hall, "Annual Review of NMR Spectroscopy", Vol. 1, p. 227, Academic Press, London, 1967.
120. N. Muller and J. Goldenson, *J. Amer. Chem. Soc.*, 1956, **78**, 5182.
121. H. Babad and T. N. Taylor, *Analyt. Chim. Acta*, 1968, **40**, 387.
122. T. R. Fukuto and R. L. Metcalf, *J. Amer. Chem. Soc.*, 1954, **76**, 5103.
123. T. R. Fukuto, E. O. Hornig and R. L. Metcalf, *J. Agric. Food Chem.*, 1964, **12**, 169.
124. M. C. Goldberg, H. Babad, D. Groothius and H. R. Christianson, *Geological Survey Res.*, 1968, D20.
125. F. J. Biros, *J. Assoc. Offic. Analyt. Chemists*, 1970, **53**, 733.
126. J. R. Plimmer, U. I. Klingebiel and B. E. Hummer, *Science*, 1970, **167**, 67.
127. J. Robinson, A. Richardson, B. Bush and K. E. Elgar, *Bull. Environ. Cont. and Toxicol.*, 1966, **1**, 127.
128. J. D. Rosen, D. J. Sutherland and G. R. Lipton, *Bull. Env. Cont. and Toxicol.*, 1966, **1**, 133.
129. R. B. Harrison, D. C. Holmes, J. Roburn and J. O'G. Tatton, *J. Sci. Food Agric.*, 1967, **18**, 10.
130. A. M. Parsons and D. J. Moore, *J. Chem. Soc. C*, 1966, 2026.
131. J. D. Rosen and D. J. Sutherland, *Bull. Env. Cont. and Tox.*, 1967, **2**, 1.
132. G. L. Henderson and D. G. Crosby, *J. Agric. Food Chem.*, 1967, **15**, 888.
133. J. D. Rosen, *Chem. Comm.*, 1967, 189.
134. J. D. Rosen, D. L. Sutherland and M. A. Q. Khan, *J. Agric. Food Chem.*, 1969, **17**, 404.
135. R. R. McGuire, M. J. Zabik, R. D. Schuetz and R. D. Flotard, *J. Agric. Food Chem.*, 1970, **18**, 319.
136. B. E. Pape and M. J. Zabik, *J. Agric. Food Chem.*, 1970, **18**, 202.
137. E. R. White, W. W. Kilgore and G. Mallett, *J. Agric. Food Chem.*, 1969, **17**, 585.
138. A. Kowalsky and M. Cohn, *Ann. Rev. Biochem.*, 1964, **33**, 481.
139. O. Jardetzky, *Naturwiss*, 1967, **54**, 149.
140. H. R. Krueger and R. D. O'Brien, *J. Econ. Entomol.*, 1959, **52**, 1063.
141. J. B. Knaak and R. D. O'Brien, *J. Agric. Food Chem.*, 1960, **8**, 198.
142. P. R. Chen, W. P. Tucker and W. C. Dauterman, *J. Agric. Food Chem.*, 1969, **17**, 86.
143. J. I. Teasley, *Environ. Sci. and Tech.*, 1967, **1**, 411.

144. P. E. Newallis, P. Lombardo, E. E. Gilbert, E. Y. Spencer and A. Morello, *J. Agric. Food Chem.*, 1967, **15**, 940.
145. R. L. Metcalf, T. R. Fukuto, C. Collins, K. Borck, S. Abd El-Aziz, R. Munoz and C. C. Cassil, *J. Agric. Food Chem.*, 1968, **16**, 300.
146. J. A. Gardiner, R. K. Brantley and H. Sherman, *J. Agric. Food Chem.*, 1968, **16**, 1050.
147. R. L. Baron, J. A. Sphon, J. T. Chen, E. Lustig, J. D. Doherty, E. A. Hansen and S. M. Kolbye, *J. Agric. Food Chem.*, 1969, **17**, 883.
148. J. Holtzman, J. R. Gillette and G. W. A. Milne, *J. Amer. Chem. Soc.*, 1967, **89**, 6341.
149. M. A. H. Fahmy, R. L. Metcalf, T. R. Fukuto and D. J. Hennessy, *J. Agric. Food Chem.*, 1966, **14**, 79.
150. W. J. Bartley and D. L. Heywood, *J. Agric. Food Chem.*, 1968, **16**, 558.
151. I. J. Belasco and R. W. Reiser, *J. Agric. Food Chem.*, 1969, **17**, 1000.
152. A. Richardson, M. Baldwin and J. Robinson, *J. Sci. Food Agric.*, 1968, **19**, 524.
153. V. J. Feil, R. D. Hedde, R. G. Zaylskie and C. H. Zachrison, *J. Agric. Food Chem.*, 1970, **18**, 120.
154. J. A. Gardiner, R. W. Reiser and H. Sherman, *J. Agric. Food Chem.*, 1969, **17**, 967.
155. R. C. Rhodes, R. W. Reiser, J. A. Gardiner and H. Sherman, *J. Agric. Food Chem.*, 1969, **17**, 974.
156. W. K. Hock and H. D. Sisler, *J. Agric. Food Chem.*, 1969, **17**, 123.
157. K. J. Packer, "Progress in NMR Spectroscopy" (J. W. Emsley, J. Feeney and L. H. Sutcliffe, Eds.), Vol. 3, p. 87, 1967.
158. J. D. Russell, M. Cruz, J. L. White, G. W. Bailey, W. R. Payne Jr., J. D. Pope Jr. and J. I. Teasley, *Science*, 1968, **160**, 1340.
159. J. J. M. Rowe, J. Hinton and K. Rowe, *Chem. Rev.*, 1970, **70**, 1.
160. R. G. Shulman, H. Sternlicht and B. J. Wyluda, *J. Chem. Phys.*, 1965, **43**, 3116.
161. A. S. Mildvan, M. C. Scrutton, *Biochemistry*, 1967, **6**, 2978.
162. R. L. Ward and J. A. Happe, *Biochem. Biophys. Comm.*, 1967, **28**, 785.
163. A. S. Mildvan, J. S. Leigh and M. Cohn, *Biochemistry*, 1967, **6**, 1805.
164. H. Sternlicht, D. E. Jones and K. Kustin, *J. Amer. Chem. Soc.*, 1968, **90**, 7110.
165. G. G. Hammes and D. L. Miller, *J. Chem. Phys.*, 1967, **46**, 1533.
166. P. G. Schmidt, G. R. Stark and J. D. Baldeschwieler, *J. Biol. Chem.*, 1969, **244**, 1860.
167. O. Jardetsky and N. G. Wade-Jardetzky, *Mol. Pharm.*, 1965, **1**, 214.
168. F. Matsumura and R. D. O'Brien, *J. Agric. Food Chem.*, 1966, **14**, 36.
169. R. T. Ross and F. J. Biros, *Biochem. Biophys. Res. Comm.*, 1970, **39**, 723.

A Simple Guide to the
use of Iterative Computer Programmes
in the Analysis of NMR Spectra

C. W. HAIGH

Department of Chemistry, University College, Swansea, Wales

I. INTRODUCTION

IN HIS introduction to this series,[1] the editor distinguished two kinds of contributions: genuine reviews; and those on some specialized aspect of NMR which was, however, of general interest. This article is of the latter type, and not the former. Two fairly recent reviews of this subject have appeared,[2,3] of which the former includes a comprehensive bibliography. In these last years, more and more papers have appeared using computer analysis for spectra; it may, in fact, now be considered to be a standard technique. Accordingly, a complete bibliography would now serve little purpose. Instead, our aim will be to present a very limited number of examples in sufficient detail to illustrate the main features of the method, and to persuade the non-specialist of its feasibility for him. We shall confine our attention to spectra arising from nuclei of spin $\frac{1}{2}$ in isotropic liquids; and we shall exclude from consideration multiple resonance and all exchange effects.

An earlier article in this series[4] has given the necessary background in adequate detail. We shall repeatedly make use of this material, and assume that the reader has a reasonable familiarity with its principal features.

311

II. COMPUTER PROGRAMMES

Although several programmes have been described[2,3] which allow iterative analysis of spectra, most published calculations follow one of two basic approaches, either that of Reilly and Swalen[5] (RS) or of Bothner-By and Castellano[6] (BBC); and our discussion will be confined to these. Any iterative programme has to be used successively in two modes. First, given the type of spin system (ABC, etc.),[4a] and a set of parameters (chemical shifts and coupling constants)[4b]—which it is hoped approximate the true values—the computer will set up and solve the secular equations, determining the energy levels and coefficients, and hence calculate the frequencies and intensities of the lines in the predicted spectrum:[4c] this is the *non-iterative* mode. When the predicted spectrum bears an adequate resemblance to that observed, the programme may then be used in the *iterative* mode. The computer is given, as additional data, the frequencies of the lines observed in the spectrum, together with their assignment. It then obtains optimum values of the parameters—in the least squares sense—to fit these data. In the iterative phase of the RS method,[5,7a,34a] this is accomplished in two stages: first a single least squares calculation obtains a best set of energy levels, then an iterative sequence of calculations obtains the best set of parameters to fit these energy levels. In the BBC method,[6,7b,34b] the iterative sequence fits the parameters directly to the transition frequencies. Accordingly, the "assignment" in the RS case consists in specifying the two *energy levels* between which an observed transition occurs, the numbering of the energy levels being derived from the non-iterative run. Correspondingly, in the BBC method, "assignment" involves matching the number of a *transition* predicted in the non-iterative run with one of the observed lines.

There can be no doubt whatsoever about the mathematical reliability of the parameters derived by either method (the question of their uniqueness, of course, is another matter). Nevertheless, of late more workers appear to have used the BBC approach; and several research groups, including the author's, have switched from RS to BBC. There are probably three main reasons for this trend.

(a) The mathematical nature of the BBC iterative sequence renders it less likely to run into convergence difficulties in tricky cases.

(b) Although different versions of the RS method, and programmes derived from them, use different methods of assessing the accuracy of the parameters, none seems to be really satisfactory. The BBC statistics, however, are mathematically impeccable.

(c) Serious difficulties have arisen from the need, in the RS method, to determine all the energy levels: these difficulties appear to be particularly severe in problems where there is chemical equivalence.[4d] A number of methods have been devised to deal with this, but none appears wholly successful. On the other hand, the BBC approach merely requires the user to specify initially a sufficient number of transitions to make the problem over-determined. It is probably this third reason which has in most cases been decisive in inducing research groups to switch from RS to BBC, though it was not so in the present author's case.

Any computer programme must firstly do precisely the calculation it was designed to perform. This may seem very obvious but, for a large and complicated programme, it will frequently take months of testing before the programmer is entirely satisfied on this point. Beside this basic requirement, two other criteria must always be firmly borne in mind by programmers: that the calculation should be achieved in the minimum *time* and, secondly, that the least possible *storage space* within the computer should be used—efficiency in this respect will enable larger spin systems to be handled on the same computer. These criteria will be mentioned several times in the sequel.

Although I have developed two modified versions of the RS and derived methods, my present programmes[8] are firmly based on the BBC philosophy. Beside the specific points considered in detail in IV and V below, these programmes do score slightly on the second of these criteria. For example, on one particular computer, LAOCOON3 could handle up to an ABCDEF system; but LAME could perform an ABCDEFG calculation.[†] The detailed examples in the next sections will be presented in terms of these programmes but the kind of data required, and the kinds of decisions needed do not greatly vary from one programme to another. The reader who follows the next few pages should have no trouble in using any standard programme, as all contain full instructions for data preparation[‡] (*e.g.* ref. 34).

III. SYSTEMS WITHOUT EQUIVALENT SPINS

Frequently an NMR spectrum can be separated into a group of multiplets whose line positions can be interpreted according to the first-order splitting rules,[4c] even though their intensities may not. It is often assumed that the centres of multiplets and the observed line separations give good approximations to the chemical shifts and coupling constants, respectively. This is usually fair, but some care must be exercised when the multiplets, though not overlapping, are quite close and/or large couplings are involved. Now perturbation theory, although it undoubtedly has its uses in this field, is unlikely to be beloved of the

† Also see appendix.
‡ Reference 2 also contains a fully worked example of the use of NMRIT and NMREN[5,7a].

non-specialist.† Nevertheless one formula is worth memorizing: the deviation of a transition frequency from its first-order position will be, correct to second order, $\pm (J_{AB}^2/2\delta_{AB})$, where J_{AB} is a coupling constant, and δ_{AB} is a chemical shift difference, both in Hz, and A and B are a pair of nuclei singled out for consideration; provided other couplings are small compared with δ_{AB}. The chief effect of this term, for moderate coupling, is to shift the whole multiplet bodily, thus changing the apparent chemical shift. Thus, if J were 15 Hz and (at 100 MHz) it was required to quote chemical shifts accurate to 0·01 p.p.m., this effect could only be neglected if the chemical shift difference were more than 1·1 p.p.m. As the strength of the coupling (measured by $|J^2/\delta|$) increases, the line positions *within* a multiplet will be affected, so that separations can no longer be equated with coupling constants. A simple three-spin example will indicate the possible magnitudes involved. If the true parameters were $\nu_A = 37\cdot0$, $\nu_B = 19\cdot0$, $\nu_C = 0\cdot0$ Hz; $J_{AB} = 1\cdot0$, $J_{BC} = 12\cdot0$, $J_{AC} = 18\cdot0$ Hz (typical for a vinyl group), the spectrum would show three nonoverlapping four-line multiplets (the separations are: A to B, 2 Hz and B to C, 3 Hz). The shifts and couplings, however, which would be obtained by using multiplet centres and line separations would be, in the same order, 39·2, 20·6 and −3·8 Hz; and 2·8, 11·6 and 16·7 Hz. The warning is clear. In cases of this sort, when well-resolved spectra are obtained, it will frequently be worth while for the research worker to invest a very little extra time in order to obtain accurate parameters by the use of an iterative programme. For the assignment will often be trivial, and the entire process mechanical. In favourable cases, information concerning relative signs of couplings may also be obtained, by refining sets of starting parameters with different likely sign combinations, and examining particularly the intensities.

It might be thought that these considerations almost only applied to proton spectra, as the total range of ^{1}H chemical shifts is minute compared with that of all other nuclei. To take the case of the next most commonly studied nucleus ^{19}F: its coupling constants can be an order of magnitude larger; nevertheless the range of chemical shifts is so enormous, when expressed in Hz at 94·1 MHz, that strongly-coupled non-equivalent nuclei are indeed rare. But an interesting recent paper[9] shows that careful work can detect effects of this kind and put them to good use. If C_6F_5SD (or C_6F_5SH) were a strictly [AM]$_2$R (or [AM]$_2$RX) system,‡ all these ^{19}F multiplets should be symmetrical. Figs. 1 and 2 of ref. 9 show that the multiplet of *ortho* fluorines is not; this is because the *meta* and *para*

---

† Thus, although the whole subject-matter of this article might often be described by the phrase "second-order effects", a quantitative treatment will almost always involve complete solution of the secular equations—as this is so easy with a computer—rather than the strict mathematical sense of the phrase, namely the use of perturbation theory to second order only.

‡ Using the notation of ref. 10 (see also ref. 4a), which will be adopted throughout.

nuclei have a coupling constant of -2×10^1 Hz, and are separated by "only" 3×10^2 Hz. The high quality of the spectra allowed the authors to suggest *all* the relative signs (and resolve an ambiguity of alternative *meta* couplings)—a suggestion which was confirmed by double resonance.

We consider next the case when just two nuclei are sufficiently strongly coupled for their multiplets to overlap. In straightforward cases, the procedure of the preceding paragraphs may still be adequate, namely the use of multiplet centres and line separations as initial estimates of parameters, which are then refined iteratively. These estimates will of course be poorer, δ_{AB} in particular being susceptible to gross errors—A and B being the strongly coupled nuclei. The alternative is to consider all chemical shifts to be effectively infinite *except* that between A and B. As the resulting secular equations involve only quadratics, the results can be expressed in closed form, *i.e.* in explicit formulae. So, once a consistent assignment of lines has been made (and this, though not difficult, does require a little care), solution of some simple equations will give values of the parameters.[4f] The appropriate formulae are given in the texts and a particularly detailed discussion of the simplest case, the ABX system, is given in ref. 11. The resulting parameters can now be taken as *good* starting values for an iterative computer refinement. As this situation is quite common, we shall present one example in considerable detail.

The proton spectrum of phenanthrene has been examined by several groups[12]† (for the numbering used, see Fig. 1). The molecule contains ten protons; but because of the symmetry, and the fact that no inter-ring coupling can be resolved, it may be divided into an A_2 system (H9, H10), and two additional four-spin systems (*e.g.* H1–4). The former gives rise to the intense singlet at 460·2 Hz from T.M.S., which has been allowed to go off scale in Fig. 1, and which will call for no further comment. H2 and H3 were expected to have similar chemical shifts, H1 to absorb at somewhat lower field, and H4 at much lower field. This pattern is easily picked out in Fig. 1: the complex multiplet to high field of the singlet being assigned to H2 and H3, that to low field of it to H1, and the isolated broadened multiplet at low field to H4.‡

---

† The spectrum in Fig. 1 was obtained in 1964. It was first analysed iteratively using a modified version of the RS programmes, written in Sirius autocode.[13] Subsequently the analysis was repeated on an I.C.T. Atlas, using a version of the RS programmes in FORTRAN, modified by the present author. Both analyses agree with the LAME calculations presented here.

‡ It may at this stage be remarked that analysis can of course proceed perfectly satisfactorily without any identifications between, on the one hand, nuclei deduced from the multiplet structure of a spectrum and, on the other, atoms in a molecular formula, which may indeed be partially or wholly unknown. Nevertheless, any information that *is* known, which will give indications concerning likely chemical shifts and coupling constants, should certainly be used, provided such assumptions do not blind the researcher to unexpected possibilities.

The multiplet centres of H1, H4 should give quite good approximations to their chemical shifts, and the centre of gravity of the H2, H3 multiplet some sort of estimate of $\frac{1}{2}(\nu_2+\nu_3)$. The fine structure of H1 consists of eight principal

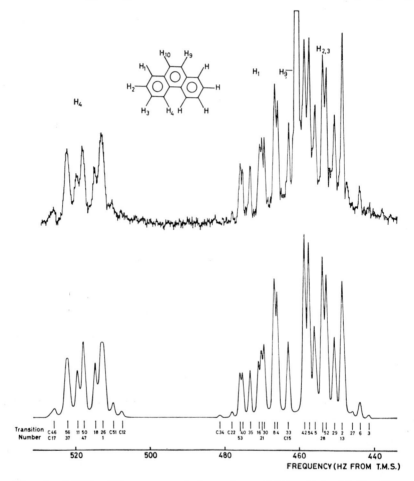

Fig. 1. 60 MHz. ^{1}H spectrum of phenanthrene (10% w/v) in CDCl$_3$. *Upper*—spectrum; *lower*—simulation (excluding A$_2$ singlet).

lines, which though clearly unsymmetrical, can be assigned on first-order grounds, and can give—after averaging—rough estimates of J_{12}, J_{13} and J_{14}.†
The broadening of the lines of H4 arises from unresolved five-bond *amphi*

---

† It is incidentally quite unusual to be able to resolve a *para* coupling so clearly in a benzenoid hydrocarbon; though well known, they are more usually deduced from analyses.

coupling between H4 and H10; this makes the multiplet less informative, but at least the separation of the outer main peaks should give a reasonable estimate of $(J_{14}+J_{24}+J_{34})$ and hence of $(J_{24}+J_{34})$. Furthermore, *ortho* and *meta* couplings in benzenoid hydrocarbons vary over comparatively narrow ranges, so that reasonable guesses at J_{24} and J_{34} may be made. At this stage, identification of J_{23} with a peak separation is not possible, but again a value may be guessed which is unlikely to be out by more than $1\frac{1}{2}$ Hz. This preliminary approach, however, gives no inkling as to the value of $(\nu_2-\nu_3)$, except that it is fairly small.

As only H2 and H3 are very strongly coupled, we turned to an ABMX calculation.[14] For small δ_{AB}, the AB part (H2, H3) should consist firstly of eight strong transitions: these are easily identified, provided the strong line furthest upfield (labelled 2, 13) is considered to consist of two overlapping transitions. Secondly, eight weaker lines are predicted, some of which can be identified. The M absorption (H1) is predicted to consist principally of the eight lines already considered, whose asymmetry is now accounted for. In addition, two pairs of weak combination bands are predicted. Of these, one at low field (C22, C for combination band) can just be discerned. At high field, the not so weak peak labelled C15, 33 is liable to contain intensity from a combination band and one of the weak AB peaks. The predicted shape for X(H4) is similar to that of M, but the asymmetry should be reversed. The pattern found, though less distinct through the broadening, is compatible with these predictions, and three combination bands are visible. It has thus been possible to make an assignment. From the observed line separations, values for the four surds involved in the four quadratics were deduced, though not with perfect consistency. Hence the ABMX parameters were calculated, in particular the previously inaccessible δ_{AB}. As the principal M absorptions only just fail to overlap the visible AB transitions, as some weak AB peaks are actually predicted in the M region, and as the M intensities have a very marked slant, the coupling of M to A and B cannot really be considered weak. But a good *approximate* set of parameters had been obtained. This could now be used in conjunction with the computer.

The form of the data for a non-iterative calculation is shown in Table I. This is a coding sheet, ready to be punched on cards (the commonest form of input for modern computers). Cards, 1, 2, 3 and 5 contain a number for filing and a title for the problem; a non-iterative run is specified, together with a number of options concerning output. Cards 4 and 6 indicate an ABCD problem, with the X approximation[4g] (see below) not required. Card 7 indicates the four chemical shifts, in order, expressed in Hz. Two points may be noted concerning these. Firstly, they have been given relative to an arbitrary origin (a particular point on the chart paper, actually very near ν_1) rather than say T.M.S.; this is quite often convenient; but of course in the iterative run, the same zero must be used for the experimental line positions. Secondly, the positive direction has been counted upfield. For most simple systems, this question of sign does not affect the results

TABLE I

Input data for programme LAME

IBM — PUNCHING INSTRUCTIONS

Name | Date | Page of | Application

Line	Columns 1–10	11–20	21–30	31–40
1	9			
2	PHENANTHRE	NE, 10 % I	N CDCL3.	EDINBURGH.
3	0 1 1			
4	4 1 1	1 1		
5	-100.	50.	0.001	
6	1 1 1	1		
7	0.	17.7	15.	-47.6
8	12 7.7			
	13 1.7			
	14 0.5			
	23 7.1			
	24 1.0			
	34 8.2			
	blank			
	blank			

Form 25-5915-2 (Revised 1/6/64) (Replaces 25-5915-1, 2-646 and X24-6299) IBM United Kingdom Limited but, technically of course, as the normal method of calculation assumes a fixed field, frequency should increase from right to left: in case of doubt, this latter correct sign-convention should be used. The next few cards indicate the coupling constants (*e.g.* that between nuclei 1 and 2 is 7·7 Hz, etc.). Finally, the blank cards indicate the end of the coupling constants, and the fact that there are no further problems to be processed in this particular "job" for the computer.

The resulting output is shown in Table II. Part (a) essentially repeats the input data as a heading. Part (b) gives the energy levels: there are $2^4 = 16$ of these. But the computer did not have to solve all 16 secular equations at once: because wave functions with different values of F_z do not mix (see ref. 4c, especially Fig. 4), the equations are broken down into $4 + 1 = 5$ blocks, whose sizes are 1, 4, 6, 4 and 1, as shown by the blank lines in the computer output. Thus the largest sub-matrix handled by the computer is of dimension 6 (ref. 4a, Table I, column 5). Most programmes do not print out the actual wave function coefficients, as these would be rather cumbersome for large systems, and of very limited usefulness in this form. Part (c) of the output shows all the predicted transitions having intensity above a specified threshold value, and gives, for each one, the numbers of the related energy levels, the frequency and the intensity; starting with the transition 1←2 and ending at 15←16. First-order theory allows 32; the ABMX formulae give 40; the computer here has printed an extra three exceedingly weak ones, making 43 in all (the maximum possible is 56). Part (d) simply re-arranges this material in ascending order of frequency.

When this last output was compared with both the ABMX calculation and the experimental spectrum, a one-to-one correspondence was easily established, the discrepancies being up to the order of a Hz. Assignment, in other words, was straightforward. The numbers in Fig. 1 correspond to the LAME line numbers. A few weak lines could not be distinguished above the noise, or were overlapped by stronger lines (two by the A_2 singlet); but 34 transitions could be identified. So we were able to proceed to an iterative calculation. The data cards required for such calculations will be mostly identical to those of Table I, though card 3 will need to specify rather more possible options. Two further items will also be needed. First, an indication of which parameters are to be refined: in this case, as is usual, all ten (four chemical shifts, six coupling constants). Second, an extra 34 cards specifying the assigned and observed transitions. A typical one would contain the numbers 46, $-56·1$ and 0·1. This means that the transition, to which was given (in the non-iterative run) the number 46, was observed 56·1 Hz down-field of the zero. As it is weak and broadened by partial overlap with the even weaker no. 17, it has been assigned a weight of 0·1 in the least squares analysis (1·0 being the standard value).

The result of the iterative calculation is given in Table III. Part (a) shows that the RMS deviation between calculated and observed line positions was 0·27 using the starting parameters, but that it quickly dropped to 0·08 Hz; and that after only

TABLE IIa

PROBLEM STARTED AT   15/57/53

COMPUTER PROGRAMME LAOCOON WITH MAGNETIC EQUIVALENCE

CASE NUMBER   9
PHENANTHRENE, 10 % IN CDCL3.   EDINBURGH.

TYPE OF SPIN SYSTEM
A1B1C1D1

NON-ITERATIVE CALCULATION

FREQUENCY RANGE   -100.000   50.000 MINIMUM INTENSITY 0.00100

INPUT PARAMETERS

ISOTOPIC SPECIES	NUCLEUS	CHEMICAL SHIFT
1	1	0.0000
1	2	17.7000
1	3	15.0000
1	4	-47.6000

NUCLEI		COUPLING CONSTANT
1	2	7.7000
1	3	1.7000
1	4	0.5000
2	3	7.1000
2	4	1.0000
3	4	8.2000

ITERATION NO.   0 STARTED AT   15/57/55

TABLE IIb

CASE NUMBER   9
PHENANTHRENE, 10 % IN CDCL3.   EDINBURGH.

ENERGY LEVELS CLASSIFIED BY SUBMATRICES
(SUBSUBMATRICES ARE SEPARATED BY BLANK LINES)

SUBMATRIX NO.   1

TOTAL SPIN QUANTUM NUMBERS FOR COMPLEX PARTICLES
   0.5   0.5   0.5   0.5

LEVEL NO.	ENERGY
1	-0.9000
2	42.1128
3	-22.4622
4	-29.5000
5	-5.0505
6	27.4118
7	15.7622
8	-44.0945
9	38.5735
10	-29.3304
11	-21.4226
12	8.1059
13	26.9434
14	18.5862
15	-38.7355
16	14.0000

CALCULATION OF FREQUENCIES STARTED AT   15/57/59

TABLE IIc

CASE NUMBER, 9
PHENANTHRENE, 10 % IN CDCL3. EDINBURGH.

TRANSITIONS, ORDERED BY LINE NUMBER

LINE NO.	ENERGY LEVELS UPPER	LOWER	CALC.FREQ.	INTENSITY
1	1	2	-43.013	1.163
2	1	3	21.562	1.304
3	1	4	28.600	0.025
4	1	6	4.150	1.508
5	2	6	14.701	1.196
6	2	7	26.351	0.230
8	2	9	3.539	1.737
11	3	7	-49.874	0.843
12	3	7	-38.224	0.123
13	3	8	21.632	1.296
14	3	9	-61.036	0.002
15	3	10	6.868	0.345
16	3	11	-1.040	0.695
17	4	6	-56.912	0.067
18	4	7	-45.262	0.982
19	4	8	14.594	0.115
21	4	10	-0.170	0.796
22	4	11	-8.077	0.064
23	5	6	-32.462	0.005

-1.127
0.053
-2.322
-1.044
0.863
0.205
0.629
0.027
0.680
0.865
0.546
0.003
2.705
0.157
0.150
0.792
0.252
0.779
0.251
2.050
0.542
2.524
0.085
0.849

-43.624
-24.280
-16.372
-19.306
8.468
7.826
11.656
-2.181
-52.824
-5.200
-30.468
11.630
19.987
-56.274
-47.917
9.405
-48.366
-40.009
17.313
-5.894
12.943
4.586
-52.735

9
10
11
13
12
14
12
15
12
13
14
13
14
15
13
15
16
16
16

5
5
5
6
6
6
7
7
7
8
8
9
9
9
10
10
11
11
11
12
13
14
15

26
27
28
29
30
31
33
34
35
37
40
41
42
43
46
47
48
50
51
52
53
54
55
56

TABLE IId

CASE NUMBER 9
PHENANTHRENE, 10 % IN CDCL3.   EDINBURGH.

TRANSITIONS, ORDERED BY FREQUENCY

LINE NO.	CALC.FREQ.	INTENSITY
14	-61.036	0.002
17	-56.912	0.067
46	-56.274	0.150
56	-52.735	0.849
37	-52.200	0.865
11	-49.874	0.843
50	-48.366	0.779
47	-47.917	0.792
18	-45.262	0.982
26	-43.624	1.127
1	-43.013	1.163
51	-40.009	0.251
12	-38.224	0.123
23	-32.462	0.005
34	-11.181	0.027
22	-8.077	0.064
53	-5.894	0.542
40	-5.359	0.546
35	-2.824	0.680
16	-1.040	0.695
21	-0.170	0.796
30	0.468	0.863
8	3.539	1.737
4	4.150	1.508
55	4.586	0.085
15	6.868	0.345
33	7.656	0.629
31	8.826	0.205
48	9.405	0.252
42	11.630	2.705
54	12.943	2.524
19	14.594	0.115
5	14.701	1.196
28	16.372	2.322
52	17.313	2.050
29	19.306	1.044
43	19.987	0.157
2	21.562	1.304
13	21.632	1.296
27	24.280	0.053
6	26.351	0.230
3	28.600	0.025
41	30.468	0.003

END OF CASE 9

TABLE IIIa

PROBLEM STARTED AT   15/58/06

COMPUTER PROGRAMME LAOCOON WITH MAGNETIC EQUIVALENCE,

CASE NUMBER   9
PHENANTHRENE, 10 X IN CDCL3.   EDINBURGH.

TYPE OF SPIN SYSTEM
A1B1C1D1

FREQUENCY RANGE -100.000   50.000 MINIMUM INTENSITY 0.00100

ITERATION NO.   0 STARTED AT   15/58/07

PARAMETERS FOR ITERATION NUMBER 0

ISOTOPIC SPECIES	NUCLEUS	CHEMICAL SHIFT
1	1	0.0000
1	2	17.7000
1	3	15.0000
1	4	-47.6000

NUCLEI		COUPLING CONSTANT
1	2	7.7000
1	3	1.7000
1	4	0.5000
2	3	7.1000
2	4	1.0000
3	4	8.2000

RMS (WEIGHTED) DEVIATION OF TRANSITION FREQUENCIES   0.2652731

```
ITERATION NO.   1 STARTED AT    15/58/13
```

```
                PARAMETERS FOR ITERATION NUMBER   1
```

ISOTOPIC SPECIES	NUCLEUS	CHEMICAL SHIFT
1	1	0.0593
1	2	17.5328
1	3	14.7589
1	4	-47.2548

NUCLEI		COUPLING CONSTANT
1	2	7.9829
1	3	1.3390
1	4	0.6926
2	3	6.9967
2	4	1.2008
3	4	8.4182

```
RMS (WEIGHTED) DEVIATION OF TRANSITION FREQUENCIES   0.0776104
ITERATION NO.   2 STARTED AT    15/58/18
```

```
                    FINAL PARAMETERS
                  (ITERATION NUMBER   2)
```

ISOTOPIC SPECIES	NUCLEUS	CHEMICAL SHIFT
1	1	0.0610
1	2	17.5301
1	3	14.7586
1	4	-47.2535

NUCLEI		COUPLING CONSTANT
1	2	7.9731
1	3	1.3471
1	4	0.6922
2	3	6.9953
2	4	1.1915
3	4	8.4278

```
RMS (WEIGHTED) DEVIATION OF TRANSITION FREQUENCIES   0.0774641
ITERATION HAS CONVERGED
```

STANDARD DEVIATION OF PARAMETERS

PARAMETER SET NO.	NUCLEUS		CHEMICAL SHIFT	STANDARD DEVIATION
1	1		0.061	0.030
2	2		17.530	0.049
3	3		14.759	0.044
4	4		-47.254	0.040

PARAMETER SET NO.	NUCLEI		COUPLING CONSTANT	STANDARD DEVIATION
5	1	2	7.973	0.059
6	1	3	1.347	0.061
7	1	4	0.692	0.045
8	2	3	6.995	0.052
9	2	4	1.192	0.078
10	3	4	8.428	0.073

CORRELATION MATRIX OF PARAMETERS

	1	2	3	4	5	6	7	8
1	1.0000							
2	-0.2842	1.0000						
3	0.0849	-0.3553	1.0000					
4	0.0021	-0.0004	0.0077	1.0000				
5	0.4602	-0.5038	0.2427	-0.0120	1.0000			
6	-0.1718	0.4829	-0.4135	0.0180	-0.4775	1.0000		
7	-0.0970	0.0212	0.0027	-0.0516	-0.0660	0.0305	1.0000	
8	-0.0292	-0.2068	0.0924	-0.0521	0.0083	-0.1448	-0.0698	1.0000
9	0.1466	-0.0278	0.0928	-0.0090	0.3414	-0.2288	-0.1421	0.0547
10	-0.0810	0.0771	-0.0481	0.0964	-0.2137	0.2334	0.0455	-0.0308

	9	10
9	1.0000	
10	-0.3842	1.0000

TABLE IIIb

CASE NUMBER   9
PHENANTHRENE,   10 % IN CDCL3.   EDINBURGH.

ENERGY LEVELS CLASSIFIED BY SUBMATRICES
(SUBSUBMATRICES ARE SEPARATED BY BLANK LINES)

SUBMATRIX NO.   1

TOTAL SPIN QUANTUM NUMBERS FOR COMPLEX PARTICLES
   0.5   0.5   0.5   0.5

LEVEL NO.	ENERGY
1	-0.7952
2	41.5876
3	-22.1610
4	-29.2952
5	-5.0352
6	27.4293
7	15.4146
8	-43.8526
9	38.1432
10	-29.1252
11	-21.3228
12	8.1303
13	26.7544
14	18.6238
15	-38.6047
16	14.1087

CALCULATION OF FREQUENCIES STARTED AT   15/58/26

TABLE IIIc

CASE NUMBER, 9 10 % IN CDCL3.   EDINBURGH.
PHENANTHRENE,

TRANSITIONS, ORDERED BY LINE NUMBER

LINE NO.	ENERGY LEVELS UPPER	LOWER	ASSIGNED WEIGHTS	OBS.FREQ.	CALC.FREQ.	DIFF.	INTENSITY
1	1	2	0.300	-42.500	-42.383	-0.117	1.176
2	1	3	0.500	21.350	21.366	-0.016	1.294
3	1	4	0.200	28.600	28.500	-0.100	0.034
4	1	5	1.000	4.200	4.240	-0.040	1.496
5	2	6	0.900	14.200	14.158	-0.042	1.205
6	2	7	1.000	26.100	26.173	-0.073	1.235
8	2	9	1.000	3.500	3.444	-0.056	0.736
11	3	6	0.600	-49.600	-49.590	-0.010	0.850
12	3	7	0.100	-37.800	-37.576	-0.224	0.112
13	3	8	0.500	21.650	21.692	-0.042	1.245
14	3	9			-60.304		0.002
15	3	10	0.500	7.000	6.964	0.036	0.419
16	3	11	1.000	-0.700	-0.838	0.138	0.667
17	4	6			-56.725		0.060
18	4	7	0.600	-44.600	-44.710	0.110	1.001
19	4	8	0.100	14.500	14.557	-0.057	0.150
21	4	10	1.000	-0.100	-0.170	-0.070	0.746
22	4	11	0.100	-8.000	-7.972	-0.028	0.077

A	B	C	D	E	i	j	No.
0.005	0.078	-32.465	-43.100	0.300	16	5	23
-1.131	-0.090	-43.178	24.000	-0.050	19	5	26
-0.060	0.001	24.090	16.300	-0.000	10	5	27
2.300	-0.075	16.288	19.300	-0.000	11	6	28
0.994		19.299	0.600	0.500	12	6	29
0.888	0.084	0.675	7.200		13	6	30
0.238		8.805		-1.000	14	7	31
0.682	-0.091	7.284	-3.300	-0.300	12	7	34
0.029	-0.117	-11.340	-52.100	-0.000	13	8	35
0.637	-0.152	-3.209	-5.400		14	9	37
0.861		-51.983		1.000	15	9	40
0.533	0.011	-5.248	11.400		12	9	41
0.003		30.013		0.100	13	10	42
0.706	-0.220	11.389	-56.100	0.300	12	10	43
2.160	-0.051	19.519	-47.800		13	10	46
0.158		-55.880		0.300	14	11	47
0.777	0.077	-47.749	-48.000	0.200	13	11	48
0.290	-0.053	9.480	-40.200	-0.000	14	11	50
0.766	0.018	-48.077	17.300	-1.000	15	13	51
0.263	-0.078	-39.947	-5.900		13	14	52
2.541	0.054	17.282	12.700	0.300	14	15	54
2.546		-5.978			15		55
2.074	0.113	12.646	-52.600		16		56
0.839		4.515					
		-52.713					

TABLE IIId

CASE NUMBER   9
PHENANTHRENE,   10 % IN CDCL3.   EDINBURGH.

TRANSITIONS, ORDERED BY FREQUENCY

LINE NO.	OBS.FREQ.	CALC.FREQ.	DIFF.	INTENSITY
14		-60.304		0.002
17		-56.725		0.060
46	-56.100	-55.880	-0.220	0.158
56	-52.600	-52.713	0.113	0.839
37	-52.100	-51.983	-0.117	0.861
11	-49.600	-49.590	-0.010	0.850
50	-48.000	-48.077	0.077	0.766
47	-47.800	-47.749	-0.051	0.777
18	-44.600	-44.710	0.110	1.001
26	-43.100	-43.178	0.078	1.131
1	-42.500	-42.383	-0.117	1.176
51	-40.000	-39.947	-0.053	0.263
12	-37.800	-37.576	-0.224	0.112
23		-32.465		0.005
34		-11.340		0.029
22	-8.000	-7.972	-0.028	0.077
53	-5.900	-5.978	0.078	0.541
40	-5.400	-5.248	-0.152	0.533
35	-3.300	-3.209	-0.091	0.637
16	-0.700	-0.838	0.138	0.667
21	-0.100	-0.170	0.070	0.746
30	0.600	0.675	-0.075	0.888
8	3.500	3.444	0.056	1.736
4	4.200	4.240	-0.040	1.496
55		4.515		0.074
15	7.000	6.964	0.036	0.419
33	7.200	7.284	-0.084	0.682
31		8.805		0.238
48		9.480		0.290
42	11.400	11.389	0.011	2.706
54	12.700	12.646	0.054	2.546
5	14.200	14.158	0.042	1.205
19	14.500	14.557	-0.057	0.150
28	16.300	16.288	0.012	2.300
52	17.300	17.282	0.018	2.015
29	19.300	19.299	0.001	0.994
43		19.519		0.160
2	21.350	21.366	-0.016	1.294
13	21.650	21.692	-0.042	1.245
27	24.000	24.090	-0.090	0.060
6	26.100	26.173	-0.073	0.235
3	28.600	28.500	0.100	0.034
41		30.013		0.003

END OF CASE   9

two iterations the convergence criterion had been achieved. This varies in different programmes; but in this case it was a less than 1% decrease in R.M.S. deviation between successive iterations. The final optimized parameters are printed, together with their standard deviations. There follow the correlation coefficients between parameters: these provide additional material for assessing their reliability: *e.g.* the significant value of -0.48 between parameter set $5(J_{12})$ and set $6(J_{13})$ means that although the standard deviation of each is quoted as 0.06 Hz, their sum is appreciably better determined than their difference, a not unusual situation for coupling constants related in this way. It should be remembered that these statistics are based solely on accuracy of internal fit of the calculated spectrum to the data presented to the computer, and take no account, say, of the reproducibility of line positions. Part (b) of the output needs no further comment; nor does part (c), except to point out that the weight assigned to each transition is also presented. Part (d) presents a final comparison of the calculated observed spectrum, which can be considered satisfactory.

A word may perhaps be in order concerning the handling of strong overlapped transitions, of which there are several pairs in this example (weak overlapped transitions, such as no. 43, are best excluded from the iterative process). Rather than setting the "observed" positions of both overlapped transitions at the centre of the observed peak, it is probably better to separate them by a judicious amount. This is the method used in this case, with fair success (but see below). In any case, a lower weight should always be assigned to them although, if there are very few, it may be feasible to omit them all from the iteration. It is clear that this is a distinct, though generally very minor, source of inaccuracy. If the matter appears crucial, very sophisticated methods are available[2,3] for analysing the experimental absorption into distinct transitions, and this could be done before iteration. A clever modification[15] by Martin and co-workers of my programme LAME allows some adjustment of this kind actually to occur during the course of the iterative sequence.

The reader will have noticed that only the observed *frequencies* are used in the iterative process, and this is true of almost all programmes. Where there is negligible overlap, and little variation in line width, a quick comparison of experimental peak heights and calculated relative intensities may be all that is needed to confirm the correctness of the solution. Not infrequently, however, one or other of these conditions is not met; and a more detailed visual comparison is worthwhile. All that is required is that a suitable line-shape function be applied to the calculated frequencies and intensities. This straightforward but tedious calculation is again suitable for a computer, and the results are normally output on an instrument called a graph-plotter, which (as the name implies) plots the calculated spectrum to scale. A number of programmes have been described,[2,3] but doubtless many more are in use; for graph-plotter instructions are much less easily transferred between installations than are programmes for the computer itself. Some research groups have an extra routine added to their principal NMR programme. The author's own preference is to output the LAME results on to some convenient intermediate storage medium (disc, tape or cards); and then to use this, often more than once, as input for the graph-plotting programme. The author's own programme NMRP† allows for variable line shape— Gaussian, Lorentzian or a combination of the two-and for different line widths for different transitions in the same spectrum. The need for this kind of flexibility is well illustrated by the difference between H4 and the rest of the spectrum in the case of phenanthrene. The simulated spectrum thus obtained is shown also in Fig. 1. The outcome on the whole is satisfactory: shapes, widths, heights and overlaps being quite well reproduced. The calculated peak heights of nos. C15 + 33 (just downfield of the singlet) and nos. 2+13 (the strong upfield AB peak) are, however, too low, indicating that the experimental separation within each of these pairs of peaks is perhaps one or two tenths of a Hz less than the calculated separations. Further adjustment would doubtless have improved the fit, and very slightly changed the parameters, so that the quoted standard deviations are very slight underestimates.

The final results, then, for a 10% (w/v) solution of phenanthrene in $CDCl_3$ at 60 MHz are:

Hz from T.M.S.:
$$\nu_1\ 469\cdot52\pm0\cdot03,\ \nu_2\ 452\cdot05\pm0\cdot05,\ \nu_3\ 454\cdot82\pm0\cdot04,\ \nu_4\ 516\cdot83\pm0\cdot04.$$
δ values (p.p.m.):
$$\delta_1\ 7\cdot825,\ \delta_2\ 7\cdot534,\ \delta_3\ 7\cdot580,\ \delta_4\ 8\cdot614.$$
Coupling constants: *ortho*: $J_{12}\ 7\cdot97\pm0\cdot06$, $J_{23}\ 7\cdot00\pm0\cdot05$, $J_{34}\ 8\cdot43\pm0\cdot07$;
$\qquad\qquad\qquad$ *meta*: $J_{13}\ 1\cdot35\pm0\cdot06$, $J_{24}\ 1\cdot19\pm0\cdot08$;
$\qquad\qquad\qquad$ *para*: $J_{14}\ 0\cdot69\pm0\cdot05$
Large correlation coefficients:
$$\nu_2/J_{12}\ -0\cdot50,\ \nu_2/J_{13}\ +0\cdot48,\ \nu_3/J_{13}\ -0\cdot41,\ J_{12}/J_{13}\ -0\cdot48.$$
Also by direct measurement: ν_9 460·2 Hz from T.M.S., δ_9 7·670 p.p.m.

These are in good accord with literature values,[12] recorded in various solvents and at various concentrations.‡

I may perhaps be allowed to quote two further papers from these laboratories which illustrate additional points. In ref. 16, a seven-spin system in an acyclic carbohydrate derivative was examined. Two different pairs of moderately closely coupled protons at either end of the molecule (and either end of the spectrum) were first treated as two ABX systems. Because a pair of protons in the middle of the molecule (and of the spectrum) were very strongly coupled, an ABMRX

---

† Based on Dr. P. Bladon's programme SAH2.

‡ Ref. 12c also presents results for a 10% solution in $CDCl_3$, but this is probably (w/w) not (w/v). In Table 3 of ref. 12c, the position of the downfield proton (536·0 Hz from T.M.S. at 60 MHz) is clearly a misprint.

calculation was also performed. These preliminaries provided data for an ABCDE, and finally an ABCDEFG iterative solution. Ref. 17 discusses the powerful carcinogen 3,4-benzpyrene which contains 12 non-equivalent protons; because of the lack of resolved inter-ring coupling these can be split into five spin systems A, AB, AB, ABC and ABCD, the last of which was investigated by methods closely related to those just described at length. These five systems overlapped extensively; so, before punching out the calculated transition intensities onto cards, LAME multiplied them by the appropriate factor to convert relative intensities for 2-, 3- and 4- spin systems to a common scale. Finally, the output of all calculations was fed together to a graph-plotter programme: this resulted in gratifying agreement.

The types of system dealt with hitherto in this section require—for large systems—patience rather than deep theoretical knowledge. If, however, a nonspecialist finds a case in which more than two non-equivalent nuclei are overlapping each other's absorptions simultaneously, and the spectrum is sufficiently well resolved that it appears to warrant detailed investigation, he might well obtain specialist advice, particularly with regard to the possibility of multiple solutions.

IV. MAGNETIC EQUIVALENCE

When a spin system contains magnetically equivalent nuclei,[4a,h]† the calculation may be simplified: a simple three-spin example is given in Fig. 5 of ref. 4h. Firstly, when there is a group of three or more magnetically equivalent spins, the number of distinct energy levels is reduced. Secondly, the solution of the secular equations is broken down into smaller parts. Both these effects, if properly used, will reduce both the computer storage requirements, and also the computing time. If the largest number of secular equations that has to be handled simultaneously (the largest "subsubmatrix") is n, then an important part of the storage requirements will vary as n^2, and the time required to perform an important part of the calculations will vary as a sum of terms, the largest of which is n^3. For large n, comparatively small reductions may thus result in very useful improvements in both respects.

The question of magnetic equivalence is not in reality as complicated as it might appear to be from the reading of certain texts; and a cumbrous notation can be avoided if one uses what is known as the "composite particle" or "complex particle" approach. A group of N magnetically equivalent spin $\frac{1}{2}$ nuclei (which we shall label A), can have a total spin I_A taking all the values $\frac{1}{2}, \frac{3}{2} \ldots \frac{1}{2}N$ for N odd, and $0, 1 \ldots \frac{1}{2}N$, for N even. The whole problem can be broken down into completely separate parts, called "submatrices", according to the values of

† Bishop uses the term "completely equivalent".

the total spins of *each* group of magnetically equivalent nuclei. Within each of these submatrices, the z component of the spin of the A group, which we denote by m_A, can take all the values I_A, (I_A-1), ..., $-(I_A-1)$, $-I_A$. As is true in the general case, secular equations need only be solved for the mixing of wave functions having the same value of F_z, the sum of the m values for all the groups. It is the splitting of the problem into submatrices before this second splitting into subsubmatrices which so markedly reduces the value of n, with the beneficial effects we have enumerated.

The [A_2B_3] system will be used as an illustration. Clearly I_A can be 1 or 0, and I_B can be $\frac{3}{2}$ or $\frac{1}{2}$. This leads to four submatrices: (1) $I_A=1$, $I_B=\frac{3}{2}$; (2) $I_A=1$, $I_B=\frac{1}{2}$; (3) $I_A=0$, $I_B=\frac{3}{2}$; (4) $I_A=0$, $I_B=\frac{1}{2}$. This is shown in Table IVb. Within the first submatrix, m_A can have the values 1, 0, -1; and m_B the values $\frac{3}{2}, \frac{1}{2}, -\frac{1}{2}$, $-\frac{3}{2}$: a total of $3 \times 4 = 12$ wave functions and therefore 12 energy levels. Of these, only three have $F_z=\frac{1}{2}$, namely $m_A=1$, $m_B=-\frac{1}{2}$; $m_A=0$, $m_B=+\frac{1}{2}$: and $m_A=-1$, $m_B=+\frac{3}{2}$. These three give rise to the three energy levels numbered 4 to 6 in Table IVb. We thus have a submatrix requiring the solution of only three secular equations (note that subsubmatrices are separated by blank lines in Table IVb): as this subsubmatrix was chosen as being one of the two largest, $n=3$ in this case. For an ABCDE five-spin case, however, $n=10$. [Note also (Table IVb) that the total number of energy levels is 24 compared with $2^5=32$.] As this is not an unusually favourable case, it can easily be seen that the savings in storage requirements and computer time can be dramatic.†

An important step forward was made when Stanley, Ferguson and Marquardt[18] incorporated these ideas into a programme DPENMR but, as it was based on the RS philosophy, it was subject to the difficulties considered in section II above. So in 1968 the present author devised a programme,[8a] whose name—LAME—is an acronym for LAocoon with Magnetic Equivalence: he wishes to acknowledge not only his obvious indebtedness to the authors of LAOCOON3[6,7b] but also to those of DPENMR.[18] It may be noted that this latter research group now routinely use LAME rather than their own programme.[19] Two other groups have independently reported work closely parallel to mine: Musso and Isaïa[20] at Nice have written NMR–LAOCN–4A, which is specifically designed for small computers; and Johannesen and Ferretti[21] in the United States have written UEAITR, an iterative version of the programme UEANMR II, produced at Norwich by Harris and Woodman.[22]

In practice, to the user there is very little difference in the application of a programme incorporating magnetic equivalence: the changes are rather the economy in storage space and execution time. So our example can be explained fairly briefly. The spectrum of tetraethyl silane, $(CH_3CH_2)_4Si$, has been previously reported,[23] and has been used[23c] as a pedagogical example to illustrate

---

† For more examples, see Appendix.

magnetic equivalence. Our 100 MHz spectrum[24] is shown† in Fig. 2. Two experimental points may be noted at this juncture. Even though the non-specialist will doubtless eschew those refinements which are necessary for *very* high resolution analysis, it is essential that spectra which are to be analysed by computer should be recorded using an expanded scale, *i.e.* with a sweep-width less than that suitable for routine measurements, and that the frequencies of the lines be stated with a precision suitable to the experimental conditions. Secondly, although with some spectrometers line positions can be read off directly from the chart, side-band calibration is more usual. Now, some spectrometers have a markedly non-linear chart scale: in this case, *two* side-bands, one at either end, are inadequate. Sufficient side-bands are to be used to allow accurate interpolation: this is shown by the faint vertical lines in Fig. 2.

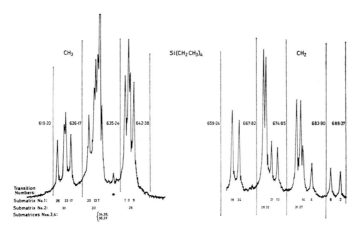

FIG. 2. 100 MHz. ^{1}H spectrum of tetraethyl silane (12% w/w) in CCl_4, with benzene as internal reference. The vertical lines are calibration markers, annotated in Hz from benzene.

The main isotopic species in tetraethyl silane gives rise in principle to an $[A_2B_3]_4$ system; but as no inter-alkyl coupling can be resolved, an $[A_2B_3]$ interpretation suffices. Now this system is a member of the wider class of $[A_pB_q]$, which have important simplifying features. Subject to a scale factor, the *shapes* of their spectra depend only on the ratio $|J_{AB}|/(\nu_A - \nu_B)$, and have been tabulated as a function of that quantity.[25] Furthermore, when—as here—*p* is

† The peak marked with an asterisk is not an impurity, but arises from the ^{29}Si satellite spectrum. Its comparatively large intensity (^{29}Si natural abundance is only 4·7%) arises from the superposition of the largest peak in the Si α subspectrum and the second largest peak in the Si β subspectrum (or *vice versa*). The resulting three-bond J_{SiH} is about 6·8 Hz (ref. 24).

even and q is odd, one peak (arising from all the $I_A = 0$ submatrices) occurs at
exactly ν_B; and the equations for the $I_A = 1$, $I_B = \frac{1}{2}$ submatrix can be solved in
closed form (the formulae are identical to those which are well-known to apply
to the A_2B case). Thus, if only five of these lines can be identified, the three
parameters J_{AB}, ν_A and ν_B can be determined. It may well be asked then why
one should wish to use a computer. There is in fact a good answer to this question: the direct method just outlined makes use of five lines—each susceptible to
experimental error −, or at best of the eight lines arising from these three submatrices. The computer on the other hand can use *all* the observed lines (25 in
this case) and so determine these three parameters that much more precisely.

In this case, no difficulty was experienced in initially using this direct method.
The form of the data input to the programme LAME only differed from that
previously described by the inclusion of the information that the A group contained two, and the B group three magnetically equivalent nuclei. A non-iterative run gave, as expected, very close agreement with experiment, assignment of
lines being obvious. The results of the iterative run are given in Table IV. The
line positions are quoted in Hz upfield from the reference peak, which was benzene in this case.† The convergence, as expected, was almost immediate. The
structure of Table IVb has already been discussed; and it will be observed, on
comparing it with Table IVc, that 17 observable peaks (nos. 1–25) arise from
submatrix 1, seven (nos. 26–33) from submatrix 2, and that the four remaining
transitions all give rise to the very strong peak at exactly ν_B, which has been
allowed to go off scale. Fig. 2 not only gives the transition numbers (from Table
IVd) but also classifies them according to submatrices. Graph-plotter confirmation was considered unnecessary, though the so-called "stick diagram" could
have been used. (For an alternative presentation of the 60 MHz results, see
Fig. 6 of ref. 23c.) The final parameters then are $(\nu_A - \nu_B) = -42 \cdot 72 \pm 0 \cdot 01$ Hz
(at 100 MHz) $= -0 \cdot 4272$ p.p.m. (methylene *upfield* from methyl), $|J_{AB}| =$
$7 \cdot 952 \pm 0 \cdot 006$ Hz, in adequate agreement with the literature.[23]

In general, spin systems containing groups of magnetically equivalent nuclei
will not have any submatrices whose secular equations can be solved in closed
form; this is true for a system as simple as [ABC₃]. If the multiplets do not overlap, the first-order splitting rules (now with binomially related intensities in
the limit) may provide approximations for the required parameters. It may be
noted that in this first-order limit, the transition frequencies depend only on
m_A, etc., for the upper and lower levels, and *not* on I_A, etc. Thus the transitions
from all the other submatrices coincide with those from that one with the maximum values of I_A, etc. It is this superposition of peaks which can be said to give

---

† The HA100 instrument "locks" onto the reference peak: the usual reference
tetramethyl silane could not be used in this case because its peak was too close.
As it was not intended to report precise δ values, but only a *difference* in chemical
shifts, benzene was not inappropriate.

Table IVa

PROBLEM STARTED AT   15/58/34

COMPUTER PROGRAMME LAOCOON WITH MAGNETIC EQUIVALENCE

CASE NUMBER 202
TETRAETHYLSILANE 16/10/69

TYPE OF SPIN SYSTEM
A2B3

FREQUENCY RANGE   300.000   1000.000 MINIMUM INTENSITY 0.00000

ITERATION NO.   0 STARTED AT   15/58/35

PARAMETERS FOR ITERATION NUMBER   0

ISOTOPIC SPECIES	NUCLEUS	CHEMICAL SHIFT
1	1	673.3000
1	2	630.6000

NUCLEI		COUPLING CONSTANT
1	2	7.9000

RMS (WEIGHTED) DEVIATION OF TRANSITION FREQUENCIES   0.0795001

ITERATION NO.   1 STARTED AT   15/58/37

PARAMETERS FOR ITERATION NUMBER   1

ISOTOPIC SPECIES	NUCLEUS	CHEMICAL SHIFT
1	1	673.2468
1	2	630.5278

NUCLEI		COUPLING CONSTANT
1	2	7.9524

RMS (WEIGHTED) DEVIATION OF TRANSITION FREQUENCIES   0.0235579

ITERATION NO.   2 STARTED AT   15/58/41

TABLE IVa *continued*

FINAL PARAMETERS
(ITERATION NUMBER 2)

ISOTOPIC SPECIES	NUCLEUS	CHEMICAL SHIFT
1	1	673.2467
1	2	630.5279

	NUCLEI		COUPLING CONSTANT
	1	2	7.9524

RMS (WEIGHTED) DEVIATION OF TRANSITION FREQUENCIES   0.0235579
ITERATION HAS CONVERGED

STANDARD DEVIATION OF PARAMETERS

PARAMETER SET NO.	NUCLEUS	CHEMICAL SHIFT	STANDARD DEVIATION
1	1	673.247	0.007
2	2	630.528	0.007

PARAMETER SET NO.	NUCLEI		COUPLING CONSTANT	STANDARD DEVIATION
3	1	2	7.952	0.006

CORRELATION MATRIX OF PARAMETERS

	1	2	3
1	1.0000		
2	-0.0770	1.0000	
3	-0.2854	0.1058	1.0000

TABLE IVb

CASE NUMBER 202
TETRAETHYLSILANE 16/10/69

ENERGY LEVELS CLASSIFIED BY SUBMATRICES
(SUBSUBMATRICES ARE SEPARATED BY BLANK LINES)

SUBMATRIX NO.   1

TOTAL SPIN QUANTUM NUMBERS FOR COMPLEX PARTICLES
   1.0   1.5

LEVEL NO.	ENERGY
1	1630.9671
2	994.4369
3	943.8417
4	357.1024
5	313.8916
6	258.8930
7	-281.5246
8	-315.5855
9	-364.5864
10	-943.4811
11	-986.8451
12	-1607.1099

SUBMATRIX NO.   2

TOTAL SPIN QUANTUM NUMBERS FOR COMPLEX PARTICLES
   1.0   0.5

LEVEL NO.	ENERGY
13	992.4868
14	354.8062
15	314.4643
16	-314.5963
17	-362.6266
18	-984.5344

TABLE IVb (*continued*)

SUBMATRIX NO.   3

TOTAL SPIN QUANTUM NUMBERS FOR COMPLEX PARTICLES
0.0   1.5

LEVEL NO.	ENERGY
19	945.7918
20	315.2639
21	-315.2639
22	-945.7918

SUBMATRIX NO.   4

TOTAL SPIN QUANTUM NUMBERS FOR COMPLEX PARTICLES
0.0   0.5

LEVEL NO.	ENERGY
23	315.2639
24	-315.2639

CALCULATION OF FREQUENCIES STARTED AT   15/58/48

TABLE IVc

CASE NUMBER 202
TETRAETHYLSILANE 16/10/69

TRANSITIONS, ORDERED BY LINE NUMBER

LINE NO.	ENERGY LEVELS UPPER	LOWER	ASSIGNED WEIGHTS	OBS.FREQ.	CALC.FREQ.	DIFF.	INTENSITY
1	1	2	1.000	636.530	636.530	-0.000	3.905
2	1	3	1.000	687.130	687.125	0.005	1.095
3	2	4	0.500	637.310	637.334	-0.024	5.549
4	2	5	1.000	680.540	680.545	-0.005	1.355
5	2	6			735.544		0.000
6	3	4			586.739		0.001
7	3	5	0.200	629.930	629.950	-0.020	2.863
8	3	6	1.000	684.960	684.949	0.011	1.231
9	4	7	1.000	638.610	638.627	-0.017	4.673
10	4	8	1.000	672.690	672.688	0.002	1.876
11	4	9			721.689		0.001
12	5	7			595.416		0.004
13	5	8	0.200	629.530	629.477	0.053	3.678
14	5	9			678.478		1.536
15	6	7			540.418		0.000
16	6	8			574.479		0.000
17	6	9	1.000	623.450	623.479	-0.029	2.231
18	7	10	1.000	661.950	661.956	-0.006	3.675
19	7	11			705.320		0.002
20	8	10	0.500	627.870	627.896	-0.026	2.477
21	8	11	1.000	671.270	671.260	0.010	2.078
22	9	10			578.895		0.001
23	9	11	0.200	622.330	622.259	0.071	2.766
24	10	12	1.000	663.600	663.629	-0.029	3.154
25	11	12	1.000	620.260	620.265	-0.005	1.846
26	13	14	0.200	637.750	637.681	0.069	2.828
27	13	15	1.000	678.010	678.023	-0.013	3.172
28	14	16	0.500	669.440	669.403	0.037	4.828
29	14	17			717.433		0.001
30	15	16	0.200	629.140	629.061	0.079	1.807
31	15	17	1.000	677.070	677.091	-0.021	3.365
32	16	18	0.500	669.990	669.938	0.052	4.634
33	17	18	0.200	622.000	621.908	0.092	1.366
34	19	20	1.000	630.530	630.528	0.002	3.000
35	20	21	1.000	630.530	630.528	0.002	4.000
36	21	22	1.000	630.530	630.528	0.002	3.000
37	23	24	1.000	630.530	630.528	0.002	2.000

TABLE IVd

CASE NUMBER 202
TETRAETHYLSILANE 16/10/69

TRANSITIONS, ORDERED BY FREQUENCY

LINE NO.	OBS.FREQ.	CALC.FREQ.	DIFF.	INTENSITY
15		540.418		0.000
16		574.479		0.000
22		578.895		0.001
6		586.739		0.001
12		595.416		0.004
25	620.260	620.265	-0.005	1.846
33	622.000	621.908	0.092	1.366
23	622.330	622.259	0.071	2.766
17	623.450	623.479	-0.029	2.231
20	627.870	627.896	-0.026	2.477
30	629.140	629.061	0.079	1.807
13	629.530	629.477	0.053	3.678
7	629.930	629.950	-0.020	2.863
34	630.530	630.528	0.002	3.000
35	630.530	630.528	0.002	4.000
36	630.530	630.528	0.002	3.000
37	630.530	630.528	0.002	2.000
1	636.530	636.530	-0.000	3.905
3	637.310	637.334	-0.024	5.549
26	637.750	637.681	0.069	2.828
9	638.610	638.627	-0.017	4.673
18	661.950	661.956	-0.006	3.675
24	663.600	663.629	-0.029	3.154
28	669.440	669.403	0.037	4.828
32	669.990	669.938	0.052	4.634
21	671.270	671.260	0.010	2.078
10	672.690	672.688	0.002	1.876
31	677.070	677.091	-0.021	3.365
27	678.010	678.023	-0.013	3.172
14		678.478		1.536
4	680.540	680.545	-0.005	1.355
8	684.960	684.949	0.011	1.231
2	687.130	687.125	0.005	1.095
19		705.320		0.002
29		717.433		0.001
11		721.689		0.001
5		735.544		0.000

END OF CASE 202

JOB FINISHED AT   15/58/54

rise to the binomial intensities. (Thus the 25 peaks of our $[A_2B_3]$ system collapse to the $3+4=7$ distinct peaks in the $[A_2X_3]$ case.)

It is surprising how few systems of this kind appear to have received detailed computer-iterated analysis. This is probably due not so much to the infrequent occurrence of groups of magnetically equivalent nuclei but to their possessing relative chemical shifts which are large compared with the appropriate coupling constants. Nevertheless it may not be out of place to suggest the type of structure where this phenomenon may (or may not) be met. CH_2 and CF_2 groups present obvious examples of possible A_2 groups; but as soon as there is more than one of them, care must be exercised. Even where the structure is not of the type which will result in non-equivalence, nevertheless strictly the pair of nuclei are almost always not magnetically but *chemically* equivalent (see below). Thus the many compounds XCH_2CH_2Y are classical examples of $[AB]_2$ rather than $[A_2B_2]$ systems and perfluorobutane, $CF_3CF_2CF_2CF_3$, which one might naïvely consider as $[A_3B_2]_2$, has actually been analysed on an $[A_3[B]_2$ basis.[26] However, in cases of this kind—in cyclic as well as acyclic structures—the magnitudes of the couplings (whether involving protons or fluorines) are often such as to obey the series of inequalities which are consistent with the appearance of deceptively simple spectra;[4i] *i.e.* the two nuclei appear to be magnetically equivalent although they are not. Strictly A_2 groups do arise in rigid structures, like the apical protons in bicyclo[1.1.1]pentane, an $[A_2B_6]$ system, or the fluorines in a linear F–M–F fragment (additional substituents on M being likely). CH_3 and CF_3 provide obvious, and strict, A_3 groups, and require no comment. A_4 groups are very rare in organic chemistry: if an $XCH_2CH_2CH_2X$ system can be analysed as $[A_4B_2]$, this is strictly an approximation, as discussed above. But the four equatorial fluorines in a *trans*-disubstituted octahedral environment, *trans* $X.MF_4.Y$, do give rise to an A_4 situation. Cyclopentadienyls (in ferrocene-type compounds) furnish possible A_5 groups. Pairs of methyl groups (particularly in iso-propyl substituents) can lead to A_6 groups: propane, $(CH_3)_2CH_2$, has been analysed as an $[A_6B_2]$ system[18,23c] and isobutane, $(CH_3)_3CH$, was solved as an $[A_9B]$ system.[18] This brief list suggests that there is indeed some scope for this method of analysis.

V. CHEMICAL EQUIVALENCE AND X FACTORIZATION

Chemical equivalence[4a,4d]† appears to be more common than magnetic equivalence in well-resolved spectra susceptible to analysis. Several examples have been mentioned incidentally in previous pages. The notation to be used is that of refs. 10 and 4a, where square brackets with suffices represent symmetry operations.

† Bishop's term is "chemical-shift equivalence".

Just as the full use of magnetic equivalence allowed the problem to be broken down into smaller parts, with advantages for storage and execution time, so also with chemical equivalence. If there is one symmetry element only, we have two submatrices, one symmetric and one anti-symmetric. Higher symmetry similarly implies more submatrices. In the simplest case, $[AB]_2$, the size (n) of the largest set of secular equations to be solved simultaneously is 4, compared with 6 for the general four-spin ABCD case.

A second simplification is particularly helpful here, though it is not irrelevant to the cases previously considered. This is the use of the X approximation.[4g] If there is no equivalence, or only *magnetic* equivalence, and if *all* chemical shifts are large compared with coupling constants, then first-order rules apply, and a computer is unnecessary. But if the same conditions hold for a system with *chemical* equivalence, first-order rules do not apply. The simplest system, $[AX]_2$, does have solutions expressible in closed form; but the $[AMX]_2$ system has $n=4$, although many transition frequencies can be given in terms of explicit formulae.[27] So we see that even in this extreme case, higher order secular equations will arise. More usual, however, will be systems where *some* chemical shifts are large compared with the related coupling constants, the simplest possible case being ABX. Some advantages accrue if one merely neglects certain terms: this is done in both LAOCOON and in LAME. But the chief gain achieved in this way is the rather technical one of reducing round-off errors in the calculations; storage requirements are unaffected, and computing time is only marginally improved. A more thoroughgoing use of the X approximation, however, can actually, yet again, break down the problem into smaller parts, with all the advantages already enumerated. For now, wave functions with different values of m_X will no longer combine with each other: the simplest case is illustrated by the dotted lines of Fig. 4 in ref. 4c. This approach we call X factorization. In approximate hand calculations, it is perfectly permissible to apply, say, the ABX formulae to a three-proton system, where one chemical shift is well removed from the other two. In computer work, however, it is generally better to reserve the X approximation to cases where the nuclei are of different isotopic species (^1H and ^{19}F most commonly); very well separated fluorine multiplets might be a legitimate exception, but for a *caveat* on this score see p. 314–5.

A computer programme was written in 1969 to incorporate both these features into the BBC framework.[8b] The name chosen—LACX—was an acronym for LAocoon with Chemical equivalence and X factorization. As this programme incorporates only one element of symmetry, the whole problem is firstly divided (if chemical equivalence is present) into two submatrices, the symmetrical and the anti-symmetrical. Secondly, the F_z values are used, as before, to define subsubmatrices. Thirdly, where the X approximation is applicable, these are further subdivided, according to the several values of m_X, into what are perhaps not very euphoniously called subsubsubmatrices. The effect of this triple division (or factorization) is illustrated in Table Vb, where now subsubsubmatrices are separated by blank lines. The problem is $[XA]_2B$. The symmetric submatrix (with 20 energy levels altogether) is divided into 6 subsubmatrices, each of which is divided into 1, 2 or 3 subsubsubmatrices. The smaller anti-symmetric submatrix (of 12 levels) is also subdivided. Clearly $n = 3$ (there are actually four subsubsubmatrices of this size); we recall that for a general five-spin ABCDE, $n = 10$; for a $[CA]_2B$ case, with chemical equivalence but no X factorization, $n = 6$; and for XYABC, with X factorization but no chemical equivalence, $n = 6$ also. It turns out then that—provided we use *both* these features where applicable—the savings in storage space and execution time can be just as dramatic as those found in connection with magnetic equivalence.† In the particular five-spin case of Table V, the time for an iterative run was *halved* by using LACX in preference to LAME.

The example chosen to illustrate the two novel characteristics of the programme is 2,6 difluoropyridine[28]‡ (for notation, see Fig. 3). The ^{19}F spectrum was recorded, but was uninformatively broad, because of the ^{14}N quadrupole.

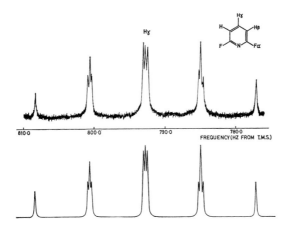

FIG. 3. 100 MHz. ^1H spectrum of 2,6 difluoropyridine,[28] downfield multiplet. *Upper*—spectrum; *lower*—simulation.

The ^1H spectrum at medium resolution[28b] shows for Hγ a binomial quintet, and for Hβ a doublet: the spectrum is thus dominated by the *ortho* Hβ–Hγ coupling and the *meta* F–Hγ coupling, whose magnitudes are clearly very similar. ^1H spectra taken on a much expanded scale are shown in Figs. 3 and 4, and exhibit

† For further examples, see Appendix.

‡ The author is grateful to Dr. Thomas and Dr. Griffin for permission to quote their results and reproduce their spectra.

considerable fine structure. Furthermore, when the strength of the radiation field is increased markedly, a series of weak outer peaks can be discerned in the Hβ absorption region (Fig. 4, wings). It is, incidentally, only through observing these weak peaks that information concerning the fluorine–fluorine coupling can be deduced from the *proton* spectrum. When use was made of the technique of sub-spectral analysis,[4f] it was possible to deduce approximate values of all the parameters (eight, apart from the fluorine chemical shift).

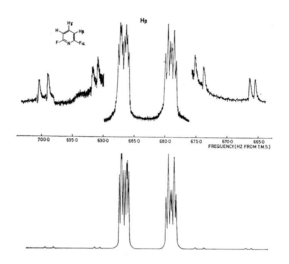

Fig. 4. 100 MHz. ^{1}H spectrum of 2,6 difluoropyridine,[28] upfield multiplet. *Upper*—spectrum (outer portions taken with high r.f. power); *lower*—simulation.

The form of data required for input to LACX is—naturally enough—closely related to that already discussed for LAME and illustrated in Table I. The computer requires to know the type of system, [XA]$_2$B in this case; and the different coupling constants, including for example J_{AA} and J_{XX}, have to be included in a consistent manner. Non-iterative runs gave good overall agreement. Interesting ambiguities were resolved both by carefully comparing the graph-plotter simulations derived from several non-iterative calculations with the experimental high resolution spectra, and also by double resonance.[28c] Once these questions were settled, refinement proceeded normally, and the final output is given in Table V. For the protons, line positions (and chemical shifts) are given with respect to an arbitrary zero, the positive direction being downfield. The shift assigned to the fluorines is quite arbitrary (the correct value is about 6×10^6 Hz !); it will not affect the calculated proton spectrum, and of course is not refined in this case. Convergence was rapid, and excellent standard deviations were obtained. The unusually large negative correlation coefficient (-0.84) between

TABLE Va

PROBLEM STARTED AT   15/56/41

COMPUTER PROGRAMME LAOCOON WITH CHEMICAL EQUIVALENCE AND X FACTORISATION

CASE NUMBER 112
2,6 DIFLUOROPYRIDINE, 100 MHZ, GRIFFIN DATA.   FINAL ASSIGNMENT.

DESCRIPTION OF SPIN SYSTEM

NUMBERING OF SETS OF NUCLEI   1   2   3

NUMBER OF SPINS IN EACH SET   2   2   1

ISOTOPIC NUMBER   1   0   0

FREQUENCY RANGE   0.000   1000.000 MINIMUM INTENSITY 0.01000

ITERATION NO.   0 STARTED AT   15/56/44

PARAMETERS FOR ITERATION NUMBER   0

ISOTOPIC SPECIES	NUCLEUS	CHEMICAL SHIFT
1 F	1	900.0000
0 Hβ	2	100.1000
0 H'γ	3	208.9200

	NUCLEI	COUPLING CONSTANT
F F	1 1	12.3500
Hβ Hβ	2 2	0.5400
ortho F H'β	1 2	-2.6500
para F Hβ	2 1	1.2960
F H'γ	1 3	8.0000
Hβ H γ	2 3	7.9700

RMS (WEIGHTED) DEVIATION OF TRANSITION FREQUENCIES   0.0738925

ITERATION NO.   1 STARTED AT   15/56/50

PARAMETERS FOR ITERATION NUMBER   1

ISOTOPIC SPECIES	NUCLEUS	CHEMICAL SHIFT
1	1	900.0000
0	2	100.1033
0	3	208.9265

NUCLEI		COUPLING CONSTANT
1	1	12.2313
2	2	0.5508
1	2	-2.4762
2	1	1.1908
1	3	7.9742
2	3	7.9418

RMS (WEIGHTED) DEVIATION OF TRANSITION FREQUENCIES   0.0455172

ITERATION NO.   2 STARTED AT   15/56/57

TABLE Va *(continued)*

FINAL PARAMETERS
(ITERATION NUMBER 2)

ISOTOPIC SPECIES	NUCLEUS	CHEMICAL SHIFT
1	1	900.0000
0	2	100.1033
0	3	208.9265

NUCLEI		COUPLING CONSTANT
1	1	12.2313
2	2	0.5507
1	2	-2.4726
2	1	1.1873
1	3	7.9742
2	3	7.9418

RMS (WEIGHTED) DEVIATION OF TRANSITION FREQUENCIES   0.0455136
ITERATION HAS CONVERGED

STANDARD DEVIATION OF PARAMETERS

PARAMETER SET NO.	NUCLEUS	CHEMICAL SHIFT	STANDARD DEVIATION
1	2	100.103	0.013
2	3	208.927	0.013

PARAMETER SET NO.	NUCLEI		COUPLING CONSTANT	STANDARD DEVIATION
3	1	1	12.231	0.039
4	2	2	0.551	0.033
5	1	2	-2.473	0.065
6	2	1	1.187	0.065
7	1	3	7.974	0.018
8	2	3	7.942	0.015

CORRELATION MATRIX OF PARAMETERS

	1	2	3	4	5	6	7	8
1	1.0000							
2	-0.0075	1.0000						
3	0.3281	0.0077	1.0000					
4	0.0050	-0.0103	-0.2887	1.0000				
5	-0.0147	0.0001	0.4093	0.0009	1.0000			
6	0.0145	0.0003	-0.4092	-0.0010	-0.8416	1.0000		
7	0.0006	-0.0010	-0.0003	0.0006	-0.0011	-0.0012	1.0000	
8	0.0417	-0.0829	-0.1004	0.1216	0.0044	-0.0057	0.0047	1.0000

EIGENVECTORS OF THE ERROR MATRIX, IN THE PARAMETER SPACE SPANNED BY THE ERRORS OF THE PARAMETERS, BEING REFINED TOGETHER WITH THEIR STANDARD DEVIATIONS, I.E. THE PRINCIPAL SEMI-AXES OF THE ERROR HYPERELLIPSOID

1	2	3	4	5	6	7	8
EIGENVECTOR NO. 1							
0.9625	-0.0387	-0.1785	-0.0611	0.0257	-0.0258	0.0003	-0.1877
STANDARD DEVIATION			0.01164				
EIGENVECTOR NO. 2							
0.0921	0.9525	-0.0083	-0.0178	0.0012	-0.0010	-0.0009	0.2898
STANDARD DEVIATION			0.01284				
EIGENVECTOR NO. 3							
0.0937	0.0049	0.7494	-0.6290	-0.1224	0.1229	-0.0004	-0.0622
STANDARD DEVIATION			0.03883				
EIGENVECTOR NO. 4							
0.1687	-0.0025	0.5996	0.7720	-0.0893	0.0873	0.0004	0.0197
STANDARD DEVIATION			0.02795				
EIGENVECTOR NO. 5							
-0.0001	0.0005	0.0005	0.0014	0.7070	0.7072	-0.0058	-0.0019
STANDARD DEVIATION			0.02595				
EIGENVECTOR NO. 6							
-0.0024	-0.0001	-0.2166	0.0108	-0.6903	0.6903	-0.0000	0.0008
STANDARD DEVIATION			0.09029				
EIGENVECTOR NO. 7							
0.0015	-0.0023	0.0001	-0.0012	0.0041	0.0041	0.9999	0.0102
STANDARD DEVIATION			0.01837				
EIGENVECTOR NO. 8							
0.1671	-0.3022	0.0041	-0.0648	0.0005	0.0023	-0.0106	0.9362
STANDARD DEVIATION			0.01479				

TABLE Va (*continued*)

parameter set no. 5 [J ortho (F−H$_\beta$)≡J_{12}] and set no. 6 [J para (F–H$_\beta$)≡J_{21}] indicates that the sum of these is much better defined than their difference. Another way of investigating this matter of the inter-relation of errors in parameters is also illustrated in Table Va (and serves to confirm and enlarge this observation); this option is identical to the method used in LAOCOON (ref. 6). Without bothering with the mathematics,[6] we may say that "eigenvector no. 6" which, looking at columns 5 and 6 is approximately the linear combination (−0·69J_{12}+0·69J_{21}) has the *comparatively* large standard deviation of 0·09 Hz; whereas all other linear combinations specified—including the sum of these parameters—have standard deviations in the range 0·012 to 0·039 Hz. In Table Vc, transition nos. 1–78 are seen to derive from the symmetric submatrix, the remainder from the anti-symmetric: the *largest* difference between calculated and observed line positions is 0·12 Hz.

As this spectrum involves sets of very close lines, a final graph-plotter simulation seemed worth while, and is also illustrated in Figs. 3 and 4. The line-width to be used was 0·2 Hz or even less. The observant reader may note that the five principal portions of the Hγ spectrum in Fig. 3 are not *exactly* vertically above the simulation: this is a measure of the non-linearity of the spectrometer used (the graph-plotter *does* have a linear scale!). In the calculation, of course, no errors arose, because proper side-band interpolation was used. Otherwise the agreement is reasonably satisfactory, and the problem can thus be considered solved. This example may serve as a cautionary tale. The spectroscopist content with a superficial examination may lose much interesting information (no less than four "hidden" coupling constants in this case) which would be revealed by careful scale-expansion and the use of strong irradiation to discern weak absorptions. For the recent resolution of an old and not dissimilar classical problem, that of β-propiolactone, in what turned out after all to be an [AB]$_2$ system, see ref. 29.

We close with a brief mention of some further examples. Many papers appear with computer-iterated analyses of [AB]$_2$ systems (see *e.g.* the work of Günther *et al.* on organic[30a] and organometallic[30b] examples). As all the six parameters may in principle be obtained explicitly, this might at first sight appear surprising: the reason is the same as that given earlier for the *computer*-analysis of an [A$_2$B$_3$] system, namely the improved accuracy of parameters derived from *all* the available information. Ref. 31 (and 34b) will serve as an excellent example of an [AB]$_2$C analysis, by a master of the art; this is in fact the standard example circulated with listings of the programme LAOCOON 3. Refs. 30 and 31 used either LAOCOON 2 or 3: when chemical equivalence is encountered, these programmes incorporate a method of maintaining the appropriate equalities of shifts and couplings during iteration, and LAME does the same. For four- and five- spin systems, storage considerations are not usually important; and the

TABLE Vb

CASE NUMBER 112
2,6 DIFLUOROPYRIDINE, 100 MHZ, GRIFFIN DATA, FINAL ASSIGNMENT.

ENERGY LEVELS

THE X FACTORISATION HAS BEEN USED, AND SUBSUBSUBMATRICES ARE SEPARATED BY BLANK LINES

SUBMATRIX NO. 1

SPIN FUNCTIONS SYMMETRIC W.R.T. SYMMETRY ELEMENT

LEVEL NO.   ENERGY

SUBSUBMATRIX NO. 1

    1   1115.07737

SUBSUBMATRIX NO. 2

    2   889.97565
    3   1011.90505

    4   211.73295

SUBSUBMATRIX NO. 3

    5   794.46789
    6   908.49158

    7   -5.41439
    8   108.18861
    9   94.62592

    10   -691.61146

TABLE Vb (*continued*)

SUBSUBMATRIX NO.   4

11	699.25544
12	-101.30567
13	-114.31186
14	3.88458
15	-900.80750
16	-796.02647

SUBSUBMATRIX NO.   5

17	-197.40014
18	-997.60728
19	-900.71857

SUBSUBMATRIX NO.   6

20	-1094.05573

SUBMATRIX NO.   2

SPIN FUNCTIONS ANTI-SYMMETRIC W.R.T. SYMMETRY ELEMENT

LEVEL NO.   ENERGY

SUBSUBMATRIX NO.   1

21	1011.09513
22	199.50168

SUBSUBMATRIX NO.   2

23	794.19442
24	-17.64565
25	107.39393
26	95.42058

SUBSUBMATRIX NO.   3

27	-101.54607
28	-114.07148
29	-8.34667
30	-796.87903

SUBSUBMATRIX NO.   4

31	-209.63141
32	-997.83141

CALCULATION OF TRANSITIONS STARTED AT   15/57/12

absolute time saved by incorporating chemical equivalence initially, in the manner of LACX, is small, even though the relative saving is still substantial. This ceases to be true for systems of six or more spins. Two recent analyses of eight-spin systems, showing chemical equivalence, may be quoted by way of illustration. The $[ABC]_2DE$ spin system of 2-ethoxybullvalene (at high temperature) has been considered in ref. 32. The $[ABCD]_2$ system of tricarbonyl cyclo-octatetraene osmium, $C_8H_8Os(CO)_3$, (at very low temperature) was examined in ref. 33; this spectrum exhibits four quite well-separated multiplets, but is very far from first order. It is interesting to note that, with the programmes then available to these two groups, a full eight-spin *iterative* analysis was beyond the capacity of their computers, so that they had to combine *partial* iteration with trial-and-error methods using non-iterative eight-spin calculations. Many of the computers commonly available can handle ABCDEFG problems using LAO-COON3 or LAME, but iterative calculations on eight-spin systems† are beyond their capacity. Such problems *can* be dealt with using LACX, provided some chemical equivalence is present.‡ Considerations of this sort are irrelevant for those fortunate enough to have access to the larger modern machines; nevertheless the saving in time is still relevant.

VI. CONCLUSION

Fortunately, most NMR groups nowadays have access to a computer and programmes of great generality are readily available.[7,8] The actual preparation of data is straightforward, as has been shown; and the form of output is designed to be readily intelligible. In many *quasi*-first-order cases, assignment is simple. There is, therefore, every encouragement to the non-specialist to use computer-iterated analysis. Skill and experience may well be needed for the achievement of a correct assignment in some systems, but there is a growing number of NMR spectroscopists trained in such matters and available to render advice. An increasing number of papers contain detailed analyses (not necessarily of exceedingly complex systems); the present author sincerely hopes that this increase will continue at an accelerating pace. All chemists will thus benefit from the availability of more accurate and reliable chemical shift and coupling constant data.

† Excluding (in the case of LAME) *magnetic* equivalence.
‡ For more details, see the Appendix.

TABLE Vc

CASE NUMBER 112
2,6 DIFLUOROPYRIDINE, 100 MHZ, GRIFFIN DATA.   FINAL ASSIGNMENT.
TRANSITIONS, ORDERED BY LINE NUMBER

LINE NO.	ENERGY LEVELS UPPER	LOWER	OBS.FREQ.	CALC.FREQ.	DIFF.	INTENSITY
1	1	2	225.000	225.102	-0.102	0.872
2	1	3	103.220	103.172	0.048	2.128
3	1	4		903.344		2.000
4	2	5	95.530	95.508	0.022	1.872
6	2	7		895.390		2.000
10	3	5	217.440	217.437	-0.003	0.986
11	3	6	103.400	103.413	-0.013	2.142
13	3	8		903.716		1.963
14	3	9		917.279		0.037
18	4	7	217.130	217.147	-0.017	0.862
19	4	8	103.580	103.544	0.036	2.098
20	4	9		117.107		0.040
21	4	10		903.344		2.000
22	5	11	95.190	95.212	-0.022	1.858
23	5	12		895.774		1.960
24	5	13		908.780		0.040
28	6	11	209.200	209.236	-0.036	1.142
31	6	14		904.607		2.000
35	7	12	95.850	95.891	-0.041	1.825
36	7	13		108.897		0.037
38	7	15		895.393		2.000
41	8	12	209.550	209.494	0.056	0.984
43	8	14	104.310	104.304	0.006	2.114
45	8	16		904.215		1.963
48	9	13	209.000	208.938	0.062	1.000
49	9	14	90.760	90.741	0.019	0.040
51	9	16		890.652		0.037
56	10	15	209.200	209.196	0.004	0.851
57	10	16	104.430	104.415	0.015	2.149
58	11	17		896.656		2.000

61	12	17	96.060	96.094	-0.034	1.809
62	12	18		896.302		1.960
64	13	17	83.070	83.088	-0.018	0.038
65	13	18		883.295		0.040
67	14	17	201.350	201.285	0.065	1.154
69	14	19		904.603		2.000
71	15	18	96.820	96.800	0.020	1.851
74	16	19	201.480	201.581	-0.101	0.981
75	16	20	104.710	104.692	0.018	2.167
76	17	20		896.656		2.000
77	18	20	96.430	96.448	0.018	1.833
78	19	23	193.220	193.337	-0.117	1.167
79	21	25	216.870	216.901	-0.031	1.000
81	21	24		903.701		1.952
82	21	24		915.675		0.048
84	22	25	217.130	217.147	-0.017	0.862
85	22	26		92.108		0.051
86	23	27	104.070	104.081	-0.011	2.087
87	23	28		895.740		1.956
88	24	27		908.266		0.041
91	25	28	83.900	83.900	-0.000	1.821
92	25	27	96.430	96.426	0.004	0.999
95	25	29	209.000	208.940	0.060	0.052
97	26	30		115.741		0.952
98	26	28		904.273		0.785
101	27	29	209.550	209.492	0.058	1.102
102	28	30	103.770	103.767	0.003	2.048
103	28	31		892.300		0.040
104	29	32		108.085		1.956
105	30	31		896.285		1.807
106		32	95.530	95.560	-0.030	0.044
107		31		883.760		1.154
110		32	201.350	201.285	0.065	1.154
			201.000	200.952	0.048	1.000

TABLE Vd

CASE NUMBER 112
2,6 DIFLUOROPYRIDINE, 100 MHZ, GRIFFIN DATA.   FINAL ASSIGNMENT.

TRANSITIONS, ORDERED BY FREQUENCY

LINE NO.	OBS.FREQ.	CALC.FREQ.	DIFF.	INTENSITY
64	83.070	83.088	-0.018	0.038
91	83.900	83.900	-0.000	0.041
49	90.760	90.741	0.019	0.040
85		92.108		0.051
22	95.190	95.212	-0.022	1.858
4	95.530	95.508	0.022	1.872
105	95.530	95.560	-0.030	1.807
35	95.850	95.891	-0.041	1.825
61	96.060	96.094	-0.034	1.809
92	96.430	96.426	0.004	1.821
77	96.430	96.448	-0.018	1.833
71	96.820	96.800	0.020	1.851
2	103.220	103.172	0.048	2.128
11	103.400	103.413	-0.013	2.142
19	103.580	103.544	0.036	2.098
101	103.770	103.767	0.003	2.102
86	104.070	104.081	-0.011	2.087
43	104.310	104.304	0.006	2.114
57	104.430	104.415	0.015	2.149
75	104.710	104.692	0.018	2.167
103		108.085		0.040
36		108.897		0.037
97		115.741		0.052
20		117.107		0.040
78	193.220	193.337	-0.117	1.167
110	201.000	200.952	0.048	1.000
67	201.350	201.285	0.065	1.154
107	201.350	201.285	0.065	1.154
74	201.480	201.581	-0.101	0.981
48	209.000	208.938	0.062	1.000
95	209.000	208.940	0.060	0.999
56	209.200	209.196	0.004	0.851
28	209.200	209.236	-0.036	1.142
100	209.550	209.492	0.058	0.985
41	209.550	209.494	0.056	0.984
79	216.870	216.901	-0.031	1.000
84	217.130	217.147	-0.017	0.862
18	217.130	217.147	-0.017	0.862
10	217.440	217.437	0.003	0.986
1	225.000	225.102	-0.102	0.872
65		883.295		0.040
106		883.760		0.044
51		890.652		0.037
102		892.300		0.048
6		895.390		2.000
38		895.393		2.000
87		895.740		1.956
23		895.774		1.960
104		896.285		1.956
62		896.302		1.960
58		896.656		2.000
76		896.656		2.000
3		903.344		2.000
21		903.344		2.000
81		903.701		1.952
13		903.716		1.963
45		904.215		1.963
98		904.273		1.952
69		904.603		2.000
31		904.607		2.000
88		908.266		0.044
24		908.780		0.040
82		915.675		0.048
14		917.279		0.037

END OF CASE 112

JOB FINISHED AT   15/57/21

APPENDIX: COMPUTER REQUIREMENTS

Storage

The following Table—which should be discussed with the reader's Computer Centre advisers—will give the potential user a *rough* idea of the maximum size of spin system on which iterative calculations may be performed on his own installation. Smaller or larger maxima are of course perfectly feasible. The quantities listed are the total amount of central processor store required for programme and variable storage, exclusive of compilers, executive and monitors; they could be substantially reduced by using the techniques of linking or overlaying.

	(a) Thousands of 48-bit words[a]	(b) Kilobytes[b]
LAME, small; ABCDEF, A_3B_3C	10	50
LAME, medium; ABCDEFG, A_4B_4CD	16	75
LAME, large; ABCDEFGH, A_3B_3CDE	30	125
LACX, small; $[AB]_2CD$	10	50
LACX, medium; $[AB]_2CDE$	14	75
LACX, large; $[AB]_2CDEF$, but *not* ABCDEFGH	22	110

[a] Multiply by two to obtain the number of "K" (i.e. thousands of 24-bit *cores*) in the I.C.L. 1900 series.
[b] Assuming a 32-bit (4 byte) word-length in single precision.

Time

No attempt will be made to quote absolute times: the same job could take a fraction of a second on a very fast computer, or many minutes on the slower machines still extant. Even on one particular installation, technical changes such as replacing magnetic tape by disc as backing store, or running the programme overlaid or not, may have substantial effects.

To obtain some estimate of the *relative* time requirements, we proceed as follows.† A slightly more accurate estimate (rather than just using n^3) can be obtained from $S \equiv \sum_i s_i^3$. Here s_i is the number of secular equations in the i'th subdivision or block [a (constant F_z) submatrix for NMREN/NMRIT or LAOCOON; a subsubmatrix for programmes using magnetic equivalence; or a subsubsubmatrix for LACX].

† For a different estimate, see ref. 34a.

E.g. for $[A_2B_3]$ from Table IVb,

$$S = [1^3 + 2^3 + 3^3 + 3^3 + 2^3 + 1^3] + [1^3 + 2^3 + 2^3 + 1^3] + [1^3 + 1^3 + 1^3 + 1^3]$$
$$+ [1^3 + 1^3] = 96.$$

And for $[XA]_2B$, from Table Vb,

$$S = \{[1^3] + [2^3 + 1^3] + [2^3 + 3^3 + 1^3] + [1^3 + 3^3 + 2^3] + [1^3 + 2^3] + [1^3]\}$$
$$+ \{[1^3 + 1^3] + [1^3 + 3^3] + [3^3 + 1^3] + [1^3 + 1^3]\} = 152.$$

For an ABCDE system, we have simply:

$$S = 1^3 + 5^3 + 10^3 + 10^3 + 5^3 + 1^3 = 2252$$

It should be noted that, for the smallest values of S, the relative time will thus be considerably underestimated, because all the other parts of the calculation will have a larger relative importance. In the last column of the following table the S values have been scaled relative to ABCDEF as unity.

These numbers can be used to estimate the relative times for non-iterative calculations; and for iterative runs, the relative time per iteration. (In actual practice, in programmes based on the BBC philosophy, convergence is almost always achieved on iteration number 2, 3 or 4.) The table of course assumes that maximum use is made of magnetic or chemical equivalence and X factorization; for example, if LAOCOON is being used, pyridine has to be considered as ABCDE rather than $[AB]_2C$.

Spin system		n	S	Approximate estimate of relative time
Six spin:	ABCDEF	20	15184	1
	$[A_2B_3C]$	6	678	0·04
	$[AB]_2CD$	12	4276	0·3
	$[AB]_2CX$	6	1264	0·08
Seven spin:	ABCDEFG	35	104960	7
	$[A_2B_3CD]$	11	4872	0·3
	$[AB]_2CDE$	21	29696	2
	$[AB]_2CDX$	12	8552	0·6
Eight spin:	ABCDEFGH	70	739162	50
	$[A_2B_3CDE]$	22	35406	2
	$[AB]_2CDEF$	42	210158	15
	$[AB]_2CDEX$	21	59392	4

REFERENCES

1. E. F. Mooney, *Ann. Rev. NMR Spectroscopy*, 1968, **1**, vii.
2. J. D. Swalen, *Prog. NMR Spectroscopy*, 1966, **1**, 205.
3. J. A. Musso and J. Metzger, *Bull. Soc. chim. France*, 1968, 463.
4. E. O. Bishop, *Ann. Rev. NMR Spectroscopy*, 1968, **1**, 91; (a) 94–100; (b) 92–94; (c) 106–112, 117–118; (d) 115–117; (e) 100–106; (f) 118–123; (g) 112; (h) 113–115; (i) 125–127.
5. J. D. Swalen and C. A. Reilly, *J. Chem. Phys.*, 1962, **37**, 21; and later privately circulated versions.
6. LAOCOON 2: S. Castellano and A. A. Bothner-By, *J. Chem. Phys.*, 1964, **41**, 3863.
7. Decks of cards and/or magnetic tapes are available to members of the Quantum Chemistry Programme Exchange (Q.C.P.E.), Department of Chemistry, Indiana University, Bloomington, Indiana 47401, U.S.A.; (a) programmes NMRIT and NMREN, Nos. 33–35 or 126–127; (b) programme LAOCOON 3, No. 111.
8. C. W. Haigh, to be published, details and listings on application to the author; (a) LAME; (b) LACX.
9. E. Lustig, E. A. Hansen and E. P. Ragelis, *Org. Magn. Resonance*, 1969, **1**, 295.
10. C. W. Haigh, *J. Chem. Soc. (A)*, 1970, 1682.
11. R. H. Bible, "Interpretation of N.M.R. Spectra, an Empirical Approach", pp. 86–96, Plenum Press, New York, 1965.
12. (a) H. J. Bernstein, W. G. Schneider and J. A. Pople, *Proc. Roy. Soc.*, 1956, **236A**, 515.
    (b) N. Jonathan, S. Gordon and B. P. Dailey, *J. Chem. Phys.*, 1962, **36**, 2443.
    (c) T. J. Batterham, L. Tsai and H. Ziffer, *Austral. J. Chem.*, 1964, **17**, 163.
    (d) R. C. Fahey and G. C. Graham, *J. Phys. Chem.*, 1965, **69**, 4417.
    (e) K. D. Bartle and J. A. S. Smith, *Spectrochim. Acta*, 1967, **23A**, 1689.
    (f) C. W. Haigh and R. B. Mallion, *Mol. Phys.*, 1970, **18**, 737.
13. P. J. Black and M. L. Heffernan, *Austral. J. Chem.*, 1963, **16**, 1051.
14. J. Lee and L. H. Sutcliffe, *Trans. Faraday Soc.*, 1958, **54**, 308.
15. J. S. Martin, G. W. Stockton and A. R. Quirt, University of Alberta, Edmonton, private communication, 1969.
16. C. W. Haigh and J. M. Williams, *J. Mol. Spectroscopy*, 1969, **32**, 398.
17. C. W. Haigh and R. B. Mallion, *J. Mol. Spectroscopy*, 1969, **29**, 478.
18. R. C. Ferguson and D. W. Marquardt, *J. Chem. Phys.*, 1964, **41**, 2087.
19. R. C. Ferguson, private communication, 1969.
20. J. A. Musso and A. Isaïa, *J. Chim. phys.*, 1969, **66**, 1676.
21. R. B. Johannensen (National Bureau of Standards, Washington, D.C.) and J. A. Ferretti (National Institute of Health, Bethesda, Md.), private communication; *J. Magn. Resonance.* 1970, **3**, 84.
22. R. K. Harris and C. M. Woodman, *Mol. Phys.*, 1966, **10**, 437.
23. (a) B. R. McGarvey and G. Slomp, *J. Chem. Phys.*, 1959, **30**, 1586.
    (b) T. Ostdick and P. A. McCusker, *Inorg. Chem.*, 1967, **6**, 98.
    (c) P. L. Corio and R. C. Hirst, *J. Chem. Educ.*, 1969, **46**, 345.
24. C. W. Haigh and M. Kinns, unpublished work.
25. (a) P. L. Corio, *Chem. Rev.*, 1960, **60**, 363.
    (b) *Idem*, "Structure of High-resolution NMR Spectra", especially p. 523, Academic Press, London, 1966.

(c) J. W. Emsley, J. Feeney and L. H. Sutcliffe, "High Resolution Nuclear Magnetic Resonance Spectroscopy", especially p. 649, Vol. 1. Pergamon Press, Oxford, 1965.

26. R. K. Harris and C. M. Woodman, *J. Mol. Spectroscopy*, 1968, **26**, 432.

27. C. Barbier, H. Faucher, D. Gagnaire and A. Rousseau, *J. Chim. phys.*, 1966, **63**, 283.

28. (a) W. A. Thomas and G. Griffin, unpublished work.
    (b) W. A. Thomas and G. Griffin, *Org. Magn. Resonance*, 1970, **2**, 503.
    (c) W. A. Thomas, G. Griffin and A. V. Cunliffe, to be published.

29. R. J. Abraham, *J. Chem. Soc. (B)*, 1968, 173. *Cf.* W. A. Anderson, *Phys. Rev.*, 1956, **102**, 51.

30. (a) J. B. Pawliczek and H. Günther, *Tetrahedron*, 1970, **26**, 1755.
    (b) H. Günther, R. Wenzl and H. Klose, *Chem. Comm.*, 1970, 605.

31. S. Castellano, C. Sun and R. Kostelnik, *J. Chem. Phys.*, 1967, **46**, 327.

32. H. Günther, H. Klose and D. Wendisch, *Tetrahedron*, 1969, **25**, 1531.

33. M. Cooke, R. J. Goodfellow, M. Green, J. P. Maher and J. R. Yandle, *Chem. Comm.*, 1970, 565.

34. For full descriptions, listing and worked examples, see in "Computer Programs for Chemistry" (D. F. De Tar, Ed.), Vol. I. Benjamin, New York, 1968; (a) J. D. Swalen, "NMRIT and NMREN", p. 54; (b) A. A. Bothner-By and S. Castellano, "LAOCOON 3", p. 10.

The Nuclear Magnetic Resonance Spectra of Polymers

M. E. A. CUDBY AND H. A. WILLIS

Imperial Chemical Industries Ltd., Plastics Division,
Welwyn Garden City, Hertfordshire, England

I. INTRODUCTION

THE DEVELOPMENT of the NMR technique has provided the polymer chemist with an outstanding method of structural analysis. The information obtainable from chemical shift, coupling constant and band area parameters is of equal importance to the investigator of polymer structure as to those concerned with smaller organic molecules.

The chemical shift parameter has provided data which have led to the identification of configurational sequences in those homopolymers which can exist in stereoisomeric forms. In copolymers this parameter has been used to obtain information on the arrangement of structural units along the polymer chains. It has proved invaluable also in both homopolymers and copolymers where it has permitted the identification of small irregularities in the polymer molecule such as branch points and end groups.

The magnitude of coupling constants (J values) is often difficult to establish from the polymer spectrum, especially in the case of aliphatic vinyl polymers, where the coupling between α- and β-protons results in second-order spectra of high complexity. A number of authors have endeavoured, however, to overcome such difficulties by either preferential deuteration of the monomer before polymerization and/or spin decoupling the relevant resonances in turn. In this way, it has been possible to obtain evidence of the molecular conformation of a number of polymers.

The third parameter, involving the measurement of the relative areas of the bands, enables the number of nuclei in different environments to be determined. This is of particular importance as it can provide a measurement of the proportions of stereochemical forms in homopolymers and an absolute determination of copolymer composition. A particular advantage of the NMR method is that it may be used directly for compositional analysis and does not require independent calibration samples. The use of NMR for routine control of polymer composition in plant laboratories is at present probably beyond the financial capabilities of most industrial organizations. On the other hand, its use as a means of calibrating other cheaper forms of analysis such as infrared methods is now commonplace.

Nuclear magnetic resonance during 1967–69, largely the extent of this review, has seen the introduction of the 220 MHz spectrometer with its promise of increased resolution and sensitivity. The use of this instrument has led to a simplification of many spectra which previously were complex as a result of the gradual transition from second-order to first-order spin–spin coupling patterns (Fig. 1). The resulting improvement in the quality of polymer spectra has allowed more structural details to be defined over a greater length of polymer chain. Even with this improvement in instrumentation the polymer spectroscopist is still involved with the analysis of broad resonance peaks and is rarely able to obtain the sharp spectra normally observed when dealing with simple organic molecules. Nevertheless, application of the NMR technique continues to provide a considerable amount of data concerning molecular structure and has greatly assisted in bridging the gap in establishing the structure–physical properties relationship in synthetic polymers.

A. Line widths of polymer spectra

It is rarely possible to obtain spectra from polymers which give resonance line widths approaching those of less complex organic molecules, but investigation of the origin of this line broadening has thrown light on ways in which the effect may be minimized. In order that a single, sharp resonance line be ob-

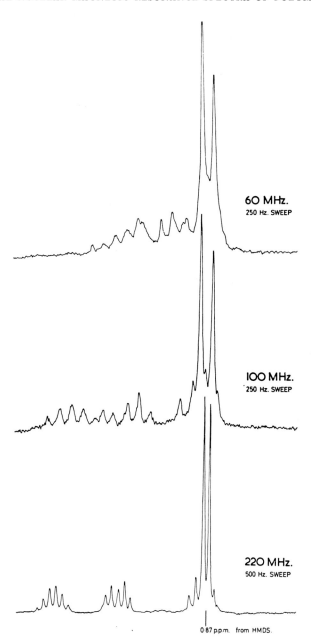

FIG. 1. The simplification of proton spectra using increasing field strengths, illustrated using isotactic polypropylene.

tained from environmentally equivalent nuclei, along a polymer chain, each must experience a similar magnetic field. This can only be achieved if there is complete freedom of rotation, which in turn depends upon rapid segmental motion of the polymer chain. Provided that all inter- and intra- molecular bonding is removed, for example with the aid of a suitable solvent, raising the temperature of the solution will result in a progressive narrowing of the line width to a constant value. It would appear that when this condition is reached maximum segmental motion has been achieved. However, in the majority of cases the line width is still much greater than that observed in the spectra of more simple molecules. Recently, an attempt has been made to establish the cause of this residual line broadening. Segré[1] has concentrated on the spectrum of isotactic polypropylene, thus reducing to a minimum the artificial broadening of lines due to the superimposition of the different spectra arising from dissimilar stereochemical sequences. The result of this work, which involved successive deuteration of the polymer molecule and measuring deuterium decoupled proton spectra, indicated that for isotactic polypropylene it is the coupling through several bonds which is the major factor contributing to the broadening of the resonance lines. It is to be hoped that further studies of this phenomenon will increase understanding of line broadening in polymer spectra.

B. Solvents for polymers

The majority of polymers are less soluble than most simple organic molecules, and therefore the spectroscopist is immediately faced with the problem of a poor signal-to-noise ratio. As previously mentioned, the advent of high field strength instruments should have improved the sensitivity of the NMR method. Unfortunately, this is true only to a limited extent, and it has also been found necessary to impose an upper limit of 160°C on the operating temperature of the variable temperature probe. Thus, the improvement in line width which may be achieved in some polymer spectra by raising the temperature is restricted. In general, the NMR spectra of polymers are much improved by raising the temperature of the solution, provided it does not result in decomposition of the polymer or overheating of the instrument with a consequent degeneration in the homogeneity of the field. Thus a solvent is required which has a high boiling point and furthermore does not contain resonance peaks in the same region of the spectrum as those due to the polymer. These requirements are sometimes difficult to satisfy, and two or more solvents may need to be used to enable the full spectrum of the polymer to be observed. Whilst this technique may be necessary it must be remembered that the frequencies of the observed resonances may well change with change of solvent. The use of an internal standard will compensate for such frequency shifts if they are due to a change in the diamagnetic susceptibility of the solution. Unfortunately, the most commonly used standard, tetramethylsilane, is extremely volatile and thus unsatisfactory for high-temperature spectroscopy. The use of hexamethyl-disiloxane is often preferred, the reference signal of this compound occurring at δ -0.06 p.p.m. with respect to T.M.S. Recently another reference standard has been offered 1,1,3,5-hexakis(trideuteromethyl)-1,3,5-trisilacyclosilane δ 0.30 p.p.m. with respect to T.M.S., and this material having a boiling point in excess of 200°C may well find favour with polymer spectroscopists.

Other effects are noticed with changes in solvent which are not due to changes in diamagnetic susceptibility. Polymers which contain polar groups will often induce a secondary electric field known as the "reaction field" in a polar solvent. This reaction field in turn affects the magnetic shielding of the nuclei and may lead to small shifts (~ 0.1 p.p.m.) in frequency. Larger shifts have been observed and were attributed to complex formation between solvent and solute. Aromatic solvents often produce these effects by taking up a pre-ferred orientation relative to the solute molecule. The well-known magnetic anisotropy of the aromatic nucleus gives rise to changes in the magnetic environment of the solute nuclei most closely involved in the complex. Many examples of the use of this technique in polymer structure determination are available.

Liu[2] has used this phenomenon in the study of the effects of chain length on the NMR spectrum of poly(dimethyl siloxanes) and poly(ethylene glycols). In the study of the proton spectrum of ethylene/vinyl acetate copolymers, Wu[3] has shown that benzene and alkyl benzenes selectively associate with the acetate methyl groups; the heats and entropies of formation of the complex were obtained by studying the temperature dependence of the spectra. It was shown that when alkyl substituents were introduced in the benzene nucleus, the strength of the complex reduced with increasing size of alkyl group. Further, introduction of polar substituents on the solvent nucleus, as for example in pyridine and halogenated benzenes, prevents the formation of such complexes. The acetate methyl protons in benzene solution appear as two resonances (Fig. 2) that at high field was assigned to the E–VA interchange unit and that at low field to vinyl acetate monomer sequences. Further solvent effects were observed on the methylene resonance peaks.

C. Deuteration as an aid to structural analysis

In vinyl polymers the interaction between α and β protons often gives rise to second-order spectra of high complexity. Removal of this interaction (coupling) by selective deuteration must lead to a simplification of the spectrum which may allow a complete interpretation of the observed resonances. Al-though this technique has been applied by many authors it has a severe limita-tion in that the monomer must be selectively deuterated before polymerization, and to date it has not been possible to preferentially deuterate the normal

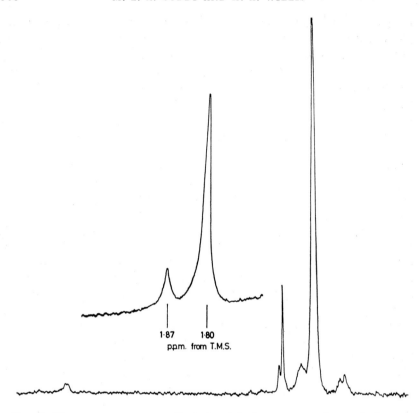

1·87   1·80
p.p.m. from T.M.S.

FIG. 2. The proton spectrum of ethylene/vinyl acetate copolymer in benzene solution.

hydrogen containing polymer. Segré et al.[4] have used this technique to establish the degree of steric purity in polystyrene prepared with a Ziegler-Natta catalyst. The same author[1] has shown the extent of through-bond interaction in polypropylene by massive deuteration and finally by deuterium decoupling. These are novel uses of this technique which has previously been used mainly to determine stereochemical configuration in vinyl polymers such as polypropylene. An extension of this type of application may be seen in a paper by Lombardi et al.,[5] where successive deuteration has provided models for the estimation of the stereoregularity of normal hydrogen-containing polymers.

D. Double resonance

This technique has been successfully used in the elucidation of the structure of organic molecules to simplify the resonance line splitting caused by spin–spin coupling. Since a study of the coupled and decoupled spectrum will often give enough information to determine the juxtaposition of various groups within a molecule it is important that this technique should be applied whenever possible to the study of polymer structure. Many applications of this technique can be found in the literature. Among the quantitative uses of this technique Schaefer[6] has interpreted the spectra of ethylene/vinyl chloride and ethylene/vinyl acetate copolymers in terms of monomer unit distribution in the polymer chains. Spin decoupled spectra are used to obtain estimates of areas of overlapping resonances with the aid of computer methods. Schaefer points out that residual spin–spin coupling can give rise to asymmetric, distorted resonance lines which may result in uncertainties in band area measurement and associated error estimations.

A recently developed use of decoupling is found in ^{13}C spectroscopy. Coupling normally occurs between the ^{13}C nucleus and associated protons, which results in complex spectra composed of many weak absorptions. The effect of complete proton decoupling (white noise decoupling) is to simplify the spectrum to single lines since, owing to the small possibility of the occurrence of adjacent ^{13}C nuclei, there is no coupling. After decoupling, the lines will be more readily observed because the total area is present at one resonance frequency rather than at many frequencies as in the proton coupled spectrum. Schaefer[7] has used this technique successfully in the ^{13}C NMR analysis of polypropylene oxide. This paper indicates the potential of ^{13}C analysis in the study of tactic sequence in homopolymers, and this could well progress to the study of the distribution of monomer units in more complex copolymers.

E. Stereospecific forms in vinyl homopolymers

It is possible to recognize the different stereospecific forms of vinyl homopolymers from a study of the α- and β-groups, i.e.

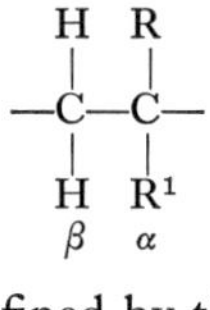

$$
\begin{array}{cc}
H & R \\
| & | \\
-C\!-\!C- \\
| & | \\
H & R^1 \\
\beta & \alpha
\end{array}
$$

The isotactic triad sequence is defined by the formula:

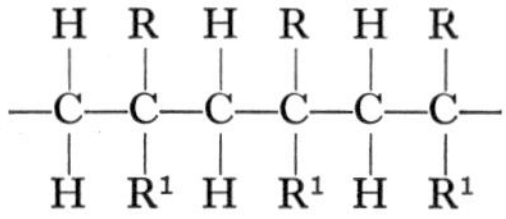

$$
\begin{array}{cccccc}
H & R & H & R & H & R \\
| & | & | & | & | & | \\
-C\!-\!C\!-\!C\!-\!C\!-\!C\!-\!C- \\
| & | & | & | & | & | \\
H & R^1 & H & R^1 & H & R^1
\end{array}
$$

the syndiotactic triad sequence by the formula:

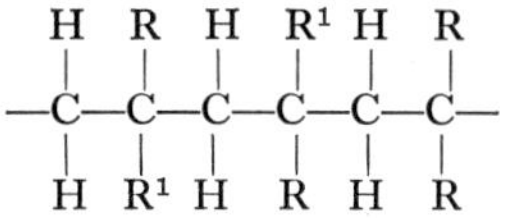

$$
\begin{array}{cccccc}
H & R & H & R^1 & H & R \\
| & | & | & | & | & | \\
-C\!-\!C\!-\!C\!-\!C\!-\!C\!-\!C- \\
| & | & | & | & | & | \\
H & R^1 & H & R & H & R
\end{array}
$$

and the heterotactic triad sequence by the formula:

$$
\begin{array}{cccccc}
\text{H} & \text{R} & \text{H} & \text{R} & \text{H} & \text{R}^1 \\
| & | & | & | & | & | \\
-\text{C}-\text{C}-\text{C}-\text{C}-\text{C}-\text{C}- \\
| & | & | & | & | & | \\
\text{H} & \text{R}^1 & \text{H} & \text{R}^1 & \text{H} & \text{R}
\end{array}
$$

The names of these sequences are usually abbreviated to i, s and h. The environment of the α-group is different in each case, and this will result in a different chemical shift enabling the presence of different tactic sequences to be observed. Unfortunately, without other evidence it is not possible to assign the observed lines to i, s and h structures. In the isotactic triad arrangement the protons of the β group are in different environments. This makes the resonance of these protons recognizable from spin–spin coupling as a quartet. In the syndiotactic triad sequence the β-protons are in an equivalent environment and give rise to a single resonance. Therefore, in a stereochemically pure polymer the appearance of the resonance of the β-protons will, in principle, establish whether the polymer is isotactic or syndiotactic. It may be seen that only two monomeric units are required to define the placement of the β-protons in terms of isotactic or syndiotactic sequences. However, the terms isotactic and syndiotactic diads lead to confusion in the case of an heterotactic polymer and therefore the authors prefer to adopt the terms suggested by Bovey, i.e. that the diad nomenclature be based on the *meso* and *racemic* forms:

$$
\begin{array}{cc}
\begin{array}{c}
\text{R}^1-\text{C}-\text{R} \\
| \\
\text{H}-\text{C}-\text{H} \\
| \\
\text{R}^1-\text{C}-\text{R} \\
\textit{meso (m)}
\end{array}
&
\begin{array}{c}
\text{R}^1-\text{C}-\text{R} \\
| \\
\text{H}-\text{C}-\text{H} \\
| \\
\text{R}-\text{C}-\text{R}^1 \\
\textit{racemic (r)}
\end{array}
\end{array}
$$

while the terms isotactic, syndiotactic and heterotactic be reserved for triad sequences.

The chemical shift of the β-protons in the *racemic* diad is defined by the adjacent R and R^1 groups, and it is logical to assume that the chemical shift is likely to be influenced further by R and R^1 groups on the next adjacent α-groups. Three distinct groups may be defined rrr, mrr, (rrm) and mrm; these are known as tetrad sequences and each might be expected to have a different chemical shift value. There are also tetrad sequences containing central groups, and these will also have different chemical shifts but the complexity arising from spin–spin coupling of the β-protons will make the observation of such groups more difficult. By a similar argument, the observation of further resonances associated with the α-group will indicate the presence of pentad sequences. Extensions of these arguments could in principle define the hexad and higher forms—the β group case and septad sequences—the case of α-groups.

II. VINYL HOMOPOLYMERS

A. Polyvinyl chloride $-(CH_2-CHCl)-_n$

In this case the monomer is substituted in the α-position, but we must expect considerable coupling between the remaining α- and β-protons which will give rise to complex spectra. Two broad resonance areas are observed at $\sim 4\cdot3$ p.p.m. and $\sim 2\cdot2$ p.p.m. due to the α- and β-protons respectively, and each broad area displays the multiplicity of resonance lines as expected from the coupling of the α- and β-protons. The α-proton resonance has been described in terms of triad and pentad sequences by Johnson and Kolbé.[8]

In a decoupled spectrum, it is possible to distinguish three lines arising from the pentad structures based on the isotactic triad, and two pentad lines for the heterotactic triad, whereas the resonance of the syndiotactic triad shows no further splitting. Thus a total of six resonances may be observed. Heatley and Bovey[9] recorded the spectrum at 220 MHz without decoupling and, with the aid of a calculated spectrum based on data of Johnson and Kolbé, have further refined this interpretation by separating the resonance of three syndiotactic pentads. The coupling constants used in this work are found to be in good agreement with those cited previously by Doskocilova.[10]

It is worthwhile describing the changes in interpretation and assignments of the methylene resonances which have occurred over the past years. Johnson[11] initially interpreted the spectrum of the β-methylene group as two overlapping triplets which he assigned to *meso* and *racemic* groups. However, Tincher[12] challenged this interpretation suggesting that the protons in the *meso* group were non-equivalent, thus necessitating that the spectrum be interpreted as the AB part of an ABX_2 spectrum with a superimposed *racemic* triplet resonance. Bovey[13] then examined the spectrum of poly-α-d_1-vinyl chloride and observed single resonances for the *meso* protons rather than a quartet. The interpretation by Tincher was then modified and the *meso* protons were regarded as fortuitously equivalent in polyvinyl chloride. Once more confusion arose after an examination of the model compound 2,4-dichloropentane by Doskocilova[14] where it was shown that the *meso* protons were markedly different in environment. A study of poly-α-*cis*-β-d_2-vinyl chloride by Yoshino[15] revealed the ten different chemical shifts expected from the six β-methylene tetrad resonances. They found that although the β protons in all three *meso* tetrads are non-equivalent only in the *rmr* tetrad were the *meso* protons sufficiently non-equivalent to be observed. This history is given more fully by Bovey *et al.*[16] where the authors also further interpret the 50 MHz spectrum of poly-α-d_1-vinyl chloride based on a slightly modified Yoshino assignment. The calculated *racemic/meso* ratio is thus altered slightly from that derived from interpretations based on the equivalence, or near equivalence, of the β-protons. The stereochemistry of polymers prepared over a wide range of temperatures was determined, and it was shown that more syndiotactic structure is evident when the polymer is prepared at low temperatures and that raising the temperature of polymerization to $100°C$ produces substantially atactic polymer. Similar results of β-proton analysis were obtained by Schneider et al.[17] based on the spectra of pure stereoisomers of 2,4-dichloropentane and 2,4,6-trichloroheptane. In this paper the authors state that $50°C$ is a high enough polymerization temperature to produce atactic polymer while polymer prepared at $-25°C$ gives 60% syndiotactic material.

B. Polypropylene

The NMR spectroscopist has concerned himself with the measurement of tacticity and sequence distribution in polypropylene since the introduction of the technique to polymer chemistry. The three years 1967–69 have produced a further quantity of papers and reviews.[18–30] In 1967, Ferguson[25] published the 220 MHz spectrum of polypropylene showing clearly the separated methine, methylene and methyl resonances in isotactic and syndiotactic polymer. Ferguson also suggested that the noticeable broadening of the multiplets arose from variation in chemical shift arising from tetrad and pentad tactic placements. At lower field strengths the spectrum of polypropylene is much more complex, and in order to assign resonances many spectroscopists have resorted to specific deuteration of the monomer before polymerization in order to reduce the coupling effects and make it possible to recognize tetrad and pentad sequences. Zambelli and Segré[26] have used this technique to partially assign the 100 MHz spectra of atactic poly(propylene cis- and trans-1,2,3,3,3-d_5). Chain conformation has been studied by Zambelli et al.[27] who have shown that, for highly isotactic polypropylene, the polymerization proceeds via the cis opening of the monomer molecule. A further paper by Zambelli, Geongo and Natta[28] shows that the production of syndiotactic polypropylene also arises from the cis opening of the monomer molecule. Conformational analysis was related to the NMR spectrum and vicinal coupling interpreted. A full tetrad assignment has been given by Heatley and Zambelli[29] based on atactic poly(propylene cis- and trans-1,2,3,3,3-d_5) using a 220 MHz spectrometer. All the proton coupling has been removed by deuteration and the remaining proton resonances appear as singlets at the chemical shifts associated with the various tetrads. The 220 MHz spectrum of a highly isotactic sample of polypropylene has been interpreted in detail by Heatley et al.[30] From the study of tetrad resonances it was shown that the interruptions in isotactic sequences occur predominantly by a reversal of the α-carbon configuration to give the following structure:

$$
\begin{array}{cccccc}
\text{CH}_3 & \text{CH}_3 & \text{CH}_3 & \text{H} & \text{H} & \text{H} \\
| & | & | & | & | & | \\
-\text{C}-\text{CH}_2-\text{C}-\text{CH}_2-\text{C}-\text{CH}_2-\text{C}-\text{CH}_2-\text{C}-\text{CH}_2-\text{C}- \\
| & | & | & | & | & | \\
\text{H} & \text{H} & \text{H} & \text{CH}_3 & \text{CH}_3 & \text{CH}_3
\end{array}
$$

The structure:

$$
\begin{array}{cccccc}
\text{CH}_3 & \text{CH}_3 & \text{CH}_3 & \text{H} & \text{CH}_3 & \text{CH}_3 \\
| & | & | & | & | & | \\
-\text{C}-\text{CH}_2-\text{C}-\text{CH}_2-\text{C}-\text{CH}_2-\text{C}-\text{CH}_2-\text{C}-\text{CH}_2-\text{C}- \\
| & | & | & | & | & | \\
\text{H} & \text{H} & \text{H} & \text{CH}_3 & \text{H} & \text{H}
\end{array}
$$

is not thought to exist to any great extent. This conclusion is supported by comparison of observed and calculated spectra and only one small discrepancy is noted. This paper shows the importance of the conformations of *meso* and *racemic* diads in determining the spectrum of tetrad sequences in polypropylene.

C. Polyethylene

The NMR spectrum of polyethylene is dominated by the resonance due to $-(\text{CH}_2)-_n$ groups. However, weak resonances may be observed, especially if spectrum accumulation be used, which arise from the protons of unsaturated groups and, particularly at 220 MHz, resonances of the protons of terminal methyl groups may be observed. It has not so far been demonstrated that information can be obtained by NMR which is not available from other studies, particularly infrared spectroscopy. Furthermore, at the present time the latter method provides more reliable results more easily and is consequently preferred.

The resonance due to the $-(\text{CH}_2)-_n$ chain has been the subject of a series of papers by Liu[31-33] who examined the spectra of a series of linear hydrocarbons of high purity between C_5 and C_{36} in a series of solvents. It was found that, apart from the separate resonances shown by the terminal $-\text{CH}_2-$ groups of the chain, hydrocarbons above C_{17} show the CH_2 resonance as a doublet in some solvents, and the degree of resolution between the halves of the doublet depend upon the solvent. The polarity of the solvent molecule was evidently not the significant factor since benzene (non-polar) and pyridine (polar) gave only a suggestion of splitting. On the other hand, the size of the solvent molecule appeared to be important, since 9-chloroanthracene gave the greatest splitting, and was the largest molecule tested. Liu interprets the splitting as indicating that different CH_2 groups in the hydrocarbon interact to a different extent with the solvent molecules, and he suggests that the conformation taken up by the molecule in solution is such that some CH_2 groups are exposed to, and others shielded from, the solvent. A possible form would be a chain-folded conformation. The low-field peak is considered to arise principally from a highly ordered structure, and that at high field from a disordered structure. Liu extended the treatment to consider the spectrum of polyethylene. A comparison of linear (high density) and chain branched (low density) shows a much broader $-CH_2-$ resonance in the spectrum of the low-density material. Liu considers that this effect is consistent with the more disordered structure expected for this chain-branched polymer.

D. Polymethyl methacrylate

Polymethyl methacrylate is, of all commonly available polymers, that best suited to tacticity measurements by nuclear magnetic resonance. As Ramey[34] points out, it is one of the few vinyl polymers in which protons within each of the α substituent groups are equivalent and there is no spin–spin coupling of the protons of the α-groups with one another, or with the β-protons. The resulting simplicity in the spectrum can only be achieved in most other vinyl polymers by spin decoupling, or by the examination of polymers prepared from selectively deuterated monomers.

This, no doubt, accounts for the great popularity of polymethyl methacrylate as a subject for study of effects such as solvent–solute interaction. Thus, Nagai and Nishioka[35] consider that the NMR spectrum of polymethyl methacrylate in benzene gives evidence for the presence of a solvent–solute π-complex. Liu[36] has extended this approach to measurements on the polymer in a series of aromatic solvents and related the change of chemical shift of particular resonances of the polymer to the intensity of the "ring current" in the solvent. Work has continued also on the assignment of those new features of the polymethyl methacrylate spectrum which are revealed by examination with higher field strength instruments. The original studies of this polymer at 40 MHz allowed interpretation in terms of diad and triad stereochemical sequences.[37] In the 100 MHz spectra reported by Ramey[34] additional structure is evident on the β-methylene resonances in both highly isotactic and highly syndiotactic samples. This is explained[34,38] by taking into account tetrad rather than diad sequences. In these 100 MHz spectra there is some indication of additional structure in the α-methyl resonances which arises from pentad effects. This fine structure is well resolved in the 220 MHz spectra shown in a recent paper of Frisch et al.[39]

The assignment of the structure to particular pentad sequences is clearly a difficult problem. These authors have examined the α-CH_3 and β-CH_2 resonances in the spectrum of a predominantly syndiotactic polymer, prepared with a free radical initiator. They assume the propagation mechanism to be a Bernoulli-trial process, and hence they are able to predict the relative concentration of triads, tetrads and pentads. The spectrum was broken down to a series of peaks with the Du Pont curve resolver and the assignment was then made by considering the position and relative area of the resolved peaks. The authors point out that their assignment is logical and consistent, rather than rigorously proved, and it is perhaps not surprising that Ferguson,[40] who also reported the 220 MHz spectrum, proposes an assignment which differs in some respects. This latter author has also made use of intensity measurements in formulating his assignments, but he has preferred to examine the spectra of a series of polymers and to propose an assignment consistent with all of these. He has taken into account also the results of spin decoupling experiments. The differences between the two assignments are chiefly concerned with the assignment of the resonances of pentads centred on the heterotactic (*mr*) triad, and as such might be considered more academic than practically important. What is probably more significant, however, is that Frisch *et al.*[39] find that the chemical shifts of resonances due to particular tetrad and pentad sequences are different in substantially isotactic and substantially syndiotactic environments. Even though the resonances do not get "out of order" when these shifts occur, it would seem to be quite a serious matter as the majority of polymers of practical interest consist of mixed forms (rather than substantially isotactic or syndiotactic materials), and if allowance has to be made for what is presumably a kind of solvent effect, the interpretation of the spectrum of an unknown polymer becomes very complicated. However, Ferguson[40] disagrees with these conclusions and finds that the resonance positions of protons in particular sequences are the same in both substantially isotactic and substantially syndiotactic environments. Certainly this disagreement between experts draws attention to some of the problems of working with a 220 MHz instrument. It has been our experience that while dispersion of the spectrum is much improved with this instrument, precise determination of chemical shift is a matter of considerable difficulty, particularly when working at elevated temperature, and it is possible that this is the reason for the present disagreement. The problem will no doubt be resolved through further careful work.

While it is evident that there are problems associated with the characterization of pentad structures, there is general agreement that measurement by NMR of tacticity of polymethyl methacrylate in terms of triads is reliable from the relative areas of the α-CH$_3$ resonances. This has become an accepted method of studying polymerization initiation[39,41,42] and chain propagation mechanisms[43] for this polymer. The effect of solvents presented during polymerization has been studied,[44] while Osawa *et al.*[45] have not only varied the solvent, but have carried out the polymerization under ultrasonic irradiation. There has been some interest in so-called "complexes" formed between isotactic and syndiotactic polymethyl methacrylate. Liquori *et al.*[46] examined a "stereo-block" polymer and were able to demonstrate, by chemical tests, that the material was a mixture containing syndiotactic and isotactic polymer chains in a 2:1 ratio. Liu and Liu[47] have examined the problem further and have produced evidence, both from the NMR spectrum and by other physical measurements of the existence of "complexes" between these species in solution. The presumption is that the inter-chain forces reach a maximum when the proportion of the two constituents is correct for complex formation. Thus, when the resonance of the protons of the O–CH$_3$ group is observed in benzene solution, the band width is strongly dependent upon the syndiotactic/isotactic ratio, and falls to a minimum at the proportions at which the viscosity of the solution reaches a maximum. These proportions are in the ratio 2:1, as found by Liquori et al.[46] It is suggested that in the "complex" the extended syndiotactic chains fit into the grooves of the isotactic helices.

E. Other methacrylate and acrylate homopolymers

The success achieved in the analysis of the polymethyl methacrylate spectrum has stimulated a search for other acrylates or methacrylates which might have equally useful spectra. In practice there are rather few suitable monomers, because the resonances of protons in substituent groups usually obscure the α-CH$_3$ or β-CH$_2$ resonances or both. However, Iwakura et al.[48] find that the α-CH$_3$ resonances may still be observed in polyglycidyl methacrylate. Furthermore, if this ester were converted to polymethyl methacrylate, the relative intensity of the three α-CH$_3$ resonances remained the same in both spectra. They take this as evidence that the α-CH$_3$ resonances have the same significance in the spectrum of polyglycidyl methacrylate as in polymethyl methacrylate, and hence may be used reliably in a tacticity study, and they have proceeded to calculate the differences of entropy and enthalpy of activation between the isotactic and syndiotactic species.

Lee et al.[49] have studied polyphenyl methacrylate in which the extra protons fall to low field, and hence do not interfere with the normal analysis, and they show spectra in their paper in which the methylene resonances are clearly seen. The authors suggest that there is some evidence of the effect of tetrad sequences. Another method which these authors have found useful is the partial or total substitution of side chain protons by fluorine, and again excellent spectra were measured. Matsuzaki et al.[50] have had considerable success with polymethyl α-chloroacrylate in which again the β-methylene resonances of the substantially pure isotactic and syndiotactic forms appear as a well-defined quartet and singlet. Matsuzaki et al.[51] have used the more familiar method of converting the polymer to polymethyl methacrylate to study polymenthyl methacrylate. The optical activity of the polymer prepared with the 1-menthyl monomer was, however, little affected by changes of tacticity. Matsuzaki et al.[52,53] have also made a study of polymethyl acrylate. Comparison of the spectra of polymethyl acrylate and that of the deuterio polymer has permitted the spectra to be analysed, and the authors have been able to match them with calculated spectra. Yoshino et al.[54] and Yoshino and Iwanaga[55] have made a detailed study of the polymerization of isopropyl acrylate oligomers, with particular emphasis on the mode of addition of the monomer unit to the growing chain.

F. Polyacrylonitrile

The analysis of the NMR spectrum of polyacrylonitrile has given rise to a great deal of confusion. The major cause of the discrepancies is found in the observations on the equivalence or otherwise of the *meso*-methylenic protons. The spectra of polyacrylonitrile and poly-α-d_1-acrylonitrile were obtained by Yamadera and Murano[56] in $NaCNS/D_2O$ solution, and the tacticity of the polymers were calculated based on the assumption that the *meso*-methylenic protons were equivalent. This result was challenged strongly by Yoshino *et al.*[57] who, in a series of experiments involving the polymerization of α,β-d_2-acrylonitrile and α-d_1-acrylonitrile, showed that in perchloric acid the *meso*-methylenic protons were very definitely non-equivalent. Clearly, some of this confusion could be the result of solvent effects on the conformation of the polymer in solution. Murano[58] in reviewing this situation states that the *meso* protons are equivalent in nitromethane/ethylene carbonate, the solvent used by Bargon *et al.*[59] in much earlier work, whereas they are non-equivalent in $NaCNS/D_2O$ and, of course, as Yoshino[57] states, non-equivalent in perchloric acid. The *meso/racemic* ratio determined by Yoshino[57] shows that polymer prepared by X-ray irradiation at $-80°C$ is largely isotactic and that polymer prepared by a radical process has a random configuration. More recently Matsuzaki *et al.*[60] have re-stated their own findings first published in 1966 that a radical catalyst produces polymer having a random configuration confirming Yoshino's[57] results. In this work, Matsuzaki *et al.* have used DMF-d_7, and this solvent must be added to those previously noted which show the *meso*-methylenic protons to be non-equivalent. Further, these authors show that in a radical polymerization the stereoregularity of the polymer is independent of the temperature of polymerization.

G. Polystyrene

In the atactic form this polymer has proved difficult to analyse both at 60 and 100 MHz. The advent of the 220 MHz spectrometer has allowed, however, an analysis to be made of the isotactic form. Heatley and Bovey[61] published spectra which show the non-equivalence of the protons of the methylene group confirming that the material under examination has an isotactic structure. Good agreement is obtained between calculated and observed spectra; the parameters used are well tabulated. The spin system found to best represent the methine and methylene resonance is that of an AA'BB'CC' six-spin cyclic dimer model with AA'BB' representing β-protons and CC' the α-protons in the polymer. Segré *et al.*[62] have studied heavily deuterated polystyrene made by either a Ziegler-Natta catalysed route or by a free-radical initiated route. The Ziegler-Natta catalysed product of the polymerization of $C_6D_6CH{=}CD_2$ gave an NMR spectrum after deuterium decoupling which showed essentially a single, narrow resonance due to the methine proton. This result was interpreted as showing that the Ziegler-Natta system produced a polymer of steric purity better than 97·5%. The free radical initiated d_7-polymer gave rise to a complex spectrum consisting of broad, poorly resolved resonances from which the authors conclude that the polymer is atactic and devoid of any appreciable degree of stereoregularity. Beachell and Smiley[63] have studied the oxidative degradation of polystyrene by combined NMR, IR and UV spectroscopic methods. Samples of deuterated polystyrenes were examined as degraded materials and their spectra compared with those of degraded non-deuterated polystyrene. Peaks associated with the degraded material were assigned to aromatic resonances similar to those observed in polystyrene containing benzoyl end groups. Consideration of all spectral data and chemical analysis lead the authors to conclude that the degradation gives rise to ketonic groups in the molecule. The authors also agree with previous studies that some evidence is obtained by NMR for the presence of conjugated unsaturated structures in polystyrene.

H. Poly α-methyl styrene

Although the resonance of the α-methyl protons of poly α-methyl styrene is sensitive to stereochemical arrangement, there has been great difficulty in assigning each of the resonances to a particular triad sequence. In the initial work of Brownstein et al.[64] the highest field methyl resonance was assigned to syndiotactic triads since the observation of the β-methylene protons of a reasonably stereoregular polymer showed no splitting due to coupling. However, Sakurada et al.[65] assigned this peak to the isotactic triad as a result of their interpretations of X-ray data on polymer prepared with a Ziegler catalyst. Ramey and Statton[66] then produced an argument which assigned the triad resonances to h, i and s sequences in order of increasing field strength based on their interpretation of the β-methylene resonances. More recently a further study of this polymer has been made by Fujii et al.[67] which includes the spectrum of poly $β$-d_1-α-methyl styrene. This spectrum indicates that the *meso* methylene protons of poly α-methyl styrene are coincidentally equivalent, thus contradicting the interpretation by Ramey.[66] Although this evidence does not enable the authors to assign the high- and low-field triad resonance to either syndiotactic or isotactic sequences it does exclude the possibility, suggested by Ramey, that the lowest field resonance is due to heterotactic sequences. The suggestion is made in this paper that tetrad analysis may provide the answer to the problem of assigning the α-methyl resonances to tactic sequences. Ramey[68] has obtained data at 220 MHz and has studied both the β-methylene and α-methyl resonances. Analysis of the β-methylene region enables the author to assign the high-field doublet to *mmm* and *mmr* tetrads. The percentage isotactic triad content is calculated and, from this data, it is suggested that the α-methyl resonances correspond to i, h and s triads in order of increasing field strength.

I. Ether polymers

Vinyl ether polymers are useful subjects for the study of stereoisomerism as the inclusion of the ether oxygen atom reduces the extent of spin–spin coupling in the molecule and thus considerably simplifies the spectrum. A further simplification is achieved if the hydrogen on the α-carbon atom is replaced by a methyl group, and Matsuzaki et al.[69] have studied α-methyl vinyl methyl ether and the corresponding isobutyl ether polymers which are of this nature. Analysis of triad sequences from the resonances of protons in the α-groups is apparently straightforward.

The authors commented that this spectrum of poly α-methyl vinyl methyl ether differed substantially from that previously reported by Goodman and Fan[70] and suggested that these workers had measured the spectra of degraded samples. These remarks drew immediate reaction from Goodman and Fan[71] who pointed out that they had added a stabilizer and were able furthermore to produce a spectrum similar to that of Matsuzaki et al.[69] by degrading their polymer. Liu and Lignowski[72] also consider that the polymers examined by Matsuzaki et al.[69] were degraded and hence their results were not valid. A short paper by Matsuzaki and co-workers[73] appears to concede the case to Goodman and Fan.

As an example of a polymer from an α,β-disubstituted olefin Ohsumi et al.[74,75] have examined the polymer $-[CH(CH_3)-CH(OCH_3)]_n-$. Resonances of the β-CH_3 and α-OCH_3 were observed in the spectra of polymers prepared with different catalysts. While the configuration of the α-carbon was always found to be isotactic, the configuration of the β-carbon differed with different catalysts.

In all the reports quoted above, the spectra were analysed in terms of triad sequences. Yuki and co-workers[76] found that the resonance of the methoxy protons in poly *ortho*-methoxystyrene was complex, and it was necessary to consider pentad sequences to account for the structure observed in the 100 MHz spectra. The overlapping resonances were resolved with the Du Pont curve resolver assuming Lorentian contours.

Studies have been made also of polymers with the ether oxygen in the backbone; again the effect of the oxygen is to remove the interaction between adjacent groups, and in principle a simplification of the spectrum results. Even so, the spectrum of polypropylene oxide reported by Ramey et al.[77] proved to be too complex for full interpretation, even after decoupling of methyl and methylene protons, and Tani et al.[78] therefore examined the monodeuterio compound in which the single proton is replaced by $-(O-CH_2-CDCH_3)-_n$. They find that, in addition to isotactic and syndiotactic arrangements, there are head-to-head and tail-to-tail structures present. Brame and Vogl[79] have made a particular study of polyacetaldehyde. By reference to model compounds they were able to predict the relative positions of the doublet resonances from the methyl protons of each of the triad forms, but only at 220 MHz were they able to resolve the methyl resonances of the syndiotactic triads from those of heterotactic triads, and even here it was necessary to use the Du Pont curve resolver. They suggest that a principal reason for the difficulty in analysing the proton resonance is that there are significant pentad effects leading to a multiplication of the structure from the isotactic and heterotactic triads. Thus the study of ether polymers has proved of interest and it has been demonstrated that useful configurational studies are possible in the examination of these substances.

J. Miscellaneous polymers

In this section, we report on some interesting studies of polymer systems which do not fall easily into the categories previously dealt with in this review.

1. Polyvinyl formate

The structure of this polymer has been studied by Ramey et al.[80] who said that the resonances of the α- and β-protons were insensitive of tactic arrangement. However, the resonance of the proton in the CHO group appears as three closely spaced peaks which, by reference to the spectrum of polyvinyl acetate prepared from the PVF, may each be ascribed to one of the three sequences. An intermediate product between the PVF and the polyvinyl acetate is polyvinyl alcohol; examination of this material in the β-proton region did not yield diad concentrations consistent with the sequence measurements on either the PVF or the polyvinyl acetate. In an attempt to resolve the difficulty, the authors examined spectra of some normal polyvinyl alcohol samples in the β-methylene region with and without spin decoupling. They concluded that the β-methylene resonance in polyvinyl alcohol is subject to tetrad effects which distort the band contour, and that this accounted for the discrepancies.

2. cis-1,4-Polyisoprene

Carman and Wilkes[81] were aware of previous attempts to estimate the steric purity of cis-1,4-polyisoprenes. However, there were no published data on the detection limit of trans-1,4 in the presence of 3,4-isomer. Both 60 MHz and 220 MHz spectra were obtained from which the authors concluded that at 60 MHz only values of above 2% trans-1,4 were reliable whereas at 220 MHz it was possible to detect as little as 0·5%.

3. *3,4,5-trideuterio-styrene polymers and copolymers*

The resonance of *ortho*-aromatic protons in the homopolymer of styrene and a number of copolymers appears to be particularly sensitive to environment. Comments have been made on the length of styrene sequence required before the *ortho* resonance becomes separated from the resonances of the *meta*- and *para*- protons. Clearly, sequence distribution measurements on copolymers could be made if the resonance of *ortho* protons was sharp and not broadened, as normally observed, by coupling with *meta* and *para* protons. This point is made by Kinstle and Harwood[82] and, to overcome this difficulty, these authors have prepared 3,4,5-trideuterio styrene homopolymer and 50:50 10:90 copolymers with methyl methacrylate. In the NMR spectrum of the homopolymer the authors find three separate peaks at low field, which were ascribed to *ortho* protons in syndiotactic, heterotactic and isotactic environments. The spectra of the two copolymers indicates that a triad analysis is possible with resonances assigned to $M\dot{S}M$, $(M\dot{S}S + S\dot{S}M)$ and $S\dot{S}S$ sequences although the use of some form of curve analysis may be necessary before a quantitative measurement of sequence distribution is possible.

4. *Poly(diphenylene ether sulphone)*

The use of NMR techniques to discover and estimate the amount of branching in a polymer chain is demonstrated in a paper by Cudby *et al.*[83] concerning poly(diphenylene ether-sulphones) obtained by polysulphonylation. A spectrum accumulation technique is used to estimate the amount of 1,2,4-trisubstituted aromatic nuclei in the polymer (Fig. 3). The results derived from the NMR spectrum are shown to be in good agreement with a chemical method.

5. *Poly(perfluorobutadiene)*

The value of ^{19}F resonance in structural analysis is demonstrated by Toy and Lawson[84] in the study of poly(perfluorobutadiene). An assignment of resonances in the spectrum of the monomer is made which is subsequently used to interpret the polymerization mechanism for a number of different catalyst systems.

6. *Tetrafluorethylene/perfluoromethyl vinyl ether copolymer*

An interesting development in the application of NMR to solid polymers is indicated by Ellett *et al.*[85] who applied pulse techniques to a TFE/PFMVE copolymer to obtain chemical shift data. The line widths shown in the spectrum are greater than one would expect from a solution, but certainly the experiment as performed gives information which would otherwise be unobtainable. It is to be hoped that more experiments of this nature will be attempted which if successful, would extend the scope of NMR into the field of cross-linked or high molecular weight insoluble polymers.

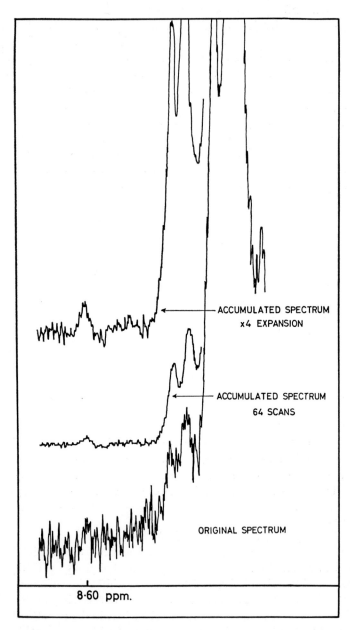

FIG. 3. The accumulated spectrum of poly(diphenylene ether-sulphone) used to determine the amount of 1,2,4-trisubstitution.

7. Fluorinated methacrylate polymers

In a most interesting paper, by Lee et al.,[86] an examination of the micro-structure of certain methacrylate polymers was made by the specific introduction of fluorine into the side chain group which deshielded the remaining protons in the side chain to such an extent that their resonances were sufficiently displaced to permit an examination of the polymer backbone protons to be made. A tacticity temperature of polymerization relationship was established in the case of methyl methacrylate which was in agreement with previous work by Bovey[87] and Fox.[88] The authors state that very long range ^{19}F–H coupling was observed over four saturated bonds in the study of a methacrylate with a 1,1-dihydroheptafluorobutyl side group. The authors now propose to investigate tetrad effects in these specifically fluorinated polymers at very high field strengths.

III. COPOLYMERS

NMR study of copolymers continues to excite interest, and this is justified as such examination may reveal a number of important features. Thus, in many cases, it is possible to determine the relative proportions of the constituents, and the sequence lengths of one or more of the polymerized species. These observations have been used in many cases to examine a number of theories of copolymerization. In a few cases it is possible to make observations on the stereochemical sequences of one or more of the polymerized species.

A. Copolymers of vinylidene chloride

Copolymers of vinylidene chloride have proved, over the years, very popular subjects for NMR study. The particular advantages arise from the absence of an α-proton which reduces coupling problems and the relatively large down-field shift of the β-proton resonance owing to the proximity of the chlorine atoms. This often has the effect of distributing the resonances of the methine and methylene protons over a comparatively wide range of chemical shift values so that the subtle effects arising in extended monomer sequences may be more readily observed.

Kinsinger and Fischer[89] have extended their earlier work,[90] on vinylidene chloride/isobutylene copolymers, to include a tetrad analysis based on methylene protons. Using previously determined copolymerization parameters obtained from a diad analysis, and assuming that only the terminal effect was operative in the mechanism of copolymerization, the authors calculated the concentration of the various tetrads as a function of the monomer feed. In some cases the concentration of the different tetrads closely fitted the expected values whereas others deviated substantially. The authors proceeded to determine the four reactivity ratios for the penultimate effect based on the micro-structure of the copolymers. Referring to their earlier work on diad analysis the authors showed that there was a marked improvement in their results with the inclusion of these new parameters. The authors ended on a note of caution by suggesting that the now improved agreement between calculated and observed values for diads and tetrads was not necessarily due to the incorporation of the penultimate effect parameter. This note of caution appears appropriate since the studies of other vinylidene chloride copolymers have evidently not required any such elaborate explanation. Thus Johnsen and Kolbé[91] working at 100 MHz on the system vinylidene chloride/vinyl acetate have measured the concentrations of pentad sequences from the resonance of the methine group and concentrations of hexads from the resonance due to the methylene group. The values obtained from the concentrations of pentads and hexads are shown to agree with the values calculated from reactivity ratios.

Ito et al.[92] have also examined vinylidene chloride/vinyl acetate copolymer and agree that there is no need to consider penultimate effects to explain the polymerization mechanism. They find that the Mayo and Lewis terminal model is satisfactory and indeed find very good agreement between experiment and theory. Similar results were obtained on copolymers of vinylidene chloride with methyl methacrylate and with styrene. A later paper by Yamashita and Ito[93] deals in more detail with the vinylidene chloride/vinyl acetate copolymer system and confirms that the results, of the NMR analysis of diad and tetrad sequence distributions, are quite compatible with the usual copolymerization theory and furthermore are very useful in characterizing the copolymer sequence over a wide range of conversions and compositions.

B. Other copolymers

Sequence distribution of monomer units in ethylene/vinyl chloride co-polymers has been determined by Wilkes et al.[94] The concentrations of the diads EE, VV and EV (or VE) were determined, and used in conjunction with monomer feed data to determine the individual reactivity ratios. The authors demonstrated that the structures observed by analysis of the diad distributions were identical to those predicted from copolymerization theory, and that the copolymerization was not random but follows first order Markoffian statistics.

In the compositional analysis by NMR of styrene/acrylonitrile copolymers, Cernicki et al.[95] have tried two different methods. In their more conventional approach they measure the spectrum of the copolymer as a solution in a proton free solvent and from the areas under the resonances calculated the composition. In their alternative method they recorded the spectrum of the copolymer and that of polystyrene, as solutions of known concentration in an aliphatic solvent. The combined styrene content was then calculated from the relative areas of the low-field resonance in the two spectra. Both methods evidently gave good results, comparable with those of chemical analysis, but the NMR methods were more simple and faster.

Murano et al.[96] have compared NMR and infrared methods of compositional analysis of styrene/methacrylonitrile copolymers, and find good agreement between them. They have also obtained evidence on the presence of triad sequences from the resonance pattern of the methine proton. The α-methyl resonance was too complex to be accounted for in terms of triad sequences; the authors suggest that this could be explained on the basis of pentad structures with a central methacrylonitrile unit. The sequence distribution of the copolymer of 3,3-bis(chloromethyl)oxacyclobutane and β-propiolactone has been studied by Yamashita et al.[97] The authors examined the possibility of applying the normal Mayo-Lewis equation to ionic copolymerizations. The copolymer composition was determined from the NMR spectrum where all four diad sequences were observed but the diad proportions showed that the copolymerization process did not follow a simple mechanism.

Monomer sequence distribution studies of ethylene/vinyl formate copolymers have been carried out at 220 MHz by Wu.[98] Several solvents were used in the study and their different effects are demonstrated. The assignments of the observed resonances were made with the help of both partial and complete spin decoupling of the methine protons. Having established the assignments the authors proceeded to the quantitative determination of diad and triad concentrations. According to this investigation, the copolymer contains more homopolymer blocks than predicted by Bernoullian statistics.

Yamadera and Murano[99] have turned their attention towards the analysis of copolyesters. Examples of the homopolymers studied were polyethylene terephthalate, polyethylene isophthalate and polyethylene sebacate, and the copolymers poly(ethylene terephthalate/ortho-phthalate), poly(ethylene terephthalate/isophthalate) and poly(ethylene terephthalate/sebacate). The analysis of the resonances due to the ethylene glycol residue showed sensitivity to sequence distribution for example in the case of the poly(ethylene terephthalate/sebacate) copolymer, three peaks were assigned to T–G–T, S–G–S and T–G–S linkages. The relative intensities of these resonances were then used to determine the average sequence length and degree of randomness of the copolymer. The transesterification reaction between polyethylene terephthalate and polyethylene sebacate was also studied. A change from block copolymer to a random copolymer was observed in a period of 3 hours at a temperature of 276°C.

The advantage of enhanced chemical shift with higher frequency instruments is well demonstrated in the work of Schaefer et al.[100] on propylene oxide/maleic anhydride and propylene oxide/citraconic anhydride copolymers. Propylene oxide may enter the polymer chain either head or tail first, thus there is a considerable number of possible structural sequences. In order to perform a sequence analysis the authors found it necessary to hydrolytically degrade the polymer and separate the dimer and trimer factors from the hydrolysate before NMR examination. Even so, it was shown that the sequence analysis was only possible in spectra measured at 220 MHz. The authors concluded that at least two different third-order Markovian statistical distributions are required to describe the structure.

The quantitative application of NMR spectroscopy has been emphasized by Mochel[101] in studies of butadiene/styrene and butadiene/isoprene copolymers. The author made no attempt to interpret the spectra of the copolymers in terms of monomer distribution, although changes in the spectra were noted which could possibly be used to study the distribution quantitatively. Reference is made to quantitative analysis by infrared techniques and modifications to the equations set up by Senn[102] are required to keep both sets of experimental data in line. Some interesting comments are made on the detection of block styrene units in the copolymers examined. Whereas Bovey *et al.*[103] suggested that runs of 8 to 10 styrene units are needed before the separation of *ortho*-protons from the main aromatic resonance is observed, Mochel considers that the effect may arise from only 2 to 3 units. This conclusion was based on different reactivity ratios for styrene than those used by Bovey. The analysis of butadiene/isoprene copolymers is not as straightforward as that of styrene/butadiene copolymer but good agreement between theoretical and observed values was obtained except for copolymers containing less than 10% of isoprene.

The distribution of monomer units in propylene oxide-sulphur dioxide copolymers is the subject of a paper by Schaefer *et al.*[104] The copolymerization was studied in some detail with various catalytic systems. Hydrolysis of the copolymers gave polypropylene glycol ethers and sodium sulphite in good yield from which the authors concluded that sulphite linkages connect the monomer units. A triad analysis was performed on the NMR spectrum of the copolymer using the methyl resonance, the concentrations being estimated by simulating the spectrum using a Du Pont curve resolver. The monomer distributions are described as a non-Markovian chain.

REFERENCES

1. A. L. Segré, *Macromolecules*, 1968, **1**, 93.
2. K-J. Liu, *Makromol. Chem.*, 1969, **126**, 187.
3. T. K. Wu, *Macromolecules*, 1969, **2**, 521.
4. A. L. Segré, P. Ferruti, E. Toja and F. Danusso, *Macromolecules*, 1969, **2**, 35.
5. E. Lombardi, A. L. Segré, A. Zambelli, A. Marinangeli and G. Natta, *J. Polymer Sci., Part C, Polymer Symposia*, 1967, **16**, 2539.
6. J. Schaefer, *J. Phys. Chem.*, 1966, **70**, 1975.
7. J. Schaefer, *Macromolecules*, 1969, **2**, 533.

8. U. Johnsen and K. Kolbé, *Kolloid-Z.*, 1967, **221**, 64.
9. F. Heatley and F. A. Bovey, *Macromolecules*, 1969, **2**, 241.
10. D. Doskocilova, J. Stokr, B. Schneider, H. Pivcova, M. Kolinsky, J. Petranik and D. Lim, *J. Polymer Sci., Part C, Polymer Symposia*, 1967, **16**, 215.
11. U. Johnsen, *J. Polymer Sci.*, 1961, **54**, 56.
12. W. C. Tincher, *J. Polymer Sci.*, 1962, **62**, 5148.
13. F. A. Bovey, E. W. Anderson and D. C. Douglass, *J. Chem. Phys.*, 1963, **39**, 1199.
14. D. Doskocilova, *J. Polymer Sci., Part B, Polymer Letters*, 1964, **2**, 421.
15. T. Yoshino and J. Komiyama, *J. Polymer Sci.*, 1965, **83**, 311.
16. F. A. Bovey, F. P. Wood, E. W. Anderson and R. L. Kornegay, *J. Phys. Chem.*, 1967, **71**, 312.
17. B. Schneider, J. Stokr, D. Doskocilova, M. Kolinsky, S. Sykora and D. Lim, *J. Polymer Sci., Part C, Polymer Symposia*, 1968, **16**, 3891.
18. H. A. Willis and M. E. A. Cudby, *Appl. Spectroscopy Review*, 1968, **1**, 237.
19. P. R. Sewell, *Ann. Rev. NMR Spectroscopy*, 1968, **1**, 165.
20. A. Zambelli, M. G. Giongo and G. Natta, *Makromol. Chem.*, 1967, **110**, 291.
21. G. Natta and P. Corrandini, *Makromol. Chem.*, 1967, **110**, 291.
22. P. J. Flory and Y. Fujiwara, *Macromolecules*, 1969, **2**, 327.
23. E. Lombardi, A. Segré, A. Zambelli, A. Marinangeli and G. Natta, *J. Polymer Sci., Part C, Polymer Symposia*, 1967, **16**, 2539.
24. T. Miyamoto and H. Inagaki, *J. Polymer Sci., Part A-2, Polymer Phys.*, 1969, **7**, 963.
25. R. C. Ferguson, *Ann. New York Acad. Sci.*, 1967, **29**, 495.
26. A. Zambelli and A. L. Segré, *J. Polymer Sci., Part B, Polymer Letters*, 1968, **6**, 473.
27. A. Zambelli, *Makromol. Chem.*, 1967, **110**, 1.
28. A. Zambelli, A. L. Segré, M. Farina and G. Natta, *Makromol. Chem.*, 1968, **112**, 281.
29. F. Heatley and A. Zambelli, *Macromolecules*, 1969, **2**, 618.
30. F. Heatley, R. Solovey and F. A. Bovey, *Macromolecules*, 1969, **2**, 619.
31. K-J. Liu, *J. Polymer Sci., Part A-2, Polymer Phys.*, 1967, **5**, 1209.
32. K-J. Liu, *J. Polymer Sci., Part A-2, Polymer Phys.*, 1968, **6**, 451.
33. K-J. Liu, *J. Polymer Sci., Part A-2, Polymer Phys.*, 1968, **6**, 947.
34. K. C. Ramey, *J. Polymer Sci., Part B, Polymer Letters*, 1967, **5**, 859.
35. M. Nagai and A. Nishioka, *J. Polymer Sci., Part A-1, Polymer Chem.*, 1968, **6**, 1655.
36. K-J. Liu, *J. Polymer Sci., Part A-2, Polymer Phys.*, 1967, **5**, 1199.
37. F. A. Bovey and G. V. D. Tiers, *J. Polymer Sci.*, 1960, **44**, 173.
38. K. Hatada, K. Ota and H. Yuki, *J. Polymer Sci., Part B, Polymer Letters*, 1967, **5**, 225.
39. H. L. Frisch, C. L. Mallows, F. Heatley and F. A. Bovey, *Macromolecules*, 1968, **1**, 533.
40. R. C. Ferguson, *Macromolecules*, 1969, **2**, 237.
41. D. Lim, J. Coupek, K. Juzl, J. Baca, S. Sykora and B. Schneider, *J. Polymer Sci., Part C, Polymer Symposia*, 1968, **23**, 21.
42. A. Blumstein and A. C. Watterson, *J. Polymer Sci., Part B, Polymer Letters*, 1968, **6**, 69.
43. T. Hirahara, T. Nakano and Y. Minoura, *J. Polymer Sci., Part A-1, Polymer Chem.*, 1968, **6**, 485.

44. W. Fowells, C. Schuerch, F. A. Bovey and F. P. Hood, *J. Amer. Chem. Soc.* 1967, **89**, 1396.
45. Z. Osawa, T. Kimura and T. Kasuga, *J. Polymer Sci., Part A-1, Polymer Chem.*, 1969, **7**, 2007.
46. A. M. Liquori, G. Anzuino, M. D'Alagni, V. Vitagliano and L. Costantino, *J. Polymer Sci., Part A-2, Polymer Phys.*, 1968, **6**, 509.
47. H. Z. Liu and K-J. Liu, *Macromolecules*, 1968, **1**, 157.
48. Y. Iwakura, F. Toda, T. Ito and K. Aoshima, *Makromol. Chem.*, 1967, **104**, 26.
49. W. M. Lee, B. R. McGarvey and F. R. Eirich, *J. Polymer Sci., Part C, Polymer Symposia*, 1969, **22**, 1197.
50. K. Matsuzaki, T. Uryu and K. Ito, *Makromol. Chem.*, 1969, **126**, 292.
51. K. Matsuzaki, A. Ishida and N. Tateno, *J. Polymer Sci., Part C, Polymer Symposia*, 1967, **16**, 2111.
52. K. Matsuzaki, T. Uryu and A. Ishida, *J. Polymer Sci., Part C, Polymer Symposia*, 1967, **16**, 2099.
53. K. Matsuzaki, T. Uryu, A. Ishida, T. Ohki and M. Takenchi, *J. Polymer Sci., Part A-1, Polymer Chem.*, 1967, **5**, 2167.
54. T. Yoshino, J. Komiyama and N. Iwanaga, *J. Amer. Chem. Soc.*, 1967, **89**, 6925.
55. T. Yoshino and H. Iwanaga, *J. Amer. Chem. Soc.*, 1968, **90**, 2434.
56. M. Murano and R. Yamadera, *J. Polymer Sci., Part A-1, Polymer Chem.*, 1967, **5**, 1855.
57. T. Yoshino, H. Kenjo and K. Kuno, *J. Polymer Sci., Part B, Polymer Letters*, 1967, **5**, 703.
58. M. Murano, *Makromol. Chem.*, 1968, **112**, 281.
59. J. Bargon, K-H. Hellwege and U. Johnsen, *Kolloid-Z.*, 1966, **213**, 51.
60. K. Matsuzaki, T. Uryu, M. Okada and H. Shiroki, *J. Polymer Sci., Part A-1, Polymer Chem.*, 1968, **6**, 1475.
61. F. Heatley and F. A. Bovey, *Macromolecules*, 1968, **1**, 301.
62. A. L. Segré, P. Ferruti, E. Toja and F. Danusso, *Macromolecules*, 1969, **2**, 35.
63. H. C. Beachell and L. H. Smiley, *J. Polymer Sci., Part A-1, Polymer Chem.*, 1967, **5**, 1635.
64. S. Brownstein, S. Bywater and D. J. Worsfold, *Makromol. Chem.*, 1961, **48**, 127.
65. Y. Sakurada, M. Matsumoto, K. Imai, A. Nishioka and Y. Kato, *J. Polymer Sci., Part B, Polymer Letters*, 1963, **1**, 633.
66. K. C. Ramey and G. L. Statton, *Makromol. Chem.*, 1965, **85**, 287.
67. K. Fujii, D. J. Worsfold and S. Bywater, *Makromol. Chem.*, 1968, **117**, 275.
68. K. C. Ramey, G. L. Statton and W. G. Jankowski, *J. Polymer Sci., Part B, Polymer Letters*, 1969, **7**, 693.
69. K. Matsuzaki, M. Hamada and K. Arita, *J. Polymer Sci., Part A-1, Polymer Chem.*, 1967, **5**, 1233.
70. M. Goodman and Y-L. Fan, *J. Amer. Chem. Soc.*, 1964, **86**, 4922.
71. M. Goodman and Y-L. Fan, *Macromolecules*, 1968, **1**, 163.
72. K-J. Liu and S. J. Lignowski, *J. Polymer Sci., Part B, Polymer Letters*, 1968 **6**, 191.
73. K. Matsuzaki, T. Uryu and C. Imai, *J. Polymer Sci., Part B, Polymer Letters*, 1968, **6**, 195.

74. Y. Ohsumi, T. Higashimura, S. Okamura, R. Chujo and T. Kuroda, *J. Polymer Sci., Part A-1, Polymer Chem.*, 1967, **5**, 3009.
75. Y. Ohsumi, T. Higashimura, S. Okamura, R. Chujo and T. Kuroda, *J. Polymer Sci., Part A-1, Polymer Chem.*, 1968, **6**, 3015.
76. H. Yuki, Y. Okamoto, Y. Kuwae and K. Hatada, *J. Polymer Sci., Part A-1, Polymer Chem.*, 1969, **7**, 1933.
77. K. C. Ramey and N. D. Field, *J. Polymer Sci., Part B, Polymer Letters*, 1964, **2**, 461.
78. H. Tari, N. Oguri and S. Watanabe, *J. Polymer Sci., Part B, Polymer Letters*, 1968, **6**, 577.
79. E. G. Brame and O. Vogl, *J. Macromol. Sci.*, 1967, **A1**, 277.
80. K. C. Ramey, D. C. Lini and G. L. Statton, *J. Polymer Sci., Part A-1, Polymer Chem.*, 1967, **5**, 257.
81. C. J. Carman and C. E. Wilkes, *Polym. Prepr. Amer. Chem. Soc. Div. Polym. Chem.*, 1969, **10**, No. 2, 1435.
82. J. F. Kinstle and H. J. Harwood, *Polym. Prepr. Amer. Chem. Soc. Div. Polym. Chem.*, 1969, **10**, No. 2, 1389.
83. M. E. A. Cudby, R. G. Feasey, S. Gaskin, V. Kendall and J. B. Rose, *Polymer*, 1968, **9**, 265.
84. M. S. Toy and D. D. Lawson, *J. Polymer Sci., Part B, Polymer Letters*, 1968, **6**, 639.
85. D. Ellett, Jr., U. Haeberlen and J. S. Waugh, *J. Polymer Sci., Part B, Polymer Letters*, 1969, **7**, 71.
86. W. M. Lee, B. R. McGarvey and F. R. Eirich, *J. Polymer Sci., Part C, Polymer Symposia*, 1969, No. 22, 1197.
87. F. A. Bovey, *J. Polymer Sci.*, 1960, **46**, 59.
88. T. G. Fox and H. W. Schnecko, *Polymer*, 1962, **3**, 575.
89. T. Fischer, J. B. Kinsinger and C. W. Wilson, *J. Polymer Sci., Part B, Polymer Letters*, 1966, **4**, 379.
90. J. B. Kinsinger, T. Fischer and C. W. Wilson, *J. Polymer Sci., Part B, Polymer Letters*, 1967, **5**, 285.
91. U. Johnsen and K. Kolbe, *Kolloid-Z*, 1967, **220**, 145.
92. K. Ito, S. Iwase and Y. Yamashita, *Makromol. Chem.*, 1967, **110**, 233.
93. K. Ito and Y. Yamashita, *J. Polymer Sci., Part B, Polymer Letters*, 1968, **6**, 219.
94. C. E. Wilkes, J. C. Westfahl and R. H. Backderf, *J. Polymer Sci., Part A-1, Polymer Chem.*, 1969, **7**, 23.
95. B. K. Cernicki, J. V. Muhl, Z. J. Janovic and K. Sliepcevic, *Analyt. Chem.*, 1968, **40**, 606.
96. M. Murano, K. Shimizu and H. J. Harwood, *Polym. Prepr. Amer. Chem. Soc., Div. Polym. Chem.*, 1969, **10**, No. 1, 193.
97. Y. Yamashita, T. Asakura, M. Okada and K. Ito, *Macromolecules*, 1969, **2**, 613.
98. T. K. Wu, *J. Phys. Chem.*, 1969, **73**, 1801.
99. R. Yamadera and M. Murano, *J. Polymer Sci., Part A-1, Polymer Chem.* 1967, **5**, 2259.
100. J. Schaefer, R. J. Katnik and R. J. Kern, *Macromolecules*, 1968, **1**, 101.
101. V. C. Mochel, *Rubber Chem. Technol.*, 1967, **40**, 1200.
102. W. L. Senn, *Analyt. Chim. Acta*, 1963, **29**, 505.
103. F. A. Bovey, G. V. D. Tiers and G. Filipovich, *J. Polymer Sci.*, 1959, **38**, 73.
104. J. Schaefer, R. J. Kern and R. J. Katnik, *Polym. Prepr. Amer. Chem. Soc. Div. Polym. Chem.*, 1968, **9**, 13.

Fluorine-19 Nuclear Magnetic Resonance Spectroscopy

K. JONES AND E. F. MOONEY†

Department of Chemistry, University of Birmingham, P.O. Box 363, Birmingham, B15-2TT, England

I. INTRODUCTION

THIS REVIEW covers the work published during 1969 which either dealt in detail with ^{19}F parameters or made use of these in structural determinations. The number of papers published which contained ^{19}F data amply justifies the intention to include a yearly review of ^{19}F NMR in future. Many of us, who entered this field at an early date, must surely be amazed at the growth of interest in many of these nuclei which at one time were but curiosities.

The reference made in Volume 3[1] to CCl_3F being an unsuitable reference material for the measurement of chemical shifts has been confirmed independently.[2] At room temperature, under high resolution conditions, the signal is a doublet, while at $-30°$ three peaks are clearly seen. Since CCl_3F has four

† Present addresses: (K.J.) I.B.M.(U.K.).Ltd., London Process Branch, Croydon, Surrey, England; (E.F.M.) Anacon (Instruments) Ltd., Bourne End, Buckinghamshire, England.

chlorine-isotopic species, namely $CF^{35}Cl_3$ (42·0%), $CF^{35}Cl_2{}^{37}Cl$ (42·9%), $CF^{35}Cl^{37}Cl_2$ (13·6%) and $CF^{37}Cl_3$ (1·5%) [the relative abundances being shown in parentheses] the three observed peaks were assigned to the three most abundant isotopic species.

Despite this fact no new universal reference standard for ¹⁹F shifts has yet emerged and the recently published ASTM recommendations[3] state that CCl_3F is the reference standard to be used. Consequently, as in the previous volume, the ¹⁹F shifts quoted in this review will all be reported with respect to CCl_3F and the following conversion factors will be used:

CF_3CO_2H	−78·5	$C_2F_2Cl_4$	−67·3
C_6F_6	−162·9	$(CF_2CCl_2)_2$	−114·1
$C_6H_5CF_3$	−63·9	C_6H_5F	−113·7

Readers are reminded that the sign convention being used in these volumes is such as to maintain the same sense of sign for proton and all other nuclei. Thus resonance signals to high field (i.e. low frequency) of the reference take a negative sign.

II. FLUOROHYDROCARBONS

A. Fluorinated aliphatic hydrocarbons

Fluorination of alkali metal salts of dicarboxylic acids afforded ω-fluorocarboxylic acids and α,ω-difluoroalkanes.[4] The ¹⁹F shift of the $-CH_2F$ groups, in all the compounds containing more than four carbon atoms, was −219 ± 0·5 with $^1J(F-H)$ of 47 to 48 Hz and $^3J(F-H)$ of 24 to 26 Hz. During the course of the reaction of N-bromobistrifluoromethylamine with vinyl fluoride, under ionic conditions, 2-bromo-1,1-difluoroethane was isolated in high yield.[5] This compound had a ¹⁹F shift of −119·0 with $^2J(F-H)$ of 56·4, $^3J(F-H)$ of 14·6 and $^3J(H-H)$ of 3·6 Hz.

Chlorination of perfluoro-penta-1,2-diene gave the 1,2,3,3-tetrachloro-octafluoro-n-pentane (1) the parameters of which are as shown.[6] The authors give

$$-79·6 \qquad -115·7$$
$$CF_3-CF_2-CFCl-CCl_2-CF_2Cl$$

| AB spectrum centred at $-116·3$ $J_{AB} = 277·0$ Hz | AB spectrum centred at $-57·0$ $J_{AB} = 163·0$ Hz |

1

the band centres of the AB systems in p.p.m. and the shift separation, $\Delta\nu$, in Hz. Unfortunately it is not stated whether 56·46 or 94·08 MHz was used to measure this particular spectrum and therefore precise shifts cannot be re-calculated.

A number of polyfluoropropanes, obtained as by-products during the fluorination of tetrahydrofuran, were isolated and characterized by NMR.[7] The appropriate ^{19}F data are shown in Table I and examination of the Table shows that the *gem* F–H coupling in $>$CFH and –CFH$_2$ groups is in the range 45 to 49 Hz while that of –CF$_2$H group is larger, 54 to 57 Hz.

TABLE I

^{19}F Parameters of some polyfluoropropanes[7]

	Chemical shifts			
	F–1	F–2	F–3	Coupling constants, Hz
(1) (2) (3) CF$_3$–CFH–CF$_2$H	−77·2	−217·0	−130·8	$J(F_1-F_2) = 11\cdot8$; $J(F_1-H_2) = 5\cdot9$ $J(F_1-F_3) = 7\cdot3$; $J(F_2-F_3) = 11\cdot8$ $J(F_2-H_2) = 45.1$; $J(F_2-H_3) = 6\cdot8$ $J(F_3-H_3) = 53\cdot9$; $J(F_3-H_2) = 7\cdot2$
(1) (2) (3) CF$_3$–CH$_2$–CF$_2$H	−64·5	. .	−116·3	$J(F_1-F_3) = 7\cdot1$; $J(F_1-H_2) = 10\cdot0$ $J(F_3-H_2) = 13\cdot4$; $J(F_3-H_3) = 54\cdot4$
(1) (2) (3) CF$_3$–CH$_2$–CH$_2$F	−65·9	. .	−209·4	$J(F_1-F_3) = 6\cdot2$; $J(F_1-H_2) = 10\cdot7$ $J(F_3-H_2) = 22\cdot8$; $J(F_3-H_3) = 47\cdot7$
(1) (2) (3) CF$_2$H–CFH–CF$_2$H	−133·1	−226·8	−133·1	$J(F_1-F_2) = 12\cdot8$; $J(F_1-H_1) = 54\cdot7$ $J(F_2-H_1) = 8\cdot0$; $J(F_2-H_2) = 46\cdot2$[a]
(1) (2) (3) CF$_2$H–CH$_2$–CH$_2$F	−119·0	. .	−223·7	$J(F_1-F_3) = 1\cdot2$; $J(F_1-H_1) = 56\cdot5$ $J(F_1-H_2) = 16\cdot0$; $J(F_3-H_2) = 25\cdot4$ $J(F_3-H_3) = 48\cdot7$
(1) (2) (3) CFH$_2$–CFH–CF$_2$H	−239·4	−208·4	−136·2	$J(F_1-H_1) = 47\cdot7$; $J(F_2-H_2) = 47\cdot1$ $J(F_3-H_3) = 55\cdot0$[a]

[a] Other couplings not measured.

The three-bond vicinal and four-bond coupling constants in fluorinated alkane derivatives have been the focus of some interest during 1969. Abraham,[8] by using reported values for $^4J(F-F)$ in conformationally rigid molecules, has determined the magnitude and signs of all the $^4J(F-F)$ values in the highly fluorinated –C–C–C fragment **2**; these were:

$$J_{tt} \text{ (trans-trans)} \quad -10 \qquad J_{tg} \text{ (trans-gauche)} \quad \sim 0$$
$$J_{gg} \text{ (gauche-gauche)} \quad +16 \qquad J_e \text{ (eclipsed)} \quad +26$$

The author pointed out that the $^4J(F-F)$ couplings in the same molecule may be of either sign and that the large F–F couplings, observed when two fluorine atoms are in close proximity, are probably always positive.

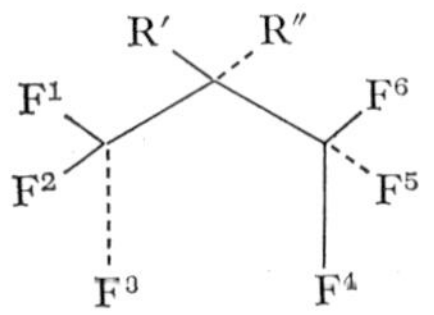

2

$$J_{tt} = J_{16}$$
$$J_{tg} = J_{14}, J_{15}. J_{26}, J_{36}$$
$$J_{gg} = J_{25}, J_{34}$$
$$J_e = J_{24}, J_{35}$$

The rotational isomers of four fluoro-halogenoethanes have been studied[9] by means of the variable temperature ^{19}F spectra over the temperature range 130° to 350°K. The ^{19}F parameters for the three separate rotomers of 1,2-dibromo-1-chloro-trifluoroethane were obtained at 148°K. The other three compounds studied were 1,1-dichloro-2-iodo-, 1,2-dichloro-1-iodo- trifluoroethanes and 1,2-dibromotrifluoroethane sulphonyl fluoride.

B. Derivatives of fluorinated aliphatic hydrocarbons

1. Oxy-compounds

The ^{19}F shifts of ω-fluoro-alcohols of the form $HO \cdot CH_2 \cdot CH_2 \cdot CH_2F$ and $CH_3 \cdot CHOH \cdot (CH_2)_x CH_2F$, where $x = 1$ to 4, have been measured[10] and found to be dependent upon the number of carbon atoms between the hydroxyl and $-CH_2F$ groups. The ^{19}F shifts of the corresponding tosylates and trifluoroacetates were also compared and, as might be expected, the change in the ^{19}F shift on esterification decreased with increasing value of x.

A number of unsaturated alcohols of the general type $HO(CF_3)_2C \cdot CH_2 \cdot CH=CHR$ and $HO(CF_3)_2C \cdot CH=CH \cdot CH_2R$, where $R = H$ or Me, have been prepared by the reaction of hexafluoroacetone with olefins.[11] The ^{19}F shifts of the $-C(CF_3)_2OH$ group fall in the range $-76 \cdot 9$ to $-79 \cdot 1$.

Ciampelli et al.[12] have drawn attention to the relationships which exist between the ^{19}F shifts of the groups in fluorinated ethers and indicated the usefulness of these relations in structural determinations. These relationships were also extended to perfluoropolyethers.

A new series of compounds, the perfluoroalkyl hypochlorites or chloroxy-perfluoroalkanes, R_fOCl, have been prepared independently by two groups of workers.[13, 14] The two sets of ^{19}F shift data vary and are compared in Table II.

TABLE II

^{19}F shifts of chloroxyperfluoroalkanes, R_fOCl

| R_f | | Chemical shifts | |
		Ref. 13[a]	Ref. 14[b]
CF_3-	$\delta\ CF_3$	-71.9	-64
$CF_3 \cdot CF_2-$	$\delta\ CF_3$	-78	-83
	$\delta\ CF_2$	-87	-90
$(CF_3)_2CF-$	$\delta\ CF_3$	-81.3	-76.5
	$\delta\ CF$	-143	-136
CF_3	$\delta\ CF_3$	-79.5	..
$\diagdown$	$\delta\ CFCl$	-68.1	..
$\diagup CF-$	$\delta\ CF^2$	-139	..
CF_2Cl			
$ClO \cdot (CF_2)_5-$	$\delta\ O \cdot CF_2$	-86.4	
	$\delta\ C \cdot CF_2 \cdot C$	-123	

[a] Measured at room temperature with external standard.
[b] Measured at $-40°$ with internal standard.

It must be emphasized, however, that the data were obtained under different circumstances. One group of workers[13] used non-spinning tubes and made the measurements at room temperature using substitution method for the CCl_3F standard while the second group[14] made the measurements at $-40°$ using internal CCl_3F.

2. Acids, esters and acid halides

The micelle formation of heptafluorobutyric acid in aqueous solution has been studied by ^{19}F NMR.[15] The use of ^{19}F NMR is particularly helpful in this type of study as the shifts of each of the separate groups (CF_3 and α- and β- CF_2) may be distinguished. All three signals show a distinct break in the shift vs. concentration curve at $0.80\ M$.

Similarly, the use of the ^{19}F resonance of derivatives of α-methoxy-α-tri-fluoromethylphenylacetic acid, as a means of determining enantiomeric composition, has been claimed to have distinct advantages.[16] This is an absolute method and accurate determinations could be made on 20 mg. samples. The chemical shifts of the enantiomers for a range of racemic alcohols and amines were listed in the paper. The resolution of 2,2,2-trifluorophenylethanol has been described[17] by conversion to the phenylethoxyacetic acid derivative. Reaction with N-bromosuccinimide gave the two mono- and the di-bromo acids **3**. The shifts of the CF_3 groups in these four compounds are shown in Table III.

TABLE III

Shifts of the CF_3 group in derivatives of 2,2,2-trifluorophenyl-ethoxyacetic acid (3)[17]

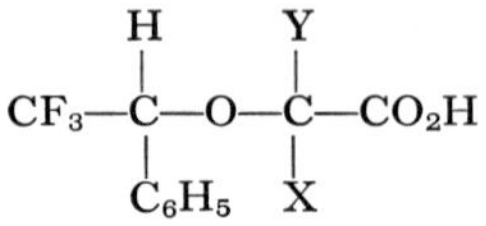

$$CF_3\text{—}\overset{\overset{\displaystyle H}{|}}{\underset{\underset{\displaystyle C_6H_5}{|}}{C}}\text{—O—}\overset{\overset{\displaystyle Y}{|}}{\underset{\underset{\displaystyle X}{|}}{C}}\text{—CO}_2H$$

3

X	Y	$\delta\ CF_3$
H	H	$-78\cdot2$
H	Br	$-77\cdot22$
Br	H	$-77\cdot56$
Br	Br	$-77\cdot60$

A number of perfluoroxydiacetic acid derivatives (**4**) have been prepared;[4]

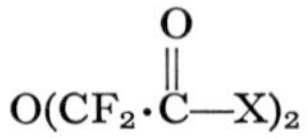

$$O(CF_2\cdot\overset{\overset{\displaystyle O}{||}}{C}\text{—X})_2$$

X = Cl, F, CO_2H, $CONH_2$ and CO_2Me

4

the ^{19}F shifts of the CF_2 groups in the acid chloride and fluoride are $-76\cdot7 \pm 1$, while in the acid, amide and methyl ester are $-77\cdot9 \pm 0\cdot2$. The chemistry of trifluorothioacetic acid and its derivatives have been investigated in more detail,[18] and the CF_3 resonance signal of the derivatives was in the range $-73\cdot5$ to $-77\cdot2$.

The greater sensitivity of ^{19}F shifts to steric and electronic effects has been used as a means of identifying carbohydrates by preparing the trifluoroacetate derivatives.[19] The range of the ^{19}F shifts of the trifluoroacetyl group varied by as much as $0\cdot5$ p.p.m. compared with $0\cdot2$ p.p.m. range found the shifts of the acetyl groups. The ^{19}F spectra of the trifluoroacetyl derivates of methyl-α-D-gluco-, methyl-α-D-manno-, methyl-α-D-galacto- and methyl-α-D-arabino-pyranosides are shown in the paper.

The shift of the trifluoromethoxy group in trifluoromethyl chloroformate, $CF_3O\cdot C(O)Cl$, has been reported as $\delta\ -61$.[14]

Banks *et al.*[20] found that hydrolysis of perfluoro-(2-methyl-2H-azirine) afforded 3,3,3-trifluoro-2,2-dihydroxypropionic acid, while ethanolysis afforded the ethyl esters of the 2,2-dihydroxy- and 2-ethoxy-2-hydroxy- derivatives. The ^{19}F shifts of the CF_3 groups in these compounds were in the range $-83 \cdot 1 \pm 1 \cdot 7$.

A number of perfluorocarboxylatodifluorophosphines of the general form $R_fCO \cdot OPF_2$ have been prepared.[21] The shifts of the $-PF_2$ groups are more appropriately dealt with later (p. 478) but the shifts of the fluorocarboxylate groups are shown in **5** to **7**.

$-76 \cdot 5$
$CF_3 \cdot CO \cdot OPF_2$
5

$-81 \cdot 4 \qquad -119 \cdot 7$
$CF_3 \!-\! CF_2 \!-\! CF_2 \!-\! CO \cdot OPF_2$
$-127 \cdot 2$
$^4J(CF_3\!-\!CF_2) = 8 \cdot 5$ Hz
7

$-83 \cdot 8 \quad -122 \cdot 1$
$CF_3 \!-\! CF_2 \!-\! CO \cdot OPF_2$
$^3J(F\!-\!F) = 1 \cdot 5$ Hz
6

Thermolysis of bromodifluoroacetic anhydride afforded the bromo-difluoro-acetyl bromide (**8**);[22] the ^{19}F shift reported is shown. The ^{19}F shifts of both

$-59 \cdot 1 \ \overset{O}{\underset{\parallel}{}}$
$BrCF_2 \!-\! \overset{\parallel}{C} \!-\! Br$
8

$CO \cdot F$
$| \quad 19 \cdot 5$
$CO \cdot F$
9

$-126 \cdot 5 \quad \overset{-121 \cdot 3}{CF_2 \!-\! CO \cdot F}$
$CF_2 \qquad\qquad 23 \cdot 1$
$CF_2 \!-\! CO \cdot F$
10

oxalyl fluoride (**9**) and perfluoroglutaryl difluoride (**10**) have also been re-ported;[23] these are again shown in the structures. The data for the difluoride in both solution and as neat liquid have also been compared by the same authors.[24] In this same paper the authors[24] gave the data for the three isomeric perfluorobutenoyl fluorides. The shift of the acid fluoride atom in perfluorobut-3-enoyl fluoride (**11**) is at δ 17·3 while those of the *cis*- and *trans*- perfluorobut-

$\underset{F}{\overset{(2)}{}} \qquad \underset{F}{\overset{(5)}{}}$
$C{=}C$
$\underset{F}{\overset{(1)}{}} \qquad \underset{CF_2 \cdot CO \cdot F}{\overset{(3)}{}} \ {}^{(4)}$
11

$\delta_1 \ -108 \cdot 9; \ \delta_2 \ -92 \cdot 5$
$\delta_3 \ -112 \cdot 3; \ \delta_5 \ -195 \cdot 5$
$|J_{12}| \ 56 \cdot 9; \ |J_{13}| \ 24 \cdot 9$
$|J_{14}| \ 3 \cdot 6; \ |J_{15}| \ 118 \cdot 4$
$|J_{23}| \ 6 \cdot 8; \ |J_{23}| \approx 0 \cdot 0$
$|J_{25}| \ 40 \cdot 2; \ |J_{34}| \ 8 \cdot 4$
$|J_{35}| \ 15 \cdot 7; \ |J_{45}| \ 4 \cdot 4$ Hz

2-enoyl fluorides (12, 13) are at δ 26·1 $\pm$ 0·2. In each case the coupling of the acoyl fluorine atom is greatest with the *cis*-olefinic fluorine or CF_3 group; the full parameters are discussed in the section on olefins (see p. 406).

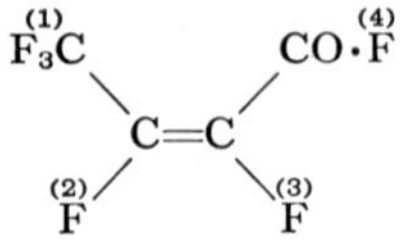

δ_1 −68·3; δ_2 −129·5
δ_3 −142·8; δ_4 26·3
$|J_{12}|$ 7·3; $|J_{13}|$ 11·9
$|J_{14}|$ 12·5; $|J_{23}|$ 9.1
$|J_{24}|$ 22·3; $|J_{34}|$ 26·3 Hz

12

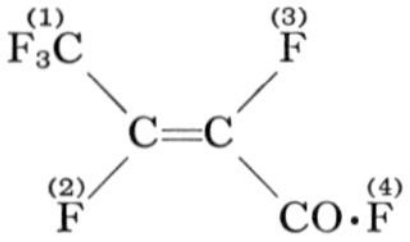

δ_1 −71·6; δ_2 −146·9
δ_3 −158·7; δ_4 25·9
$|J_{12}|$ 7·7; $|J_{13}|$ 21·1
$|J_{14}| \leqslant$ 0·3; $|J_{23}|$ 138·2
$|J_{24}|$ 55·6; $|J_{34}|$ 21·5 Hz

13

Pyrolysis of fluoro-(4-fluorocarbonyl-2-methyl-1,2-oxazetidine) (14) at 560° afforded perfluoro-(3-azabut-2-enoyl) fluoride (15) together with other

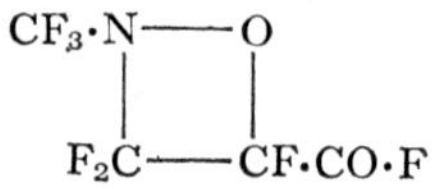

14

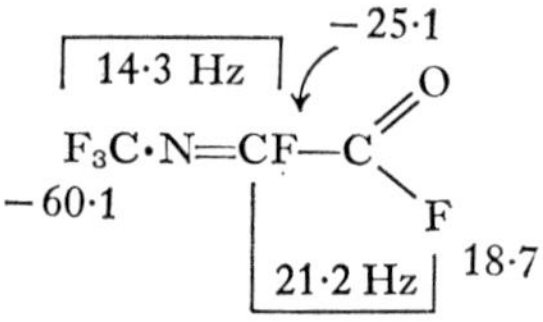

15

products; the ^{19}F parameters of the acid fluoride are shown.[25] The ^{19}F shift of the –CO·F group in 4 (X = F) is 13·3 with ^3J(F–F) of 2·1 Hz (see p. 396).[4]

The relationships found by Ciampelli *et al.*[12] for fluorinated ethers was extended by these authors to fluorinated acid fluorides. Thus a nearly linear relationship was found for the ^{19}F shift of the acid fluoride group, –C(O)F, against the ^{19}F shift of the α-group which varied from –CF_3, $>CF_2$ to $>CF$. Since the ^{19}F shift of the –C(O)F group is at low field, and therefore usually very easily recognized, this relationship should prove to be useful in structural determinations.

Roesky[26] has given the ^{19}F data of a series of N-alkyl-N-(fluoro-carbonyl)-sulphonylfluoridamide derivatives (16) and these data are given in Table IV. The four-bond F–F coupling was 7·6 to 8·0 Hz. It is of some concern to note that in this paper Roesky used negative delta values for ^{1}H shifts in order to maintain the sense of chemical shifts for the two nuclei.

3. Nitro, amino, nitriles, etc.

2-Fluoro-2,2-dinitroethanol and sulphur tetrafluoride gave an ethoxysulphur trifluoride derivative (p. 483) but, in addition, also gave the 1,2-difluoro-1,1-

TABLE IV

^{19}F Parameters of N-alkyl-N-(fluorocarbonyl)-sulphonyl-fluoridamide[26]

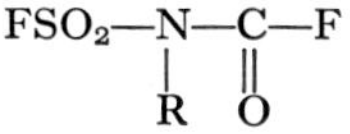

$$FSO_2—N—C—F$$
$$\underset{R}{|} \quad \underset{O}{\|}$$

16

	R = CH$_3$	R = C$_2$H$_5$	R = n-C$_3$H$_7$
δ –C(O)F	−2·94	−1·93	−1·51
δ –SO$_2$F	52·1	55·7	55·1
J(F–F), Hz	7·6	7·6	8
J[-C(O)F–H]	0·8	0·5	..
J[SO$_2$F–H]	1·8	2·0	2·0

dinitroethane (**17**).[27] Only the shift of the FC(NO$_2$)$_2$– group was given in the paper.

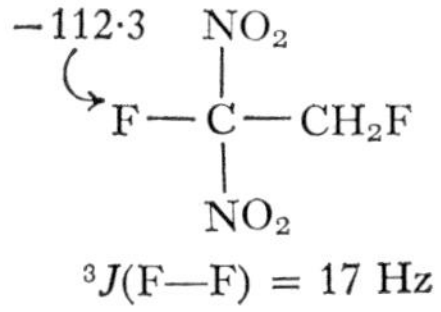

$$\overset{-112\cdot3}{\underset{\text{NO}_2}{F—\underset{\text{NO}_2}{C}—CH_2F}}$$
$$^3J(F—F) = 17 \text{ Hz}$$
17

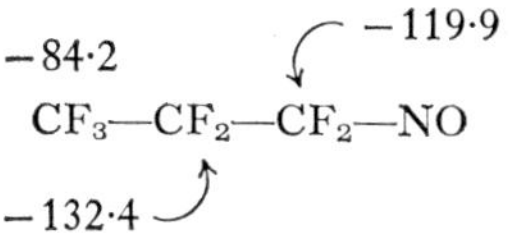

$$\overset{-84\cdot2}{CF_3}—CF_2—CF_2—NO \overset{-119\cdot9}{\underset{-132\cdot4}{}}$$
18

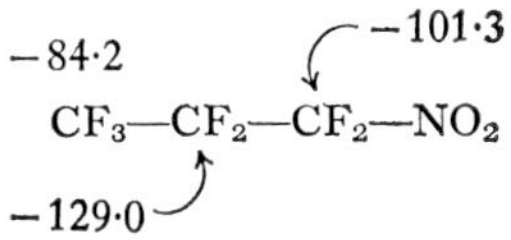

$$\overset{-84\cdot2}{CF_3}—CF_2—CF_2—NO_2 \overset{-101\cdot3}{\underset{-129\cdot0}{}}$$
19

Lee et al.[28] have studied the ^{19}F spectra of a number of nitro-, azo- and azoxy- alkane derivatives. The shifts of the CF$_3$ groups are:

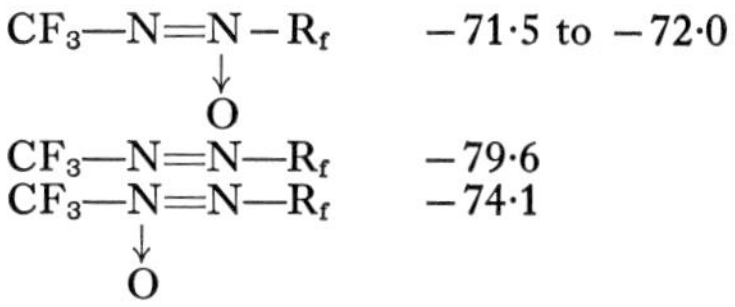

$$CF_3—N{=}N–R_f \qquad -71\cdot5 \text{ to } -72\cdot0$$
$$\underset{O}{\downarrow}$$

$$CF_3—N{=}N—R_f \qquad -79\cdot6$$
$$CF_3—N{=}N—R_f \qquad -74\cdot1$$
$$\underset{O}{\downarrow}$$

and of the CF$_2$ groups:

$$—CF_2—N{=}N—R_f \qquad -112\cdot3 \text{ to } -113\cdot4$$
$$\underset{O}{\downarrow}$$

$$—CF_2—N{=}N—R_f \qquad -100\cdot9 \text{ to } -101\cdot4$$
$$\underset{O}{\downarrow}$$

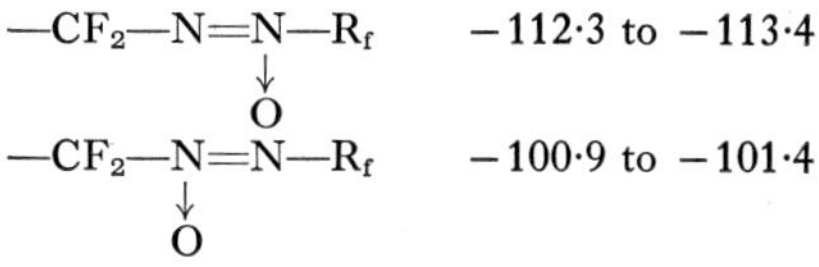

The shifts of the heptafluoro- 1-nitroso- and 1-nitro- propanes are shown in **18** and **19**. The authors also studied the temperature dependence of the spectra and the variable temperature spectra (137° to 230°K) of trifluoronitromethane were shown in the paper. The $^{19}F-^{15}N$ coupling in this compound was found to be 15·1 Hz.

Vinyl fluoride and N-bromobistrifluoromethylamine afforded the 2-bromo-2-fluoro-N,N-bistrifluoromethylamine while addition of bromine to *trans-* and *cis-* 2-fluoro-N,N-bistrifluoromethylvinylamine gave respectively the *erythro-* and *threo-* 1,2-dibromo-2-fluoro-N,N-bistrifluoromethylethylamine.[5] The shifts of these compounds are shown in Table V. The conformations of the *erythro-* and *threo-* isomers, as shown in **20** and **21** respectively, were assigned

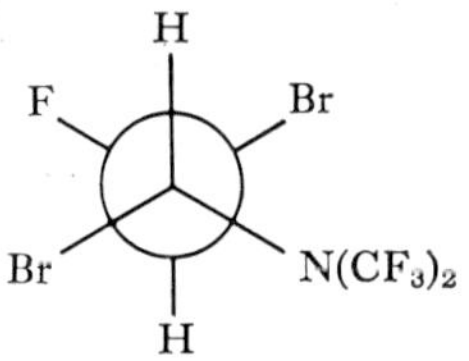

on the basis that the value of $^3J(H-H)$ of 8·0 Hz was more in keeping with *trans-* rather than *gauche-* couplings. Similarly, the values of $^3J(F-H)$ of 8·0 and 3·0 Hz are too small for *trans-*coupling while the CF_3-F coupling of 3·0 and 1·1 Hz for the *threo-* and *erythro-* isomers respectively are consistent with the required *gauche-* and *trans-* couplings. In both this paper and a second by the same authors,[29] the data on a number of N,N-bis-trifluoromethylaminoethylene derivatives were reported which are shown in Table V. It is of importance to notice that the ^{19}F-shifts of the $(CF_3)_2N-$ groups in the *cis-* and *trans-* isomers do not differ significantly from each other and therefore of little use in assigning the geometry of unknowns. The couplings involving the CF_3 group and the other fluorine atoms are also included in the Table. The four-bond F–H coupling of the geminal trifluoromethylamino group and the hydrogen in $(CF_3)_2N-C-H$ was about 1·8 to 1·9 Hz while the *cis-* and *trans-* (CF_3-H) coupling in the $(CF_3)_2N-C=CH$ group are much smaller, 0·5 to 0·9 Hz. The shifts of the $(CF_3)_2N-$ groups in the two bistrifluoromethylamino acetylene derivatives $(CF_3)_2N \cdot C \equiv C \cdot X$, where $X = CH_3$[5] and Br,[29] were also reported and included in Table V.

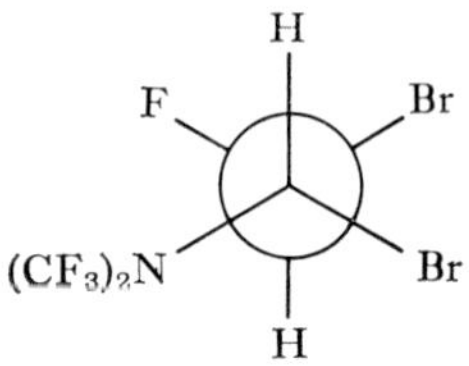

Magnetic non-equivalence of trifluoromethyl groups in N,N-bistrifluoromethylalkylamines of the type $(CF_3)_2N \cdot CXYZ$, where the adjacent carbon atom is chiral, has been reported.[30] The coalescence temperatures, rates and free energies of activation were also calculated and the reasons for the magnetic non-equivalence discussed.

The ^{19}F shift of bis(trifluoromethyl)hydroxylamine is at $-70 \cdot 02$ and the complexes with amines of the form $[R_3N \cdot (CF_3)_2NOH]$ or $\{R_3N[(CF_3)_2NOH]_2\}$ all show ^{19}F resonance signals in the range $-69 \cdot 4$ to $-69 \cdot 9$.[31]

TABLE V

^{19}F shifts of bistrifluoromethylamino groups in $(CF_3)_2N–R$ [5,29]

R	$\delta\ (CF_3)$	R	$\delta\ (CF_3)$
$-CHF \cdot CH_2Br$ [a]	$-56 \cdot 9$	$-CH_2 \cdot CHFBr$ [b]	$-59 \cdot 3$
$-CHBr \cdot CHFBr$ [c] (*erythro*)	$-54 \cdot 3$ and $-59 \cdot 1$	$-CHBr \cdot CHFBr$ [d] (*threo*)	$-57 \cdot 5$
$-CH{=}CBr \cdot CH_3$ (*cis*)	$-58 \cdot 3$	$-CH{=}CBr \cdot CH_3$ (*trans*)	$-58 \cdot 8$
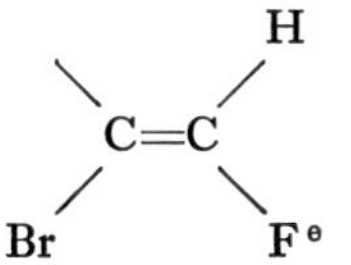 (C=C: Br / H at top, F[e] at bottom)	$-58 \cdot 2$	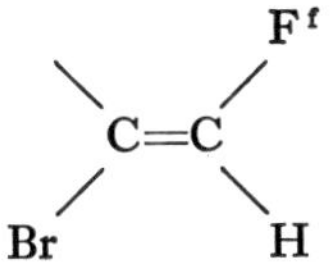 (C=C: Br / F[f] at top, H at bottom)	$-58 \cdot 1$
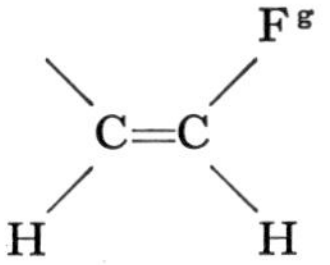 (C=C: H / F[g] at top, H at bottom)	$-59 \cdot 7$	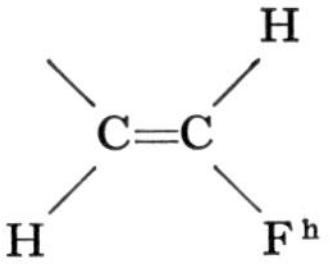 (C=C: H / H at top, F[h] at bottom)	$-59 \cdot 9$
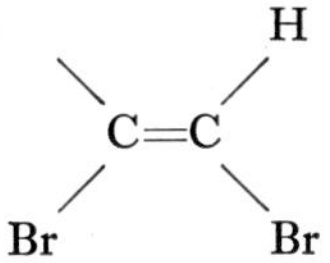 (C=C: Br / H at top, Br at bottom)	$-57 \cdot 3$	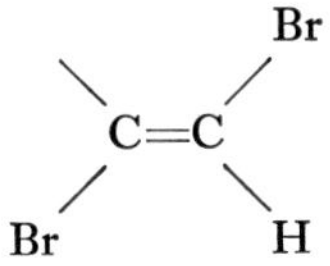 (C=C: Br / Br at top, H at bottom)	$-57 \cdot 1$
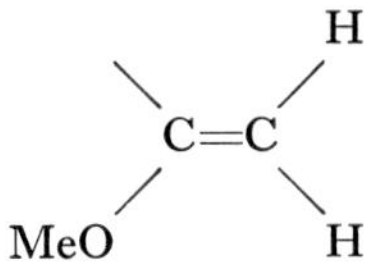 (C=C: MeO / H at top, H at bottom)	$-57 \cdot 6$	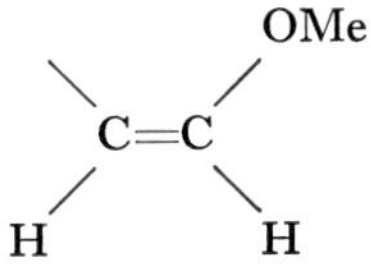 (C=C: H / OMe at top, H at bottom)	$-59 \cdot 1$
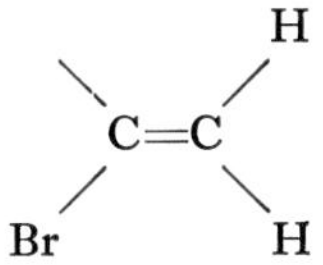 (C=C: Br / H at top, H at bottom)	$-58 \cdot 9$	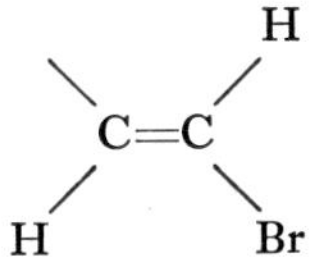 (C=C: H / H at top, Br at bottom)	$-58 \cdot 4$
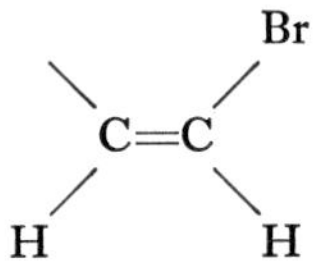 (C=C: H / Br at top, H at bottom)	$-58 \cdot 6$	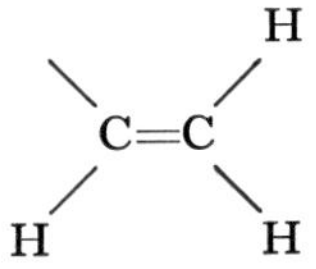 (C=C: H / H at top, H at bottom)	$-58 \cdot 7$
$-C{\equiv}C \cdot CH_3$	$-60 \cdot 0$	$-C{\equiv}C \cdot Br$	$-61 \cdot 0$

Shifts of other fluorine atoms:

		CF₃–F coupling constants:	
[a] $-144 \cdot 5$	[e] $-109 \cdot 9$	[a]	[e] $0 \cdot 9$ Hz
[b] $-147 \cdot 9$	[f] $-105 \cdot 9$	[b] $6 \cdot 2$Hz	[f] $3 \cdot 4$Hz
[c] $-138 \cdot 9$	[g] $-126 \cdot 9$	[c] $1 \cdot 1$Hz	[g] $5 \cdot 1$Hz
[d] $-134 \cdot 7$	[h] $-132 \cdot 1$	[d] $3 \cdot 0$Hz	[h] $0 \cdot 0$Hz

Krespan[32] has described a number of fluorinated imines and differentiated the *syn-* and *anti-* isomers by ^{19}F NMR on the basis that the *syn-* CF_3–H coupling is larger than that of the *anti-* arrangement. The parameters are shown in Table VI. The imines were formed by reaction of ammonia and fluoroalkyl-

TABLE VI

^{19}F parameters of imines and hydrozones[32]

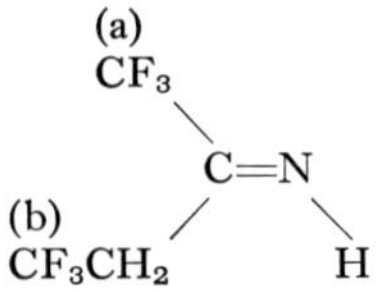

(a) CF₃ ... C=N ... (b) CF₃CH₂ ... H		(a) CF₃ ... C=N ... (b) CF₃CH₂ ... H	
δ CF$_3$(a)	− 77·2 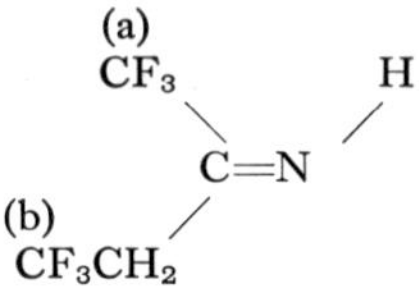	δ CF$_3$(a)	−75·7
δ CF$_3$(b)	− 63·8	δ CF$_3$(b)	−64·1
^5J(F$_a$–F$_b$) =	2·6	^5J(F$_a$–F$_b$) =	1·9
^3J(F$_b$–H) =	9·9	^3J(F$_b$–H) =	10·0
^4J(F$_a$–NH) =	1·3	^4J(F$_a$–NH) =	2·6
^5J(F$_b$–NH) =	1·1	^5J(F$_b$–NH) =	0·5

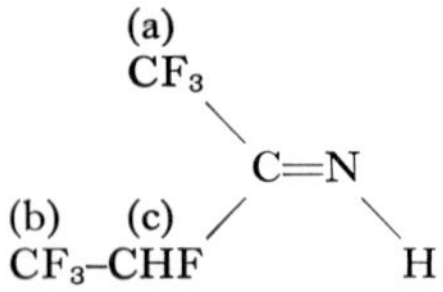

(a) CF₃ ... C=N ... (b) (c) CF₃–CHF ... H		(a) CF₃ ... C=N ... (b) CF₃–CHF ... H	
δ CF$_3$(a)	− 75·2 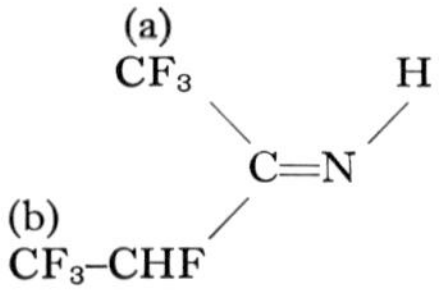	δ CF$_3$(a)	−73·2
δ CF$_3$(b)	− 78·3	δ CF$_3$(b)	−79·0
δ CF (c)	−208·8	δ CF(c)	−206·1
^5J(F$_a$–F$_b$) =	3·4	^5J(F$_a$–F$_b$) =	5·5
^4J(F$_a$–F$_c$) =	10·2	^4J(F$_a$–F$_c$) =	2·7
^3J(F$_b$–F$_c$) =	11·9	^3J(F$_b$–F$_c$) =	12·8
^3J(F$_b$–H$_c$) =	5·9	^3J(F$_b$–H$_c$) =	5·5
^2J(F$_c$–H$_c$) =	43·8	^2J(F$_c$–H$_c$) =	43·6
^4J(F$_a$–NH) =	1·1	^4J(F$_a$–NH) =	2·7

acetylenes; with hydrazine substituted hydrazones were obtained. The parameters of these hydrazones are shown in **22** and **23** and for the two hydrazino-hydrazones **24** and **25**.

− 62·9 and − 65·1
$[(CF_3)_2CH]_2C{=}N{\cdot}NH_2$
22

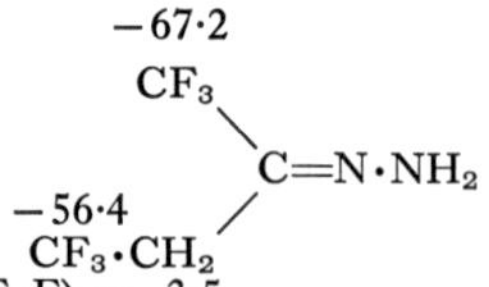

−67·2
CF_3
$\diagdown$
$C{=}N{\cdot}NH_2$
$\diagup$
−56·4
$CF_3{\cdot}CH_2$
^5J(F–F) = 3·5
^3J(F–H) = 10·5
23

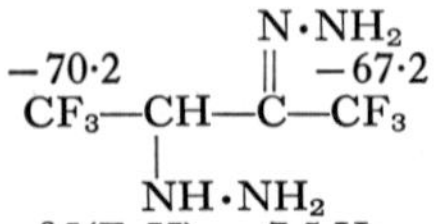

$\qquad$ N·NH₂
−70·2 $\quad$ ‖ −67·2
$CF_3{-}CH{-}C{-}CF_3$
$\qquad$ |
$\qquad$ NH·NH₂
^3J(F–H) = 7·5 Hz
^5J(F–F) = 3·7 Hz
24

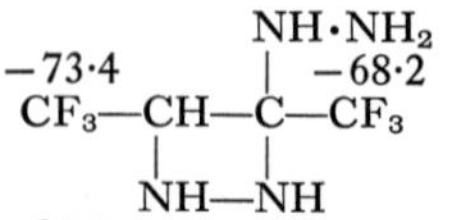

$\qquad$ NH·NH₂
−73·4 $\quad$ | −68·2
$CF_3{-}CH{-}C{-}CF_3$
$\qquad$ |
$\qquad$ NH—NH
^3J(F–H) = 7·3 Hz
^5J(F–F) = 3·2 Hz
25

The reaction of azide salts with fluorovinyl methyl ether afforded an azirine **26** and the carbamate **27**.[33] Isomerization of the azirine **26** afforded the isocyanate **27**. The reaction of sodium hydride with 2-methylhexafluoro-2-

propanol and 2-phenyl-hexafluoro-2-propanol afforded respectively a cyanate **28** and isocyanate **29** derivatives.

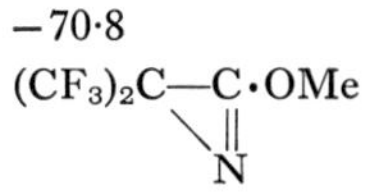

$$-70\cdot8$$
$$(CF_3)_2C\!-\!C\cdot OMe$$
$$\underset{N}{\overset{\|}{\diagdown}}$$

26

$$\overset{O}{\overset{\|}{-74\cdot7}}$$
$$(CF_3)_2CH\cdot NH\cdot C\cdot OCH_3$$
$$^3J(F\!-\!H) = 7\ Hz$$

27

$$-79\cdot6$$
$$CH_3\cdot C(CF_3)_2\cdot N\!=\!C\!=\!O$$
$$^4J(F\!-\!H) = 1\cdot1\ Hz$$

28

$$-78\cdot7$$
$$CH_3.C(CF_3)_2\!-\!O\!-\!C\!\equiv\!N$$
$$^4J(F\!-\!H) = 1\cdot2\ Hz$$

29

4. *Fluoroalkyl iodide polyfluorides*

A new class of organic polyvalent iodine compounds has been described.[34] Reaction of perfluoroalkyl iodides with fluorine and bromine, or chlorine trifluoride, gave the iodonium salts of the general form R_fIF_n, where $n = 2$ or 4. The ^{19}F shifts are shown in Table VII, and it will be observed that the

TABLE VII

^{19}F shifts of fluoroalkyl iodide polyfluorides

R_f	R_fIF_n n	IF_n	Shifts, $\alpha-CF_2$	$\beta-CF_2$	$\delta-CF_2$	CF_3
	0	..	$-65\cdot4$	..	..	$-86\cdot5$
$CF_3\cdot CF_2-$	2	$-167\cdot2$	$-77\cdot6$	..	..	$-82\cdot4$
	4	$-30\cdot6$	$-90\cdot6$	..	..	$-82\cdot4$
	0	..	$-59\cdot7$	$-122\cdot1$	..	$-80\cdot7$
$CF_3\cdot CF_2\cdot CF_2-$	2	$-167\cdot2$	$-81\cdot4$	$-121\cdot5$	..	$-82\cdot5$
	4	$-25\cdot0$	$-84\cdot0$	$-125\cdot6$	..	$-82\cdot5$
	0	..	$-60\cdot3$	$-126\cdot1$	$-115\cdot0$	$-82\cdot5$
$CF_3\cdot CF_2\cdot CF_2\cdot CF_2-$	2	$-169\cdot8$	$-75\cdot8$	$-126\cdot6$	$-119\cdot2$	$-82\cdot4$
	4	$-29\cdot0$	$-83\cdot1$	$-126\cdot6$	$-121\cdot3$	$-82\cdot3$

fluorines of the IF_2 group in R_fIF_2 are strongly shielded, while those of the IF_4 groups in R_fIF_4 are not. It is also noticeable that the α-CF_2 group is more strongly shielded in the perfluoroalkyl iodide tetrafluorides. Since the resonance signals of the parent iodides and of the complex fluorides are easily differentiated, mixtures of heptafluoropropyl iodide difluoride and nonafluorobutyl iodide were examined by NMR and no exchange reactions of the type:

$$R_fIF_n + R_f'I \rightleftharpoons R_fI + R_f'IF_n$$

were observed.

5. *Carbonium ions*

Despite the enormous interest over the past few years, in the study of carbonium ions derived from fluorohydro-carbons, during 1969 to our knowledge only one further example has been cited. This was found when perfluorocyclopropene was dissolved in excess of antimony pentafluoride which led to the formation of perfluorocyclopropyl hexafluoroantiminate;[35a] the ^{19}F shift of the cyclopropyl cation was $\delta -63 \cdot 1$.

C. Fluoro- olefins and acetylenes

For the purpose of comparing the F–F couplings in tetrafluoroethylene complexes with those of the parent olefin it was necessary to determine the values of the couplings in the tetrafluoroethylene. This was done by observing and analysing the ^{13}C satellite spectrum of the ^{19}F–^{12}C resonance signal.[35b]

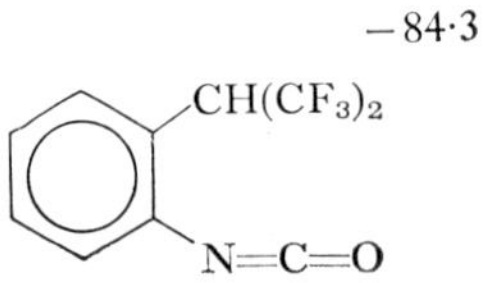

$$-84 \cdot 3$$

$$^3J\text{(F–H)} = 8 \cdot 5 \text{ Hz}$$

30

Banks *et al.*[36] have isolated three fluorobutene derivatives and the ^{19}F parameters are shown in Table VIII. A series of 1-perfluoroalkyl-2-iodoethylenes (**31a** and **31b**) have also been prepared[37] and the ^{19}F parameters are included in Table VIII. In each case the α-fluorine atoms *cis* to the iodo-group (i.e. **31a**) occur at lower field. [These authors[37] also used negative δ values for

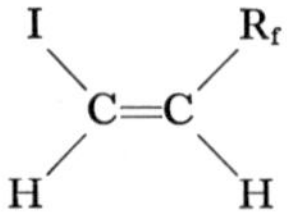

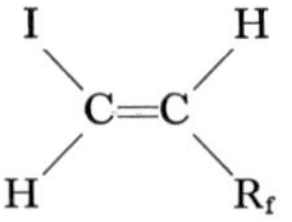

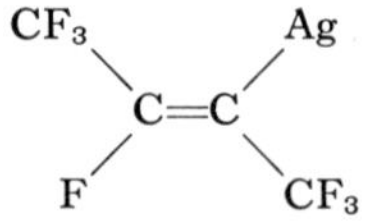

^{1}H shifts to maintain the same sense in the relation of the ^{1}H and ^{19}F shifts.] Hydrolysis of *trans*-perfluoro-1-methylpropenylsilver (**32**) afforded the *trans*-2H-perfluorobut-2-ene,[38] while with methyl iodide the *trans*-2-methyl-perfluorobut-2-ene was obtained. The *cis*-isomer of the latter but-2-ene, together with the *trans*-2-bromo-derivatives were prepared for the purposes of comparison. The shifts of these compounds are also included in Table VIII. Banks *et al.*[6] analysed the spectra of the *cis*- and *trans*-2H-nonafluoropentenes, 3H-2-bromo-octafluoropent-1-ene, *trans*-2H-octafluoro-1-methoxy- and *cis*-1H-2-

TABLE VIII

^{19}F parameters of some fluoro-olefin derivatives

R_1	R_2	R_3	R_4	$\delta\,R_1$	$\delta\,R_2$	$\delta\,R_3$	$\delta\,R_4$	Ref.
H	I	H	CF_3	..	..	..	−65·85	37
I	H	H	CF_3	..	..	..	−61·95	37
F	CF_3	Ag	CF_3	−95·1	−70·0	..	−50·7	38
F	CF_3	H	CF_3	−120·5	−74·7	..	−60·5	38
CF_3	F	Br	CF_3	−69·3	−104·2	..	−63·8	38
F	CF_3	Br	CF_3	−97·2	−67·0	..	−61·0	38
F	CF_3	CH_3	CF_3	−119·9	−69·1	..	−66·2	38
CF_3	F	CH_3	CF_3	−68·7	−119·0	..	−63·3	38
CF_3	H	CF_3	CF_3	−66·5	..	−60·6	−60·6	36
NH_2	CF_3	H	CF_3	..	−72·8	..	−58·7	32
NH_2	CF_3	CN	F	..	−67·0	..	−165·2	32
NH_2	CF_3	CF_3	Cl	..	−63·9	−59·5	..	32
NH_2	CF_3	CN	Cl	..	−66·8	..	..	32
CF_3	H	F	$-CF_2CF_3$	−58·5	..	−113·7	$\delta\,CF_2$ −124·7 $\delta\,CF_3$ −87·1	6
H	CF_3	F	$-CF_2CF_3$	..	−62·05	−115·4	$\delta\,CF_3$ −86·3 $\delta\,CF_2$ −124·7	6
CF_2H	Br	F	$-CF_2CF_3$	−114·5	..	−119·8	$\delta\,CF_2$ −118·7 $\delta\,CF_3$ −86·5	6
H	CF_2OMe	F	$-CF_2CF_3$	..	−70·7	−118·8	$\delta\,CF_2$ −124·1 $\delta\,CF_3$ −85·3	6
H	I	H	$-CF_2CF_3$	..	..	..	$\delta\,CF_2$ −116·1 $\delta\,CF_3$ −85·7	37
I	H	H	$-CF_2CF_3$	..	..	..	$\delta\,CF_2$ −114·5 $\delta\,CF_3$ −85·85	37
F	F	F	$-CH(CF_3)_2$	−117·7	−95·5	−185·6	−65·6	36
F	F	OMe	$-CH(CF_3)_2$	−97·7	−107·8	..	−67·2	36
H	I	H	$-CF(CF_3)_2$	..	..	..	$\delta\,CF$ −196·3 $\delta\,CF_3$ −77·7	37
I	H	H	$-CF(CF_3)_2$	..	..	..	$\delta\,CF$ −189·4 $\delta\,CF_3$ −77·6	37
F	F	Br	$-CFH.CF_2$ CF_3	−79·5	−75·0	..	$\delta\,CFH^a$ $\delta\,CF_2{}^b$ $\delta\,CF_3$ −85·2	6

[a] Resonance not observed.
[b] AB system centred at −129·7 with $\Delta\nu = 297$ Hz. (Frequency at which measured not stated, either 54·46 or 94·10 MHz.)

bromo-octafluoro- pent-2-enes; the shifts are shown in Table VIII. Also included in Table VIII are the data for a number of vinylamines which have been
reported.[32] A number of bis(trifluoromethyl)amino-substituted ethylenes and
propenes have also been prepared and the shifts of the olefinic fluorine atoms
were included, for convenience, in Table V.[5]

The data for the three isomeric butenoyl fluorides (**11, 12, 13**) were included
in the section on acid derivatives (p. 397). The assignments, however, were
made[24] on the basis of comparison with the parameters of perfluoropropene[39]
and perfluoroacryloyl fluoride.[40] It is of interest that, while the *trans-* F–F
coupling across the double bond are larger (118·4 to 138·2 Hz) than the corresponding *cis-* couplings (9·1 to 40·2 Hz in these particular instances), the
coupling between the acyl fluorine and the *cis*-substituent group is larger than
that to the *trans*-group.

The analysis of hexafluoro-1,3-butadiene (**33**) has been undertaken[41] and

δ_a $-93\cdot86$ J_{ab} $+50\cdot737$ $J_{bc'}$ $+14\cdot195$
δ_b $-107\cdot96$ J_{ac} $+31\cdot911$ $J_{aa'}$ $+4\cdot800$
δ_c $-179\cdot69$ J_{bc} $-118\cdot577$ $J_{bb'}$ $+11\cdot313$
$J_{ab'}$ $+2\cdot449$ $J_{cc'}$ $-30\cdot305$
$J_{ac'}$ $+2\cdot409$

33

the parameters obtained are as shown; the signs of the long-range $^5J(\text{F–F})$ in
33 were found to be positive. The available data on other fluorobutadienes were
also discussed and the mechanism for the five-bond F–F coupling suggested.
The authors also suggested that the two trifluorovinyl groups in **33** were not
coplanar and the general features of the AA′BB′CC′ spin system were discussed. Perfluoroisoprene has been isolated[36] and the ^{19}F parameters are
shown in **34**.

$\delta\ CF_3$ $-63\cdot5$ J_{cd} $120\cdot1$
$\delta\ F_a$ $-70\cdot9$ J_{ce} $36\cdot4$
$\delta\ F_b$ $-70\cdot9$ J_{de} $61\cdot4$
$\delta\ F_c$ $-176\cdot3$ J_{ad} or J_{bd} $7\cdot3$
$\delta\ F_d$ $-117\cdot1$ J_{ae} or J_{be} $2\cdot7$
$\delta\ F_e$ $-100\cdot3$

34

Reaction of cyclohexylisocyanide, perfluorobut-2-yne and ethanol afforded
both a butene derivative (**35**) and a ketenimine (**36**);[42] the assignments, however, were not given. Perfluoro-(3-methylbuta-1,2-diene) has also been prepared[36] and the ^{19}F parameters found at $-50°$ are shown in **37**.

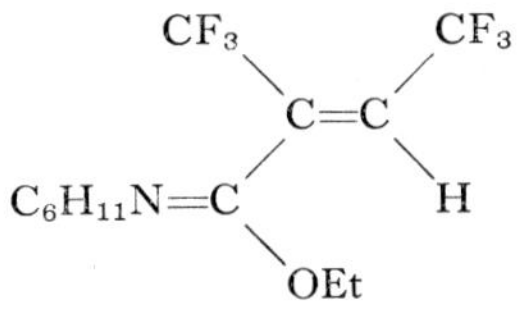

35

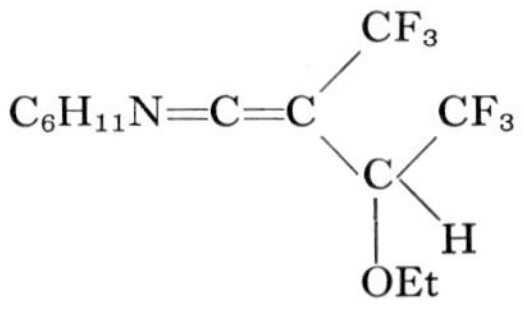

36

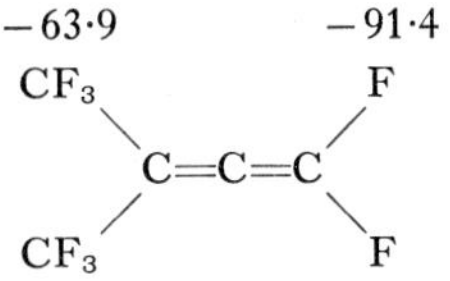

$^5J(\text{F–CF}_3) = 3{\cdot}3$ Hz

37

The data for the monoperfluoro- methyl-, ethyl- and isopropyl- acetylenes have been reported[37] and the data are shown in Table IX. Banks *et al.*[6] have described the preparation of two fluoropent-2-yne derivatives and the data for these two compounds are also included in Table IX. It was perhaps fortuitous

TABLE IX

^{19}F parameters of acetylene derivatives

$$\text{R–C}{\equiv}\text{C–R}^1$$

			Shifts			
				R^1		
R	R^1	R	CF	CF_2	CF_3	Ref.
H	CF_3	..	..	..	$-55{\cdot}55$ a	37
H	$-CF_2CF_3$	..	..	$-105{\cdot}9$	$-88{\cdot}7$ b	37
$CH_3{\cdot}O{\cdot}CF_2-$	$-CF_2CF_3$	$-61{\cdot}9$	..	$-106{\cdot}1$	$-86{\cdot}5$ c	6
CF_3	$-CF_2{\cdot}CF_3$	$-54{\cdot}3$	..	$-107{\cdot}3$	$-86{\cdot}5$ c	6
H	$-CF(CF_3)_2$	..	$-171{\cdot}8$	..	$-90{\cdot}7$ d	37

a $^4J(\text{F–H}) = 3{\cdot}5$ Hz.
b $^3J(\text{F–F}) = 3{\cdot}6$ Hz, $^4J(\text{F–H}) = 5{\cdot}3$ Hz, $^5J(\text{F–H}) = 0{\cdot}5$ Hz.
c $^3J(\text{F–F}) = {}^5J(\text{F–F}) = 3{\cdot}3$ Hz.
d $^3J(\text{F–F}) = 9{\cdot}9$ Hz, $^4J(\text{F–H}) = 6{\cdot}0$ Hz, $^5J(\text{F–H}) = 0{\cdot}6$ Hz.

that in these two compounds the values of $^3J(\text{F–F})$ of the pentafluoroethyl group and $^5J(CF_2\text{–C}{\equiv}\text{C–}CF_2)$ were the same, namely $3{\cdot}3$ Hz.

D. Fluorinated cyclohydrocarbons

1. *Saturated monocyclic systems*

The spectra of both 2,3,3-trichloro-1,2,2-trifluoro- and 3,3-dichloro-1,1,2-trifluoro-2-iodo- cyclopropanes have been analysed.[43] The same authors also analysed the spectra of 2,3-dichloro-1,1,2-trifluoro-, 2,3,3-trichloro-1,1,2-tri-fluoro- and 3,3-dichloro-1,1,2-trifluoro-2-iodo- cyclobutanes and the data are summarized in Table X. The trichloro- derivative was studied at two different concentrations but there was little variation in the parameters. There was the usual large difference between the magnitudes of the *gem*-F–F couplings in the cyclobutane (~ 200 Hz) and the cyclopropane (~ 150 Hz) derivatives.

Reduction of N-cyclohexyl-3-perfluoromethyl-3-[1,2,3-tris(perfluoro-methyl)cyclopropenyl]- ketenimine and acetamide derivatives—afforded the corresponding cyclopropyl derivatives (38).

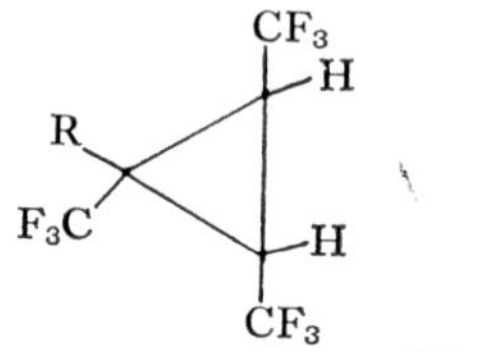

$$38; \text{ a, R} = \text{R'NH}-\overset{\displaystyle CF_3}{\underset{\displaystyle O}{\overset{\displaystyle |}{\underset{\displaystyle ||}{C}}}}-\overset{\displaystyle CF_3}{\underset{\displaystyle H}{\overset{\displaystyle |}{\underset{\displaystyle |}{C}}}}-$$

$$\text{b, R} = \text{R'N}=\text{C}=\underset{\displaystyle CF_3}{\overset{\displaystyle |}{C}}-$$

The adducts of 1,1-dichloro-2,2-difluoroethylene with 1,4-dichloro-1,3-butadiene are the 2,2,4-trichloro-3,3-difluorocyclobutane derivatives.[44] The F–F and F–H couplings constants found in the four isomers are shown in structures **39** to **42**, but there was no unambiguous method of assigning the configuration of the fluorine atoms from the F–H coupling constants.

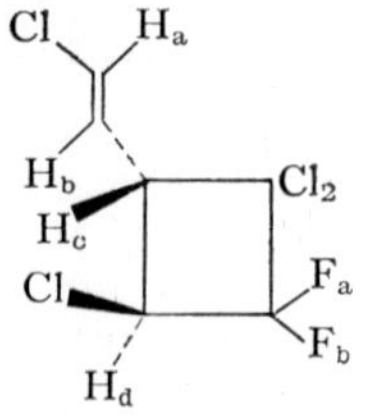

$J(F_a-H_b) = 0.8$
$J(F_a-H_d) = 10.7$
$J(F_b-H_d) = 6.1$
$J(F_a-H_c) = 3.0$
$J(F_b-H_c) = 1.8$

39

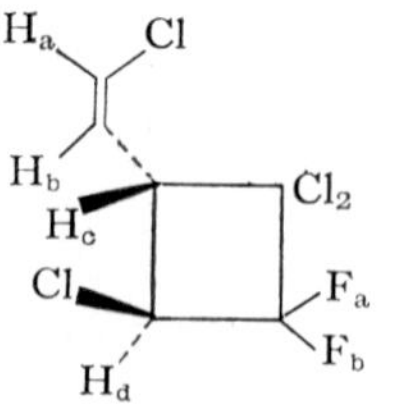

$J(F_a-H_b) = 0.8$
$J(F_a-H_d) = 10.2$
$J(F_b-H_d) = 6.0$
$J(F_a-H_c) = 3.5$
$J(F_a-H_b) = 0.8$
$J(F_a-F_b) = 179.2$

40

The 1-chloro-2,3,3-trifluorocyclobutane has been prepared[45] from tri-fluoroethylene and vinyl chloride and the NMR spectra examined in detail. The parameters are shown in Table X. The authors also gave the various dihedral angles calculated, assuming that the cyclobutane ring was puckered to

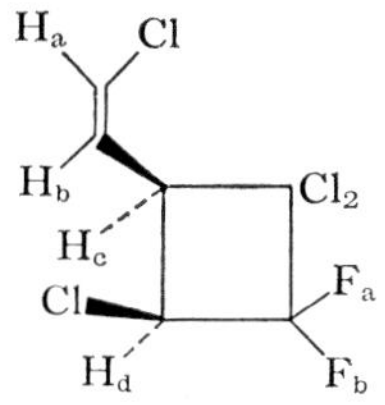

$J(F_a–H_d) = 9\cdot2$
$J(F_b–H_d) = 7\cdot3$
$J(F_b–H_c) = 7\cdot2$
$J(F_a–H_b) = 1\cdot3$
$J(F_a–F_b) = 182\cdot7$

41

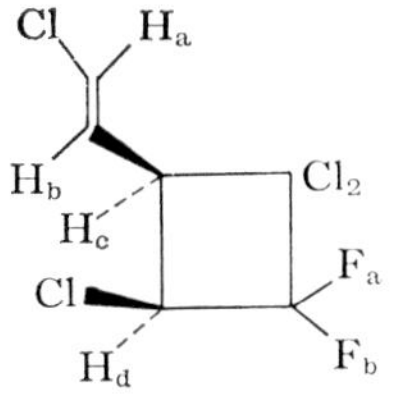

$J(F_a–H_b) = 1\cdot4$
$J(F_a–H_d) = 9\cdot6$
$J(F_b–H_d) = 7\cdot2$
$J(F_b–H_c) = 7\cdot2$
$J(F_a–F_b) = 187\cdot5$

42

TABLE X

The ^{19}F parameters of cyclobutane derivatives

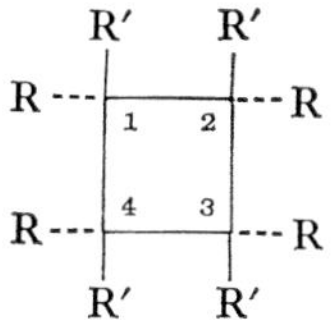

R_1	F	F	F	F	F
R_1'	F	F	F	F	F
R_2	I	I	Cl	H	Cl
R_2'	F	F	F	F	F
R_3	Cl	Cl	Cl	Cl	Cl
R_3'	H	Cl	Cl	H	Cl
R_4	H	H	H	H	H
R_4'	H	H	H	H	H
$\delta-R_1$	$-87\cdot95$	$-86\cdot86$	$-101\cdot94$	$-93\cdot72$	$-102\cdot75$
$\delta-R_1'$	$-108\cdot53$	$-112\cdot30$	$-111\cdot35$	$-124\cdot64$	$-112\cdot22$
$\delta-R_2$	..	..	..	..	..
$\delta-R_2'$	$-129\cdot72$	$-109\cdot27$	$-114\cdot44$	$-188\cdot76$	$-115\cdot20$
$J(R_1–R_1')$	$+197\cdot62$	$+200\cdot07$	$+202\cdot89$	$210\cdot09$	$+202\cdot65$
$J(R_1–R_2')$	$-5\cdot56$	$-5\cdot05$	$+2\cdot82$	$0\cdot93$	$+2\cdot84$
$J(R_1'–R_2')$	$-8\cdot92$	$-8\cdot76$	$-9\cdot46$	$-3\cdot69$	$-9\cdot46$
$J(R_1–R_4)$	$+8\cdot45$	$+8\cdot99$	$+10\cdot47$	$9\cdot16$	$+10\cdot46$
$J(R_1–R_4')$	$+11\cdot71$	$+9\cdot49$	$+9\cdot76$	$2\cdot49$	$+9\cdot57$
$J(R_1'–R_4)$	$+10\cdot23$	$+10\cdot59$	$+10\cdot69$	$20\cdot02$	$+10\cdot46$
$J(R_1'–R_4')$	$+13\cdot23$	$+11\cdot78$	$+11\cdot86$	$15\cdot99$	$+12\cdot03$
$J(R_2'–R_4)$	$-2\cdot53$	$-3\cdot03$	$-3\cdot1$	$-3\cdot32$	$-2\cdot92$
$J(R_2'–R_4')$	$+5\cdot92$	$+6\cdot87$	$+7\cdot5$	$11\cdot58$	$+7\cdot40$
$J(R_1–R_3')$	$+5\cdot64$	..	..	$2\cdot70$	..
$J(R_1'–R_3')$	$+1\cdot13$	..	..	$3\cdot45$	..
$J(R_2'–R_3')$	$+6\cdot85$	..	..	$14\cdot70$	..
Ref.	43	43	43	45	46

the extent of 27°. The equatorial-axial and diaxial cross-ring F–H couplings were smallest (~ 3 Hz) while the diequatorial couplings were larger (~ 10 Hz). It was also claimed that this was the first instance of the determination of the signs of the cross-ring F–H coupling constants in cyclobutanes.

43   44

The analysis of the spectra of the two cyclobutanes, namely 1,1,2,2-tetra-chlorotetrafluoro- (43) and 1,1,2-trichloro-2,3,3-trifluoro- (44) has also been considered in detail.[46] The ^{19}F spectrum of 43 consisted of a single line and analysis was effected by using the ^{13}C satellite spectrum, which was treated as an *aa'bb'* subspectrum. The ^{19}F shift was $-114\cdot20$ with ^2J(F–F), *cis* ^3J(F–F) and *trans* ^3J(F–F) being $+200\cdot0$, $-11\cdot93$ and $+5\cdot86$ Hz respectively. The isotopic shift between the ^{13}CF and ^{12}CF resonance was $0\cdot1248$ p.p.m. The cyclobutane 44 was treated as an ABMRX spin system and again the *cis*- and *trans*- ^3J(F–F) were found to be of opposite sign with the former being nega-tive. The conclusions regarding these signs in this compound are in agreement with those of Park *et al.*[43] and the two sets of data are compared in Table X. It must be mentioned, however, that Park *et al.* found the *cis*- and *trans*- F–F coupling to be of like sign, namely negative, in the two iodo-compounds examined (Table X). Therefore it would seem to be too early to predict any possible rules regarding the signs of this three-bond F–F coupling.

The cyclo-addition reactions of 1,1-difluorobuta-1,3-diene with various fluoro-olefins afforded vinylcyclobutane derivatives.[47] It was stated that the ^{19}F spectra were very complex and were being considered in greater detail. Only preliminary generalizations of the ^{19}F shifts were given which, however, could be useful for structural assignment.

One of the most significant advances in the simplification of spectra, in which there is coupling between heteronuclei, is the use of noise-decoupling. A wide band of r.f. radiation is applied over the range of the resonance frequencies of one of the nuclei resulting in the effective decoupling of all the nuclei of one type, e.g. ^{1}H, resulting in the simplification of the spectrum of the second type of nuclei, e.g. ^{19}F. This elegant approach has been amply demonstrated by Ernst,[48] who first described this method in 1966,[49] by application to the study of some cyclobutane derivatives. The data for the *cis*- and *trans*- trifluorochloro-cyclobutanes 45 and 46, which exist in equilibrium between the two forms **a** and **b**, are shown in Table X. The author considered the overall problem of the

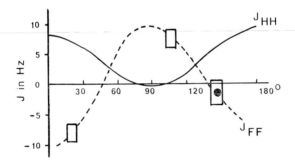

assignment of the ^{19}F shifts and the variation in the vicinal F–F coupling constants. The variation of this vicinal coupling with dihedral angle was compared with the same relationship of the vicinal H–H coupling; the variations are shown in Fig. 1. The effects of temperature and dielectric constant of the

FIG. 1. Vicinal F–F coupling constants in trifluorochlorocyclobutanes as a function of dihedral angle ϕ. The rectangles indicate the probable ranges of values. The two values designated ● are corresponding values for trifluorochlorocyclopropane. The solid curve represents the Karplus relationship which holds for vicinal H–H coupling constants. (From Ernst.[48])

solvent were also considered and the variations reported may prove useful in making future assignments.

The chemical shifts of the *cis*- and *trans*- 2H-octafluorocyclopentyl- and decafluorocyclohexyl- methyl ethers have been recorded as a basis of differentiation between the *cis*- and *trans*- isomers.[50]

2. *Unsaturated monocyclic systems*

1,2-Bis(trifluoromethyl)-3,3-difluorocyclopropene has been prepared[51] and the shifts of the CF_3 groups were $\delta = -63.0$ and that of the $>CF_2$ group, $\delta = -107.2$ with $^4J(CF_3\text{–}F) = 2.4$ Hz. The parent perfluorocyclopropene has also been prepared[35a] and the shifts of the two types of fluorine atoms were $\delta = -96.7$ and -145.1, but no precise assignments were given. The coupling between the olefinic F and the $>CF_2$ group was 43.5 Hz.

The three 1-perfluoro- methyl-, ethyl- and isopropyl- 2,2-difluorocyclopropenes have been prepared[37] by insertion reactions on the acetylenic derivatives; the data are as shown in Table XI. Isocyanides were found to react in

TABLE XI

^{19}F parameters of fluorocyclopropenes[37]

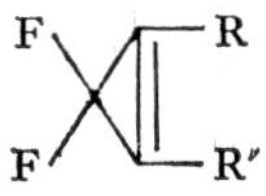

R	R'	δF_2	R'
H	CF_3	-102.8	$\delta CF_3 \ -63.3$ [a]
H	CF_2CF_3	-104.6	$\delta CF_2 \ -115.8; \ \delta CF_3 \ -85.85$ [b]
H	$-CF(CF_3)_2$	-104.9	$\delta CF \ -128.9; \ \delta CF_3 \ -77.05$ [c]

[a] $^4J(CF_3\text{–}CF_2) = 2.8$; $^3J(CF_2\text{–}H) = 1.3$; $^4J(CF_3\text{–}H) = 0.4$ Hz.
[b] $^4J(CF_2\text{–}CF_2) = 5.2$; $^5J(CF_2\text{–}CF_3) = 0.9$; $^3J(CF_2\text{–}CF_3) = 2.55$; $^4J(CF_2\text{–}H) = 0.35$; $^3J(CF_2\text{–}H) = 1.2$ Hz.
[c] $^4J(CF_2\text{–}CF) = 6.8$; $^5J(CF_2\text{–}CF_3) = 0.9$; $^3J(CF\text{–}CF_3) = 9.2$; $^3J(CF_2\text{–}H) = 1.4$; $^4J(CF\text{–}H) = 1.4$ Hz.

inert solvents with two mol. of hexafluorobut-2-yne to afford cyclopropenyl-ketenimine derivatives **47**.[42] Hydrolysis of **47** in turn afforded the corresponding acetamide derivatives (**48**).

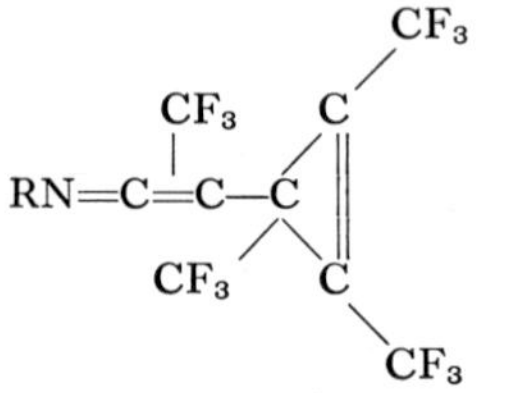

47

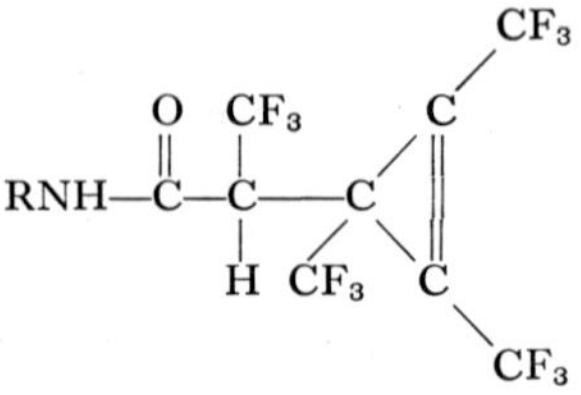

48

The spectra of 3,3,4,4-tetrafluoro- (**49a**) and 1,2-dichlorotetrafluoro- (**49b**) cyclobutenes have been analysed in detail.[46] The spectrum of **49a** is of an

[AA′X]₂ type, the analysis of which has been dealt with previously, but, as in the cyclobutanes, the *cis*- and *trans*- ^3J(F–F) values were of opposite sign, the former being negative. The magnitudes of these couplings warrant comment as both are very much larger than in cyclobutanes, being in the range: *cis* $-12\cdot5 \pm 0\cdot5$ and *trans* $+28 \pm 3$ Hz. The ^{19}F spectrum of **49b** consists of a

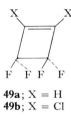

49a; X = H
49b; X = Cl

50a; Z = I	50b; Z = Cl
δ F$_A$ $-92\cdot43$	δ F$_A$ $-102\cdot97$
δ F$_B$ $-111\cdot32$	δ F$_B$ $-110\cdot49$
δ F$_C$ $-101\cdot88$	δ F$_C$ $-108\cdot04$
$J_{AB} = +190\cdot08$	$J_{AB} = +192\cdot33$
$J_{AC} = +21\cdot78$	$J_{AC} = +28\cdot62$
$J_{BC} = -11\cdot74$	$J_{BC} = -12\cdot21$
$J_{AX} = -2\cdot50$	$J_{AX} = -2\cdot04$
$J_{AY} = +12\cdot63$	$J_{AY} = +11\cdot85$
$J_{BX} = -1\cdot65$	$J_{BX} = -1\cdot62$
$J_{BY} = +9\cdot72$	$J_{BY} = +10\cdot19$
$J_{CX} = +4\cdot77$	$J_{CX} = +6\cdot85$
$J_{CY} = -0\cdot86$	$J_{CY} = -0\cdot85$

single line and analysis was performed by using the ^{13}C satellite spectrum. The isotopic shift between ^{13}CF and ^{12}CF was 0·1213 p.p.m.

The spectra of 3-chloro- and 3-iodo- 3,4,4-trifluorocyclobutenes have been analysed[43] and the parameters are as shown in **50a** and **b**. The couplings of the olefinic protons to the two fluorine atoms were different and the four bond (F–H) coupling was larger than that of the three-bond (F–H) coupling. Cyclo-addition of 1,1,4,4-tetrafluorobuta-1,3-diene to dichlorodifluoro- and chloro-trifluoro- ethylenes gave chlorocyclobutene derivatives which, on further re-action, gave the four cyclobutene derivatives **51** to **54**;[52] the shifts were as shown. A seven-bond F–F coupling in the F–C–C=C–C=C–C–F entity in dicyclobutene derivatives **55** has been reported[53] to be in the range 2·8 to 4·3 Hz. The only other seven-bond F–F coupling reported occurs in fluorinated

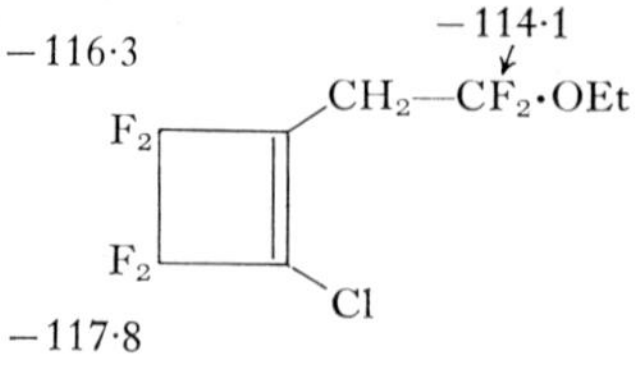

51

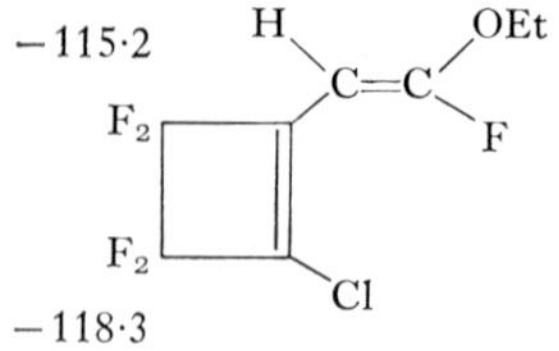

52

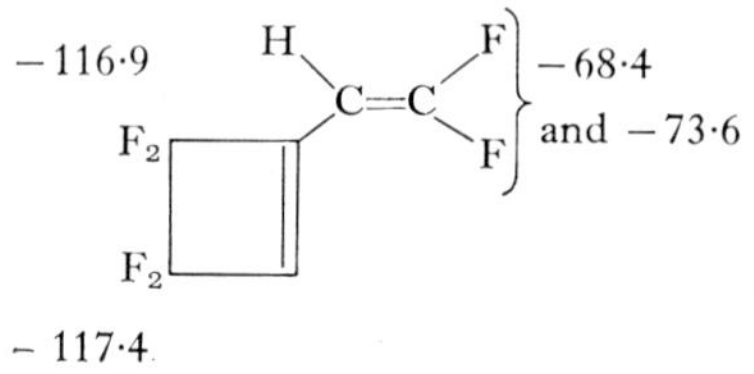

53

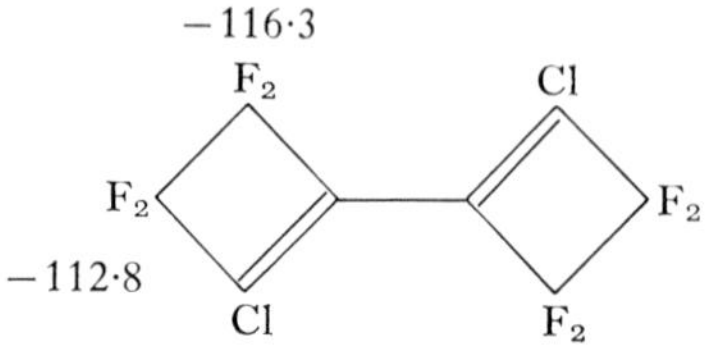

54

styrenes.[54, 55] In **55a** no five-bond F–F coupling was observed, which is rather surprising since five-bond couplings are more frequently encountered.

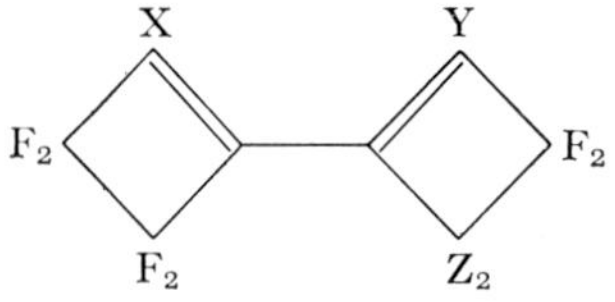

55

55 **a**; X=Cl, Y=Z=F
  b; X=Cl, Y=OEt, Z=F
  c; X=Cl, Y=Z=OEt
  d; X=Y=Z=OEt
  e; X=I, Y=Z=OEt

Using homonuclear spin tickling techniques the signs of all the F–F and F–H couplings in 3-chloro-, 3-iodo-, 3,4,4-trifluoro-, 1,4-dichloro-3,3,4-trifluoro-1-ethoxy-2-chlorotetrafluoro-, 1-chloropentafluoro- and 1,4,4-trifluorocyclobutenes were determined.[55a] The spectrum of 1,2,4,4-tetrafluorocyclobutene-3-one ethylene ketal was used to determine the sign of the cross-ring and vicinal couplings between the vinylic and allylic fluorines. Typical couplings in these compounds are:

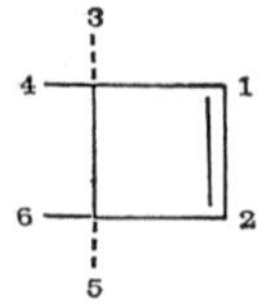

	J_{34}	$J_{12}(\sim 0°)$	$J_{13}(\sim 52°)$	J_{15}	$J_{35}(\sim 0°)$	$J_{36}(\sim 104°)$
J_{FF}	+180 to +200	−8	+4 to +8	+16 to +19	−12 to −17	+24 to +30
J_{FH}	..	−7	−1 to −2	+6 to +12		
J_{HH}	−12 to −15	+3	+1 to +2	−0·5	+4 to +6	+1 to +4

The values in parentheses are the approximate dihedral angle.

The opposite signs, and order of magnitude, of the *cis* and *trans* vicinal ^3J(F–F) values are in agreement with the observations of Harris and Robinson.[46]

The chemical shifts of 1-chloro-2-methoxy-hexafluorocyclopentane and octafluorocyclohexene have also been recorded, but no assignments made,[50] although the data for the former compound had been given earlier[56] and reported in Volume One of this series.[57]

The shift of the $>CF_2$ group in the symmetrical 1*H*,2*H*,4*H*,5*H*-tetrafluoro-cyclohexa-1,4-diene has been given as δ −170·1.[58] The spectra of the two isomeric 2- and 3- fluorocyclohexa-2,5-dien-1-one system have been analysed in some detail.[59] The shifts of the two 4-methyl-4-allyl- derivatives considered are as shown in **56** and **57**, together with the relevant coupling constants. It

^3J(F–HC=) = 15·3 Hz
^4J(F–HC=) = 12·0 Hz
^5J(F–HC=) = 1·5 Hz

56

^3J(F–HC=) = 13·8 Hz
^4J(F–HC=) = 7·2 Hz
^5J(F–HC=) = 0·9 Hz

57

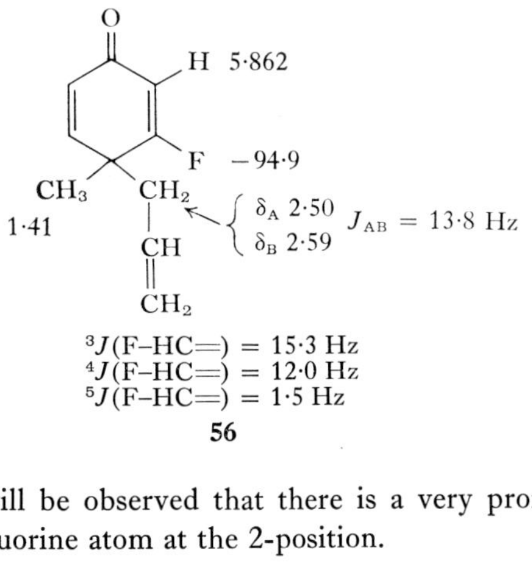

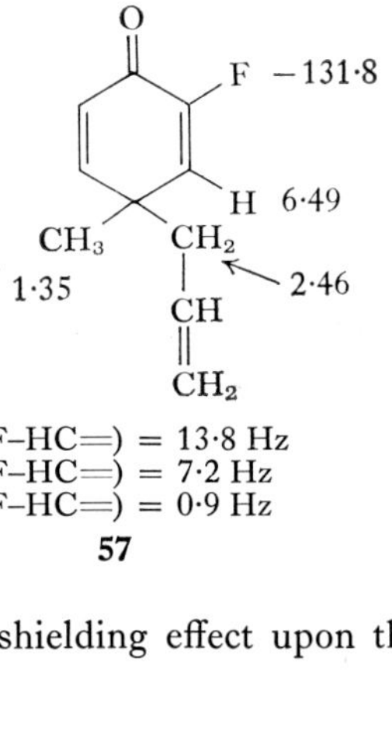

will be observed that there is a very pronounced shielding effect upon the fluorine atom at the 2-position.

3. *Bicyclic systems*

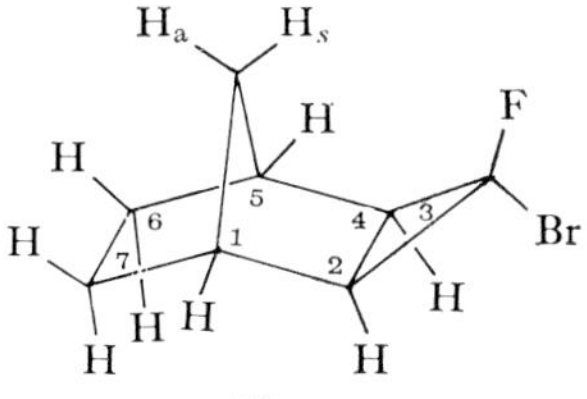

The study of rigid bi- and tri- cyclic alkanes afford excellent examples of the stereochemical dependence of coupling constants. Thus, Jefford *et al.*[60] have used *syn*-3-fluoro-*anti*-3-bromo-*exo*-tricyclic[3.2.1.0^{2,4}]octane (**58**) as the spatial arrangement of the fluorine with the protons is precisely defined by virtue of the rigid molecular framework. The fluorine resonance signal is a

58

simple pentet, i.e. coupling to four protons. The fluorine nucleus will obviously couple to H_2 and H_4 and it was shown that, rather surprisingly, the fluorine also couples nearly equally to both the *syn*- and *anti*- H_8 protons. Thus, despite the difference in the distance between the nuclei involved, the five-bond F–H couplings are nearly identical, 3·6 and 3·0 Hz. The authors comment upon the five-bond couplings between *syn*-diaxially disposed fluorine atoms and methyl groups in the cyclohexane rings of steroids.

Roberts and Dence[61] have investigated the variation of the ^{19}F shifts of 2,2-difluoronorbornane derivatives substituted in various positions and found a pronounced effect of the vicinal orientation on the fluorine shielding. A large upfield shift occurs with a methyl-fluorine dihedral angle of 0°; the effect is smaller at 60° and virtually absent at 120°. The ^{19}F shifts of the bridgehead fluorine atoms, in bicyclo- alkanes and alkenes, have been considered in some detail by Anderson and Stock.[62] The substituent chemical shifts calculated for the series studied showed anomalous behaviour in that the presence of electron withdrawing groups in the 4-position, of 4-substituted-1-fluorobicyclo[2.2.2]-octanes, caused the fluorine to experience large shifts to high field. This behaviour was contrasted with that in the rigid bridge anthracene derivatives. These authors draw attention to the remarkable range of shifts for the tertiary fluorine which varied from δ −132 for t-butyl fluoride to −194 for 1-apocamphyl fluoride. These variations were ascribed to changes in bond-order resulting from interaction between non-bonding orbitals of fluorine atom and the endocyclic carbon-carbon bond orbitals.

The ^{19}F spectrum of hexafluorobicyclo[2.2.0]hexa-2,5-diene has been analysed as an AA′XX′X″X‴ spin system.[63] The refined parameters are shown in **59**. The spectrum of **59** has also been studied in greater detail by Kaiser[64]

59

δ F^1, F^4 = −191·0; δ F^2, F^3, F^5, F^6 = −122·8
J_{15} or J_{16} = ±9·92 or ∓7·12*
J_{14} = ∓9·36
J_{35} = ±0·10
J_{25} or J_{23} = ±14·03 or ∓3·01*

* This pair of couplings cannot be distinguished in the analysis.

using subspectral analysis; the parameters were essentially similar to those found by Cavalli and Rigatti.[63] Camaggi and Gozzo[65] have extended the studies to a whole series of derivatives of bicyclo[2.2.0]hexa-2,5-diene, Tables XII to XIV. Hexafluorobicyclo[2.2.0]hexa-2,5-diene is an active dipolarophile

TABLE XII

^{19}F shifts of fluorinated bicyclo[2.2.0]hexa-2,5-dienes

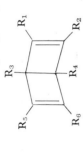

Substituents						Chemical shifts[a]					
R_1	R_2	R_3	R_4	R_5	R_6	δ_1	δ_2	δ_3	δ_4	δ_5	δ_6
H	H	F	F	F	H	··	··	(−183·9)	(−186·9)	−95·8	··
OEt	F	F	F	F	OEt	··	−136·1	−185·7	−185·7	−136·1	··
OEt	F	F	F	OEt	F	··	−133·9	(−180·0)	(−192·0)	··	−133·9
OEt	OEt	F	F	F	F	··	··	−185·1	−185·1	−124·3	−124·3
F	CH₃	F	F	CH₃	F	−109·7	··	−190·5	−190·5	··	−109·7
CH₃	F	F	F	CH₃	F	··	−111·1	−185·2	−193·5	··	−111·1
F	F	Cl	Cl	F	F	−124·9	−124·9	··	··	−124·9	−124·9
F	F	Cl	F	F	F	−125·1	−122·1	··	−192·8	−125·1	−122·1
F	F	I	F	F	F	−126·2	−118·9	··	−194·5	−126·2	−118·9
H	F	F	F	F	F	··	−94·5	(−189·0)	(−191·0)	(−121·0)	(−124·9)
F	F	CF₃	F	F	F	−123·0	−122·0	−67·5	−195·9	−123·0	−122·0
CF₃	F	F	F	F	F	−64·8	−84·9	(−192·0)	(−192·9)	(−119·1)	(−123·0)
F	F	CF₃	CF₃	F	F	−139·0	−139·0	−57·6	−57·6	−139·0	−139·0
F	F	F	F	F	F	−122·8	−122·8	−191·0	−191·0	−122·8	−122·8

[a] Shifts in parentheses may be interchanged.

TABLE XIII

¹⁹F shifts of fluorinated bicyclo[2.2.0]hexenes

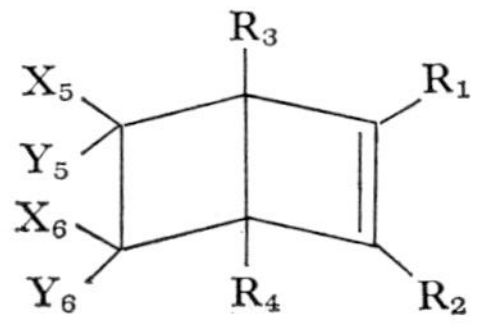

Substituents								Chemical shifts[a]					
R_1	R_2	R_3	R_4	X_5	Y_5	X_6	Y_6	δ_1	δ_2	δ_3	δ_4	δ_5	δ_6
OEt	OEt	F	F	Br	F	Br	F	··	··	−166·1	−166·1	−114·0	−114·0
OEt	OEt	F	F	Br	F	F	Br	··	··	(−163·6)	(−183·5)	(−93·0)	(−93·6)
F	F	Cl	F	Br	F	Br	F	(−118·0)	(−120·0)	··	−169·3	(−109·4)	(−109·8)
F	F	Cl	F	Br	F	F	Br	(−118·3)	(−119·8)	··	−169·3	(−94·4)	(−97·0)
F	F	Cl	Cl	Br	F	Br	F	(−120·0)	(−120·0)	··	··	(−104·0)	(−104·0)
F	F	Cl	Cl	Br	F	F	Br	(−118·2)	(−121·9)	··	··	(−91·8)	(−92·8)
F	F	CF₃	F	Br	F	Br	F	(−116·9)	(−117·5)	−64·6	−169·1	(−93·5)	(−102·2)
CF₃	F	F	F	Br	H	Br	F	−62·6	−81·5	−173·9	−173·9	(−111·9)	(−115·0)
F	F	F	F	CF₃	F	F	F	(−115·9)	(−124·9)	(−177·3)	(−194·5)	−67·4	δ_A −105·0[b] δ_B −112·1
F	F	F	F	F	F	d	CF₃	(−110·0)	(−121·4)	(−174·0)	(−186·0)	δ_A −100·3[c] δ_B −109·8	−65·8

[a] Values in parenthesis are tentative assignments.
[b] $J_{AB} = 221$ Hz.
[c] $J_{AB} = 228$ Hz.

[d] $X_6 =$

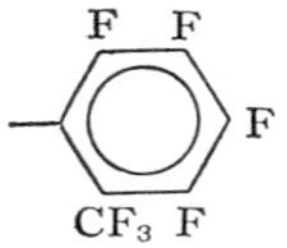

TABLE XIV

¹⁹F shifts of fluorinated bicyclo[2.2.0]hexanes

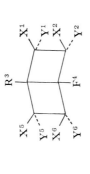

Substituents									¹⁹F Chemical shifts					
X^1	Y^1	X^2	Y^2	R^3	X^5	Y^5	X^6	Y^6	δ_1	δ_2	δ_3	δ_4	δ_5	δ_6
Br	F	Br	F	F	Br	F	Br	F	-118.4	-118.4	-141.3	-141.3	-118.4	-118.4
F	H	F	H	F	F	H	F	H	-206.6	-206.6	-161.1	-161.1	-206.6	-206.6
H	F	H	F	CF_3	H	F	H	F	-210.5	-202.5	-70.5	-156.0	-210.5	-202.5

and reacts with phenylazide and diazomethane to give mono- and di- adducts of the type **60** and **61**.[66] The vinylic fluorine atoms in the parent bicyclohexa-diene and in adducts of type **60** are all fairly constant at $\delta = -121\cdot4 \pm 1\cdot2$ while the bridgehead fluorine atoms exhibit more variable shifts, e.g. in the symmetrical adducts **61a** $-183\cdot5$, **61b** $-186\cdot4$, **61c** $-171\cdot6$ and **60c** $-182\cdot5$.

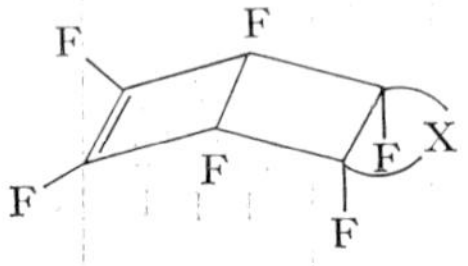

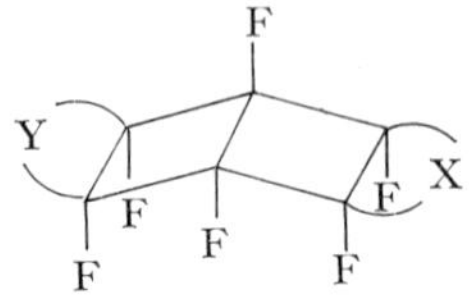

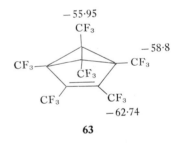

60, a $X = -N-N{=}N-$
                 $|$
                  C_6H_5

  b $X = -CH_2-N{=}N-$
  c $X = {>}N-C_6H_5$

61, X or Y $=$
a $-N-N{=}N-$
        $|$
        C_6H_5

b $-CH_2-N{=}N-$
c ${>}N-C_6H_5$

Concurrent with the work by Haszeldine *et al.*,[67] on the photoisomerism of hexakis(trifluoromethyl)benzene, Lemal *et al.*[68] have reported their work on the same topic. The most abundant product was hexakis(trifluoromethyl)-bicyclo[2.2.0]hexadiene (**62**), the next most abundant being the hexakis(tri-

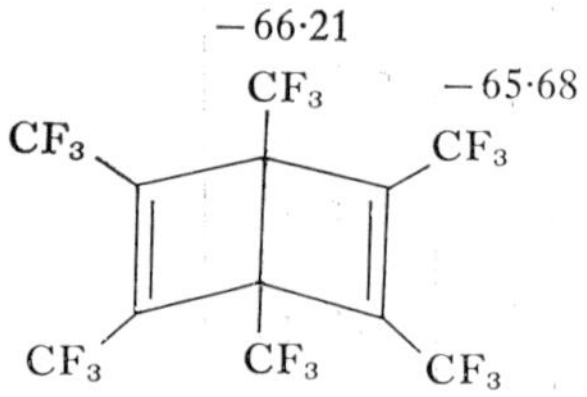

62

63

fluoromethyl)benzvalene (**63**) and the least abundant hexakis(trifluoromethyl)-prismane (**64a**); the ^{19}F resonance of the latter compound is a single sharp signal at $\delta -63\cdot48$. The ^{19}F data for the prismane derivative (**64a**) was also reported,[67] as was that for the benzvalene compound (**63**), although the precise assignments in the latter case were not given. One further prismane derivative **64b** was reported by these authors.[67] The shifts of the trifluoromethyl groups in a series of adducts, bicyclooctatrienes **64**, formed by the addition of hexa-fluorobut-2-yne with various aromatic hydrocarbons have been reported.[69] Perfluorocyclohexa-1,3-diene reacts with alkynes to form a range of 2,3-di

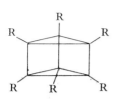

64a R = CF$_3$, δ CF$_3$ −63·48[68], −65·8[67]

b R = CF$_2$CF$_3$, $\begin{cases} δ \text{ CF}_2 & -111·3 \\ δ \text{ CF}_3 & -82·7 \end{cases}$

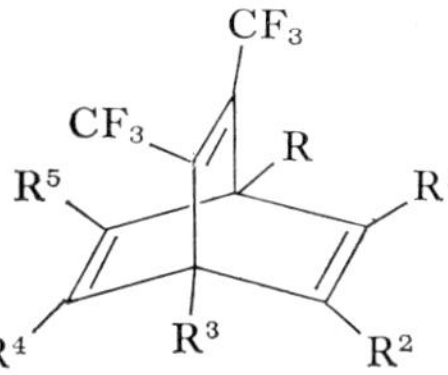

R, R^1, R^2, R^3, R^4, R^5 = Me or H

65

substituted-1,4,5,6,7,7,8,8-octafluorobicyclo[2.2.2]octa-2,5-dienes of the type **66**.[70] The ^{19}F shifts of these compounds are shown in Table XV.

TABLE XV

^{19}F parameters of 2,3-disubstituted-1,4,5,6,7,7,8,8,-
octafluorobicyclo[2.2.2]octa-2,5-dienes (66)[70]

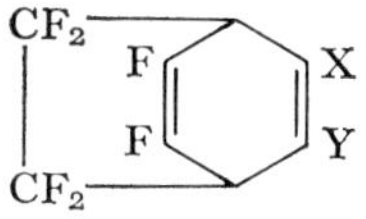

66

X	Y	\multicolumn{4}{c}{Chemical shifts, δ}

X	Y	CF$_2$–CF$_2$	CF=CF	$\diagdown$CF	X, Y
H	Me	−122·5	−154·5 −155·4	−210·1 −212·6	
H	CF$_3$	−122·9	−152·3 −153·3	−209·7 −214·9	CF$_3$ −63·1
H	CH$_2$Cl	−121·1	−152·6 −154·3	−209·5 −214·8	
H	C$_6$H$_5$	−121·9	−153·5 −154·5	−208·1 −210·3	
Me	Me	−123·7	−155·1	−213·0	
CF$_3$	CF$_3$	−121·5	−150·5	−213·2	CF$_3$ −54·1
Me	CF$_3$	−122·7	−152·3	−210·7 −214·5	CF$_3$ −59·1
CH$_2$Cl	CH$_2$Cl	−122·1	−154·0	−215·6	
CO$_2$Et	CO$_2$Et	−121·3	−152·6	−213·4	

The adducts of tetrafluoro- and 1,2-bis(trifluoromethyl)-3,3-difluorocyclo-propenes with various dienes have also been investigated[51] and the data for these adducts are shown in **67** to **68**. The products containing the cyclopropane ring were identified by the magnitude of the *gem* F–F coupling of approximately 170 Hz. Perfluorocyclopropene and buta-1,3-diene gave the adduct **79** (1,6,7,7-tetrafluorobicyclo[4.1.0]hepta-3-ene) with shifts as shown.[35a]

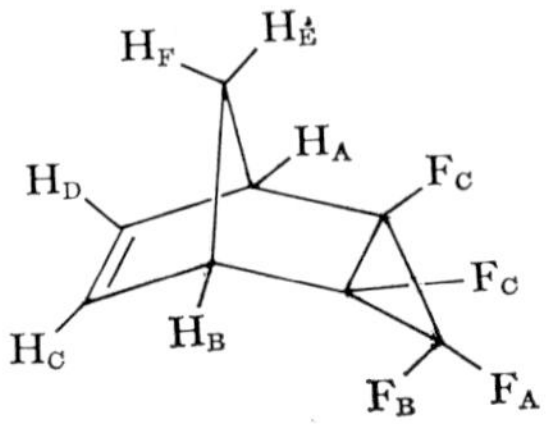

$\delta\,F_A\,-134{\cdot}8;\,\delta\,F_B\,-128{\cdot}1$
$\delta\,F_C\,-221;\,J(F_AF_B) = 177$
$J(F_A\text{–}H_C,\,H_D) = 1{\cdot}8;\,J(F_AF_C) = 24{\cdot}3$
$J(F_A\text{–}H_A,\,H_B) = 4{\cdot}3,\,J(F_C\text{–}H_A,\,H_B) = 2{\cdot}3$
$J(F_BF_C) = 1{\cdot}4$

67

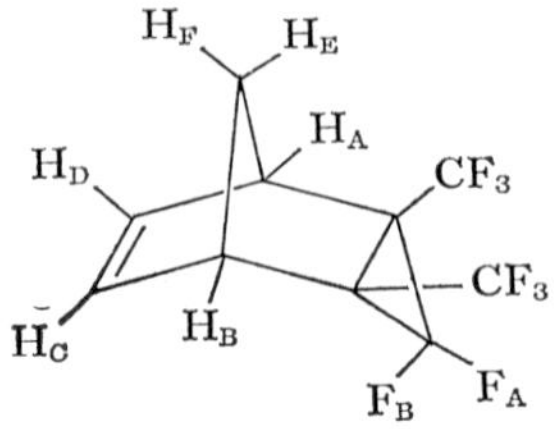

$\delta\,F_A\,-113{\cdot}7;\,\delta\,F_B\,-129{\cdot}9;\,\delta\,CF_3\,-59{\cdot}9$
$J(F_A\text{–}CF_3) = 19{\cdot}0;\,J(F_B\text{–}CF_3) = 2{\cdot}6$
$J(F_AF_B) = 178$

68

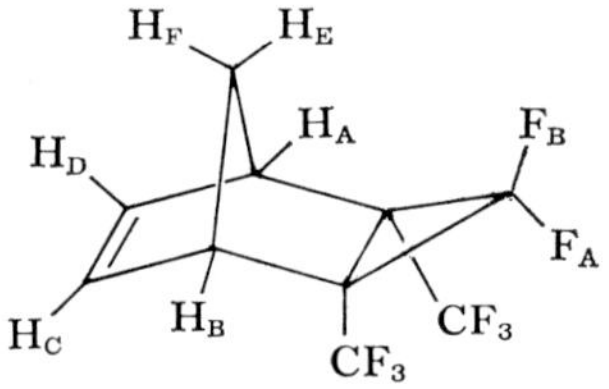

$\delta\,F_A\,-109{\cdot}4;\,\delta\,F_B\,-136{\cdot}0;\,\delta\,CF_3\,-61{\cdot}7$
$J(F_A\text{–}CF_3) = 19{\cdot}0;\,J(F_B\text{–}CF_3) = 2{\cdot}6$
$J(F_AF_B) = 177$

69

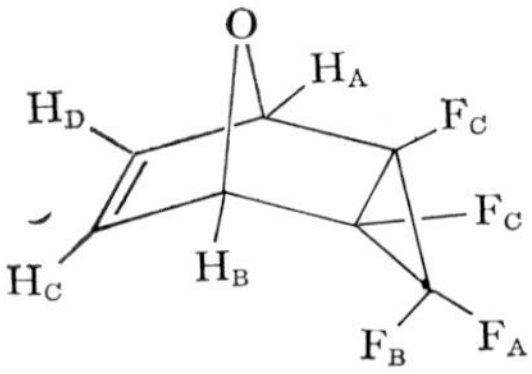

$\delta\,F_A\,-139{\cdot}3;\,\delta\,F_B\,-129{\cdot}9;\,\delta\,F_C\,-227{\cdot}8$
$J(F_AF_B) = 175;\,J(F_BF_C) = 0;$
$J(F_AF_C) = 23{\cdot}4;\,J(F_A\text{–}H_A,\,H_B) = 3{\cdot}2$

70

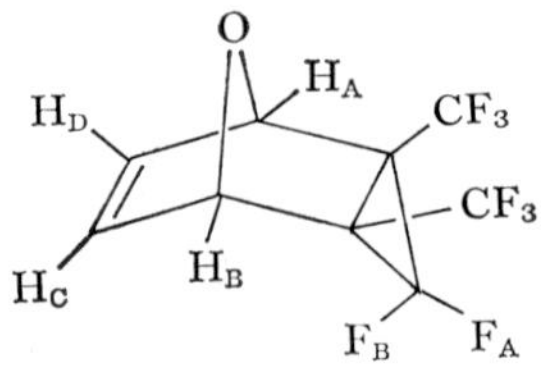

$\delta\,F_A\,-116{\cdot}7;\,\delta\,F_B\,-137{\cdot}0;\,\delta\,CF_3\,-59{\cdot}7$
$J(CF_3\text{–}F_A) = 16;\,J(CF_3\text{–}F_B) = 2{\cdot}2$
$J(F_AF_B) = 166;\,J(F_B\text{–}H_A,\,H_B) = 1{\cdot}2$

71

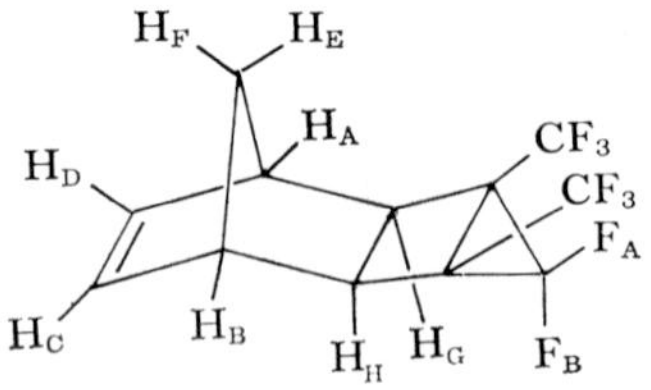

$\delta\,F_A\,-140{\cdot}2;\,\delta\,F_B\,-142;\,\delta\,CF_3\,-61{\cdot}8$
$J(CF_3\text{–}F_A) = 11{\cdot}5;\,J(CF_3\text{–}F_B) = 5{\cdot}6;$
$J(F_AF_B) = 172$

72

The variable temperature spectra of fluoro-chloro-bullvalen (**80**) have been studied and the four signals observed at low temperature were assigned to the positional isomers **80a** to **80d**.[71]

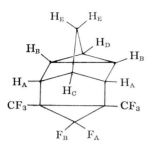

δ F$_A$ $-127\cdot3$; δ F$_B$ $-133\cdot2$; δ CF$_3$ $-59\cdot8$
J(CF$_3$–F$_A$) $= 18\cdot6$; J(CF$_3$–F$_B$) $= 4\cdot0$;
J(F$_A$F$_B$) $= 176$

73

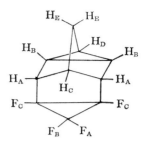

δ F$_A$ $-142\cdot7$; δ F$_B$ $-152\cdot4$; δ F$_C$ -218
J(F$_A$F$_C$) $= 22\cdot7$; J(F$_A$F$_B$) $= 179$;
J(F$_B$F$_C$) $= 0$

74

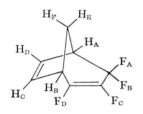

$\left.\begin{array}{l}\delta\text{ F}_A\\ \delta\text{ F}_B\end{array}\right\}$ $-100\cdot3$ and $-117\cdot4$; J(F$_A$F$_B$) $= 263$
δ F$_C$ $-174\cdot5$; δ F$_D$ $-127\cdot8$

75

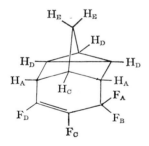

$\left.\begin{array}{l}\delta\text{ F}_A\\ \delta\text{ F}_B\end{array}\right\}$ $-88\cdot0$ and $-108\cdot1$; J(F$_A$F$_B$) $= 251$
δ F$_C$ $-160\cdot0$; δ F$_D$ $-132\cdot1$

76

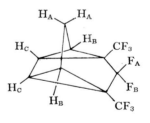

$\left.\begin{array}{l}\delta\text{ F}_A\\ \delta\text{ F}_B\end{array}\right\}$ $-85\cdot6$ and $-107\cdot8$; J(F$_A$F$_B$) $= 266$
δ F$_C$ $-173\cdot7$; δ F$_D$ $-128\cdot8$

77

δ F$_A$ $-101\cdot1$; δ F$_B$ $-108\cdot3$; δ CF$_3$ $-65\cdot8$
J(F$_A$F$_B$) $= 242$; J(CF$_3$–F$_A$) $= 10\cdot1$;
J(CF$_3$–F$_B$) $= 3\cdot1$

78

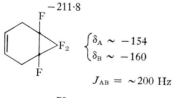

$\begin{cases}\delta_A \sim -154\\ \delta_B \sim -160\end{cases}$

$J_{AB} = \sim 200$ Hz

79

80

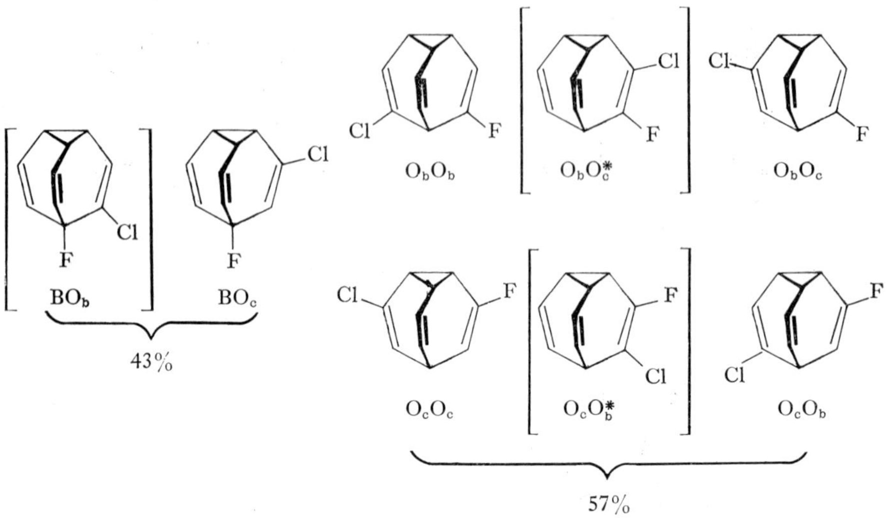

O_bO_b $O_bO_c^*$ O_bO_c

BO_b BO_c

43%

O_cO_c $O_cO_b^*$ O_cO_b

57%

80a **80b** **80c** **80d**

E. Fluoroaromatics

1. *Monocyclic*

The spectra of α,α,α-trifluorotoluene and 2-chloro-5-nitro-α,α,α-trifluoro-toluene have been analysed in detail and the spectral parameters discussed.[72] The proton and fluorine-19 spectra of six *ortho*-substituted fluorobenzenes of the type **81** have also been analysed in detail;[73] fluorine decoupled spectra were used to obtain the initial parameters.

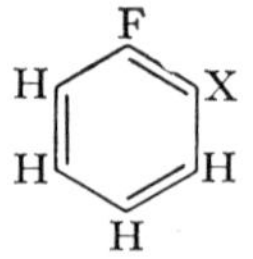

X = F, Cl, Br, I,
CN or NO$_2$

81

The deuterium isotope effect in fluorobenzenes has been investigated[74] by a study of the 2-*d*-, 3-*d*- and 4-*d*- fluorobenzene. The effect on the fluorine resonance is about 25 to 35 times greater when the deuterium atom is in the *ortho*-position compared with that when in the *meta*- or *para*- position. The ^{19}F–^{2}H coupling constants were *ortho*- $^3J(F–^2H) \approx 1\cdot4$, *mets*- $^4J(F–^2H) \approx 0\cdot9$ and *para*- $^5J(F–^2H) < 0\cdot2$ Hz. The effect of substituents on the F–^{1}H couplings in fluorobenzene derivatives has been considered by Goldstein *et al.*[75] There appears to be an additivity of substituent effects although the total range of substituent effects on the ^{19}F–^{1}H couplings is only 2·4 Hz. The study of some 3- and 3,5- substituted fluorobenzenes has shown that in these compounds the effects of the substituents were not additive.[76] The authors, however, found that there was a correlation between the rate constants of methoxydefluorination and the ^{19}F shifts of some 5-substituted-3-nitrofluorobenzenes. The ^{19}F shifts are shown in Table XVI.

The ^{19}F parameters of 1,2-dichloro-4-fluorobenzene, a product obtained by the direct fluorination of *o*-dichlorobenzene, have been reported.[77] The ^{19}F shift was at −110·5 with $^{3}J(F–H) = 8·3$, $^{4}J(F–H) = 5·4$ and $^{5}J(F–H) = 7·6$ Hz. Diehl *et al.*[78] have used the principle of subspectral analysis to determine the NMR parameters of 1,2,4-trifluorobenzene; the analysis of the ABCMXZ spin system was discussed in detail.

Pyrolysis of 2,3-disubstituted octafluorobicyclo[2.2.2]octa-1,3-dienes results in the elimination of tetrafluoroethylene with the formation of 1,2-disubstituted tetrafluorobenzenes.[70] The shifts of the tetrafluorobenzenes obtained in this work are included in Table XIII. Reaction of methyllithium with 1,2-dibromo-tetrafluorobenzene gave[79] two products, 2,3,4,5-tetrafluoro-*o*-xylene and 2,3,4,5 tetrafluorotoluene; the shifts are shown in Table XVI. Perfluorobi-cyclo[2.2.0]hexa-2,5-diene and phenyllithium gave[65] the 1,4-difluorotetra-phenyl- and fluoropentaphenyl- benzenes (**82** and **83** respectively); the

1-chloro-4-iodo-tetrafluorobenzene was also obtained in this work. The data on some trifluoromethyl-substituted benzenes have been given,[80] although some of the data had been reported by the same author at an earlier date.[81] The spectra were recorded at the low frequency of 30 MHz on an early instrument and the reliability of some of the data is suspect. The shifts of the compounds included in the two papers[65, 80] are included in Table XVI.

Cooper[82] has studied the ^{19}F spectra of bromo- and iodo- pentafluoroben-zenes, 1,2-dibromo- and 1,2-diiodo- tetrafluorobenzenes, 3,5-difluoro-iodo-benzene and 2,5-difluorobromobenzene. The *meta*- and *para*- F–F coupling constants were found, as previously reported[83] in other instances, to follow an additive substituent constant basis. The presence of a pronounced solvent dependence of $^{3}J(F–F)$ was found (2 to 3 Hz), and it was suggested this may

TABLE XVI

¹⁹F shifts of fluoroaromatics

1	2	3	4	5	6	δ_1	δ_2	δ_3	δ_4	δ_5	δ_6	Ref.
F	H	NO_2	H	H	H	−159·5	..	..	..	..	..	76
F	H	SO_2Me	H	H	H	−159·7	..	..	..	..	..	76
F	H	CF_3	H	H	H	−160·5	..	..	..	..	..	76
F	H	F	H	H	H	−159·8	..	−159·8	..	..	..	76
F	H	Cl	H	H	H	−160·6	..	..	..	..	..	76
F	H	Br	H	H	H	−160·3	..	..	..	..	..	76
F	H	I	H	H	H	−160·3	..	..	..	..	..	76
F	H	OMe	H	H	H	−161·7	..	..	..	..	..	76
F	H	CO_2H	H	H	H	−162·3	..	..	..	..	..	76
F	H	OH	H	H	H	−162·2	..	..	..	..	..	76
F	H	NH_2	H	H	H	−163·6	..	..	..	..	..	76
F	H	Me	H	H	H	−164·1	..	..	..	..	..	76
F	H	NO_2	H	NO_2	H	−154·7	..	..	..	..	..	76
F	H	SO_2Me	H	NO_2	H	−155·4	..	..	..	..	..	76
F	H	CF_3	H	NO_2	H	−155·7	..	..	..	..	..	76
F	H	F	H	NO_2	H	−155·5	..	−155·5	..	..	..	76
F	H	Cl	H	NO_2	H	−156·8	..	..	..	..	..	76
F	H	I	H	NO_2	H	−157·5	..	..	..	..	..	76
F	H	OMe	H	NO_2	H	−158·1	..	..	..	..	..	76
F	H	CO_2H	H	NO_2	H	−158·1	..	..	..	..	..	76
F	H	NH_2	H	NO_2	H	−160·6	..	..	..	..	..	76

(1)	(2)	(3)	(4)	(5)	δ_a	δ_b	δ_c	δ_d	δ_e	Ref.
F	NO_2	H	Me	H	−160·6	:	:	:	:	76
F	CF_3	H	CF_3	H	−157·1	:	:	:	:	76
F	Br	H	Br	H	−158·6	:	:	:	:	76
F	I	H	I	H	−158·3	:	:	:	:	76
F	NH_2	H	NH_2	H	−164·3	−138·0	:	:	:	76
F	H	F	H	H	−138·0	:	:	:	:	73
F	H	Cl	H	H	−115·3	:	:	:	:	73
F	H	Br	H	H	−107·0	:	:	:	:	73
F	H	I	H	H	−93·15	:	:	:	:	73
F	H	CN	H	H	−107·3	:	:	:	:	73
F	H	NO_2	H	H	−118·4	:	:	:	:	73
F	H	OMe	H	H	−135·2	:	:	:	:	73
F	H	OH	H	H	−140·9	:	:	:	:	73
F	H	Me	H	H	−117·7	:	:	:	:	77
F	C_6H_5	H	Cl	C_6H_5	−110·5	:	:	:	:	65
I	C_6H_5	C_6H_5	C_6H_5	C_6H_5	−115·0	:	:	:	:	65
Br	H	C_6H_5	C_6H_5	H	−76·0	−111·2	−76·0	−111·2	:	82
$-O{\cdot}CH_2CH_2OH$	F	F	F	F	:	:	:	−119·7	:	82
$-NH{\cdot}CH_2CH_2OH$	F	H	H	F	:	−166·6	−174·3	−166·1	−161·1	84
$-NH{\cdot}CH_2CH_2NH_2$	F	F	H	F	−114·0	−166·0	−166·3	−166·0	−157·9	84
$-N(CH_2CH_2OH)_2$	F	F	F	F	−161·1	−166·1	−174·6	−166·1	−161·1	84
$-O{\cdot}CH_2{\cdot}CO_2H$	F	F	F	F	−157·9	−145·3	−56·3	−145·3	−150·9	84
$-N(CH_2CH_2OH)_2$	F	F	F	F	−161·1	−165·6	−165·2	−165·6	−157·2	84
H	F	F	CF_3	F	−150·9	−147·5	−152·4	−147·5	−152·3	84
H	F	F	Cl	F	−157·2	−130·49	−152·4	−155·4	−138·1	85
H	F	F	F	F	−152·3	−113·07	−132·6	−154·2	−137·9	85
H	F	Cl	F	F	−117·19	:	−124·5	−163·2	−134·1	85
H	F	Br	Cl	F	−109·4	:	−111·9	−156·1	−133·0	85
H	F	I	Br	F	−97·5	:	:	−162·2	−131·6	85
H	F	F	I	F	−138·3	−141·4	:	−141·4	−138·3	85
H	F	F	H	F	−137·5	−132·8	:	−132·8	−137·5	85
H	F	F	H	F	−137·2	−120·2	:	−120·2	−137·2	85

Substituents						Chemical shifts, δ						Ref.
1	2	3	4	5	6	δ₁	δβ	δ₃	δ₄	δ₅	δ₆	
NO₂	Cl	F	F	F	F	··	··	−135·5	−149·1	−152·7	−145·9	85
NO₂	Br	F	F	F	F	··	··	−126·5	−148·5	−151·2	−145·2	85
NO₂	I	F	F	F	F	··	··	−111·4	−148·1	−149·6	−144·0	85
NO₂	F	Cl	F	F	F	··	−124·1	··	−126·0	−158·5	−140·8	85
NO₂	F	Br	F	F	F	··	−116·1	··	−117·9	−158·0	−139·5	85
NO₂	F	I	F	F	F	··	−106·5	··	−108·6	−157·8	−138·0	85
NO₂	F	F	Cl	F	F	··	−146·5	−136·7	··	−136·7	−146·5	85
NO₂	F	F	Br	F	F	··	−145·6	−128·5	··	−128·5	−145·6	85
NO₂	F	F	I	F	F	··	−145·1	−115·5	··	−115·5	−145·1	85
NO₂	H	F	F	F	F	··	··	−135·9	−144·6	−155·7	−141·8	85
NO₂	F	H	F	F	F	··	−121·9	··	−124·1	−160·6	−138·5	85
H	Me	F	F	F	F	··	··	−135·9	−157·6	−135·5	−148·3	70
H	Me	F	F	F	F	··	··	−145·5	−158·3	−160·7	−141·2	79
H	CF₃	F	F	F	F	··	(−62·9)	−143·8	−153·3	−161·3	−141·8	70
H	CH₂Cl	F	F	F	F	··	··	−139·5	−159·6	−149·6	−137·1	70
Me	C₆H₅	F	F	F	F	··	··	−152·5	−156·5	−159·6	−154·5	70
Me	Me	F	F	F	F	··	··	−139·2	−161·9	−158·0	−135·3	70
CF₃	Me	F	F	F	F	(−54·1)	··	−143·9	−162·0	−161·9	−143·9	79
CF₃	CF₃	F	F	F	F	(−56·9)	(−56·9)	−144·5	−145·4	−162·0	−144·5	70
CF₃	CF₃	F	F	F	F	··	(−56·9)	−132·3	−149·2	−145·4	−132·3	80
Cl	CF₃	F	I	F	F	··	··	−136·9	−159·7	−149·2	−136·9	80
CF₃	F	CF₃	F	F	F	(−59·0)	−116·8	−141·3	−128·1	−152·5	−141·3	80
CF₃	F	CF₃	CF₃	F	OMe	(−59·5)	−140·9	−119·0	(−59·5)	−119·0	−128·1	65
CF₃	F	OMe	CF₃	F	NH₂	(−58·5)	−102·5	(−59·0)	−102·5	(−58·5)	−140·9	80
CF₃	F	CF₃	F	F	F	(−58·4)	−134·2	−140·9	−135·8	−134·2	−102·5	80
Br	F	F	F	F	F	··	−119·1	··	−135·8	−134·2	−134·2	80
I	F	F	F	F	F	··	··	−126·8	−154·4	−164·2	−135·8	80
NO₂	Br	F	F	F	CH₃	··	··	−107·2	−152·1	−154·4	−164·2	82
NO₂	I	F	F	F	F	··	··	−139·3	−156·2	−152·1	−154·4	82
NO₂	CH₃	F	F	F	F	··	··	−140·3	··	−151·4	−152·1	85
NO₂	F	F	CH₃	F	F	··	−149·0	−140·3	··	−140·3	−149·0	85

NO₂	F	F	CF₃	F	:	-144.9	-135.6	-57.2	-135.6	-144.9
NO₂	F	F	$-OCH_2CH_3$	F	:	-148.4	-155.4	..	-155.4	-148.4
$-CH_2Br$	F	F	F	F	:	-143.3	-162.3	-154.0	-162.3	-143.3
$-CH_2COCl$	F	F	F	F	:	-143.6	-162.2	-153.6	-162.2	-143.6
$-CH_2OH$	F	F	F	F	:	-145.0	-163.1	-155.6	-163.1	-145.0
$-C(O)C_6F_5$	H	F	F	F	:	-141.5	-160.2	-146.4	-160.2	-141.5
$-C(O)C_6F_4H\text{-}o$	F	F	OMe	F	:	..	-137.6	-147.7	-154.2	-138.4
$-C(O)C_6F_4OMe\text{-}p$	H	F	OMe	F	:	-143.9	-157.9	..	-157.9	-143.9
$-C(O)C_6F_3HOMe$	F	F	F	F	:	..	-133.0	..	-151.6	-140.4
$2\text{-}C_5F_4N$	F				:	-140.8	-161.7	-150.9	-161.7	-140.8

85
85
92
92
92
93
93
93
93
113

be the cause of the discrepancies of the values of $^3J(F–F)$ found in the literature.

Reaction of fluoroaromatics with ethanolamine and diethanolamine afforded the N-oxyethylfluoroanilines while with ethylene glycol the fluorophenoxy-ethanol was obtained;[84] the ^{19}F shifts of these compounds are shown in Table XVI. The ^{19}F shifts of a number of halo-tetrafluorobenzenes and nitro-tetrafluorobenzenes examined in our laboratories are also included in Table XVI.[85]

Pentafluoroaromatics still continue to attract considerable attention. Manatt et al.[86] have reanalysed the spectra of chloro-, bromo- and iodo-pentafluoro-benzenes, pentafluorobenzonitrile, the pentafluorophenol and phenylate ion, and pentafluoroaniline and anilinium ion, paying particular attention to the signs of the three-, four- and five- bond F–F coupling constants. It was found that the magnitudes of the $F_2–F_4$ and $F_2–F_6$ couplings were dramatically effected in changing from the phenol or aniline to the corresponding ion. These authors suggest that some of the assignments previously made by Bruce[87] are incorrect and that $J(F_3–F_5)$ is not necessarily larger than $J(F_2–F_6)$. The mechanism of the F–F constants was also considered and compared with similar couplings in fluoro-olefins and fluoro-1,3-dienes. Dean and McFar-lane[88] have made both a homo- and hetero- nuclear double resonance study of four pentafluoro-phenyl derivatives, C_6F_5X where $X = CHO, CH_3, CF_3$ and H, to facilitate the analysis and determination of the signs of coupling. A novel decoupling method was described which was particularly suitable for the study of very small coupling constants. Lustig et al.[89] have studied the spectrum of pentafluorothiophenol in great detail and used spin-tickling to determine the signs of the coupling constants and refined J values were given. In this case only one coupling, namely the para J_{25}, was positive in sign. Examination of the spectrum of pentafluorothiophenol-d revealed small upfield isotope shifts.

Although the present-day tendency is to measure NMR spectra at increasingly higher fields, the application of low-field resonance studies to the analysis of spectra, especially for the determination of the signs of meta F–F coupling, has been demonstrated for a series of pentafluorophenyl derivatives.[90] The variation of the fluorine shifts and the meta F–F couplings of pentafluorophenol in various solvents was also discussed.

The shifts of hexakis(pentafluoroethyl)benzene **84**, prepared by reaction of hexafluorobenzene and tetrafluoroethylene, have been recorded[91] and evidence was obtained for restricted rotation of the perfluoroethyl groups. The ^{19}F data for some pentafluorobenzyl derivatives have been determined[92] as a means of comparing the electronic effects in fluorophenylsilane derivatives; the shifts of these compounds are included in Table XVI. The ^{19}F data of a number of derivatives of benzophenone and fluorenone have also been recorded[93] and the data for the former compounds are also included in Table XVI and of the

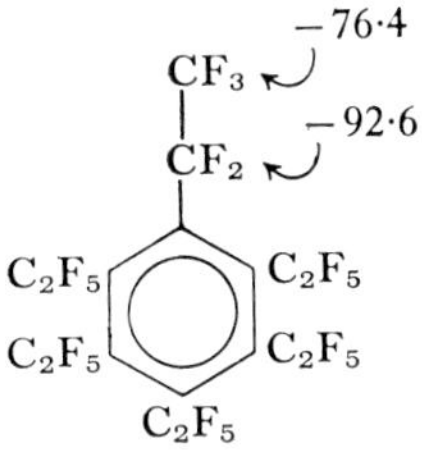

$$-76\cdot4$$
$$\text{CF}_3$$
$$-92\cdot6$$
$$\text{CF}_2$$

C$_2$F$_5$ C$_2$F$_5$
C$_2$F$_5$ C$_2$F$_5$
C$_2$F$_5$

84

fluorenones in Table XVII. The shifts resulting in protonation of the octafluorofluoren-9-one and decafluorobenzophenone were also considered.

TABLE XVII

^{19}F shifts of fluoren-9-one derivatives

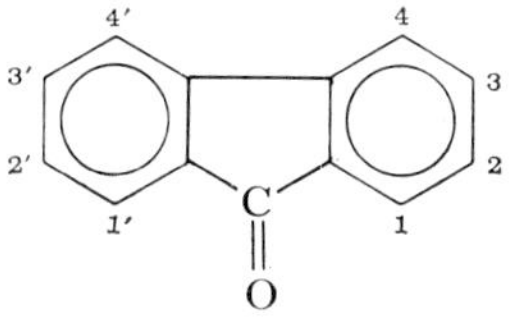

4' 4
3' 3
2' 2
1' C' 1
O

Substituents				Chemical shifts			
1,1'	2,2'	3,3'	4,4'	δ (1,1')	δ (2,2')	δ (3,3')	δ (4,4')
F	F	F	F	−132·6	−143·3	−151·0	−138·0
F	F	OMe	F	−136·0	−140·3	..	−133·1
F	OMe	F	F	−127·5	..	−149·6	−140·8
F	OMe	F	OMe	−130·1	..	−144·5	..
F	OMe	OMe	F	−129·4	..	..	−134·6

2. Polynuclear aromatics

The ^{19}F spectra have been used to elucidate the structure of the products obtained on nucleophilic substitution of octafluoronaphthalene.[94] The very large *peri*-coupling between F_1–F_8 and F_4–F_5 (about 60 to 80 Hz) was clearly seen and was therefore used to establish that substitution had not occurred at position-1; monosubstitution occurs in position 2 and the second substituent enters at position 6. The chemical shifts and the *peri*- F_1–F_8 and F_4–F_5 couplings are shown in Table XVIII. It is of interest to note that the *ortho*-F–F couplings in general had smaller values (14 to 18 Hz) than is usual. The *peri* F–F couplings in perfluoronaphthalene, acenaphthylenes and acenaphthene-1,2-quinones have also been investigated in some detail.[95] The *peri* F–F

TABLE XVIII

The ^{19}F shifts and *peri* F–F coupling constants in fluoronaphthalenes

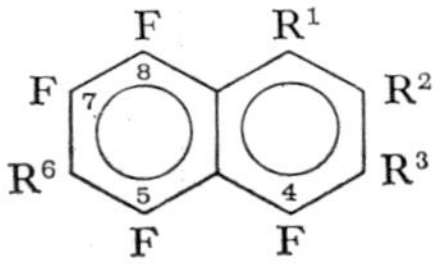

Structure: naphthalene skeleton bearing substituents F, R^1, R^2, R^3 (positions 1–4) and R^6, F, F, F (positions 5–8); ring positions 4, 5, 7, 8 labelled with F.

Substituents				^{19}F Chemical shifts							Coupling constants, Hz	
R^1	R^2	R^3	R^6	δ_1	δ_3	δ_4	δ_5	δ_6	δ_7	δ_8	$J(F_1\text{–}F_8)$	$J(F_4\text{–}F_5)$
F	$C_5H_{10}N$	F	F	−134.2	−143.1	−150.2	−148.3	−159.4	−158.1	−147.5	68	55
F	C_4H_8N	F	F	−140.1	−144.3	−150.5	−149.2	−162.7	−158.5	−149.2	74	58
F	$C_6H_{12}N$	F	F	−131.4	−140.9	−149.5	−147.9	−158.9	−157.4	−147.1	70	58
F	C_4H_8NO	F	F	−133.4	−142.9	−148.9	−147.3	−157.3	−156.6	−146.5	73	58
F	$C_5H_{10}NO$	F	F	−119.0	−132.9	−147.5	−144.3	−150.8	−153.4	−142.1	81	59
F	$NOH\cdot[CH_2]_4\cdot CH{=}CH_2$	F	F	−126.6	−140.6	−148.4	−146.6	−154.2	−155.9	−144.6	68	58
F	OMe	F	F	−141.1	−149.9	−148.0	−147.4	−157.3	−156.8	−146.7	68	60
F	NH_2	F	F	−147.8	−153.1	−150.4	−149.0	−161.6	−157.8	−148.2	58	60
F	$C_5H_{10}N$	F	$C_5H_{10}N$	−135.5	−146.0	−151.2	−135.5	··	−146.0	−151.2	67	67
F	C_4H_8NO	F	C_4H_8NO	−134.6	−144.8	−150.2	−134.6	··	−144.8	−150.2	66	66
C_4H_8NO	$C_5H_{10}N$	F	F	··	−142.1	−147.4	−148.3	−158.1	−158.6	−142.1	··	67
$C_5H_{10}N$	C_4H_8NO	F	F	··	−142.6	−147.3	−148.5	−158.0	−158.9	−141.6	··	68
F	$C_5H_{10}N$	C_4H_8NO	F	−132.3	··	−132.3	−148.1	−159.4	−159.4	−148.1	65	65
$C_5H_{10}N$	$C_5H_{10}N$	$C_5H_{10}N$	F	··	··	−128.4	−150.5	−160.6	−159.7	−148.1	··	82
MeO	$C_5H_{10}N$	F	MeO	··	−145.3	−150.0	−143.0	··	−154.3	−151.5	··	67
H	$C_5H_{10}N$	F	F	··	−145.7	−145.0	−148.4	−161.5	−158.9	−150.4	··	50
F	MeO	F	$C_5H_{10}N$	−183.2	−152.9	−149.3	−135.6	··	−144.5	−150.9	62	69

couplings in naphthalenes (85) and naphthalic anhydrides (86) were in the range 59 to 70 Hz, while in the acenaphthylenes (87) and quinones (88) the values were found to be appreciably smaller (Table XIX). It was suggested that

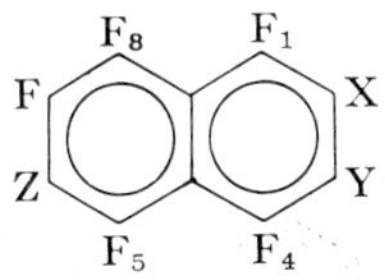

85 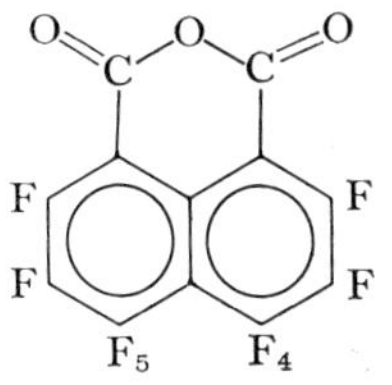   86

in the latter cases the presence of the five-membered ring may introduce ring-strain and thus cause geometric changes. It was further shown that the *peri*-F–F coupling was of opposite sign to that of the *ortho* F–F coupling and is therefore presumably positive.

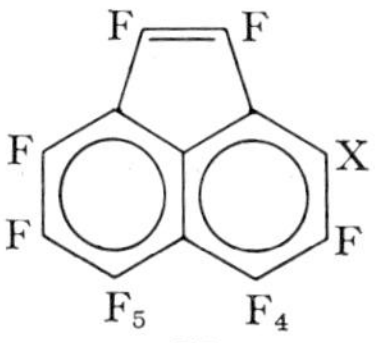

87 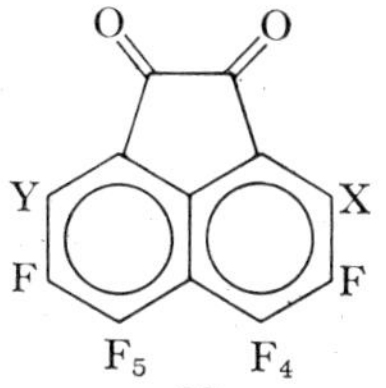   88

TABLE XIX

Peri F–F couplings in naphthalene and acenaphthene derivatives

	X	Y	Z	$J(F_1-F_8)$	$J(F_4-F_5)$
85	H	F	F	65·7	59·4
	H	F	OMe	63·7	65·2
	H	OMe	OMe	61·8	68·2
	OMe	OMe	H	63·4	69·3
	H	F	NMe$_2$	62·6	69·7
86	H	..	..	..	53·9
	OMe	..	..	..	58·2
87	H	..	..	..	32·7
	OMe	..	..	..	35·7
88	OMe	F	..	..	29·4
	OMe	OMe	..	..	30·7

Octafluorobiphenylene (**89**), formed by pyrolysis of the disilver salt of tetra-fluorophthalate, shows two doublets in the ^{19}F spectrum at $-138\cdot8$ and $-148\cdot5$.[96] It is claimed that a single coupling of 12·6 Hz is present as this is the separation between the two peaks of the doublet. This, however, is obviously an incorrect conclusion and the simplicity of the spectrum arises from the similarity in the chemical shifts of the A and B fluorine nuclei in the $[AB]_2$ spin system; such a situation has also been encountered in the cases of the tetra- and octa- fluorophenazine (**90**).[97]

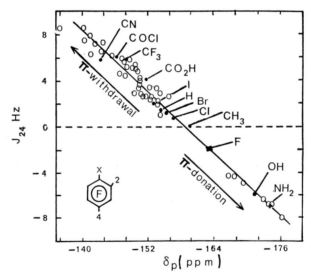

89   **90**

F. Relationship of ^{19}F shifts and electronic effects

Hogben and Graham[98] have considered the relationship of the chemical shifts and coupling constants in some sixty-one pentafluorophenyl derivatives. It was found that there was a linear relationship between the shift of the 4-fluorine atom and the value of the *meta*-coupling, $J(F_2-F_4)$, shown in Fig. 2.

FIG. 2. The relationship of the coupling constant between the *ortho*- and *para*-fluorine atoms (J_{24}) to the chemical shift of the *para*-fluorine (δ_p) for pentafluoro-phenyl derivatives. The point representing fluorine as substituent is interpolated from the chemical shift of hexafluorobenzene. (From Hogben and Graham.[98])

The authors conclusively showed that there was a definite change in the sign of the *meta*-F_2–F_4 coupling constants. Further, it is evident from Fig. 2 that the results conveniently fall into two classes, related to the π-donating or π-withdrawing character of the substituent group. Spiesecke and Schneider[99] showed that the *para*-^{13}C chemical shifts in monosubstituted benzenes was dependent upon the change in π-electron density at the *para*-carbon arising from the resonance effects of the substituent group. Although the ^{13}C shifts of the pentafluorophenyl compounds were not available to the authors it was

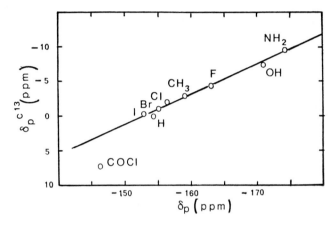

Fig. 3. The relationship of the chemical shift of the *para*-fluorine of certain pentafluorophenyl derivatives (δ_p) to the chemical shift of the *para*-carbon in corresponding phenyl derivatives (δ_p ^{13}C). (From Hogben and Graham.[98])

shown[98] that a linear relationship existed between the *para*-^{13}C shifts of the hydrocarbon phenyl derivatives with the *para*-^{19}F shifts of the corresponding pentafluorophenyl compound, Fig. 3. It was found[100] that a precisely similar relationship existed between the ^{13}C shift and the ^{19}F shift of the 4-CF group in the pentafluorophenyl compounds, Fig. 4. It is therefore evident that the shift of the 4-fluorine atom is dependent upon the resonance effect of the substituent group. The ^{19}F shifts of the *meta*- and *para*- fluorine atoms in *p*- and *m*- fluorophenyl derivatives are related to the Taft parameters by the following two equations:

$$\delta_p^F = -29{\cdot}5\sigma_{R^\circ} - 7{\cdot}1\sigma_I + 0{\cdot}60$$
$$\delta_m^F = -7{\cdot}1\sigma_I + 0{\cdot}60$$

Thus the difference in the chemical shift ($\delta_p^F - \delta_m^F$) is directly related to the resonance effect; this fact had previously been observed by Parshall[101] during

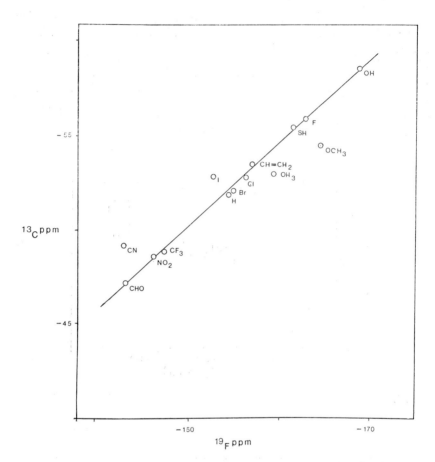

FIG. 4. The relationship of the *para*-fluorine and *para*-carbon-13 chemical shifts of some pentafluorophenyl derivatives. (From Mooney and Winson.[100])

the study of fluorophenylplatinum compounds. The relationship in pentafluorophenyl derivatives is, however, not so convenient and takes the form:

$$\delta_p^{C_6F_5} = -49 \cdot 05\sigma_{R^\circ} - 16 \cdot 00\sigma_I + 153 \cdot 72$$
$$\delta_m^{C_6F_5} = -8 \cdot 31\sigma_I + 164 \cdot 64$$

Consequently, the relation $(\delta_p^{C_6F_5} - \delta_m^{C_6F_5})$ does not eliminate the inductive parameters and the use of $(\delta_p^{C_6F_5} - \delta_m^{C_6F_5})$ as a measure of the resonance interaction has little theoretical foundation. Both $\delta_p^{C_6F_5}$ and $J(F_2-F_4)$, however, may be separately related to the Taft resonance parameters σ_{R° by:

$$\delta_p^{C_6F_5} = -52 \cdot 28\sigma_{R^\circ} + 148 \cdot 74$$
$$J(F_2-F_4) = 22 \cdot 26\sigma_{R^\circ} + 3 \cdot 81$$

thus consideration of these two parameters, $\delta_p^{C_6F_5}$ and $J(F_2–F_4)$, are useful in accessing the π-electron interaction. These authors and their coworkers[102] have used these parameters as a basis for the study of the bonding in phosphines and Group IV derivatives (see p. 453).

Taft and his coworkers have used the ^{19}F shifts of p-fluorophenol to study hydrogen bonding complex formation.[103] These workers studied the basic strengths of a whole series of fifty-fifty bases ranging in strength from hexamethylphosphoramide to diethyl sulphide; the log formation constant, K_f, being 3·56 and 0·11 respectively—this corresponding to a limiting shift difference of 3·71 and 1·10 p.p.m. respectively. Taft and Uschold[104] have also used the ^{19}F shifts of 4-fluoro- and 3,4-difluoro- phenyl derivatives, with nitro-, nitrile and benzoyl cyanide substituents, to study the self-association of these compounds in solution. The dissociation constants calculated from these studies indicated that both polar and steric effects are important.

A study[105] of the concentration dependence of the ^{19}F shifts of $ortho$-, $meta$-, and $para$- trifluoromethylphenol has been interpreted in terms of an intramolecular F····OH bonding being predominent in the $ortho$-isomer. Using pyridine-d_5 as solvent there was over 1 p.p.m. shift in the CF$_3$ resonance of the $ortho$-isomer on dilution.

Schindlbauer and Prikoszovich[106, 107] have studied the ^{19}F shifts of 3- and 4- fluorophenylphosphorus compounds, containing tri- tetra- and pentavalent phosphorus, in relation to the Taft substituent functions. The solvent effect on the ^{19}F shift of four of the 3-fluorophenyl compounds was also considered.[107]

III. HETEROCYCLIC COMPOUNDS

A. Nitrogen heterocyclics

The study of fluorinated pyridines still continues to attract considerable attention and the data for a number of di- and tri- fluoropyridine derivatives have been published.[108] The spectra were essentially used to determine the position of the fluorine atoms and, although the $meta$-F–F coupling constants were determined, no comment was made, on the comparison with $meta$-F–F coupling constants in fluoroaromatics which has caused some interest over the past year or so. It is of interest that, as previously observed, the $para$-F$_2$–F$_5$ coupling was of similar magnitude (22 to 26·5 Hz) to the $ortho$-F–F coupling constants. The relevant shift data and coupling constants are shown in Table XX.

The spectra of 2-fluoro-3-methylpyridine have been fully analysed[109] and, by using double and triple resonance techniques, the signs of the F–H and H–H couplings were determined. The sign $J(o$-F–CH$_3)$ was positive and

TABLE XX

^{19}F parameters of fluorinated pyridines

Substituents					Chemical shifts				
2	3	4	5	6	δ_2	δ_3	δ_4	δ_5	δ_6
F	Cl	F	Cl	$C_5H_{10}N$	−71·4	..	−98·3	..	..
F	Cl	F	Cl	NMe_2	−71·5	..	−98·2	..	..
F	Cl	F	Cl	$O \cdot NC_5H_{10}$	−65·5	..	−91·4	..	..
F	Cl	NMe_2	Cl	F	−72·4	..	..	..	−72·4
F	Cl	$C_5H_{10}N$	F	F	−74·7	..	..	−155·9	−92·0
F	Cl	F	F	$C_5H_{10}N$	−73·2	..	−123·4	−157·8	..
F	Cl	NMe_2	F	F	−75·0	..	..	−156·4	−92·8
F	Cl	F	F	NMe_2	−73·4	..	−124·2	−161·0	..
F	F	$OC_5H_{10}N$	F	F	−85·6	−142·9	..	−142·9	−85·6
OMe	F	NMe_2	F	F	..	−145·8	..	−151·4	−90·6
OMe	F	$ONMe_2$	F	F	..	−147·9	..	−154·3	−88·5
$[CH_2]_5N\text{-}O$	F	$C_5H_{10}N$	F	F	..	−118·7	..	−137·9	−85·4
F	F	$\overset{\ominus\oplus}{ONH_2C_5H_{10}}$	F	F	−96·6	−165·6	..	−165·6	−96·6
F	F	SH	F	F	−91·2	−141·4	..	−141·4	−91·2
F	F	SC_6H_5	F	F	−91·9	−138·0	..	−138·0	−91·9
F	F	SO_3H	F	F	−90·0	−140·6	..	−140·6	−90·0
F	F	SC_5F_4N	F	F	−89·0	−137·5	..	−137·5	−89·0
F	F	$S \cdot SC_5F_4N$	F	F	−88·7	−136·0	..	−136·1	−88·7
F	F	SOC_6H_5	F	F	−90·2	−140·3	..	−140·3	−90·2
F	F	$SO_2C_6H_5$	F	F	−90·9	−143·5	..	−143·5	−90·9
F	F	$SO_2C_5F_4N$	F	F	−89·9	−142·2	..	−142·2	−89·9
F	F	SOC_5F_4N	F	F	−88·2	−138·5	..	−138·5	−88·2
CF_3	F	F	F	F	−65·4	−141·5	−134·9	−149·4	−80·9
Br	F	F	F	F	..	−129·7	−133·6	−155·4	−80·3
C_6F_5	F	F	F	F	(c)	−140·2	−138·2	−154·7	−81·2
(a)	F	F	F	F	(d)	−139·5	−134·9	−148·9	−79·7
(b)	F	F	F	F	(e)	−139·5	−136·1	−150·5	−80·6

ª $[CF_2]_3 \cdot CN$.
ᵇ $[CF_2]_3 \cdot C_5F_4N$.
ᶜ See Table XVI.
ᵈ αCF_2 −111·7; βCF_2 −123·1 and $\gamma CF_2 \cdot CN$ −104·9.
ᵉ αCF_2 −112·9; βCF_2 −123·9.

therefore the same as that in *o*-fluorotoluene; the significance of π-contributions to the coupling was discussed.

Haszeldine *et al.*[110] have reported the data for a series of 4-substituted tetra-fluoropyridines, formed by direct substitution, and the shifts of the compounds are shown in Table XX; no details of the coupling constants were given. Sutcliffe *et al.*,[111] during the investigation of perfluoro-isopropyl pyridines, found that at room temperature the spectrum of **91** showed broad resonance signals. At −30° to −40°, however, the resonance lines were sharp and a large through-space coupling between F_a and F_3 were observed while the coupling to F_5 was zero; similarly the CF_3 groups shows a marked coupling to F_5. The

| | | | | Coupling constants, Hz | | | | | | |
J_{23}	J_{24}	J_{25}	J_{26}	J_{34}	J_{35}	J_{36}	J_{45}	J_{46}	J_{56}	Ref.
..	15·0	..	..	..	..	..	..	..	..	108
..	14·6	..	..	..	..	..	..	..	..	108
..	..	..	..	..	..	..	..	..	..	108
..	..	..	..	..	..	..	..	..	..	108
..	..	22·6	13·7	..	..	..	..	..	20·8	108
..	11·4	26·5	..	..	..	..	17·4	..	..	108
..	..	22·2	13·2	..	..	..	..	..	21·2	108
..	11·0	26·0	..	..	..	..	16·8	..	..	108
..	..	..	..	..	..	..	..	..	..	108
..	..	..	..	..	..	..	..	..	..	108
..	..	..	..	..	..	..	..	..	..	108
..	..	..	..	..	..	..	..	..	..	108
18·1	..	22·3	14·4	..	6·9	..	..	..	..	108
..	..	..	..	..	..	..	..	..	..	110
..	..	..	..	..	..	..	..	..	..	110
..	..	..	..	..	..	..	..	..	..	110
..	..	..	..	..	..	..	..	..	..	110
..	..	..	..	..	..	..	..	..	..	110
..	..	..	..	..	..	..	..	..	..	110
..	..	..	..	..	..	..	..	..	..	110
..	..	..	..	..	..	..	..	..	..	110
..	..	..	..	17·7	10·1	28·1	17·0	19·8	24·1	113
..	..	..	..	18·2	4·6	25·6	17·2	17·0	22·7	113
..	..	..	..	17·4	4·7	25·4	17·2	17·8	24·9	113
..	..	..	..	17·8	..	26·5	17·8	18·8	24·3	113
..	..	..	..	18·2	..	27·4	18·2	18·6	24·2	113

two fluorine atoms F_3 and F_5 become equivalent at 150°. The 2,4-bis(hepta-fluoro-isopropyl)trifluoropyridine (**92**) showed two sets of resonances arising from the two conformations **92a** and **92b**. The spectra of 2,4,6- and 2,4,5-tris-(heptafluoro-isopropyl)difluoropyridines indicate single conformations **93** and **94**. The perfluoro-*s*-butyl derivative **95** appears to have a greater barrier to rotation since even at +30° the fluorine F_a couples only to F_3 while at +150° F_3 and F_5 again become equivalent.

Emsley and Phillips[112] have considered the ^{19}F spectra of a series of tetra-fluoropyridines and the substituent shifts found in these pyridines were compared with those of the corresponding substituted benzenes. In some cases the

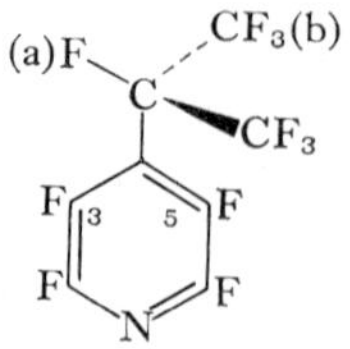

91 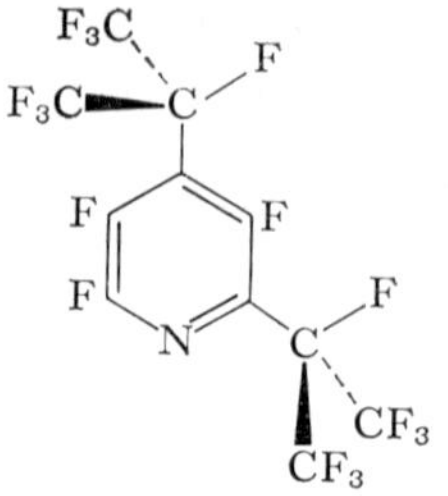   92a 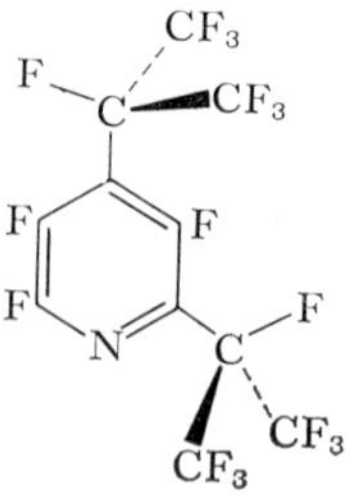   92b

para-substituent shifts were compared with the π-electon densities. The authors also calculated the three different "substituent coupling contributions" for the nitrogen heteroatom and, by combining with the coupling contributions for fluorobenzenes, were able to confirm the signs of some of the coupling constants observed.

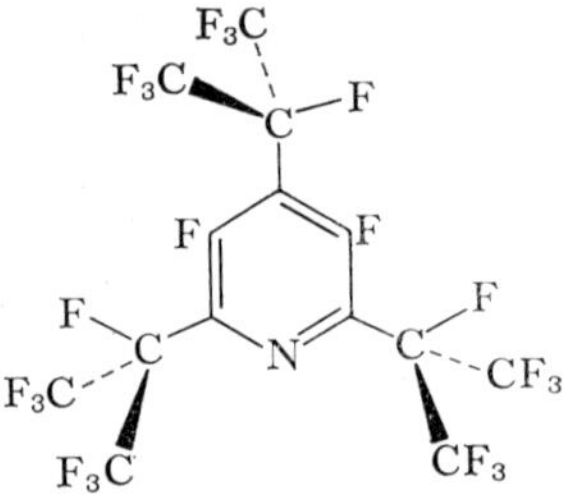

93 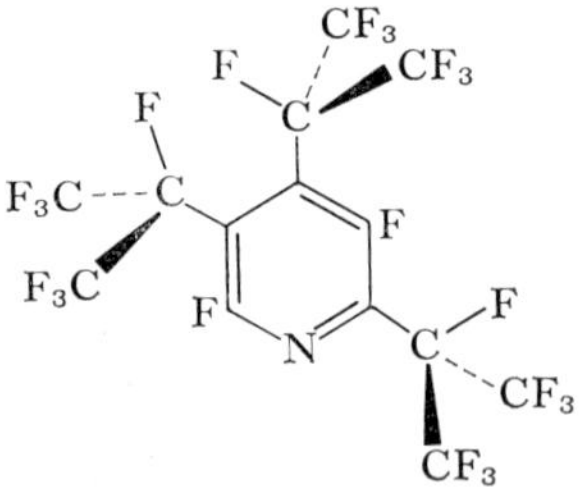   94 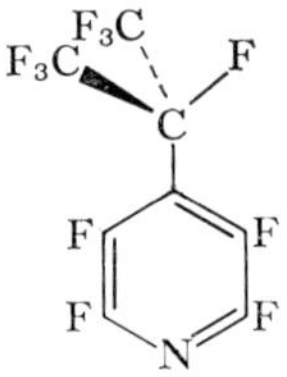   95

Perfluorocyclohexa-1,3-diene undergoes 1,4 addition with nitriles to give adducts of type **96** and although the shifts were quoted in the paper[113] no precise assignments were made. The adducts **96** were unstable and readily afforded some 2-substituted tetrafluoropyridines, the shifts of which are included in Table XX. As has been observed in previous work the five-bond *para*-F_3–F_5 coupling is large (25 to 28 Hz).

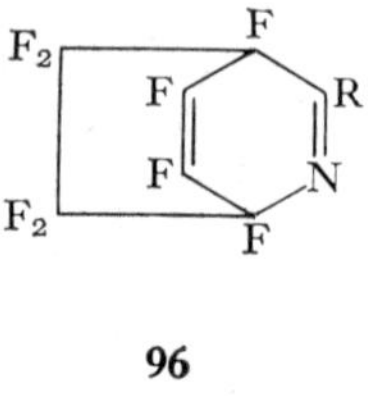

96

The ^{19}F shifts of trifluoromethyl substituted bis-tetrafluoroethane derivatives of triazines **97** have been recorded.[114] The ^{19}F shifts of 2-substituted-4,6-difluoro-s-triazines **98** were found to be dependent upon the nature of the

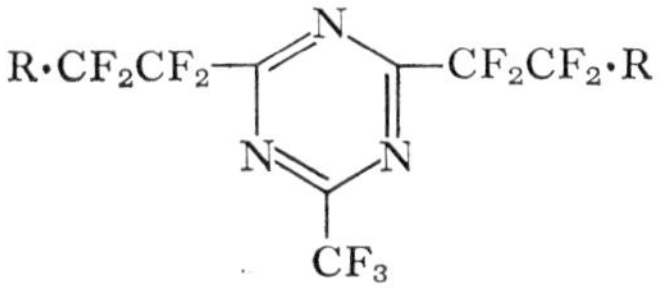

97

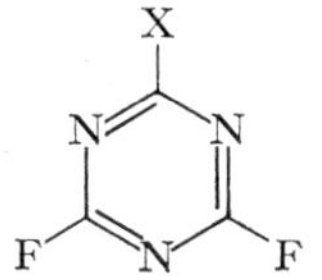

98

2-substituent.[115] In the series, $X = -N=P(C_6H_5)_nCl_{3-n}$, the shift progressively increases to high field with increasing value of n. The shifts of the other derivatives, $X = -N-SO$, $-NHCONHSO_2F$, $-NHCCl=NSO_2F$, $-NHPOCl_2$ and $-NHSO_2F$, fall into the range $-36\cdot4 \pm 0\cdot8$. The data for 2,3-dihydro-5,6,7,8-tetrafluorobenzopyrazine (**99**) have also been reported and the ^{19}F shifts are as shown.[84] Fluoroazirines have now been prepared, by the reaction of azide salts with fluorovinyl methyl ether, and the data are shown in **100**.[33]

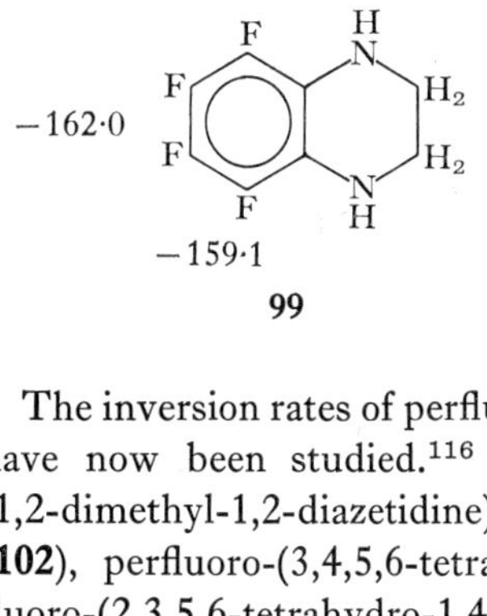

99

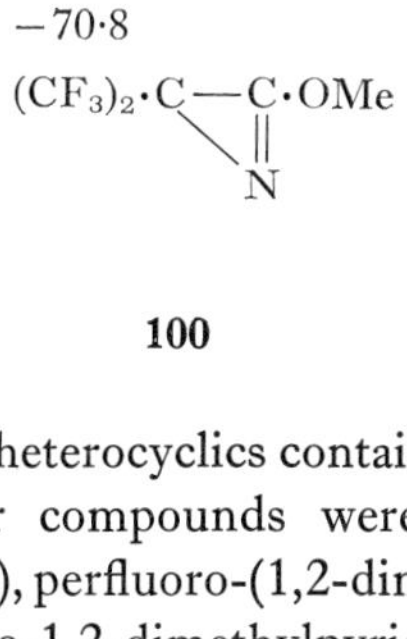

100

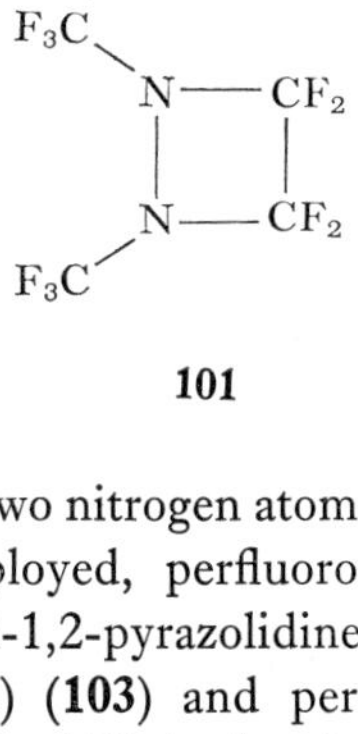

101

The inversion rates of perfluoro-heterocyclics containing two nitrogen atoms have now been studied.[116] Four compounds were employed, perfluoro-(1,2-dimethyl-1,2-diazetidine) (**101**), perfluoro-(1,2-dimethyl-1,2-pyrazolidine) (**102**), perfluoro-(3,4,5,6-tetrahydro-1,2-dimethylpyridazine) (**103**) and perfluoro-(2,3,5,6-tetrahydro-1,4-dimethyl-1,4-diazine) (**104**). In **103** the barrier

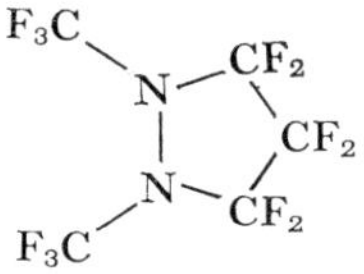

102

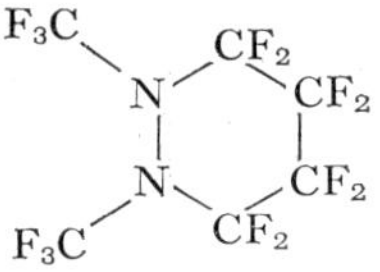

103

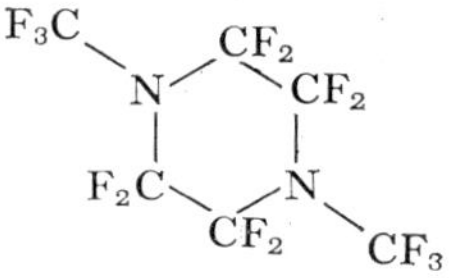

104

to inversion is sufficiently high for the molecule to have a preferred conformation even at 100°, while in **104** the barrier is so low that rapid inversion occurs at $-100°$. The structural assignments of **101** at 65° and $-85°$ and **102** at 84°

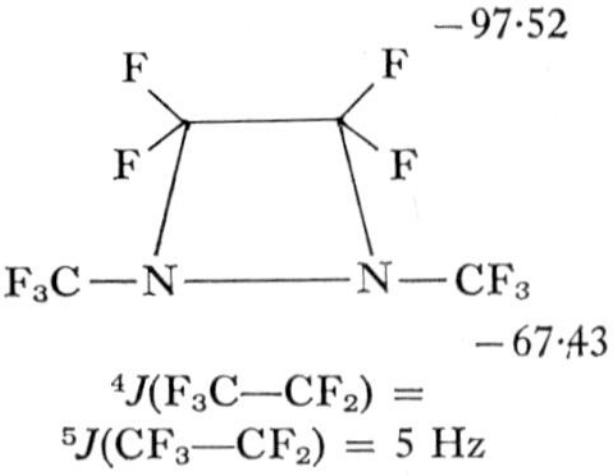

105

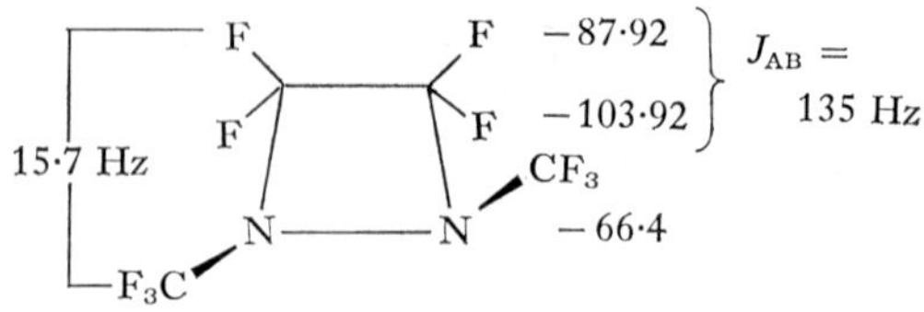

106

and $-58°$ are shown in **105** to **108** respectively. The variation in the rates of inversion were rationalized on steric grounds (in **104** there is no steric hindrance at all) but the author points out that this explanation may be an oversimplification.

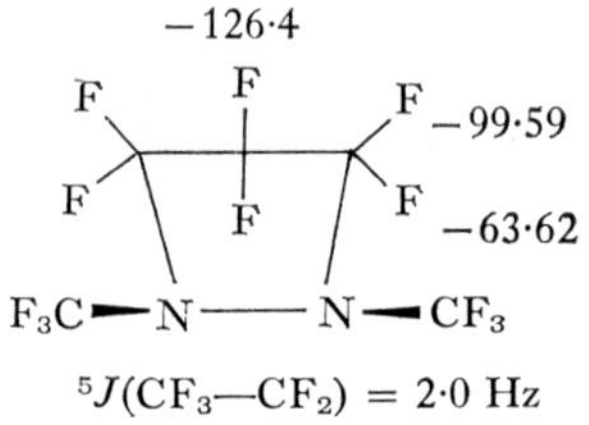

107

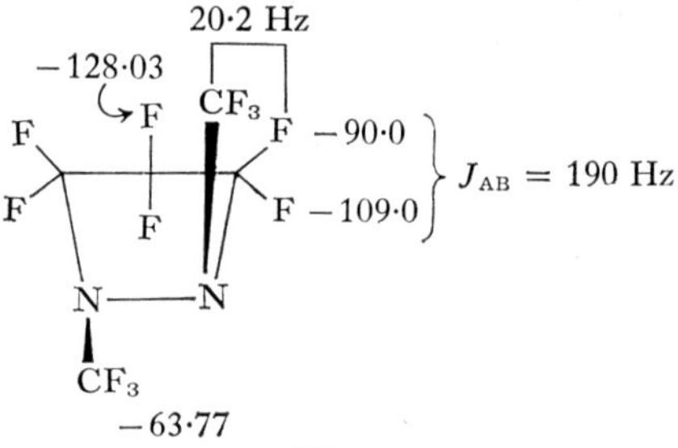

108

B. Oxygen heterocyclics

Fluorination of tetrahydrofuran using potassium tetrafluorocobaltate afforded 2,2,5,5-tetrafluoro-2,5-dihydrofuran (**109**) and 2,2,5-trifluoro-2,5-dihydrofuran (**110**);[117] the parameters were as shown. The direct fluorination

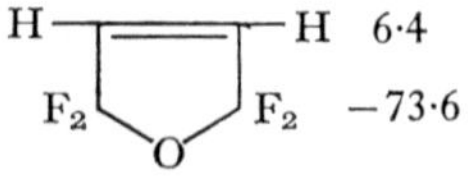

109

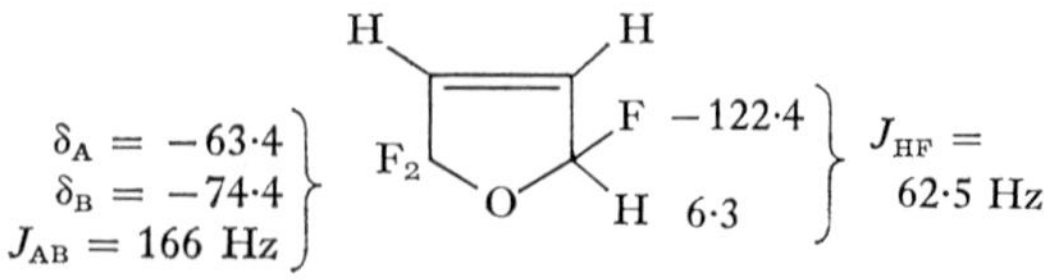

110

of tetrahydrofuran afforded a number of polyfluoro-oxolan derivatives.[7] The different types of fluorine atom were readily recognized from the relative chemical shift ranges as shown in Table XXI; the identity of the $>CF_2$ (not adjacent to oxygen) and $>CFH$ (adjacent to oxygen) groups with similar ^{19}F

TABLE XXI

^{19}F chemical shift and J value ranges in polyfluoro-oxolans

$>$CF$_2$, adjacent to oxygen,	-70 to -88
$>$CF$_2$, *not* adjacent to oxygen,	-115 to -142
$>$CHF, adjacent to oxygen,	-123 to -138
$>$CHF, *not* adjacent to oxygen,	-202 to -226
^2J(H–F), of 2-CHF group.	57 to 64 Hz
^2J(H–F), of 3-CHF group,	47 to 52 Hz
^2J(F–F), of 2-CF$_2$ group.	136 to 150 Hz
^2J(F–F), of 3-CF$_2$ group,	251 to 283 Hz

shift ranges are differentiated as the former exhibit AB spectra with characteristic large value of J_{AB}. Further the 2-CF$_2$ and 3-CF$_2$ groups are additionally differentiated by the smaller value of the *gem* F–F coupling in the former instance being in the range 136 to 150 Hz compared with 251 to 283 Hz. The main problem became one of the assignment of the relative configuration of the hydrogen atoms in the di-, tri- and tetra- *H*-polyfluoro compounds. While precise chemical shift substituent parameters could not be calculated it was found that, as in the case of the polyfluorocyclopentanes and cyclohexanes, the effect of *trans* hydrogen is very small and the effects of *cis* hydrogen atoms further removed than adjacent positions may be ignored. Thus the authors were concerned with the effects on the groups in three situations, (a) with no *cis*-H, (b) with one *cis*-H and (c) with two *cis*-H; the latter situation can only effect the 3-CF$_2$ and 3-CFH groups since the 2-CF$_2$ or 2-CFH groups can only have no or one *cis*-H atom in the adjacent position. The chemical shifts for these arrangements are shown in Table XXII. Using this as a basis, the configura-

TABLE XXII

The effect of *cis*-hydrogen atoms on the ^{19}F chemical shift ranges in polyfluoro-oxolans[7]

Type of fluorine	Position ring	Number of *cis*-H atoms on adjacent carbon atoms		
		None	One	Two
$>$CF$_2$	2	$-78\cdot9$ to $-87\cdot8$	$-70\cdot6$ to $-76\cdot3$	$\cdot\,\cdot$
$>$CF$_2$	3	$-125\cdot1$ to $-141\cdot1$	$-123\cdot3$ to $-130\cdot0$	$-115\cdot1$ to $-118\cdot4$
$>$CFH	2	$-129\cdot3$ to $-137\cdot5$	$-123\cdot7$ to $-128\cdot7$	$\cdot\,\cdot$
$>$CFH	3	$-213\cdot3$ to $-225\cdot6$	$-205\cdot7$ to $-219\cdot8$	$-202\cdot2$ to $-204\cdot4$

TABLE XXIII

^{19}F parameters of polyfluoro-oxolans

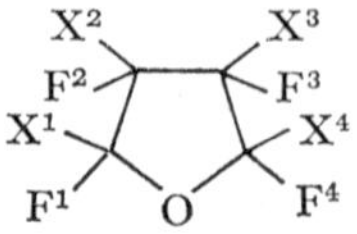

Chemical shifts							
	X¹	X²	X³	X⁴	X¹	F¹	X²
2H-Heptafluoro-	H	F	F	F	..	−135·5	−126·9
3H-Heptafluoro-	F	H	F	F	−74·7	−83·6	..
2H/4H-Hexafluoro-	H	F	H	F	..	−132·9	−126
3H/4H-Hexafluoro-	F	H	H	F	−75·2	−82·7	..
2H,5H/3H-Pentafluoro-	H	H	F	H	..	−125·2	..
3H,5H/2H-Pentafluoro-	H	H	F	H	..	−128·4	..
2H,3H/5H-Pentafluoro-	H	H	F	H	..	−129·3	..
2H,3H,5H/-Pentafluoro-	H	H	F	H	..	−133·0	..
2H,4H/3H-Pentafluoro-	H	H	H	F	..	−126·8	..
2H,3H/4H-Pentafluoro-	H	H	H	F	..	−136·6	..
3H,4H/2H-Pentafluoro-	H	H	H	F	..	−128·7	..
2H,4H/3H,5H-Tetrafluoro-	H	H	H	H	..	−126·3	..
2H,3H,5H/4H-Tetrafluoro-	H	H	H	H	..	−134·7	..
2H,3H/4H,5H-Tetrafluoro-	H	H	H	H	..	−132·0	..
2H,5H-Hexafluoro-[a]	H	F	F	H	..	−132·6	−125·5
2H,5H-Hexafluoro-[a]	H	F	F	H	..	−133·0	−127·9

[a] Configuration not assigned.

tion of the polyfluoro-oxolans were derived as shown in Table XXIII; the only two isomers for which the shifts were ambiguous were those of the 2H,5H-hexafluoro-oxolans but for convenience the shift data for these two isomers are included in Table XXIII.

Cyclization of *trans*-1,1-bis(trifluoromethyl)pent-3-en-1-ol with aluminium trichloride gave 2,2-bis(trifluoromethyl)-5-methyltetrahydrofuran and the ^{19}F spectrum of this product exhibited two quartets at −77·6 and −80·1 with $^4J(F–F) = 9$ Hz.[11]

Perfluoro-β-oxaglutaric anhydride (perfluoro-1,4-dioxan-2,6-dione) **111**,

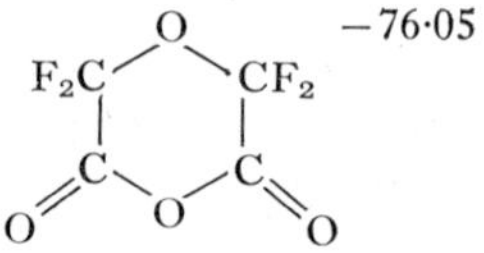

111

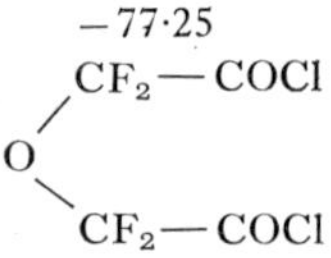

112

F^2	X^3	F^3	X^4	F^4	Coupling constants, Hz			
					X^1F^1	X^2F^2	X^3F^3	X^4F^4
−137·1	−127·7	−133·9	−82·1	−84·1	58·4	256·6	264·4	137·7
−213·3	−123·3	−130·2	−85·4	−87·8	142·7	49·5	259·4	136·3
−128	..	−225·4	−70·6	−80·6	∼60	∼260	48·9	141·2
−207·6	..	−207·6	−75·2	−82·7	144·8	..	..	144·8
−219·5	−123·9	−128·6	..	−132·0	58·6	50·6	264·4	59·8
−208·1	−118·4	−134·8	..	−130·0	59·8	50·9	282·4	60·0
−220·0	−125·7	−130·0	..	−136·3	62·1	52·0	251·8	62·7
−214·1	−115·1	−125·1	..	−137·5	62·1	50·1	267·0	61·0
−202·2	..	−205·7	−75·0	−80·8	58·3	48·5	47·9	150·0
−212 to −213	..	−212 to −213	−71·3	−78·9	59·4	..	..	140·0
−215·2	..	−225·6	−76·3	−79·4	60·6	51·6	49·4	144·5
−204·4	..	−204·4	..	−126·3	62·3	..	..	62·3
−210·9	..	−204·1	..	−123·7	61·9	50·8	50·8	60·9
−219·8	..	−219·8	..	−132·0	63·3	..	..	63·3
−141·1	−125·5	−141·1	..	−132·6	57·0	264·2	264·2	57·0
−129·7	−127·9	−129·7	..	−133·0	58·7	264·1	264·1	58·7

prepared by reaction of perfluoro-N-fluoromorpholine with aqueous sodium iodide or hydrolysis of perfluoro-5,6-dihydro-2H-1,4-oxazine, has been examined and the shifts are shown in **111**.[23] By comparison the shift of the CF_2 group in the perfluoro-β-oxaglutaryl chloride (**112**) is at a similarly low field. Thus, the replacement of the CF_2 group in the entity **113** by oxygen, as in **111**, results in a deshielding of the $-CF_2 \cdot C(O)$-group by about 50 p.p.m. The shift of the $-CF_2 \cdot C(O)$-group in tetrafluorosuccinic anhydride (**114**) is δ −130·3

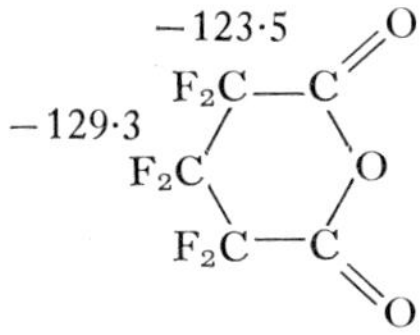

113 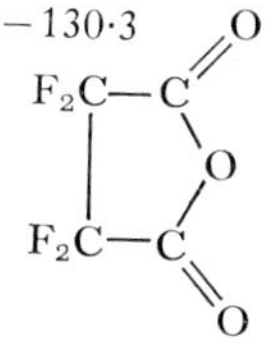   **114**

while the shifts for perfluoroglutaric anhydride are shown in **113**.[24] The data

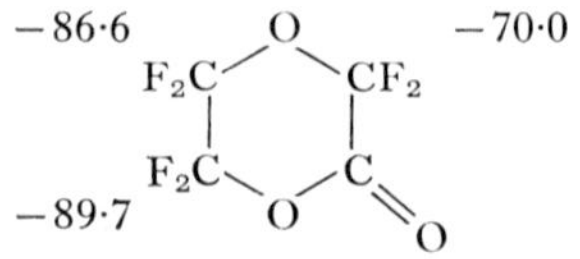

$$-86\cdot6 \qquad \overset{O}{\underset{F_2C \diagdown}{\overset{F_2C \diagup}{\bigg|}}} \qquad -70\cdot0$$

115

for perfluoro-β-oxa-δ-valerolactone (**115**), prepared from perfluoroxydiacetyl chloride, and for perfluoro-1,3-dioxolane (**116**), prepared from the lactone **115**, have been reported.[4]

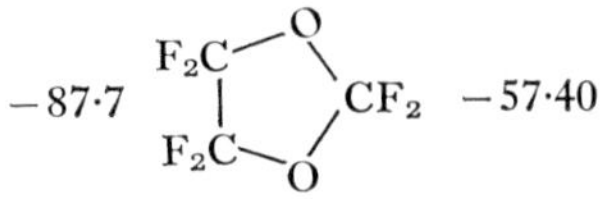

$$-87\cdot7 \qquad \overset{F_2C \diagup O}{\underset{F_2C \diagdown O}{\bigg|}} CF_2 \quad -57\cdot40$$

$$^4J(F\!-\!F) = 3\cdot8 \text{ Hz}$$

116

C. Sulphur heterocyclics

The ^{19}F parameters of tetrafluorothiophen and the 4- and 5- methoxy derivatives have been reported[118] and these parameters are shown in Table XXIV. It is noteworthy that the α-fluorine atoms are to higher field than those of the β-fluorine atoms. As in the case of the fluorofurans (see p. 443) it would be expected, from electronegativity considerations, that the β-fluorine atoms would be at higher field. The other point of interest is the very large four-bond F–F coupling (J_{25}) across the sulphur atom, approximately 30 Hz.

Thermal decomposition of the thiadiazoline derivatives (**117** and **118**) re-

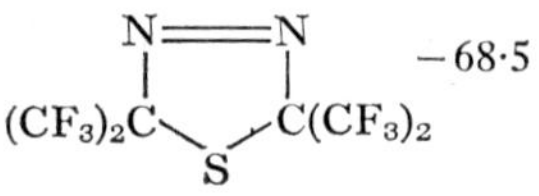

$$\overset{N\!=\!\!=\!\!N}{(CF_3)_2C\diagdown_{S}\diagup C(CF_3)_2} \quad -68\cdot5$$

117

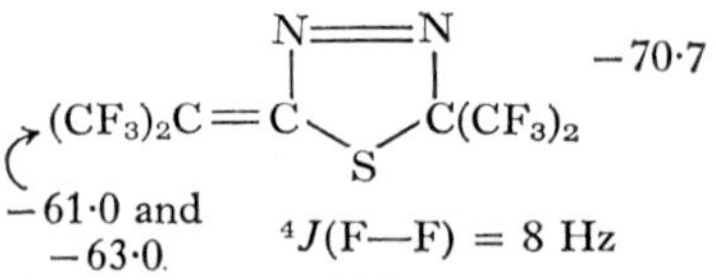

$$\overset{N\!=\!\!=\!\!N}{(CF_3)_2C\!=\!C\diagdown_{S}\diagup C(CF_3)_2} \quad -70\cdot7$$

$$-61\cdot0 \text{ and} \quad ^4J(F\!-\!F) = 8 \text{ Hz}$$
$$-63\cdot0.$$

118

sults in the elimination of nitrogen with the formation of the corresponding thiiranes (**119** and **120**);[119] the shifts of the CF_3 groups are shown.

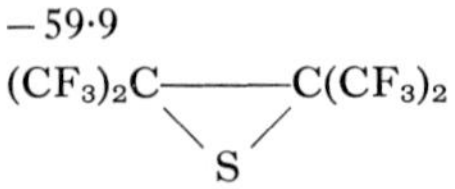

$$-59\cdot9$$
$$(CF_3)_2C\text{———}C(CF_3)_2$$
$$\diagdown_{S}\diagup$$

119

$$-61\cdot0 \text{ and} \qquad -67\cdot4$$
$$-63\cdot0$$
$$(CF_3)_2C\!=\!C\text{———}C(CF_3)_2$$
$$\diagdown_{S}\diagup$$

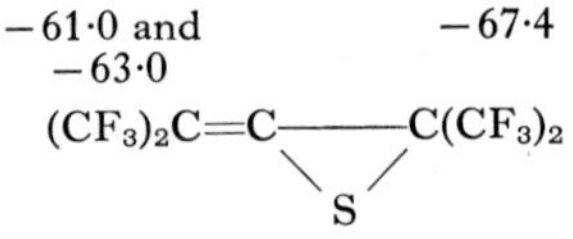

$$^4J(F\!-\!F) = 6 \text{ Hz}$$
$$^6J(F\!-\!F) = 4 \text{ Hz}$$

120

TABLE XXIV

^{19}F parameters of fluorothiophen derivatives

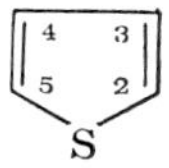

Substituents				Chemical shifts				Coupling constants (Hz)					
2	3	4	5	2	3	4	5	2,3	2,4	2,5	3,4	3,5	4,5
F	F	F	F	−164·9	−155·6	−155·6	−164·9	7	17	31	7	17	7
F	F	F	OMe	−164·0	−156·1	−154·6	..	5·4	17·8	..	10·0	..	..
F	F	OMe	F	−166·8	−153·1	..	−164·9	5·4	..	30·6	..	15·4	..

D. Mixed nitrogen-oxygen and nitrogen-sulphur heterocyclics

A number of new 4-substituted perfluoro-oxazetidines have been prepared[120] and the ^{19}F parameters of some of these compounds given. The available data are summarized in Table XXV. These authors, however, have given the shifts

TABLE XXV

^{19}F parameters of 4-substituted perfluoroxazetidines

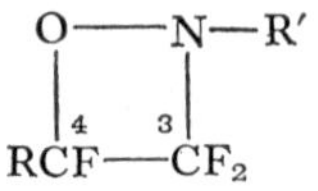

$$
\begin{array}{c}
O\!\!-\!\!-\!\!-N\!\!-\!\!R' \\
| \; 4 \quad 3 \; | \\
RCF\!\!-\!\!-CF_2
\end{array}
$$

R	R'	3-CF_2	4-CF	R'
			Chemical shifts, δ	
F	$-CF_2CFClOCH_2CH_3$	$\sim -95\cdot4$	$-84\cdot5$	$-CF_2$: $\sim -103\cdot7$ and $\sim -108\cdot0$
		$\sim -98\cdot8$		$-CFCl$: $-69\cdot6$
Cl	$-CF_2CFClOCH_2CH_3$	$\sim -88\cdot8$	$-65\cdot7$	$-CF_2$: $\sim -103\cdot8$ and $\sim 108\cdot1$
		$\sim -93\cdot8$		$-CFCl$: $\sim -70\cdot0$
Br	$-CF_2CFClOCH_2CH_3$	$\sim -84\cdot2$	$-58\cdot2$	$-CF_2$: $\sim -103\cdot9$ and $\sim -108\cdot2$
		$\sim -93\cdot5$		$-CFCl$: $\sim -69\cdot9$
F	H	$-97\cdot8$	$-81\cdot4$	
Cl	H	$\sim -87\cdot9$		
		$\sim -95\cdot6$	$-62\cdot5$	
Br	H	$\sim -81\cdot6$	$-53\cdot4$	
		$\sim -95\cdot1$		
F	$-CF_2CO_2CH_2CH_3$	$-97\cdot3$	$-83\cdot1$	$-CF_2$: $\sim -97\cdot3$
F	Cl	$\sim -95\cdot3$	$\sim -78\cdot0$	
		$\sim -110\cdot4$	$\sim -81\cdot9$	
F	F	$\sim -104\cdot4$	$\sim -78\cdot0$	$-NF$: $25\cdot0$
		$\sim -107\cdot6$	$\sim -80\cdot3$	
F	$-COF$	$-95\cdot1$	$-84\cdot4$	$-COF$: $-5\cdot8$

of all the individual lines and no AB analysis have been undertaken. It was thus not indicated how the values of J_{AB} varied for the CF_2 groups adjacent to oxygen and nitrogen; more detailed analysis of the N-fluoro compounds was being undertaken. Pyrolysis of N-fluoro-formyl-1,2-oxazetidine gave the trifluoromethyl isocyanate (121).[120]

$$
\begin{array}{c}
-48\cdot2 \\
CF_3\!\!-\!\!N\!\!=\!\!C\!\!=\!\!O \\
\textbf{121}
\end{array}
$$

Reaction of hexafluorobenzene with diethanolamine or ethylenediamine in the presence of pyridine yielded respectively N-β-oxyethyl-2,3-dihydro-5,6,7,8,-tetrafluorobenzoxazine and the 2,3-dihydro-5,6,7,8-tetrafluorobenzopyrazine.[84]

Reaction of hexafluorothioacetone and bis(trifluoromethyl)thioketone and bis(trifluoromethyl)diazomethane afforded the thiadiazoline derivatives **117** and **118** respectively.[119] The shifts of the CF_3 groups are as shown.

IV. SOME THEORETICAL CONSIDERATIONS

The rigid-lattice second moment of the ^{19}F resonance of XeF_2 has been measured as a function of the external field.[121] The experimental shielding anisotropy $|\Delta\sigma| = 105 \pm 10 \times 10^{-6}$ did not agree with the value of $\sigma_\perp - \sigma_\parallel = -506 \times 10^{-6}$ previously calculated[122] using a localized orbital method. The field-independent rigid-lattice second moment was ~ 0.4 G^2 larger than that calculated from crystallographic data,[123] probably because of large amplitude vibrations in XeF_2. The temperature dependence of the second moment and of the spin-lattice relaxation time were also reported. The field dependence of the ^{19}F second moments have also been investigated[124] and gave a value of 280 p.p.m. for $\sigma_\parallel - \sigma_\perp$ in both tetrafluorohydroquinone and trifluoroacetanilide; the ^{19}F second moment of trifluoroacetamide, however, showed virtually no field dependence.

The ^{19}F spin-lattice relaxation time T_1 has been measured as a function of temperature in both solid and liquid arsenic trifluoride.[125] Three mechanisms were suggested as being responsible for spin-lattice relaxation in the liquid.

The number of studies in nematic phase, involving either simple molecules or molecules with a high degree of symmetry, are increasing, especially with the greater availability of suitable liquid crystal material. From a study of fluoromethanes in p,p'-di-n-hexyloxazoxybenzene the indirect F–H coupling was shown to be positive.[126] The values of the ^{19}F magnetic shielding anisotropies were determined and found to be consistent even using several different referencing techniques. Using methyl fluoride enriched with 55% ^{13}C in nematic phase as unexpectedly large apparent anisotropy in the ^{13}C–^{19}F indirect coupling was found;[127] possible reasons for this large value were discussed. 1,1-Difluoroethylene has also been studied in the nematic phase.[128]

The fluorine chemical shift anisotropies of some $para$-substituted fluorobenzenes have been determined in nematic phase.[129] The changes in anisotropy, relative to fluorobenzene, have been correlated with Taft's inductive and resonance parameters.

Cowley and White[130] have considered the theoretical aspects for the calculation of nuclear spin-coupling constants and, in a subsequent paper,[131] the one- and two- bond fluorine couplings with Group III, IV and V elements.

The relative signs of the one-bond ^{19}F coupling with ^{11}B, ^{13}C, ^{29}Si, ^{14}N and ^{31}P were also considered.

Homer and Callaghan[132] have reconsidered the relation of ^{19}F screening with intramolecular electric fields. The general type of relation used by previous workers was of the form:

$$\Delta\sigma = -A\,\Delta E_z - B[\Delta(E^2) + \Delta\langle E^2\rangle]$$

These authors saw no justification for including the electric field contribution term $\langle E^2\rangle$ with that due to the square of the steady field E^2, and accordingly introduced a new equation:

$$\Delta\sigma = -X\,\Delta E_z - Y\,\Delta(E^2) - Z\,\Delta\langle E^2\rangle$$

The point of origin of the electric fields associated with the C–F bonds was also investigated, together with validity of including contributions from C–C bonds to the $\langle E^2\rangle$ term. Using this approach the authors calculated the ^{19}F shifts for perfluorobicyclo[2.2.1]heptane, *trans*-perfluorodecalin and perfluoro-cyclohexane and, by excluding the C–C bond contribution, there was fair agreement between calculated and observed shifts.

V. ORGANO-METALLIC COMPOUNDS

Group I. Silver and gold

The first example of a perfluorovinylsilver has been reported,[38] namely *trans*-heptafluoro-1-methyl propen-1-ylsilver (**122**) and the parameters are as

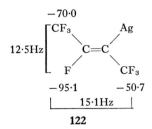

122

shown. Remarkably few studies of fluoroalkyl and fluoroaryl gold compounds have been reported. Four fluorophenyl (fluorophenylisocyanide)gold(I) isomers have been described[133] and the ^{19}F shifts indicate that the gold atom strongly withdraws electrons from the isocyanide ligand but is a weak donor to the fluorobenzene ring. The ^{19}F data are tabulated in Table XXVI. The authors compared the general effects on ^{19}F shifts with those reported for fluorophenyl-copper compounds.

TABLE XXVI

^{19}F chemical shifts on fluorophenyl gold derivatives

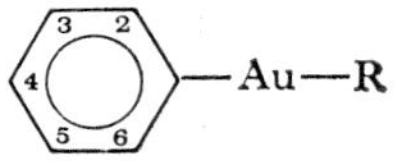

Substituents						Chemical shifts, δ					
2	3	4	5	6	R	2	3	4	5	6	R
H	H	F	H	H	$-CN-C_6H_4F-p$	..	..	$-116\cdot29$	..	..	$-106\cdot62$
H	H	F	H	H	$-CN-C_6H_4F-m$	..	..	$-116\cdot36$	..	..	$-109\cdot68$
H	F	H	H	H	$-CN-C_6H_4F-p$	..	$-115\cdot93$	..	..	..	$-106\cdot62$
H	F	H	H	H	$-CN-C_6H_4F-m$	..	$-115\cdot90$	..	..	..	$-109\cdot67$
H	H	F	H	H	$-P(C_6H_5)_3$	..	..	$-116\cdot93$	..	..	..
H	F	H	H	H	$-P(C_6H_5)_3$	..	$-116\cdot02$	..	..	..	..
F	F	F	F	F	$-P(C_6H_5)_3$	$-116\cdot48$	$-163\cdot0$	$-159\cdot1$	$-163\cdot0$	$-116\cdot48$	..

Group II. Mercury

Ethyl 3-bromoperfluorobutanoate when treated with mercury afforded the ethyl 3-(bromomercuri)perfluorobutanoate (**123**)[134] which was characterized by ^{19}F NMR; the shifts were as shown.

$$\begin{cases} \delta_A\ -110\cdot26 \\ \delta_B\ -113\cdot58 \end{cases}$$

$$-188\cdot54\ \diagdown \qquad \diagdown$$

$$\underset{\underset{\displaystyle CF_3}{|}}{BrHg—CF—CF_2\cdot CO_2C_2H_5}$$

$$-68\cdot99$$

123

Group III. Boron

Hogben *et al.*,[102] using the $\delta_p^{C_6F_5}$ and $J(F_2\text{–}F_4)$ relationship (see p. 434), have reconsidered the pentafluorobenzonitrile-boron trihalide complexes. The boron tribromide adduct, however, gave anomalous results (Fig. 5) and indicates that in this complex the π-acceptor propensity of the nitrile group is decreased even

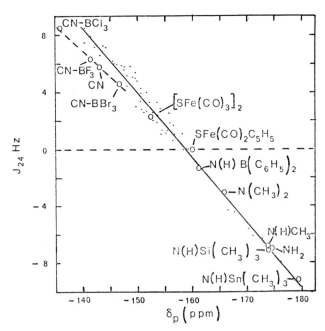

FIG. 5. The $J_{24} - \delta_p$ relationship for certain pentafluoroaniline, pentafluorobenzonitrile and thioiron carbonyl complexes and derivatives. (From Hogben *et al.* [102])

below that of the parent nitrile. It is of interest to note that the shift of the *para*-fluorine atom measured by Hogben and Graham,[98] using hexafluorobenzene as internal reference and converted to the CCl_3F scale by the relation $\delta_{CCl_3F} = \delta - 163 \cdot 0$, was found to be $\delta_p^{C_6F_5} = -146 \cdot 9$ and compares favourably with an independent investigation[135] which gave $\delta_p^{C_6F_5} = -146 \cdot 33$ (measured direct to internal CCl_3F in methylene dichloride solution). The latter workers also measured the ^{11}B shift which indicated that complex formation had indeed occurred. This problem would seem to be analogous to that of the increase in the $-C\equiv N$ stretching frequencies of the nitriles on complex formation.[136]

Group IV. Silicon, germanium, tin, lead and zirconium

Using the $\delta_p^{C_6F_5}$ relationship with $J(F_2-F_4)$ in pentafluoro- phenoxy and thiophenyl derivatives of silicon, germanium, tin and lead showed[102] that the parameters for the oxygen and sulphur compounds fell into two distinct clusters. This arises from the back-donation of the ring π-electrons to the vacant d orbitals of sulphur thus reducing the net π-donor strength of the sulphur substituents. There are two possible ways in which the oxygen or sulphur lone-pairs may bond. Firstly, with the C_6F_5 group resulting in an increase in the π-electron density of the ring and secondly, with the Group IV metal thus decreasing the ring π-electron density. The parameters indicate that the tendency to form π-bonds with oxygen or sulphur decreases in the order:

$$Si > Ge > Sn > Pb$$

Using this principle these authors[102] also investigated the nature of the silicon-nitrogen bonding in the *N*-trimethylsilylaniline (**124**), using the penta-

ArNHSi(CH₃)₃
a. Ar = C₆H₅—
b. Ar = C₆F₅—
124

fluoroaniline derivative (**124b**). Previous investigation[137] of **124a** was based upon the magnitude of the $^{15}N-H$ coupling which, being the same magnitude as that in aniline, indicated no increase in the s character of the nitrogen atom in **124a** and therefore absence of any double-bond character involving the nitrogen atom. It was, however, suggested[138] that a non-planar geometry would not exclude π-bonding and therefore the matter was still open to some doubt. The relation[102] of $\delta_p^{C_6F_5}$ and $J(F_2-F_4)$ of **124b** was the same as that of pentafluoroaniline and *N*-methylpentafluoroaniline (Fig. 5). and therefore indicates the absence of any appreciable π-character of the Si–N bond. It is of interest to note the position of the trimethylstannyl derivative, $C_6F_5NHSn(Me)_3$ (see Fig. 5), which indicates an enhanced π-donation to the ring. This argument makes considerable sense for, in the pentafluorophenyl-aminodiphenylborane, $C_5F_5NHB(C_6H_5)_2$, the parameters substantiate the presence of B–N π-bonding.

The ^{19}F shifts of a number of polyfluorophenylsilane derivatives have been recorded,[139] although no precise assignments were made. The ^{19}F shifts of similarly related pentafluorophenylsilane derivatives have also been listed.[92] The ^{19}F data for the methyl difluorosilane (125) has been reported after analysis of the spectrum as an A_3P_2X system;[140] the compound was obtained by treating the monochloro-derivative, $MeSiH_2Cl$, with phosphorus penta-fluoride.

The parameters for the two 2-bromotetrafluorophenyltin compounds, $[(2\text{-}BrC_6F_4)_nSnMe_{4-n}$, where $n=1$ and 2] have been determined.[141] The ^{19}F spectrum of 126 consisted of a broad singlet of $-123\cdot3$ with $J(\text{Sn–F})=12\cdot2$ Hz.

$$CH_3\text{—}\overset{\overset{\displaystyle F}{|}}{\underset{\underset{\displaystyle F}{|}}{Si}}\text{—}H$$

125

$$Me_3Sn\text{—}\langle\!\langle F \rangle\!\rangle\text{—}SnMe_3$$

126

The spectra of the adducts 127 to 130 of trimethyltin hydride with a number of fluoro-olefins have been studied by Akhtar and Clark.[142] The data for these adducts was as shown. In this paper the ^1H shifts were shown as negative delta

$$\underset{-213}{\overset{-72}{\underset{CF_3}{|}}}Me_3Sn\text{—}CF\text{—}\underset{\overset{\displaystyle H}{\diagup}}{\overset{\displaystyle F}{\diagdown}}C\text{—}F\ \begin{cases}-120\\-124\cdot5\\J_{AB}=320\end{cases}$$

127

$$\overset{-97\cdot67}{Me_3Sn\text{—}CH_2\text{—}CF_2H}$$

128

$$Me_3SnCF_2\cdot CFH_2$$
$$\overset{-229\cdot32}{}\qquad{-111\cdot48}$$

129

$$Me_3Sn\text{—}\overset{\overset{\displaystyle F}{|}}{\underset{\underset{\displaystyle H}{|}}{C}}\text{—}\underset{\underset{\displaystyle H}{\diagdown}}{\overset{\overset{\displaystyle F}{\diagup}}{C}}\text{—}F\ \begin{cases}-117\cdot54\\-124\cdot1\\J_{AB}=294\cdot1\end{cases}$$
$$-237\cdot43$$

130

(δ) values in order to maintain the same sense in signs of ^1H and ^{19}F shifts. Abel et al.[143] found that monochloropentafluoroacetone was inserted in silicon-oxygen, -nitrogen and -arsenic bonds to give compounds of the type 131. Since the carbon atom is asymmetric the ^{19}F spectrum of the $-CF_2Cl$ group constitutes an AB system with $\delta_A-\delta_B$ varying from 0·6 to 1·7 p.p.m. with $J_{AB}=170\pm3$ Hz; the authors dealt at some length with the ABX_3 analysis.

The variable temperature ^{19}F studies of tri(hexafluoroacetylacetonato)-π-cyclopentadienyl-zirconium have been undertaken[144] and at $-30°$ four bands were observed corresponding to the pentagonal-bipyramidal structure; a

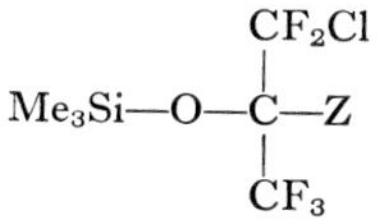

$$CF_2Cl$$
$$Me_3Si—O—\overset{|}{\underset{|}{C}}—Z$$
$$CF_3$$

Z = OMe, SMe, NMe$_2$ and AsMe$_2$

131

rather rare type of hepta-coordination. The proton and ^{19}F spectra of the corresponding trifluoroacetylacetonate derivative were similarly interpreted. The ^{19}F spectrum of the bis(hexafluoroacetylacetonato)-π-cyclopentadienyl-titanium chloride also shows two sets of four-equally intense bands and an additional relatively weak set due to another isomer.

Group V. Phosphorus, arsenic and antimony

The ^{19}F shifts of the trifluoromethyl groups in the boron phosphinites **132** to **134** are in the range $-66 \cdot 8$ to $-67 \cdot 5$,[145] and the ^{19}F–^{31}P coupling is in the

$-67 \cdot 0$
$(CH_3)_2B \cdot O \cdot P(CF_3)_2$
$^2J(F–P) = 88$ Hz
132

$-67 \cdot 5$
$CH_3 \cdot B[O \cdot P(CF_3)_2]_2$
$^2J(F–P) = 90 \cdot 4$ Hz
133

$-66 \cdot 8$
$B[O \cdot P(CF_3)_2]_3$
$2J(F–P) = 91 \cdot 4$ Hz
134

region of 87 to 91·5 Hz. The values of $^2J(F–P)$ in bis(trifluoromethyl)phosphine, $(CF_3)_2PH$, were found[146] to be solvent dependent and could, with the exception of the cases in which benzene was the solvent, be linearly related to the ^1H shift of the PH group. The results were thus in accord with specific hydrogen bonding between the phosphorus and solvent.

A novel tetra(trifluoromethyl)diphosphorus disulphide (**135**) has been

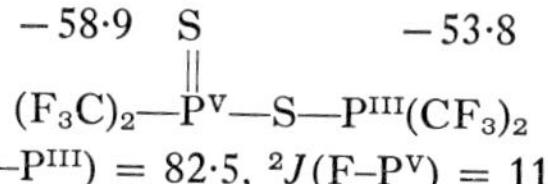

$-58 \cdot 9$ S $\quad -53 \cdot 8$
$(F_3C)_2—\overset{\|}{P^V}—S—P^{III}(CF_3)_2$
$^2J(F–P^{III}) = 82 \cdot 5$, $^2J(F–P^V) = 111 \cdot 7$,
$^4J(F–P–P^{III}) = 5 \cdot 0$
135

described[147] in which the two phosphorus atoms exhibit different valencies; the parameters were found to be as shown. Tetrakis(monochloromethyldifluorophosphine)nickel(0), $Ni(ClCH_2PF_2)_4$, has been prepared,[148] by reaction of the fluorophosphine and nickelocene, and the spectrum analysed. The ^{19}F shift of the complex at $-62\cdot0$ is to low field of that of the fluorophosphine ($-96\cdot7$). The $^1J(\text{F–P})$ is approximately the same value in the complex (1149 Hz) as in the phosphine (1196 Hz); the analysis of the spectrum was briefly discussed.

Cowley and Taylor[149] have considered the ^{19}F shifts and coupling constants in a series of trifluorovinylphosphine derivatives. The details of the parameters are shown in Table XXVII. The shifts of the vinylic fluorine atoms fall into discrete ranges but caution must be exercised in extending these correlations to other derivatives as is illustrated in the paper by data taken from other references. The authors, however, found that an approximately linear relationship existed between the shift of F_1, i.e. the vinyl fluorine *trans* to the substituent (136), and the *gem* F_1–F_2 coupling. These two authors have also examined the ^{19}F spectra of trifluorovinyl tetrafluorophosphorane (137) and bis(trifluorovinyl)trifluorophosphorane (138).[150] It was not possible to detect the F–P resonances in the latter compound at ambient temperature but they were resolved at $-60°$; the data are shown below the structures. No further resolution of the phosphorane fluorine atoms could be obtained in 137, even on

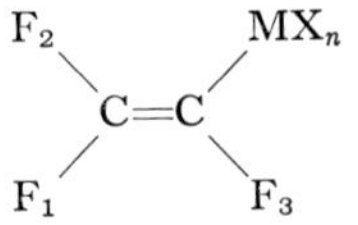

$$-79\cdot4 \qquad -54\cdot9$$
$$\text{F} \qquad\qquad \text{PF}_4$$
$$\diagdown\qquad\diagup$$
$$\text{C}=\text{C}$$
$$\diagup\qquad\diagdown$$
$$\text{F} \qquad\qquad \text{F}$$
$$-64\cdot7 \qquad -177\cdot8$$
$$^1J(\text{F–P}) = 927\ \text{Hz}$$

137

$$\text{F}_2 \qquad\qquad \text{MX}_n$$
$$\diagdown\qquad\diagup$$
$$\text{C}=\text{C}$$
$$\diagup\qquad\diagdown$$
$$\text{F}_1 \qquad\qquad \text{F}_3$$

136

cooling to $-100°$. It was suggested that, on the basis of the NMR data, the structure of 138 was probably that of an equatorially substituted trigonal-bipyramid.

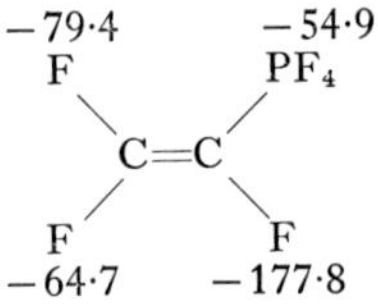

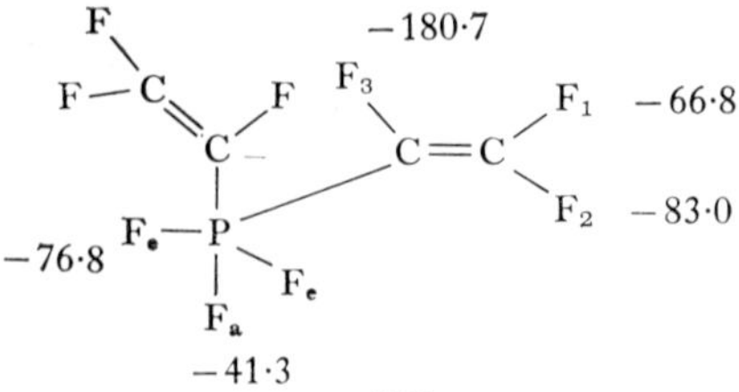

$J(\text{F}_e\text{–P}) = 975,\ J(\text{F}_a\text{–P}) = 641$
$J(\text{F}_e\text{–P–F}_a) = 52,\ J(\text{F–C–P}) = 91$
$J(\text{F–C–P–F}_e) = 0,$
$J(\text{F–C–P–F}_a) = 2\cdot5,$
cis $J(\text{F–C–C–P}) = 15,$
trans $J(\text{F–C–C–P}) = 31,$
cis $J(\text{F–C–C–P–F}_e) = 5,$
cis $J(\text{F–C–C–P–F}_a) = 58,$
trans $J(\text{F–C–C–P–F}_e) = 0,$
trans $J(\text{F–C–C–P–F}_a) = 12$

Structure 138 with shifts: $-180\cdot7$ (F$_3$), $-76\cdot8$ (F$_e$–P), $-41\cdot3$ (F$_a$), F_1 $-66\cdot8$, F_2 $-83\cdot0$

138

Hogben *et al.*,[102] using the relationship between $\delta_p^{C_6F_5}$ and $J(\text{F}_2\text{–F}_4)$ found in pentafluoroaromatics (see p. 434), have studied the bonding in pentafluorophenyl phosphines and complexes. It was deduced that the π-acceptor

TABLE XXVII

^{19}F parameters of perfluorovinyl phosphines

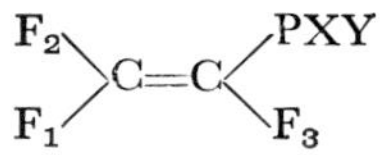

$$\begin{array}{ccc} F_2 \diagdown & & \diagup PXY \\ & C{=}C & \\ F_1 \diagup & & \diagdown F_3 \end{array}$$

X	Y	Chemical shifts, δ			Coupling constants, Hz						
		F_1	F_2	F_3	F_1–F_2	F_1–F_3	F_2–F_3	P–F_3	P–F_2	P–F_1	
$CF_2{=}CF-$	$CF_2{=}CF-$	−82·6	−106·3	−175·9	··	··	··	··	··	··	$^5J(\text{F–NCH}_3)$ = 0·6
$CF_2{=}CF-$	NMe_2	−89·04	−110·05	−179·28	53	32	119	24	53	8	$^5J(\text{F–NCH}_3)$ = 0·8
NMe_2	NMe_2	−89·4	−107·8	−181·3	··	··	··	··	··	··	$^1J(\text{F–P})$ = 995; $^4J(\text{F–NCH}_3)$ = 6·2; $^5J(\text{F–NCH}_3)$ = 0·9
F	NMe_2	−90·1	−113·0	−190·0	··	··	··	··	··	··	δ PF = −126·3
$CF_2{=}CF-$	Cl	−81·87	−103·92	−180·97	36	··	121	··	70	··	$^1J(\text{F–P})$ = 1202; $^3J(\text{FPCF})$ = 11·1; $^4J(\text{FP–CF}_1)$ = 13·2;
Cl	Cl	−82·50	−103·59	−186·43	39	32	123	17	84	7	$^4J(\text{FP–CF}_2)$ = 2·8
F	F	−79·90	−112·00	−119·14	42·4	31·0	123·5	20·8	69·6	4·8	δ PF = −103·60

character of the phosphorus atom in phosphines and their complexes increases along the series:

$$\text{free phosphines} < \text{carbonyl complexes} < S < O < BCl_3 < H^{\oplus}Cl^{\ominus}$$

presumably reflecting decreasing back donation by the complexed group. The lone-pair on phosphorus is effectively removed when the coordination number of the phosphorus atom is increased to five; thus the π-withdrawal from the C_6F_5-group increases in the series:

$$(C_6F_5)_3P < (C_6H_5)_3PF_2 < (C_6F_5)PS < (C_6F_5)_3PO$$

Similarly the relationship of $\delta_p^{C_6F_5}$ and $J(F_2-F_4)$ shows that the order of increasing π-acceptor power of X in the series C_6F_5X is

$$P[N(CH_3)_2]_2 < P(CH_3)_2 < P(C_2H_5)_2 < P(C_6H_5)_2 < PF_2 < PCl_2$$

The presence of a large four-bond $^{19}F-^{31}P$ coupling (52 to 55 Hz) in a series of *ortho*-trifluoromethylphenylphosphines of the type $(o\text{-}CF_3C_6H_4)_nP(C_6H_5)_{3-n}$, where $n = 1$, 2 or 3, and its positive temperature dependence has been taken[151] as evidence for through-space coupling between the fluorine and phosphorus atoms. It was emphasized that no F–P coupling was present in the corresponding *meta*- or *para*- compounds. The temperature dependence of the $^{19}F-^{31}P$ coupling (Fig. 6) was very similar to that previously observed for the $^{19}F-^{19}F$ coupling in 2-fluoro-trifluoromethylbenzene.[152]

The nucleophilic substitution of pentafluorophenyldiphenylphosphine and the oxide and sulphide have been studied[153] and the ^{19}F shift data are summarized in Table XXVIII. Reaction of triphenylphosphine with 1,2-dichloro-perfluorocycloalkenes afforded the triphenylphosphonium betaines **139**.[154] The

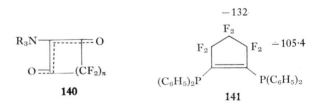

a, $n = 1$; δ $-118 \cdot 1$, $J(F-P) = 20 \cdot 5$ Hz
b, $n = 2$; δ $-127 \cdot 2$, $J(F-P) = 1 \cdot 1$ Hz

139

shifts found, as shown in structures, were very similar to the corresponding quarternary ammonium betaines **140**. It is of interest to note the large variation

140   **141**

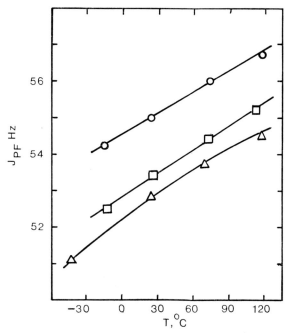

FIG. 6. Temperature dependence of $J(F–P)$ of $(o\text{-}CF_3C_6H_4)_3P$ ○, $(o\text{-}CF_3C_6H_4)_2PC_6H_5$ △, and $o\text{-}CF_3C_6H_4P(C_6H_5)_2$ □. (From Miller *et al.*[151])

in the four-bond F–P coupling with ring size. Diphenylphosphine reacted smoothly with octafluorocyclopentene to afford the 1,2-bis(diphenylphosphino)-hexafluorocyclopentene **141**.[155] Although it was obvious from the multiplicity of the resonance signals that each of the CF_2 groups couple to the phosphorus atoms no precise values were quoted in the paper.

The ^{19}F chemical shifts and the $^1J(F–P)$ values of a series of pentafluoro-phenyl fluorophosphoranes and fluorophosphines, and corresponding oxides, have been recorded[156] and the data are included in Table XXVIII. The ^{19}F shifts of the pentafluorophenyl entity do not warrant any comment but the shifts and coupling constants of the PF_n groups are very variable. For convenience this aspect is considered in the section on p. 478. The authors did, however, consider the electronic interaction between the pentafluorophenyl groups and the phosphorous atom.

Nichols[157] has studied a whole range of pentafluorophenyl phosphines, arsines and stilbenes and considered the variation of F–F couplings within the ring. In the phosphines a large *ortho* F–P coupling was found, 31 to 38 Hz, which was much more variable in the oxides and appeared to depend upon the number of pentafluorophenyl groups attached to the phosphorus atom. Thus,

TABLE XXVIII

^{19}F chemical shifts of fluorophenylphosphorus compounds

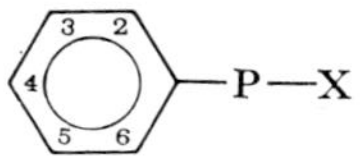

Substituents					X	Chemical shifts						Ref.
2	3	4	5	6		2	3	4	5	6		
F	F	OMe	F	F	$-(C_6H_5)_2$	-130.6	-156.9	: :	-156.9	-130.6		153
F	F	NHMe	F	F	$-(C_6H_5)_2$	-131.4	-161.2	: :	-161.2	-131.4		153
F	F	NHMe	F	F	$-(O)(C_6H_5)_2$	-132.7	-162.1	: :	-162.1	-132.7		153
F	F	OMe	F	F	$-(S)(C_6H_5)_2$	-129.9	-156.5	: :	-156.5	-129.9		153
F	F	NHMe	F	F	$-(S)(C_6H_5)_2$	-131.7	-162.9	: :	-162.9	-131.7		153
F	F	F	F	F	F_2	-140.3	-164.5	-149.0	-164.5	-140.3	δ PF -94.5; ^1J(F–P) $= 1215$	156
F	F	F	F	F	$(F)(C_6F_5)$	-138.4	-166.0	-152.6	-166.0	-138.4	δ PF -216.6; ^1J(F–P) $= 1002$	156
F	F	F	F	F	$(O)F_2$	-133.0	-163.2	-145.0	-163.2	-133.0	δ PF -57.5; ^1J(F–P) $= 1128$	156
F	F	F	F	F	$(O)(F)C_6F_5$	-136.8	-164.4	-147.2	-164.4	-136.8	δ PF -55.8; ^1J(F–P) $= 1090$	156
F	F	F	F	F	F_4	-135.8	-163.2	-149.0	-163.2	-135.8	δ PF -40.6; ^1J(F–P) $= 1000$	156
F	F	F	F	F	$(C_6F_5)F_3$	-138.4	-165.2	-151.0	-165.2	-138.4	δ PF 7.0; ^1J(F–P) $= 912$	156
F	F	F	F	F	$(C_6F_5)_2F_2$	-137.8	-164.8	-151.6	-164.8	-137.8	δ PF 2.5; ^1J(F–P) $= 713$	156

in the series $(C_6F_5)_nPh_{3-n}P{=}O$, the *ortho*-F–P coupling increased in the order $n=1$ (6·5 Hz) $< n=2$ (15·0 Hz) $< n=3$ (37·4 Hz). When the phosphines were complexed with $PtCl_2$ or $RhCOCl$ no appreciable *ortho*-F–P coupling was observed.

Glemser *et al.*[158] have reported the ^{19}F data of a number of alkylamino-pentafluorophosphazines. The shifts of the $>PF_2$ groups are fairly constant, $-70·7$ to $-71·2$, while those of the $>P{<}^X_F$ groups are naturally more variable depending upon the nature of X.

Groups VI to VIII

Bis(pentafluorophenyl)phosphine with Group VI metal carbonyls afforded a series of complexes, $[(C_6F_5)_2PH]M(CO)_5$ where $M = Cr$, Mo, W, $[(C_6H_5)_2PH]_2M(CO)_4$ where $M = Cr$ and Mo and $[(C_6H_5)_2PH]_3Mo(CO)_3$, have been characterized[159] and the ^{19}F shifts of the pentafluorophenyl entity are shown in Table XXIX. In addition $(C_6H_5)_4P_2$ reacted with chromium and

TABLE XXIX

[19]F shifts of bis(pentafluorophenyl)phosphine complexes

$[(C_6F_5)_2PX]_mM(CO)_n$ **A** and $(C_6F_5)_4P_2M(CO)_n$ **B**

	M	m	n	X	Chemical shifts, δ F_2, F_6	F_3, F_5	F_4
A	Cr	1	5	H	$-129·4$	$-158·0$	$-146·1$
A	Mo	1	5	H	$-130·1$	$-158·5$	$-146·8$
A	W	1	5	H	$-130·5$	$-157·1$	$-145·6$
A	Cr	2	4	H	$-129·6$	$-157·6$	$-146·0$
A	Mo	2	4	H	$-130·1$	$-158·1$	$-146·7$
A	Mo	3	3	H	$-131·3$	$-158·6$	$-143·9$
A	Cr	1	5	Li	$-130·0$	$-162·5$	$-149·0$
A	Mo	1	5	Li	$-129·0$	$-161·7$	$-149·2$
B	Cr	..	5	..	$\begin{cases} -128·9 \\ -128·9 \end{cases}$	$\begin{cases} -158·5 \\ -159·9 \end{cases}$	$\begin{cases} -146·5 \\ -147·7 \end{cases}$
B	Mo	..	5	..	$\begin{cases} -130·4 \\ -133·9 \end{cases}$	$\begin{cases} -157·5 \\ -159·2 \end{cases}$	$\begin{cases} -146·6 \\ -148·8 \end{cases}$

molybdenum hexacarbonyls to give polymeric complexes and $(C_6H_5)_2PCl$ with the Co and Mo carbonyl anions afforded complexes of the type $(C_6H_5)_4P_2$-$M(CO)_5$; the ^{19}F shifts of these two types of complexes are also included in Table XXIX. The variation in the F–P coupling constants and ^{19}F shifts on coordination of ethylaminobisdifluorophosphine with chromium, molybdenum and tungsten carbonyls has been studied.[160] The value of $^2J(PMP')$ was dramatically decreased on coordination and was variable within the series of complexes **142** (Table XXX). The ^{19}F shifts in the complexes are to higher

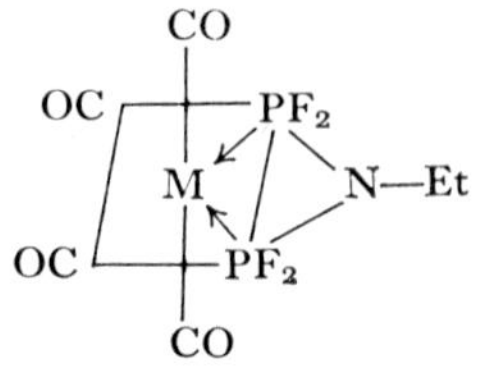

$$M = Cr, Mo, W$$

142

TABLE XXX

^{19}F **parameters of ethylaminobisdifluorophosphine complexes, 142**

M	δ F	$^4J(F–F^1)$	$^1J(F–P)$	$^3J(F^1–P)$
Cr	−47·8	9·52	−1301	+56·5
Mo	−49·6	7·0	−1284	+40
W	−51·4	5·4	−1277	+46·0

frequency (low field), and this type of shift is characteristic of all fluorophosphine complexes of zero-valent transition metals. In the tungsten complex, the fluorine nuclei coupled to the ^{183}W nucleus (14·3% abundance) with $^2J(F–W) = 27 \pm 2$ Hz. The NMR study of the pentafluorophenylhydrido-complexes of molybdenum and tungsten has been used to ascertain the structure of these complexes;[161] the ^{19}F data of only the molybdenum hydride was given in any detail.

The NMR spectra of the rhodium complexes, π-cyclopentadienyldiethylenerhodium, π-cyclopentadienylethylene(sulphur dioxide)rhodium and π-cyclopentadienylethylenetetrafluoroethylenerhodium, have been used to elucidate the nature of the bonding.[35] In the case of the tetrafluoroethylene adduct there was a problem in assigning the fluorine atoms as it was not clear whether to assign the largest F–F coupling to the *trans-* or *gem-* fluorine atoms. The authors preferred the geminal coupling on the supposition that the rhodium-carbon bonding resulted in a system similar to that found in a cyclopropane derivative.

Bis(trifluoromethyl)diazomethane reacts with bis(benzonitrile)palladium dichloride leading to the insertion of a $(CF_3)_2C$ group into a metal-chlorine bond with the formation of two complexes **143** and **144**;[162] the shifts were as shown.

PhCN   Cl   C(CF$_3$)$_2$Cl

Pd   Pd

$-62\cdot3$ Cl(CF$_3$)$_2$C   Cl   NCPh
(PhCN)$_2$Pd[C(CF$_3$)$_2$Cl]$_2$ $-62\cdot9$

143   **144**

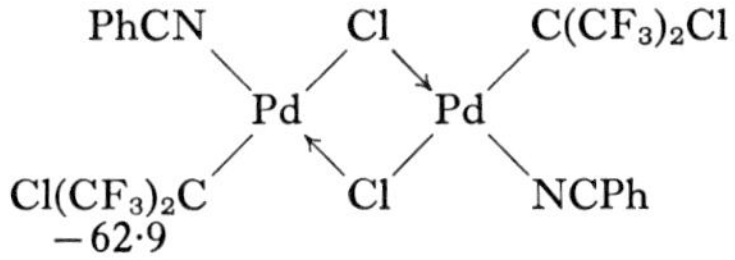

A similar insertion into metal-hydrogen bonds occurs on reaction of the same diazomethane with manganese and platinum hydrides;[163] the parameters of the three compounds obtained are shown in **145** to **147**. The coupling of the

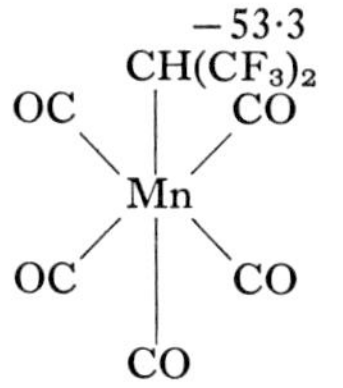

$-53\cdot3$
CH(CF$_3$)$_2$
OC   CO

Mn

OC   CO

CO

^3J(F–H) = 12 Hz
145

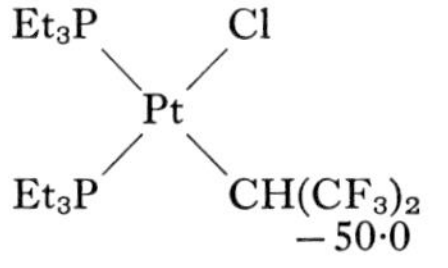

Et$_3$P   Cl

Pt

Et$_3$P   CH(CF$_3$)$_2$
          $-50\cdot0$

^3J(F–^{195}Pt) = 132$\cdot$0 Hz
^4J(F–P) = 18$\cdot$0 Hz
^3J(F–H) = 12$\cdot$0 Hz
146

CF$_3$ groups to a single phosphorus atom in **146** was assigned to that of the *trans*-Et$_3$P group on the basis that *trans* J(F–P) is greater than *cis* J(F–P). This was substantiated as in **147**, in which both phosphine groups occupy *cis*-positions, there is no evidence of F–P coupling. π-Cyclopentadienyl iron carbonyl, [(π-C$_5$H$_5$)Fe(CO)$_2$]$_2$, also reacts with the diazomethane to afford a

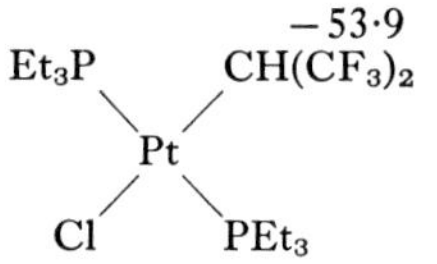

$-53\cdot9$
Et$_3$P   CH(CF$_3$)$_2$

Pt

Cl   PEt$_3$
^3J(F–^{195}Pt) = 152$\cdot$2 Hz
^3J(F–H) = 12$\cdot$0 Hz
147

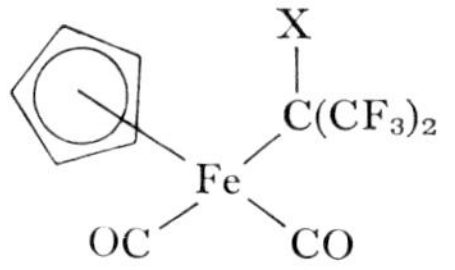

X
|
C(CF$_3$)$_2$
Fe
OC   CO

δ(CF$_3$), X = H, $-53\cdot4$
          X = D, $-53\cdot6$
148

similar complex containing a metal-CH(CF$_3$)$_2$ bond (**148**). The hydrogen atom appears to come from the tetrahydrofuran used as solvent as the use of tetrahydrofuran-d_8 resulted in the formation of a C–D bond and the CF$_3$ resonance signal was then a singlet. Octacarbonyldicobalt and (CF$_3$)$_2$CN gave the complexes **149a** and **b**. The two CF$_3$ groups in **149a** are non-equivalent, yet only a single resonance signal at $-49\cdot5$ was observed. This suggests that either the two shifts are coincident or, more probable, a dynamic equilibrium of **149a**$\rightleftharpoons$ **149b** exists.

The ^{19}F shifts of trifluoromethylthio-groups in a series of derivatives of

149a

149b

metal carbonyls, prepared by interaction of silver trifluoromethylmercaptide and the metal carbonyl, have been reported.[164] The NMR data of a series of trifluoromethyl-, pentafluoroethyl- and heptafluoroisopropyl- derivatives of cyclopentadienyl metal carbonyls of iron and molybdenum with tertiary phosphines have also been reported.[165] There was coupling of the CF_3 groups of the trifluoromethyl and heptafluoroisopropyl groups to the phosphorus atom (~1·6 and 6 to 12 Hz respectively).

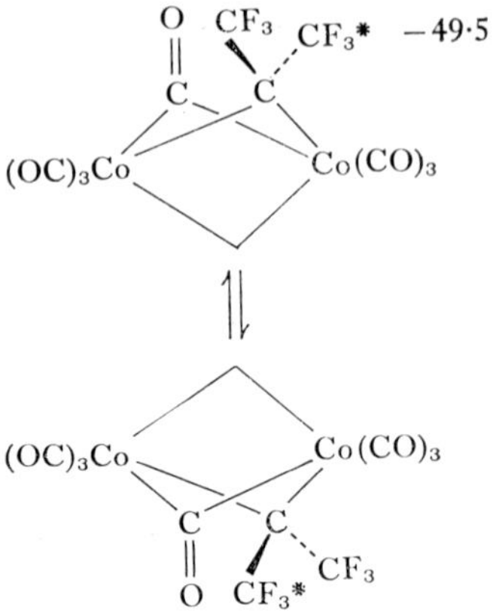

Cook and Green[166] have examined a series of complexes of hexafluoroacetone and 1,1-dicyano-2,2-bis(trifluoromethyl)-, *trans*-1,2-bis(trifluoromethyl)- and tetrafluoro- ethylenes with ruthenium. The shifts of the trifluoromethyl groups are shown in **150** to **152**. The spectra of the tetrafluoroethylene adducts

150

L = EtC(CH_2O)$_3$P–
^4J(F–P) = 13·0 Hz

X = CO, Y = L; X = L, Y = CO

151

L = EtC(CH_2O)$_3$P–
^4J(F–P) = 11·5 Hz

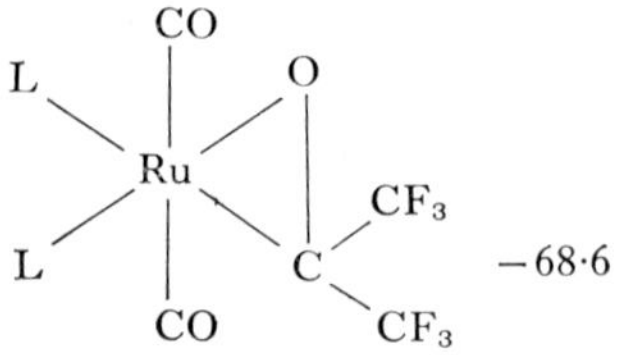

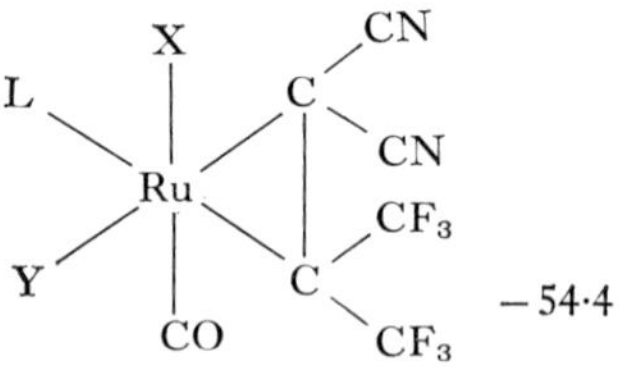

153 were analysed as $X_2AA'X'_2$ spin systems and the shifts were in the range −113·2 to −115·5, about 19 p.p.m. to lower field of uncoordinated tetrafluoroethylene. The CF_3 shift of **150** is about 9·0 p.p.m. to lower field than of the uncomplexed hexafluoroacetone, which therefore excludes any possibility of a Ru–CF_3 bond being formed. Stone *et al.*[167] have also studied a series of

nickel complexes of hexafluoroacetone and thioacetone of the general structure **154**. In all cases *trans* J(F–P) is larger than *cis* J(F–P) and the non-equality of these couplings confirms the presence of the rigid $\overline{\text{Ni–C–O}}$ and $\overline{\text{Ni–C–S}}$ rings.

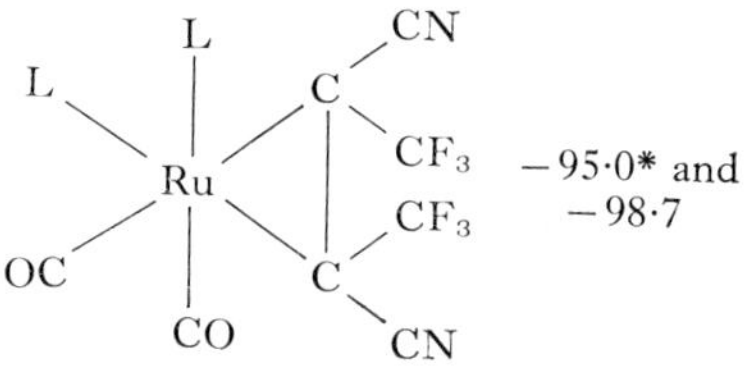
L
CN
L
C
Ru
CF3
CF3
−95·0* and
−98·7
OC
C
CO
CN

L = EtC($CH_2O)_3$P–
* ^4J(F–P) = 6·0 Hz
152

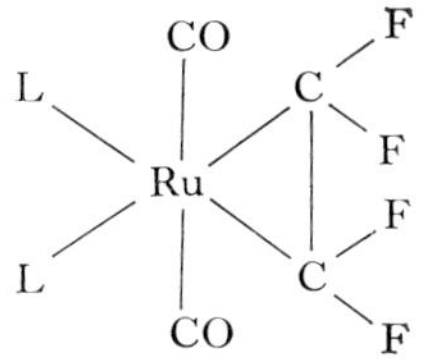
CO
F
L
C
F
Ru
F
L
C
CO
F

L = (EtO)$_3$P–, (MeO)$_3$P–, or EtC($CH_2O)_3$P–
153

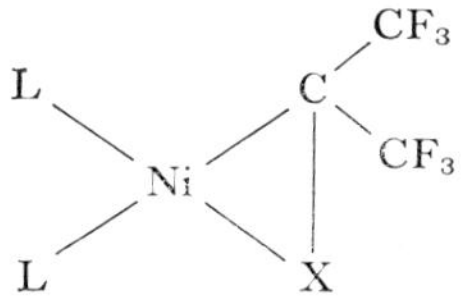
CF3
L
C
CF3
Ni
L
X

X = O or S
154

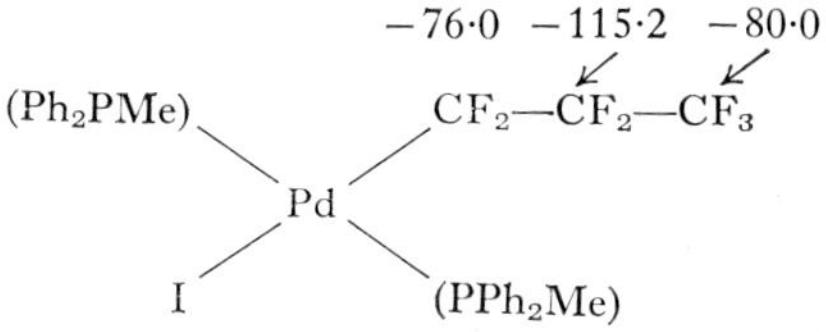
−76·0 −115·2 −80·0
(Ph2PMe)
CF2—CF2—CF3
Pd
I
(PPh2Me)

$^3J(CF_2–CF_2)$ = 2·0 Hz
$^4J(CF_2–CF_3)$ = 5·5 Hz
$^3J(CF_2–P)$ = 18·5 Hz
155

The data for a series of *trans* phenylphosphine palladium halide complexes of fluoro-olefins and fluoroaromatics have been recorded.[168] The same paper also reported the shifts of heptafluoropropyl- (**155**) and the *n*-heptafluorobutyryl (**156**) compounds; the parameters were as shown. It is significant that the shifts

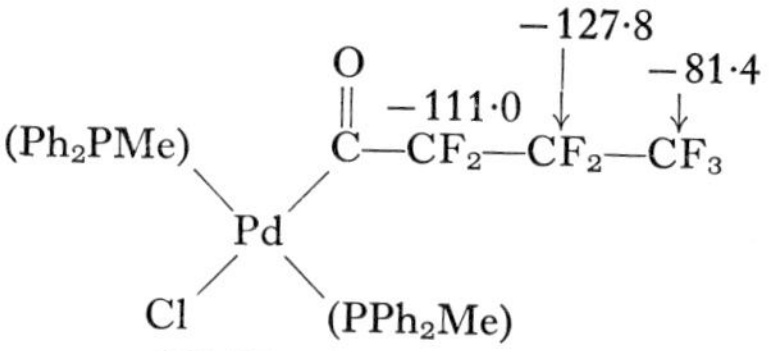
−127·8
O
−81·4
−111·0
(Ph2PMe)
C—CF2—CF2—CF3
Pd
Cl
(PPh2Me)

$^3J(CF_2–CF_2)$ = 2·8 Hz
$^4J(CF_2–CF_3)$ = 5·1 Hz
$^4J(CF_2–P)$ = 8·0 Hz
156

of the CF_2 groups directly bonded to palladium is to particularly low field. The similar complexes of nickel have also been investigated by the same school of workers.[169] It was noticeable in this work that the geminal $\underset{F}{\overset{F}{>}}C=$ coupling was particularly large and variable (72 to 114 Hz) depending upon the nature of the third vinylic substituent. The data for the hexafluorocyclobutene complex **157** were as shown. Further reactions of the π-cyclopentadienyliron car-

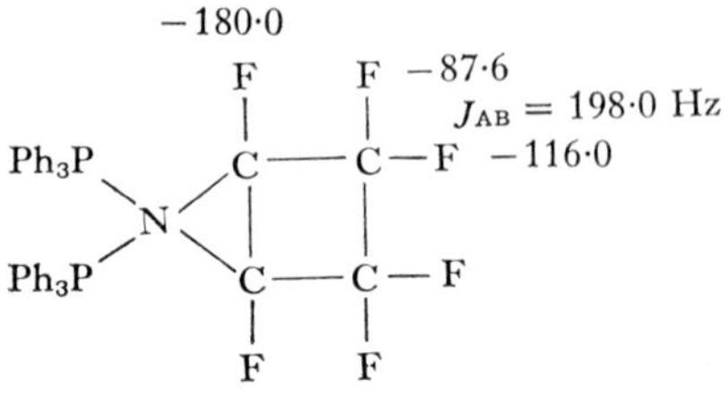

157

bonyl anion with fluoroaromatics have been studied and the ^{19}F data of the derivatives are shown in Table XXXI.[170]

The preparation of pentafluoro- phenyl and benzoyl, and of 4-methoxy-tetrafluorophenyl substituted ferrocenes has been described. There was essentially no coupling between the 2,6-fluorine atoms and the pentadienyl ring protons. Tetrafluorophthalonitrile and iron pentacarbonyl afforded hexadeca-fluorophthalocyaninatoiron(II) (**158**)[171] and the ^{19}F shifts of the bis-pyridine

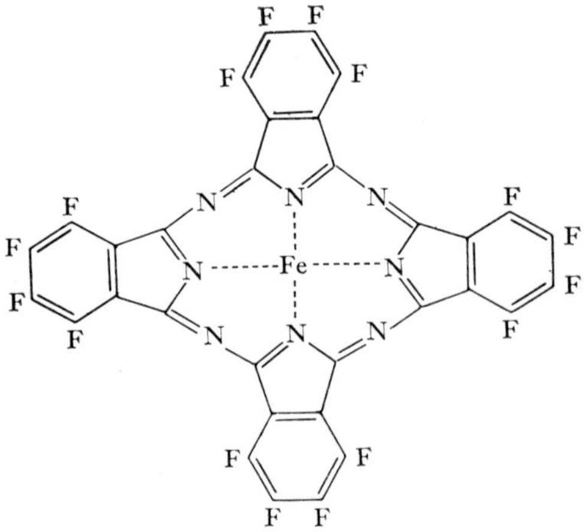

158

adduct at $-126 \cdot 5$ and $-141 \cdot 5$ are very similar to these of the parent phthalo-nitrile, namely $-128 \cdot 5$ and $-144 \cdot 4$.

TABLE XXXI

^{19}F parameters of fluoraromatic metallic derivatives

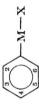

M	X	Substituents 2	3	4	5	6	Chemical shifts, δ — 2	3	4	5	6	Ref.
Fe	$(CO)_2(\pi\text{-}C_5H_5)$	F	F	Me	F	F	−109.3	−145.9	···	−145.9	−109.3	170
Fe	$(CO)_2(\pi\text{-}C_5H_5)$	F	F	$CH{=}CH_2$	F	F	−108.6	−145.6	···	−145.6	−108.6	170
Fe	$(CO)_2(\pi\text{-}C_5H_5)$	F	F	$CH_2{=}CHCH_2$	F	F	−108.8	−146.9	···	−146.9	−108.8	170
Fe	$(CO)_2(\pi\text{-}C_5H_5)$	F	F	$CH_3{\cdot}CH{=}CH$	F	F	−109.4	−146.5	···	−146.5	−109.4	170
Fe	$(CO)_2(\pi\text{-}C_5H_5)$	F	F	Br	F	F	−105.2	−134.0	···	−134.0	−105.2	170
Fe	$(CO)_2(\pi\text{-}C_5H_5)$	F	F	OMe	F	F	−108.3	−158.5	···	−158.5	−108.3	170
Fe	$(CO)_2(\pi\text{-}C_5H_5)$	F	OMe	F	F	F	−111.2	···	−170.6	−166.2	−104.8	170
Fe	$(CO)_2(\pi\text{-}C_5H_5)$	OMe	F	F	F	F	···	−168.0	−163.6	−161.6	−104.8	170
Fe	$(CO)_2(\pi\text{-}C_5H_5)$	F	H	F	F	H	−83.5	···	−158.8	−138.5	···	170
Fe	$(CO)_2(\pi\text{-}C_5H_4)$	H	F	F	H	F	···	−156.2	−141.1	···	−101.2	170
Ni	$(Ph_3P)_2Cl$	F	F	F	F	F	−120.5	−163.7	−162.6	−163.7	−120.5	169
Pd	*trans*-$(Ph_2PMe)_2Cl$	F	F	F	F	F	−119.1	−165.2	−162.1	−165.2	−119.1	168
Pd	*trans*-$(Ph_2PMe)_2Br$	F	F	F	F	F	−117.6	−162.8	−162.1	−162.8	−117.6	168

The spectra of a series of fluorophosphine-molybdenum complexes of the type cis-$L_2Mo(CO)_4$ have been analysed as $X_nAA'X_n'$ spin-system and accurate values of $|^1J_{PF}|$ and $|^3J_{PF}|$ obtained.[172] The ^{19}F spectra were used to establish the *trans* configuration in some trifluorophosphine rhodium complexes[173] and the exchange of triphenylphosphine and trifluorophosphine groups in **159**.

−15·4

F₃P   PPh₃

Rh

Ph₃P   Cl

$^1J(F–P) = 1286\ Hz$
$^2J(F–^{103}Rh) = 32\ Hz$
$^3J(F–P) = 7\ Hz$

159

Addition of Ph_3P results in the disappearance of the triplets from loss of $^3J(F–P)$, while addition of PF_3 results in additional loss of $^2J(F–Rh)$ (Fig. 7).

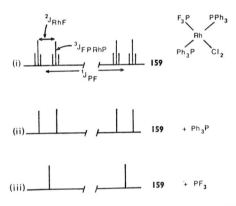

FIG. 7. Line diagram showing effect of ^{19}F NMR spectrum of **159** on adding small amounts of triphenyl phosphine and phosphorus trifluoride. (From Nixon *et al.*[173])

The shift in **159** is similar to that reported[174] for $[RhCl(PF_3)_2]_2$, namely −16·25 with $^1J(F–P) = 1300\ Hz$ and $^2J(F–^{103}Rh) = 32\ Hz$.

VI. FLUORINATED DERIVATIVES OF THE ELEMENTS

Hydrogen fluoride

Borodin *et al.*[175] have investigated the $DF–D_2O$ and $DF–D_2O–H_2O$ systems. The results were compared with those obtained[176] in the $HF–H_2O$ and $HF–D_2O$ systems which had been studied earlier. The ^{19}F spectra of bifluoride salts (HF$_2^\ominus$) of primary, secondary, tertiary and quaternary butyl ammonium ions have also been studied.[177] The shifts of these ions and, for the purpose of comparison, those of the fluoride ions are shown in Table XXXII. The in-

TABLE XXXII

^{19}F shifts of fluoride and bifluoride ions,

R$^\oplus$HF$_2^\ominus$ and R$^\oplus$F$^\ominus$

R$^\oplus$	δ (HF$_2^\ominus$)	δ (F$^\ominus$)
BuNH$_3$	−150·4	−123·1
Bu$_2$NH$_2$	−158·4	..
Bu$_3$NH	−162·1	..
Bu$_4$N	−167·9	−128·3

creasing size of the cation results in a ^{19}F shift to higher field possibly owing to steric effects preventing close approach of the anion.

Boron

Elegant et al.[178] have reported the ^{19}F shifts of the boron trifluoride complexes with phosphorus halides and esters. In a study of the complexes of 1,3-diketones with boron trifluoride, which in turn afforded boron difluoride complexes of the type **160**, the ^{19}F shifts of the BF$_2$ entity were found to be in the

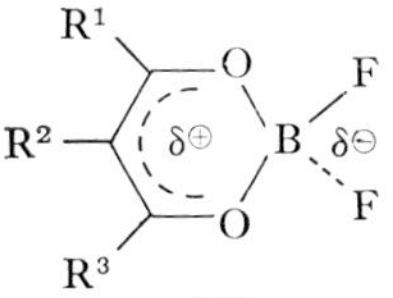

160 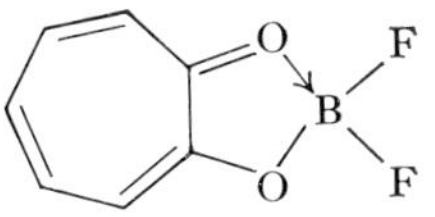   161

the range −138 to −142.[179] No B–F coupling was observed, but in each case a second low field signal was observed which, on the basis of the intensity, was assigned to the ^{10}BF$_2$ resonance, thus giving a ^{10}B–^{11}B isotopic shift of about 0·05 p.p.m. In the tropolone complex (**161**) a B–F coupling of 5 Hz was observed while in the 3-anilino- and 3-benzylamino- 1-phenylbut-2-enone complexes (**162**) a much larger B–F coupling of 15 to 17 Hz was observed. The B–F coupling is usually found when a B–N bond is formed but is generally absent in B–O compounds.

The signs of ^{11}B–^{19}F coupling in boron trifluoride and mixed halogeno-fluoroborons have been determined[180] and a change in the sign of coupling was found. In addition a linear relationship between the value of $J(^{11}$B–^{19}F$)$ and

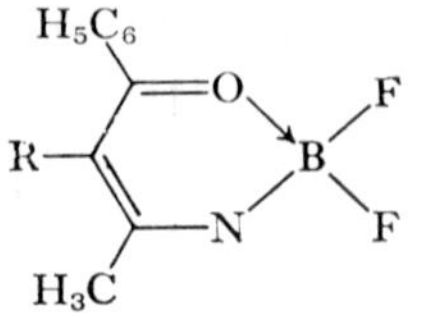

162

$\delta\ ^{19}F$ was observed. This relationship was also extended to the alkylboron difluorides. The value of $J(^{11}B-^{19}F)$ was considered to be related to the extent of π-bonding between the fluorine and boron atoms.

Two new silicon-boron fluorides have been reported,[181] namely SiB_2F_6 (**163**) and SiB_3F_7 (**164**), and the shifts reported were as shown.

$$-146\cdot9 \qquad -48\cdot2$$
$$F_2\text{—Si—}(BF_2)_2$$
163

$$-234 \qquad -39\cdot0$$
$$F\text{—Si—}(BF_2)_3$$
164

Silicon

Airey and Sheldrick[182] have described the preparation of the trifluorosilyl pseudohalides, F_3SiX, and they have recorded the appropriate ^{19}F data. These compounds showed some tendency to disproportionate, giving difluorosilyl dipseudohalides, and so the ^{19}F assignments made were only tentative.

Reaction of silicon difluoride with hydrogen sulphide resulted in the formation of a disilane **165** and of two silanethiols **166** and **167**;[183a] the parameters

$$-142\cdot4 \qquad -125\cdot3$$
$$F_2HSi\cdot SiF_3$$
$^2J(F-H) = 53\cdot2\ Hz$
$^3J(F-F) = 12\cdot7\ Hz$
$^3J(F-H) = 12\cdot7\ Hz$
165

$$-122\cdot9$$
$$F_2HSi\cdot SH$$
$^2J(F-H) = 75\cdot2\ Hz$
$^3J(F-H) = 5\cdot6\ Hz$
166

$$-143\cdot0 \qquad -118\cdot1$$
$$F_2HSi\cdot SiF_2\cdot SH$$
$^2J(F-H) = 54\cdot9\ Hz$
$^3J(F-F) = 10\cdot8\ Hz$
167

found were as shown in the structures. The value of the *gem* F–H coupling of the HF_2Si- group is rather variable.

Titanium

The ^{19}F spectra of titanium tetrafluoride complexes of pyridine oxide still continue to receive attention. Dyer and Raysdale,[183b] in an extension of their earlier work, have obtained evidence for the formation of *trans*-$TiF_4\cdot2D$ complexes from the recorded ^{19}F spectra, (where D is a pyridine oxide with 2-, 2,4- or 2,6- substituents).

Reaction of bis(cyclopentadienyl)titanium dichloride with silver trifluoromethylmercaptide afforded[164] the corresponding difluoride, $(C_5H_5)_2TiF_2$, with a ^{19}F shift of 73·3.

Nitrogen

Chlorodifluoramine has a ^{19}F shift of 141·5 and the signal consists[184] of a triplet arising from $^{19}F-^{14}N$ coupling (122 Hz). This latter coupling is similar to that found in tetrafluorohydrazine $[^1J(F-N)=117]$ and trifluoroamine $[^1J(F-N)=155$ Hz].

A number of 2,2-bis(difluoramino)- derivatives of pentane and hexane of the form **168** have been prepared and the ^{19}F shifts of the NF_2 groups were all

$$CH_3 \cdot C(NF_2)_2 \cdot (CH_2)_n X$$
$$n = 2 \text{ or } 3$$
$$X = CH_2OH, CO_2H, CNO, NHCONH_2, CH(NO_2)_2$$
168

in the range $27·0 \pm 0·3$.[185] The same workers also prepared α-bromo-α-fluor-iminotoluene, $C_6H_5CBr{=}NF$, with ^{19}F shift of 64·1.

The ^{19}F data of a series of α-difluoramino-fluorimines have been tabulated.[186] The same paper contained information on 1,1-bis(difluoramino)-1-haloalkanes and 1,1,1-tris(difluoramino)alkanes; the data for all these compounds are shown in Table XXXIII. The reaction of chloro-olefins having keto or

TABLE XXXIII
^{19}F shift parameters of difluoramine derivatives

(a) Difluoramino- fluorimine derivatives

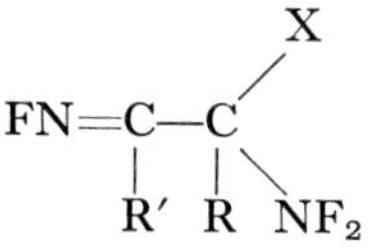

$$FN{=}C-C\begin{smallmatrix} X \\ | \quad | \quad \backslash \\ R' \ R \ NF_2 \end{smallmatrix}$$

R	R'	X	δ NF_2			δ NF
CH_3	CH_3	CH_3	27·4			27·7
C_6H_5	CH_3	CH_3	δ_A 30·0	J_{AB}	580	28·5
			δ_B 25·0			
CH_3	C_6H_5	CH_3	29·5			38·6
CH_3	CH_3	Cl	δ_A 40·9	J_{AB}	580	34·6
			δ_B 29·5			
CH_3	CH_3	Br	δ_A 48·6	J_{AB}	568	34·4
			δ_B 32·2			
$4\text{-}BrC_6H_4-$	CH_3	Cl	δ_A 46·2	J_{AB}	563	36·3
			δ_B 34·8			
CH_3	CH_3	NF_2	28·2			40·2
	$-(CH_2)_4-$	CH_3	δ_A 26·3	J_{AB}	582	22·3
			δ_B 18·5			
	$-(CH_2)_3-$	NF_2	35·4			60·2
	$-(CH_2)_5-$	NF_2	29·1			37·1
C_6H_5	C_2H_5	NF_2	31·7			42·5
$4\text{-}ClC_6H_4-$	CH_3	NF_2	31·0			48·3
$4\text{-}CH_3OC_6H_4-$	CH_3	NF_2	32·2			49·5
$4\text{-}BrC_6H_4-$	CH_3	NF_2	30·9			48·8

(b) Difluoamino derivative

$$R-\underset{\underset{R''}{|}}{\overset{\overset{R'}{|}}{C}}-NF_2$$

R	R'	R	δ (NF$_2$)		
CH$_3$	Cl	$-CH_2CO_2H$	δ_A 32·63 δ_B 36·16	J_{AB} 563	
CH$_3 \cdot$C(O)NH$-$	H	$-CCl_2NF_2$	δ_A 27·37 δ_B 45·34	J_{AB} 614	δ CCl$_2$NF$_2$ 42·66
CH$_3$	Cl	Cl	43·4		
CH$_3 \cdot$CH$_2 \cdot$CH$_2-$	Cl	Cl	41·92		
CH$_3 \cdot$CH$_2 \cdot$CH$_2-$	Br	Br	56·0		
CH$_3 \cdot$CH$_2-$	Br	F	34·3		(δ_{CF} = $-102·0$)
C$_6$H$_5$	Br	Br	57·5		
C$_6$H$_5$	Cl	Cl	44·88		
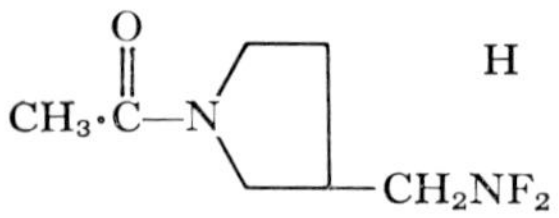 $CH_3 \cdot \overset{\overset{O}{\|}}{C}-N\overset{CH_2NF_2}{\diagdown}$	H	H	56·7		
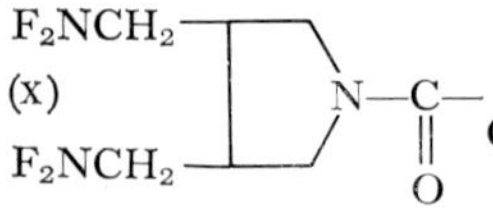 $\overset{F_2NCH_2-}{\underset{F_2NCH_2-}{}}(x)\overset{}{N-\overset{\|}{\underset{O}{C}}-CH_3}$	$-CH_2NF_2$(Y)		27·5		δ_X 56·5 and 56·8 δ_Y 54·3
$-CO \cdot NMe_2$	CH$_3$	CH$_2$NF$_2$	26·7		δ CH$_2$NF$_2$ 54·3
$\overset{Me}{\underset{F_2N}{\diagup}}CH-$	H	H	$\sim$56·5 (CH$_2$NF$_2$) $\sim$37·5 (CHNF$_2$)		
$\overset{Et}{\underset{F_2N}{\diagup}}CH-$	H	H	$\sim$56·7 (CH$_2$NF$_2$) $\sim$38·0 (CHNF$_2$)		
$\overset{Me}{\underset{F_2N}{\diagup}}CH$	CH$_3$	H	41·5		
$\overset{Me}{\underset{F_2N}{\diagup}}CH$	CH$_3$	CH$_3$	$\sim$41·0 (CHNF$_2$) $\sim$25·5 ($>$CNF$_2$)		

(c) Bis(difluoramino) derivatives

$$\begin{array}{c} R \\ \diagdown \\ C(NF_2)_2 \\ \diagup \\ X \end{array}$$

R	X	NF_2	
CH_3	Cl	34·7	
C_6H_5	Cl	37·1	
C_6H_5	Br	44·0	
C_6H_5	F	23·6	$(\delta_{CF} = -152\cdot4)$
$-(CH_2)_4CN$	Cl	δ_A 35·2 J_{AB} = 605	
		δ_B 33·9	
$-(CH_2)_4CN$	CH_3	27·5	
$-(CH_2)_4CN$	OSO_2F	25·6	$(\delta_{SF} = 48\cdot3)$
$4\text{-}BrC_6H_4-$	Cl	37·5	
$-NHC(O)\cdot(CH_2)_4-$		24·7	
$-C(O)NH\cdot(CH_2)_4-$		26·5	
$-C(=NF)\cdot NH\cdot(CH_2)_4-$		27·4 and 26·7	$(\delta_{NF} -41\cdot2)$
CH_3	$-N=CF\cdot C_6H_5$	27·5	$(\delta_{CF} -25\cdot4)$
C_6H_5	$-N=CF\cdot C_6H_5$	28·1	$(\delta_{CF} -15\cdot7)$
CH_3	$-CH_2C(NF_2)_2\cdot CH_3$	28·24	
CH_3	$-CH=CCl_2$	30·02	
$CH_3CH_2CH_2-$	Br	δ_A 35·11 J_{AB} 604	
		δ_B 46·27	
$CH_3\cdot CH_2-$	Cl	δ_A 29·91 J_{AB} 611	
		δ_B 36·91	
$CH_3\cdot CH_2\cdot CH_2$	Cl	δ_A 30·42 J_{AB} 609	
		δ_B 37·35	

(d) Tris(difluoramino) derivatives $R-C(NF_2)_3$

R	$\delta (NF_2)$
CH_3	28·0
C_6H_5	27·8
$4\text{-}CH_3O\cdot C_6H_4-$	26·9
$4\text{-}Cl\cdot C_6H_4-$	28·0
$NC(CH_2)_3-$	27·7
$NC(CH_2)_4-$	27·7
$NC(CH_2)_5-$	27·5

carboxyl groups with difluoramine affords a range of halogenated difluoramino compounds.[187] The ^{19}F data of these compounds are also shown in Table XXXIII. Similarly nitro- and nitroso- compounds have been used as alkylating agents for difluoramine and an extensive series of difluoraminoalkanes were prepared,[188] the shifts of which are also shown in Table XXXIII. The addition of tetrafluorohydrazine to a range of unsaturated amides, carbamates, iso-cyanates, nitriles and nitro compounds afforded a series of bis-difluoramino compounds.[189] The shifts for the $-NF_2$ groups are shown in Table XXXIII.

Frear and Tipping[190] found that trifluoronitrosomethane reacted with N,N-bistrifluoromethylamino-substituted acetylenes, $(CF_3)_2N \cdot C \equiv CR$ [R= H, Br, CF_3, CH_3 and $N(CF_3)_2$] to yield 1:1 adducts of the type $(CF_3)_2N \cdot CO \cdot CR = NCF_3$ and $(CF_3)_2N \cdot C(COR) = NCF_3$. The shifts of the bistrifluoro-methylamino groups fall into the range $-55 \cdot 4$ to $-58 \cdot 5$, while the shifts of the $=NCF_3$ groups are more variable falling in the range $-56 \cdot 1$ to $-70 \cdot 1$ depending upon the nature of R. The shifts are shown in Table XXXIV. The

TABLE XXXIV

[19]F shifts of N-trifluoromethyl groups

	$\delta (CF_3)_2N$	$\delta (CF_3 \cdot N=)$
$(CF_3)_2N \cdot CO \cdot CH = N \cdot CF_3$	$-56 \cdot 5$	$-68 \cdot 8$
$(CF_3)_2N \cdot CO \cdot CBr = N \cdot CF_3$	$-56 \cdot 3$	$-64 \cdot 1$
$(CF_3)_2N \cdot CO \cdot C(CF_3) = N \cdot CF_3$	$-55 \cdot 9$	$-61 \cdot 1$
$(CF_3)_2N \cdot CO \cdot C[N(CF_3)_2] = N \cdot CF_3$	a $-56 \cdot 5$	$-57 \cdot 6$
(a) (b)	b $-58 \cdot 0$	
$(CF_3)_2N \cdot CO \cdot C(CH_3) = N \cdot CF_3$	$-55 \cdot 4$	$-58 \cdot 2$
$(CF_3)_2N \cdot C(CHO) = N \cdot CF_3$	$-56 \cdot 9$	$-60 \cdot 7$
$(CF_3)_2N \cdot C(COBr) = N \cdot CF_3$	$-56 \cdot 1$	$-56 \cdot 1$
$(CF_3)_2N \cdot C(CO \cdot CF_3) = N \cdot CF_3$	$-58 \cdot 5$	

[19]F shifts of some trifluoromethyl substituted azo- and azoxy- compounds have been recorded.[191] The shift of the CF_3 group appeared to be independent of whether or not the compound was an azo- or azoxy- compound, but was affected by the presence of a phenyl group on the second nitrogen atom. The ^{19}F shifts of 1-cyclohexyl-2,4,4,4-tetrafluoro-1,3-diazabut-2-ene (169) have been reported and were as shown.[192]

Bistrifluoromethylnitroxide radicals react with mercury to afford the mercury(II) bistrifluoromethylnitroxide, which reacts readily with carbon-chlorine and non-metallic-chlorine compounds to give bistrifluoromethyl-nitroxide derivatives.[193] The ^{19}F shifts of these compounds are shown in Table XXXV.

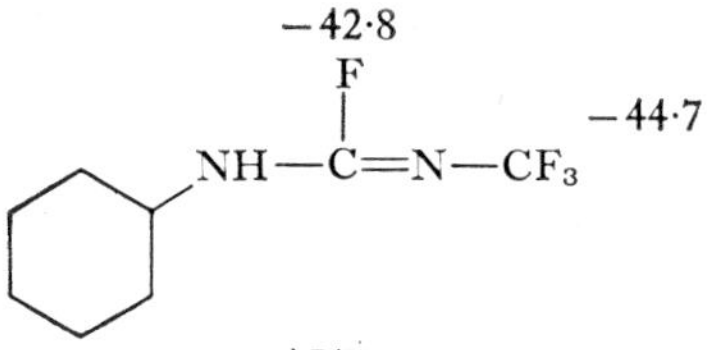

$$-42\cdot8$$
$$\underset{\underset{\text{NH}-\text{C}=\text{N}-\text{CF}_3}{|}}{\text{F}}$$
$$-44\cdot7$$

$$^4J(\text{F}-\text{F}) = 11\cdot5 \text{ Hz}$$

169

TABLE XXV

^{19}F shifts of bistrifluoromethylnitroxide groups

$Hg[ON(CF_3)_2]_2$	$-71\cdot0$
$CO[ON(CF_3)_2]_2$	$-68\cdot6$
$C_6H_5C(O)ON(CF_3)_2$	$-68\cdot3$
$CH_3ON(CF_3)_2$	$-70\cdot5$
$B[ON(CF_3)_2]_3$	$-70\cdot4$
$Si[ON(CF_3)_2]_4$	$-70\cdot3$
$Ge[ON(CF_3)_2]_4$	$-69\cdot2$
$P[ON(CF_3)_2]_5$	$-67\cdot4$

Direct fluorination of alkyl carbamates afforded the corresponding fluoro- and difluoro- carbamates.[194] The ^{19}F shifts for the N-fluoro compounds, $R \cdot O \cdot C(O) \cdot NHF$, are in the range -114 to $-119\cdot5$, and for the N-difluoro-compounds, $R \cdot O \cdot C(O) \cdot NF_2$, $32\cdot7$ to 33.

The temperature and solvent dependence of nitrogen inversion in a number of bis(N,N-difluoramino)alkanes has been studied by ^{19}F NMR.[195] The rates of inversion were slow at, or below, room temperature and it was found that the pyrimidal stability of the 2-methyl-2,3-bis(N,N-difluoramino)butane **(170)**

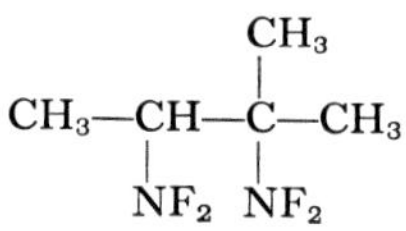

$$\underset{\underset{\text{NF}_2 \quad \text{NF}_2}{|\qquad\;|}}{\text{CH}_3-\text{CH}-\overset{\overset{\text{CH}_3}{|}}{\text{C}}-\text{CH}_3}$$

170

$$J_{AB} = 86\cdot0 \text{ Hz}$$

$$\begin{array}{c} -28\cdot8 \\ -44\cdot8 \end{array} \left\{ \begin{array}{c} \text{F} \\ \\ \text{F} \end{array} \right\} \overset{-94\cdot8 \quad -74\cdot0}{\underset{}{\text{C}=\text{N}}} \overset{\text{CF}_2-\text{CF}_2\text{Cl}}{\diagup}$$

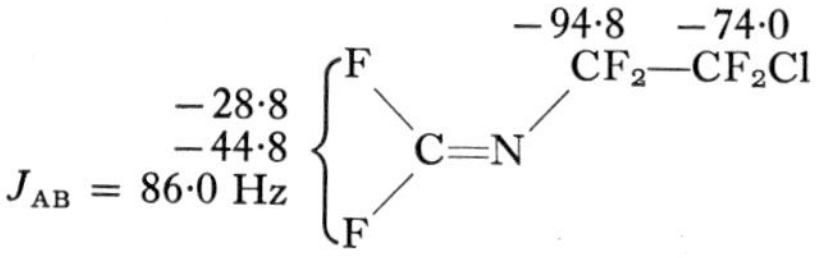

171

was the greatest yet found for an acyclic amine. The shifts of the NF_2 groups at room temperature in $CFCl_3$ are included in Table XXXIII. A note of caution was, however, given by these authors. The appearance of the spectra with small $\Delta\nu_0$ $(= \delta_A - \delta_B)$ cannot always be used to indicate rate of inversion processes since this parameter often varies with solvent, concentration and temperature. In addition, spectral line broadening from nitrogen-quadrupole relaxation (also solvent- and temperature- dependent) may change, or even collapse, the AB spectra with small values of $\Delta\nu_0$.

A rather unusual temperature dependence of the ^{19}F spectra of 4-chloro-hexafluoro-2-aza- but-1-ene (171) and but-2-ene (172) has been found.[196]

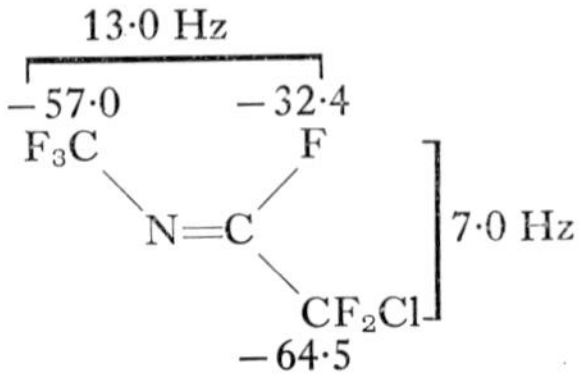

$$
\begin{array}{c}
\overset{13\cdot 0 \text{ Hz}}{\overbrace{}} \\
\underset{F_3C}{-57\cdot 0} \qquad \underset{F}{-32\cdot 4} \\
\diagdown \qquad \diagup \\
N = C \qquad \Big] \; 7\cdot 0 \text{ Hz} \\
\diagdown \\
\underset{-64\cdot 5}{CF_2Cl} \\
\mathbf{172}
\end{array}
$$

Although this might be explained by the presence of rotational isomers in 171, the same explanation cannot pertain to 172 since only one set of signals were found. It was suggested that this effect could arise from the effective decoupling of the $^{19}F-^{14}N$ coupling at low temperature owing to the more effective quadrupole relaxation of the nitrogen nucleus at these lower temperatures. Caution was advised in considering the free energy of activation derived from temperature dependence of line-widths in compounds of the type $\diagup\!\!\!\!C\!=\!\!N\diagdown^F$, because of the possible contribution of ^{14}N quadrupole relaxation to the signal line-width.

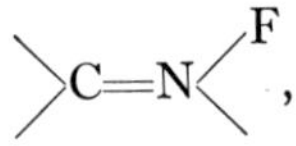

Phosphorus, arsenic and antimony

The reaction of phosphorus tri- and penta- fluorides with trialkyl phosphites results in the formation of a number of disproportionation products together with complex ions.[197] Thus, phosphorus pentafluoride and trimethyl phosphite afforded trimethoxymethylphosphonium hexafluorophosphate (173) and

$$
\begin{array}{cc}
-77 & -87\cdot 5 \\
[(MeO)_3PMe]^{\oplus}PF_6^{\ominus} & MeOP(O)F_2 \\
{}^1J(F\!-\!P) = 707 \text{ Hz} & {}^1J(F\!-\!P) = 1008 \text{ Hz} \\
\mathbf{173} & \mathbf{174}
\end{array}
$$

methyl phosphorodifluoridate (174) depending upon conditions used; the ^{19}F parameters were as shown. With triethyl phosphite the ethoxydifluoro- and diethoxyfluoro- phosphines (175 and 176 respectively) were formed together with other products.

$$
\begin{array}{cc}
-47 & -57 \\
EtOPF_2 & (EtO)_2PF \\
{}^1J(F\!-\!P) = 1271 \text{ Hz} & {}^1J(F\!-\!P) = 1189 \text{ Hz} \\
\mathbf{175} & \mathbf{176}
\end{array}
$$

The spectra of pyrophosphoryl tetrafluoride (177) and μ-oxobis(thiophosphoryl difluoride) (178) have been analysed[198] as AA'XX'A"A''' spin systems

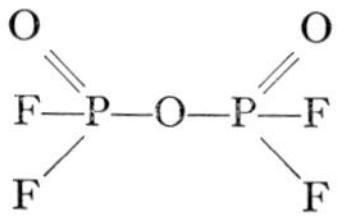

$$
\begin{array}{ccc}
O & & O \\
\diagdown & & \diagup \\
F-P-O-P-F \\
\diagup & & \diagdown \\
F & & F
\end{array}
$$

$^1J(F-P) = \pm 1062 \cdot 9$ Hz
$^3J(F-P) = \mp 2 \cdot 9$ Hz
$^2J(F-F) = 300$ Hz
$^4J(F-F) = 2 \cdot 4$ Hz

177

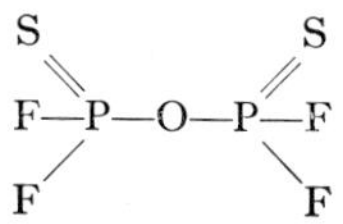

$$
\begin{array}{ccc}
S & & S \\
\diagdown & & \diagup \\
F-P-O-P-F \\
\diagup & & \diagdown \\
F & & F
\end{array}
$$

$^1J(F-P) = \pm 1168 \cdot 2$ Hz
$^3J(F-P) = 3 \cdot 7$ Hz
$^2J(F-F) = 300$ Hz
$^4J(F-F) = 2 \cdot 3$ Hz

178

and the derived coupling constants are as shown. Two interesting tetrafluorodiphosphorus compounds, having the two phosphorus atoms in different valency states, have separately been described by two groups of workers.[199, 200] The data, obtained at 40°, for difluorothiophosphoryl-μ-thio- and difluorophosphoryl-μ-oxo-difluorophosphines (179 and 180) are as shown.[199] The

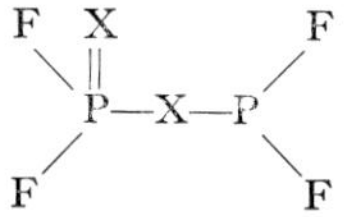

$$
\begin{array}{ccccc}
F & X & & & F \\
\diagdown & \parallel & & & \diagup \\
& P-X-P \\
\diagup & & & & \diagdown \\
F & & & & F
\end{array}
$$

179, X = S; δ (F$_2$P^V) $-13 \cdot 7$, $^1J(F-P^V) = 1321 \cdot 5$ Hz
δ (F$_2$P^{III}) $-60 \cdot 5$, $^1J(F-P^{III}) = 1216 \cdot 9$ Hz

180, X = 0; δ (F$_2$P^V) $-38 \cdot 3$, $^1J(F-P^V) = 1396 \cdot 4$ Hz
δ (F$_2$P^{III}) $-80 \cdot 0$, $^1J(F-P^{III}) = 1032 \cdot 5$ Hz

spectra are, however, temperature dependent, and at low temperatures further coupling is evident; for **179** the following J parameters were obtained: $^3J(F-P-P^V) = 22 \cdot 0$, $^3J(F-P-P^{III}) = 15 \cdot 0$ and $^4J(F-F) = 5 \cdot 9$ Hz. This same data had earlier been given in a preliminary note describing this work.[147] Photolysis of $P(O)F_2Br$ in the presence of mercury gave[200] the same difluorophosphoryl-μ-oxo-difluorophosphine (see **180** above); the ^{19}F shifts found at 34·5°C were as shown in **181**, at which temperature two simple doublets were observed. At

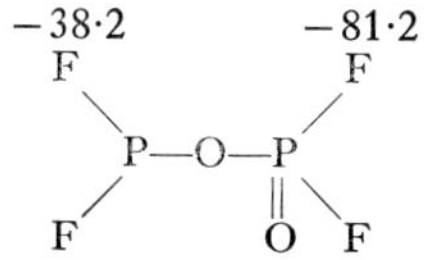

$$
\begin{array}{cccc}
-38 \cdot 2 & & -81 \cdot 2 \\
F & & F \\
\diagdown & & \diagup \\
& P-O-P \\
\diagup & & \parallel \diagdown \\
F & & O \quad F
\end{array}
$$

$^1J(F-P^{III}) = 1412$ Hz
$^1J(F-P^V) = 1033$ Hz

181

$-26°C$, however, the complex multiplet of an A_2B_2XX' spectrum was observed from the $F_2P(O)O-$ group, while that of the $-OPF_2$ group still remained reasonably sharp.

Reaction of hydrothiophosphoryl difluoride with trimethylamine afforded the salt **182** containing the $S_2PF_2^{\ominus}$ ion.[199] The thiophosphorylfluorobromoamide, **183**, has been prepared and the shift was as shown;[201] the direct fluorine-phosphorus coupling was 1141 Hz.

$$
\begin{array}{cc}
\overset{\oplus}{Me_3NH}[S_2PF_2]^{\ominus} & \overset{\overset{\textstyle 2\cdot63}{\textstyle F}}{\underset{\underset{\textstyle Br}{\textstyle |}}{S{=}P{-}NH_2}} \\
-34\cdot0 & \\
{}^1J(F\text{–}P) = 1180\ Hz & \\
\mathbf{182} & \mathbf{183}
\end{array}
$$

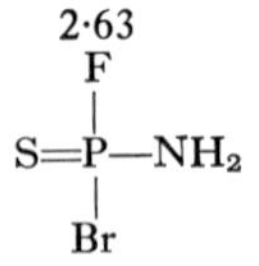

Reaction of halodifluorophosphines, XPF_2, where $X = Cl$, Br or I, with silver salts of perfluorocarboxylic acids afforded compounds of the type $R_fCO \cdot OPF_2$.[21] The ^{19}F shift of the PF_2 group was $-49\cdot8 \pm 0\cdot1$ with $^1J(F\text{–}P)$ of 1388 ± 1 Hz; the shift for the single acyl derivative cited, namely $CH_3CO \cdot O-$, was $-54\cdot4$ with $^1J(F\text{–}P)$ of 1361 Hz. The shifts of the fluoroacyl groups are, for convenience, included in the section on acid derivatives (p. 397).

The ^{19}F shifts and $^1J(F\text{–}P)$ values of a series of pentafluorophenyl fluorophosphoranes, fluorophosphines and the corresponding oxides have been recorded.[156] The shift and $^1J(F\text{–}P)$ values are very variable depending upon the nature of the P–F groups; the data are reproduced in Table XXXVI. The range

TABLE XXXVI

^{19}F shifts of pentafluorophenyl fluorophosphine derivatives[a]

P–F

	δ_F	$^1J(^{19}F\text{–}^{31}P)$
$C_6F_5PF_2$	$-94\cdot5$	1215
$(C_6F_5)_2PF$	$-216\cdot6$	1002
$C_6F_5POF_2$	$-57\cdot5$	1128
$(C_6F_5)_2POF$	$-55\cdot8$	1090
$C_6F_5PF_4$	$-40\cdot6$	1000
$(C_6F_5)_2PF_3$	$7\cdot0$	912
$(C_6F_5)_3PF_2$	$2\cdot5$	713

[a] See Table XXVIII for ^{19}F shifts of pentafluorophenyl groups.

of shifts for the P–F groups of over 200 p.p.m. clearly indicates the usefulness of ^{19}F data in structural determinations for fluorophosphines.

Parry et al.[202] have studied the difluorophosphine complexes of tetraborane. The ^{19}F spectrum of the complex (**184**) showed the expected doublet of doublets arising from F–P and H–F coupling. The spectrum of the complex with dimethylaminodifluorophosphine exhibited two sets of doublets at δ $-70\cdot5$ [^1J(F–P) = 1110 Hz] and at δ $-71\cdot5$ [^1J(F–P) = 1150 Hz] and these two signals were assigned to the two isomers **185a** and **185b**; at temperatures of about 25°C the two signals coalesced.

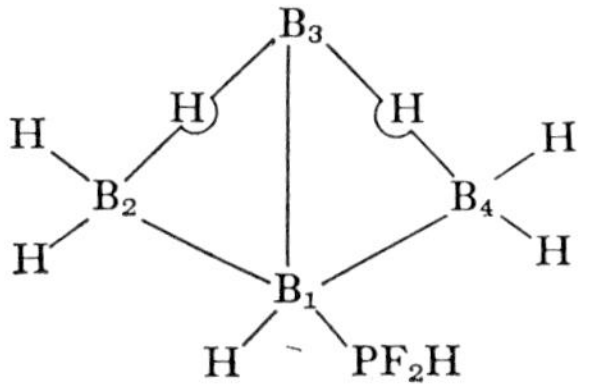

^1J(F–P) = 1120 Hz
^2J(F–H) = 54 Hz
184

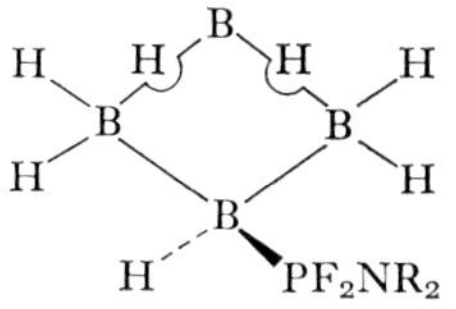

185a

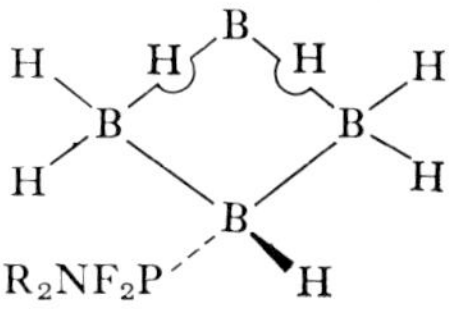

185b

The ^{19}F spectrum of bis(ethylthiophosphorylfluoride) trisulphide (**186**) consisted of a doublet at $-48\cdot1$ with ^1J(F–P) of 1144 Hz.[203] The same author also reported the data for the two compounds, trifluorophosphorarylidensulphonyl chloride (**187**) and chlorodifluorophosphorarylidensulphonyl chloride (**188**).[204]

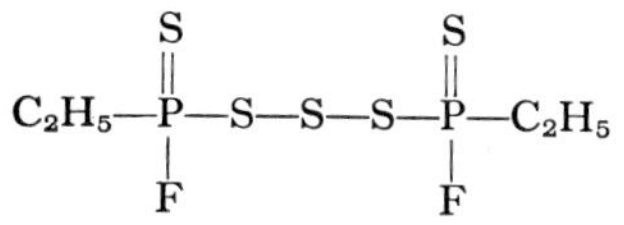

186

$-84\cdot6$
ClSO$_2$N=PF$_3$
^1J(F–P) = 1078 Hz
187

$-50\cdot4$
ClSO$_2$N=PF$_2$Cl
^1J(P–F) = 1120 Hz
188

Not only is the shift of the PF group effected by the chlorine atom, but the direct-bonded F–P coupling is increased. Roesky[205] has also tabulated the ^{19}F data for a number of aminofluorophosphine derivatives; these data are reproduced in Table XXXVII. It is of interest to note that the ^1J(F–P) values apparently fall into fairly concise ranges, namely –PF$_2$, 1197 Hz; –PFCl, $\sim$1168 Hz; and $>$ PF$_2$, $\sim$1040 Hz.

The spectra of a number of aminobis(difluorophosphines), RN(PF$_2$)$_2$, have been analysed as XX′AA′X″X‴ spin systems.[206] The essential features of the ^{19}F spectra are two strong lines separated by $|^1J_{\mathrm{PF}} + {}^3J_{\mathrm{PF'}}|$ and four AB-type sub-spectra. The ^{19}F parameters are shown in Table XXXVIII.

The ^{19}F shifts and the F–P coupling constants in a series of three-coordinate alkyl or aryl phosphorus fluorides have been tabulated.[207] A number of new trifluorophosphazo compounds have been prepared[208] and the ^{19}F data are shown in **189** to **191**.

An example of stereochemical non-rigidity in five co-ordinate phosphorus

TABLE XXXVII

^{19}F parameters of amino fluorophosphines

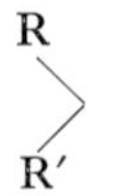

R	R′	δ_F	$^1J(F-P)$
Me$_2$N–	Cl	−70·0	1170
Me$_2$N–	F	−65·3	1197
Et$_2$N–	Cl	−67·3	1164
Et$_2$N–	F	−64·8	1197
Me$_2$N–	Me$_2$N–	−100·6	1046
Et$_2$N–	Et$_2$N–	−98·1	1037

TABLE XXXVIII

^{19}F parameters of aminobis(difluorophosphines)

$$RN(PF_2)_2$$

R	δ_F	$^1J(F-P)$	$^3J(F-P)$	$^4J(F-F)$
Me	−74·6	1264	47	11·7 and 1·7
Et	−72·5	1261	52	11·1 and 2·2
C$_6$H$_5$	−68·2	1252	40	10·0 and 4·4
m-ClC$_6$H$_4$–	−68·1	1285	41·5	11·6 and 2·6

−86·7   −60·9

F$_3$P=NSO$_2$F

$^1J(F-P) = 1090$ Hz
$^3J(F-P) = 16$ Hz
$^4J(F-F) = 4$ Hz

189

$$\overset{S}{-85\cdot2 \quad \overset{\|}{F_3P{=}N{-}PF_2} \quad -38\cdot0}$$

$^1J[F-P(S)] = 1112$ Hz
$^1J[F-P(=N)] = 1045$ Hz

190

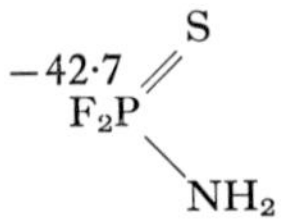

$$\overset{S}{-42\cdot7 \quad \overset{/\!\!/}{F_2P}} \diagdown_{NH_2}$$

$^1J(F-P) = 1078$ Hz

191

$$\underset{F}{\overset{F}{\diagdown}}C{=}C\underset{PX_2}{\overset{F}{\diagup}}$$

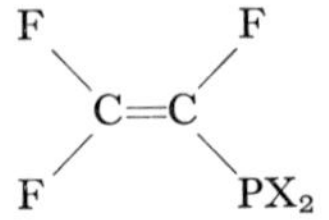

X = Cl or F

192

compounds of the form $CF_3Co(PF_3)(CO)_3$ has been demonstrated.[209] Below −30°C the resolution of the ^{19}F resonance signal is gradually lost but at −70°

it is regained and the new spectrum is consistent with the presence of two isomers.

The signs of F–P and F–F couplings are still causing considerable interest and the trifluorovinyl dichloro- and difluoro- phosphines (192) have been used in a further study.[210] By selective decoupling it was demonstrated that the sign of the P–C–F coupling in dichlorophosphine was opposite to that of the *cis* P–C–C–F coupling. In the difluorophosphine, however, selective decoupling confirmed that both these couplings were of the same sign. Taking the direct bonded F–P coupling to be negative then, in the difluorophosphine, the signs of the P–C–F, *cis* P–C–C–F and *trans* P–C–C–F couplings were considered to be absolutely positive. If the *cis* and *trans* P–C–C–F coupling in the dichlorophosphine are also positive then, in this compound, the P–C–F coupling is negative. It is most unlikely that the *cis* P–C–C–F coupling in the dichlorophosphine had changed sign, as this would involve a very large alteration of about 155 Hz. It was also of interest that the *cis* P–C–C–F coupling was larger than that of the *trans*-coupling. The signs and magnitudes of the F–F and F–P couplings are shown in Table XXXIX.

TABLE XXXIX

Signs and magnitudes of the coupling constants of $CF_2{=}CFPCl_2$ and $CF_2{=}CFPF_2$ (192)

		Sign	Hz
$CF_2{=}CFPCl_2$	$^2J(\text{F–F})$	$\pm$	39·1
	cis $^3J(\text{F–F})$	$\pm$	32·0
	trans $^3J(\text{F–F})$	$\mp$	123·4
	$^2J(\text{F–P})$	$-$	17·2
	cis $^3J(\text{F–P})$	$+$	85·7
	trans $^3J(\text{F–P})$	$+$	7·3
$CF_2{=}CFPF_2$	$^2J(\text{F–C–F})$	$\pm$	42·5
	cis $^3J(\text{F–F})$	$\pm$	31·0
	trans $^3J(\text{F–F})$	$\mp$	123·5
	$^3J(\text{F–P–C–F})$	$\pm$	11·1
	cis $^4J(\text{F–P–C–C–F})$	$\pm$	2·9
	trans $^4J(\text{F–P–C–C–F})$	$\pm$	13·2
	$^1J(\text{P–F})$	$-$	1202
	$^2J(\text{P–C–F})$	$+$	20·9
	cis $^3J(\text{P–C–C–F})$	$+$	69·6
	trans $^3J(\text{P–C–C–F})$	$+$	4·8

The ^{19}F data for triethylamine and dimethyl ether complexes of phosphorus and arsenic pentafluorides have been reported.[211] The data were consistent with structure **193** and the shifts of the apical and basal (equatorial) fluorines were in the range -81 ± 7 and -66 ± 5 respectively. The $^{19}F-^{31}P$ coupling in **193**, (M=P) were 762 ± 15 and 834 ± 14 Hz for the apical and equatorial fluorine atoms respectively. The F–F coupling was very much greater (120 Hz) in the arsenic complexes than in the phosphorus complexes $(60 \pm 8$ Hz).

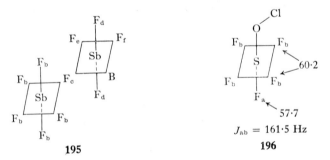

$$B = Me_3N \text{ or } Me_2O$$
$$M = P \text{ or } As$$

193   **194**

Dean and Gillespie[212] have studied the ^{19}F spectra of the system SbF_5 with SO_2ClF, SO_2F_2, $CH_3SO_2F-SO_2FCl$, SOF_2, SOF_2-SO_2ClF and SO_2-SO_2ClF at low temperatures. Two series of complexes were found, namely 1:1 and 2:1, but no complex formation was observed with SO_2F_2. In all these complexes the oxygen atom was considered to be the donor. The 1:1 complexes have structures as in **194**; the resonance of F_a (a quintet) was in the range δ $-133 \cdot 7$ to $-141 \cdot 8$ while that of F_b (a doublet) was $-100 \cdot 9$ to $-105 \cdot 1$ with $J(F-F) = 92$ to 100 Hz. The 2:1 complexes contain a fluorine-bridged Sb_2F_{10} group with the donor molecule *cis* to the bridging fluorine (**195**). The shift of

the bridge fluorine F_c was at lowest field, δ_c -83 to -90, and, with the exception of the SO_2 complex, the shifts of the remaining fluorine atoms fell into fairly narrow ranges: F_a -141 ± 1, F_b -110 ± 1, F_d $-94 \cdot 5 \pm 1 \cdot 5$, F_e $-128 \cdot 5 \pm 1 \cdot 5$, F_f -141 ± 1 with $J(F_a-F_b) = 95 \pm 3$ Hz and $J(F_b-F_c) = 47 \pm 3$ Hz. Some of the spectra were shown in the paper. These authors have also considered the complexes of the SbF_5 in SO_2 with H_2O in which the complexes of the type

$SbF_5 \cdot OH_2$ and $SbF_5 \cdot OH_2 \cdot SbF_5$ were formed.[213] With sulphuric acid the complexes $SbF_5 \cdot OSO(OH)_2$ and $SbF_5 \cdot OS(OH)_2O \cdot SbF_5$ were formed. It was shown that ligand redistribution occurred: e.g.

$$2SbF_5 \cdot OH_2 \rightleftharpoons SbF_4(OH_2)_2^{\oplus} + SbF_6^{\ominus}$$

Addition of excess SbF_5, however, resulted in the formation of the ion $Sb_2F_{11}^{\ominus}$ (see also p. 488); the sulphuric acid system undergoes similar redistribution reactions.

Sulphur and selenium

Substituted alkyl sulphur pentafluorides still continue to attract considerable interest, and one of the latest papers described the UV-initiated addition of sulphur chloride pentafluoride to trifluoroethylene.[214] The spectra of the compounds obtained, 2-chloro-1,2,2-trifluoro- and 2-chloro-1,1,2-trifluoro- ethyl sulphur pentafluoride, were discussed in detail. Lee *et al.*[215] have also considered the spectra of a number of halogen tri- and hexa- fluoroalkyl suphur pentafluorides. The couplings between the fluoroalkyl and SF_5 groups were also discussed. The addition of SF_5Br to fluoroolefins affords the 2-bromo-fluoroalkylsulphur pentafluorides;[216] not all exhibit the characteristic A_4M spectrum of the SF_5 group, but when an asymmetric centre is present in the alkyl chain additional splittings are found in the SF_5 resonance signal.

The preparation of the pentafluorosulphur hypochlorite has been described;[13] the ^{19}F parameters are as shown in **196**. The data for the same compound, chloroxysulphur pentafluoride, have also been reported.[217] A related colpound, pentafluorosulphur chloroformate, formed by reaction of **196** with carbon monoxide, was also described in the same paper and the ^{19}F data was as shown in **197**.

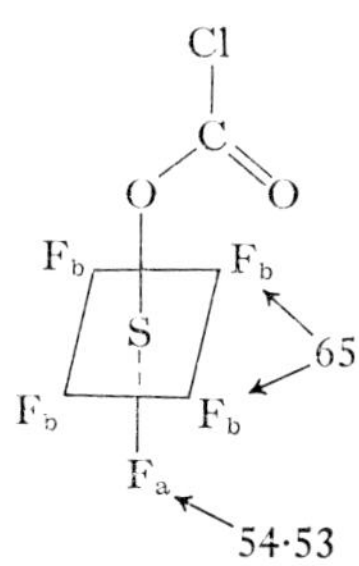

$$J_{ab} = 156 \text{ Hz}$$

197

The 2-fluoro-2,2-dinitroethoxysulphur trifluoride (**198**), prepared from the ethanol derivative and sulphur tetrafluoride, has shifts as shown.[37] The ^{19}F

shift of trifluoromethyl thionitrite, CF_3SNO, has been reported[218] as $-37\cdot7$, which is in a similar range to that of CF_3SCF_3 and CF_3SCN. The compound gradually decomposes and, although the spectrum was measured at $-60°$, an appreciable signal from the disulphide, $CF_3S\cdot SCF_3$, at $\delta\ -46\cdot9$ was present which increased in intensity at the expense of that of the thionitrite. A new simple disulphuryl compound, the methyldisulphuryl fluoride (**199**), has been described.[219] The shift was as shown and the decomposition was also followed by ^{19}F NMR. A doublet was observed at $\delta\ 70\cdot3$, $J(F-H) = 5\cdot8$ Hz, and this was attributed to the methyl sulphonyl fluoride, CH_3SO_2F.

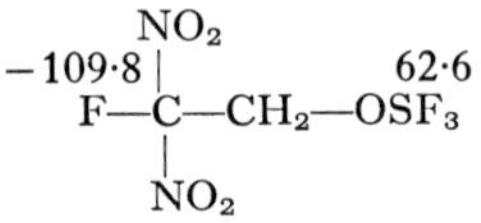

$$\overset{\displaystyle NO_2}{\underset{\displaystyle NO_2}{-109\cdot8\ |\atop F-C-CH_2-OSF_3}}\qquad\qquad CH_3S_2O_5F$$

62·6   46·3

198   **199**

Fluorosulphonyliminosulphuroxy difluoride, FSO_2NSO_2F, reacts with amines to give fluorosulphonylimino-sulphuroxyamino fluorides, FSO_2 $NSOFNRR'$, where R and $R' = H$, Me or Et.[220] The ^{19}F shifts of the FSO_2- groups are in the range $58\cdot2 \pm 0\cdot6$, while those of the SOF group are more variable ranging from $50\cdot4$ for NMe_2 to $68\cdot2$ for NH_2. The four-bond F–F coupling constant was in the range 8·0 to 8·5 Hz in all these compounds.

The data for a number of sulphurdifluoridimides have been published[221] and the data are summarized in Table XL. The ^{19}F shifts of the $N=SF_2$

TABLE XL

[19]F parameters of sulphurdifluoridimides

$$R-N=SF_2$$

R	$\delta\,(SF_2)$	
$(CF_3)_2C=N-$	31·6	$\delta\,(CF_3)$ *cis* $-66\cdot8$; *trans* $-70\cdot5$
$(CF_3)_2CF-$	58·2	$\delta\,(CF_3)\quad -82\cdot7$;
		$\delta\,(CF)\quad\ \ -144\cdot7$
$(CF_3)_2C(N=SF_2)-$	62·8	$\delta\,(CF_3)\quad -78\cdot9$
$(CF_3)_2(F_2S=N)C-N=S=N-C(CF_3)_2$	66·2	$\delta\,(CF_3)\quad -77\cdot5$
Br $\qquad\qquad\qquad\qquad\qquad\qquad |$	57·6	
ClF_2C-CF_2-	53·4	$^4J(SF-F_\alpha)$ 18·5; $^5J(SF-F_\beta)$ 3·2
BrF_2C-CF_2-	54·4	$^4J(SF-F_\alpha)$ 18·7; $^5J(SF-F_\beta)$ 3·2
$ClF_2C-(CF_2)_3-$	53·9	$^4J(SF-F_\alpha)$ 19·5
$F_3C\cdot CFCl\cdot CF_2-$	53·8	
$F_3C\cdot CFBr\cdot CF_2-$	53·9	

groups are very sensitive to the nature of the substituent in the α-position. The chemical shift of the N-bromo derivative, prepared by the action of bromine on the mercury bis-sulphurdifluoridimide, $Hg(NSF_2)_2$,[222] is included in Table XL. The addition of N-chloro- and N-bromo- sulphurdifluoridimide to fluoro-olefins afforded polyfluoroalkyl sulphurdifluoridimides;[223] the shifts of these compounds are included in Table XL. The shifts of the SF_2 groups fall into a characteristic range.

The ^{19}F shift data for two sulphur difluoroimide derivatives have been reported and the data were as shown in **200** and **201**;[224] for convenience the datum

$$-79\cdot6 \qquad\qquad 41\cdot6$$
$$F_3C-C-N=SF_2$$
$$\underset{O}{\overset{\|}{}}$$
$$^5J(F\text{--}F) = 2\cdot1Hz$$
200

$$-81\cdot2 \qquad\qquad 63\cdot4$$
$$(F_3C)_2C(NH_2)-N=SF_2$$
$$^5J(F\text{--}F) = 3Hz$$
201

$$-77\cdot1$$
$$F_3C-C-N=SCl_2$$
$$\underset{O}{\overset{\|}{}}$$
202

$$-77\cdot7 \qquad 16\cdot7$$
$$F-N=SF_2$$
$$^3J(F\text{--}F) = 44\cdot6Hz$$
203

for the dichloro- compound is shown in **202**. The ^{19}F data for N-fluorosulphur difluoride imide **203**, an isomer of thiazyl fluoride $N\equiv SF_3$, have also been reported by Glemser et al.[225] The parameters found at $-30°$ were as shown; no coupling between ^{19}F and ^{14}N in the –NF group was observed. The ^{19}F data of a series of N-alkyl-N-(fluorocarbonyl)sulphonylfluoridamide derivatives have also been reported;[26] these results were discussed earlier (see p. 398). A number of new fluorosulphonyl compounds have been prepared which are basically all N-fluorosulphonyl derivatives of amides.[226] The ^{19}F shifts of the –SO_2F groups are shown in Table XLI.

Gillespie et al.[227] have investigated the adducts of SF_4 with a number of fluoride acceptors, BF_3, PF_5, AsF_5 and SbF_5, in hydrogen fluoride. In all cases a signal was observed at low field (δ 25 to 30) which was assigned to the $SF_3^\oplus$ ion, while the high field resonance was attributed to the complex anion exchanging with the solvent. Addition of potassium fluoride to a solution of SF_4, BF_3 resulted in a new resonance at δ $-153\cdot5$, arising from the $BF_4^\ominus$ ion, and the simultaneous disappearance of that of the $SF_3^\oplus$ ion. The addition of fluoride ions suppresses the exchange between the complex fluoride anion and solvent but, at the same time, promotes the exchange between $SF_3^\oplus$ ion and solvent. In the AsF_5 system no peak was observed for $AsF_6^\ominus$ ion because of exchange with solvent and quadrupole relaxation of the ^{75}As nucleus. In a solution of SF_4,SbF_5 a peak at δ 27·6 was observed for $SF_3^\oplus$ ion but again no peak was observed for the complex anion, $SbF_6^\ominus$, because of exchange with solvent and

TABLE XLI

^{19}F parameters of fluorosulphonyl derivatives

$$R-SO_2F$$

R	δ (F)	R	δ (F)
$CH_3 \cdot CO \cdot NH-$	51·4	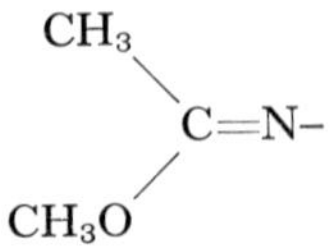 CH_3 ⟍ C=N–, CH_3O ⟋	51·0
$ClCH_2 \cdot CO \cdot NH-$	52·4	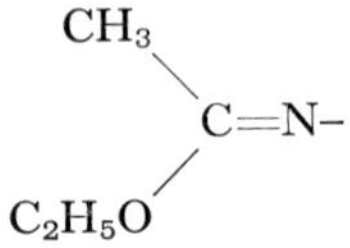	
$Cl_2CH \cdot CO \cdot NH-$	54·9	CH_3 ⟍ C=N–, C_2H_5O ⟋	51·1
$Cl_3C \cdot CO \cdot NH-$	53·3	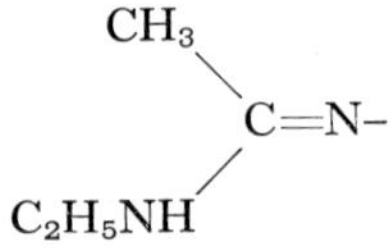	
CH_3 ⟍ C=N–, Cl ⟋	53·8	CH_3 ⟍ C=N–, CH_3NH ⟋	51·7
$ClCH_2$ ⟍ C=N–, Cl ⟋	54·9	CH_3 ⟍ C=N–, C_2H_5NH ⟋	51·6
Cl_2CH ⟍ C=N–, Cl ⟋	56·0	CH_3 ⟍ C=N–, $(C_2H_5)_2N$ ⟋	52·6
Cl_3C ⟍ C=N–, Cl ⟋	57·3	CH_3 ⟍ C=N–, H_2N ⟋	50·5
O=C–N, H_2N ⟋ ⟍ CH_3	49·2	CH_3O ⟍ C=N–, H_2N ⟋	53·0

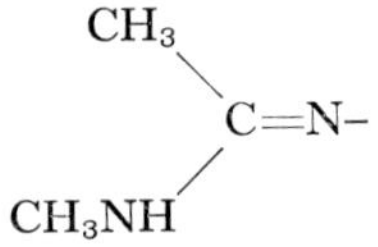

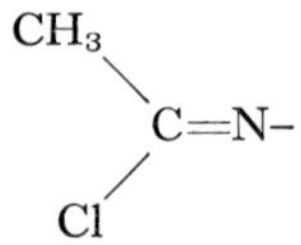

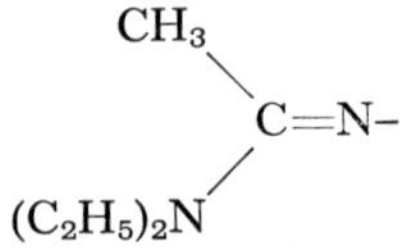

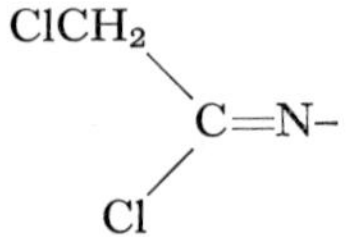

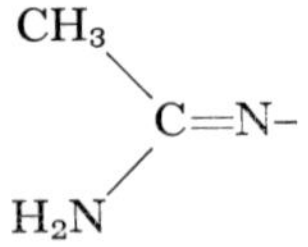

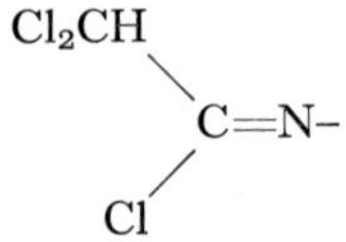

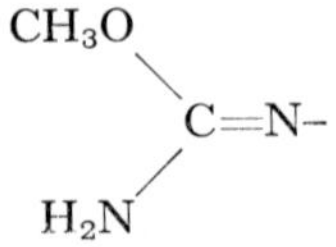

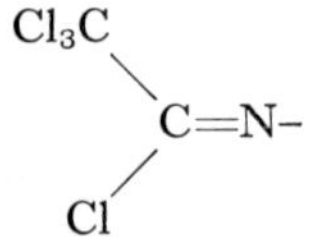

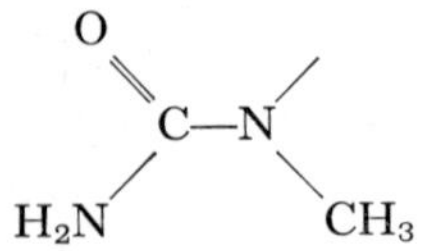

because of partially relaxed coupling due to ^{121}Sb ($I=\frac{5}{2}$) and ^{127}Sb ($I=\frac{7}{2}$). Addition of SbF_5 to the solution gave signals assigned to the complex ions $SbF_6^{\ominus}$ and $Sb_2F_{11}^{\ominus}$. Thus, ^{19}F data supported the conclusion that the adducts were completely ionized in solution.

The selenium(IV)-oxyfluorosulphate has been prepared by a number of new routes.[228] The shift of the fluorosulphate group was at 48·6, a region which is characteristic for this group.[229] Gillespie and Whitla[230] have examined the adduct of selenium tetrafluoride with sulphur trioxide, trifluoroselenium fluorosulphate. The ^{19}F spectrum in HSO_3F solution showed a resonance line at δ −8·1 arising from the fluorine atom bonded to selenium and a solvent line at δ −40·9. The appearance of the spectra, apart from a slight shift, remained essentially the same down to −85°C, and it was evident that the SO_3F group was exchanging with the solvent; at lower temperatures considerable line broadening occurred. The expected ^{77}Se satellites could only be observed at −85°, with $J(Se–F) = 1088$ Hz, being larger than that found in $SeOF_2$ (837 Hz).

Chlorine

The ^{19}F shifts of chloryl fluoride $FClO_2$ have been compared[231] with the isoelectronic SOF_2 and some other compounds. The shift of $FClO_2$ at 328 is the lowest for a second-period element and certainly lower than that of SOF_2.

Xenon

The shift of xenon dioxide difluoride, XeO_2F_2, is 105·10 with $J(F–^{129}Xe) = 1178$ Hz, while that of xenon oxide tetrafluoride, $XeOF_4$, is 100·27 with $J(F–^{128}Xe) = 1124$ Hz.[232] The authors also studied the ^{19}F spectra of a 1:1 mixture of these two fluorides and found only small differences in the chemical shift values.

Complex anions

The novel hydridopentafluorophosphate ion, $[PF_5H]^\ominus$, has been characterized[233] and the data for the potassium salt are shown in **204**, The authors,

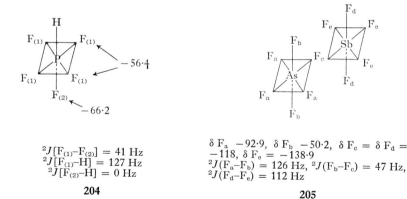

$^2J[F_{(1)}–F_{(2)}] = 41$ Hz
$^2J[F_{(1)}–H] = 127$ Hz
$^2J[F_{(2)}–H] = 0$ Hz

204

δ F_a −92·9, δ F_b −50·2, δ F_c = δ F_d = −118, δ F_e = −138·9
$^2J(F_a–F_b) = 126$ Hz, $^2J(F_b–F_c) = 47$ Hz, $^2J(F_d–F_e) = 112$ Hz

205

Nixon and Swain, also considered the variation of the value of $^2J(\text{H–P–F})$ with the HPF bond angle in this ion and other pentavalent phosphorus derivatives; these data are shown in Table XLII. The value of the coupling was, however, not only dependent upon the bond angle but also upon the nature of the substituents.

TABLE XLII

Variation of ^2J(HPF) with H–P–F bond angle in pentavalent phosphorus derivatives

Compound	Approximate bond angle		
	180°	120°	90°
$(\text{HPF}_5)^\ominus$	0	..	127
$(\text{CF}_3\text{CF}_4\text{H})^\ominus$	..	..	120
$[(\text{CF}_3)_2\text{PF}_3\text{H}]^\ominus$	18·0	..	69·5
MePF_3H	..	29·9	117
EtPF_3H	..	30	121
$\text{C}_6\text{H}_5\text{PF}_3\text{H}$	..	31·5	124
$\text{Me}_2\text{PF}_2\text{H}$	..	..	98·4
$\text{MeC}_6\text{H}_4\cdot\text{PF}_3\text{H}$	..	34	118

During the study of complexing, fluorine exchange and mutual redistribution reaction, of BF_3, PF_5, AsF_5 and SbF_5 with the corresponding ions $\text{BF}_4^\ominus$, $\text{PF}_6^\ominus$, $\text{AsF}_6^\ominus$ and $\text{SbF}_6^\ominus$, Brownstein[234] reported the ^{19}F shifts of the two ions $\text{PSbF}_{11}^\ominus$ and $\text{AsSbF}_{11}^\ominus$. The parameters for the latter ion are shown in **205**.

The systems *tert*-butyl fluoride and chloride, tetramethylammonium hexafluoroantimonate and cesium fluoride with antimony fluoride have been further investigated by ^{19}F NMR.[235] In all these systems, in which sulphur dioxide is used as solvent, the ion $\text{Sb}_2\text{F}_{11}^\ominus$ was present. In the absence of sulphur dioxide, however, it was concluded that higher polymeric ions of the type $\text{Sb}_n\text{F}_{5n+1}^\ominus$, where $n > 2$, were present. The spectra for the $\text{Sb}_2\text{F}_{11}^\ominus$ ion formed in the above systems were the same as those found for $\text{Sb}_2\text{F}_{11}^\ominus$ obtained from a 20% solution of SbF_5 in hydrogen fluoride.[236]

TABLE XLIII

^{19}F parameters of some salts of the form $\text{MF}_6^{2\ominus}$

Ion	δ (F)	Ion	δ (F)
$\text{TiF}_6^{2\ominus}$	73·7	$\text{SnF}_6^{2\ominus}$	−157·8
$\text{ZrF}_6^{2\ominus}$	−4·6	$\text{NiF}_6^{2\ominus}$	−321·5
$\text{HfF}_6^{2\ominus}$	−45·4	$\text{PdF}_6^{2\ominus}$	−351·5
$\text{SiF}_6^{2\ominus}$	−129·5	$\text{PtF}_6^{2\ominus}$	−365·5
$\text{GeF}_6^{2\ominus}$	−124·9		

The diamagnetic salts $MF_2{}^{2\ominus}$ of nickel(IV), palladium(IV) and platinum(IV) have been prepared and found to exhibit extremely large diamagnetic shifts.[237] The shifts, which were essentially temperature invariant, are compared with those of other tetravalent metals in Table XLIII. The $F-{}^{195}Pt$ coupling in the $PtF_6{}^{2\ominus}$ ion was of the order of 2080 Hz. No coupling between F and Pd in the $PdF_6{}^{2\ominus}$ ion was found and reasons for this were discussed. The authors drew attention to the large diamagnetic shifts found in nuclei adjacent to a transition metal having a spin-paired d^6 electronic configuration.

REFERENCES

1. K. Jones and E. F. Mooney, *Ann. Reports on NMR Spectroscopy*, 1970, **3**, 261.
2. P. P. Carey, H. W. Kroto and M. A. Turpin, *Chem. Comm.*, 1969, 188.
3. *Manual of Recommended Practices in Spectroscopy—Terms, Symbols, Conventions and References Relating to Nuclear Magnetic Resonance Spectroscopy*, E386-6GT, ASTM publication 1969.
4. V. Grakauskas, *J. Org. Chem.*, 1969, **34**, 2446.
5. J. Freear and A. E. Tipping, *J. Chem. Soc. (C)*, 1969, 1955.
6. R. E. Banks, A. Braithwaite, R. N. Haszeldine and D. R. Taylor, *J. Chem. Soc. (C)*, 1969, 454.
7. J. Burdon, G. E. Chivers, E. F. Mooney and J. C. Tatlow, *J. Chem. Soc. (C)*, 1969, 1739.
8. R. J. Abraham, *J. Chem. Soc. (B)*, 1969, 1922.
9. R. R. Dean and J. Lee, *Trans. Faraday Soc.*, 1969, **65**, 1.
10. P. E. Peterson, R. J. Bopp and W. A. Sheppard, *J. Amer. Chem. Soc.*, 1969, **91**, 1251.
11. V. A. Pattison, *J. Org. Chem.*, 1969, **34**, 3650.
12. F. Ciampelli, M. Tacchi Venturi and D. Sianesi, *Org. Magn. Resonance*, 1969, **1**, 281.
13. D. E. Gould, L. R. Anderson, D. E. Young and W. B. Fox, *J. Amer. Chem. Soc.*, 1969, **91**, 1310.
14. C. J. Schack and W. Maya, *J. Amer. Chem. Soc.* 1969, **91**, 2902.
15. R. E. Bailey and G. H. Cady, *J. Phys. Chem.*, 1969, **73**, 1612.
16. J. A. Dale, D. L. Dull and H. S. Mosher, *J. Org. Chem.*, 1969, **34**, 2543.
17. W. H. Pirkle, S. D. Beare and T. G. Burlingame, *J. Org. Chem.*, 1969, **34**, 470.
18. W. V. Rochat and G. L. Gard, *J. Org. Chem.*, 1969, **34**, 4173.
19. B. A. Dmitriev, A. V. Kessenich, A. Ya. Chernyak, A. D. Naumov and N. K. Kochetkov, *Carbohydrate Res.*, 1969, **11**, 289.
20. R. E. Banks, D. Berry and G. J. Moore, *J. Chem. Soc. (C)*, 1969, 2598.
21. G. G. Flaskerud, K. E. Pullen and J. M. Shreeve, *Inorg. Chem.*, 1969, **8**, 728.
22. G. A. L. Gant, *J. Org. Chem.*, 1969, **34**, 1968.
23. R. E. Banks, E. D. Burling, B. A. Dodd and K. Mullen, *J. Chem. Soc.(C)*, 1969, 1706.
24. R. E. Banks, M. G. Barlow and K. Mullen, *J. Chem. Soc. (C)*, 1969, 1331.
25. R. E. Banks, R. N. Haszeldine, M. J. Stevenson and B. G. Willoughby, *J. Chem. Soc. (C)*, 1969, 2119.
26. H. W. Roesky, *Inorg. Nuclear Chem. Letters*, 1969, **5**, 173.
27. K. Baum, *J. Amer. Chem. Soc.*, 1969, **91**, 4594.

28. R. Fields, J. Lee and D. J. Mowthorpe, *Trans. Faraday Soc.*, 1969, **65**, 2278.
29. J. Freear and A. E. Tipping, *J. Chem. Soc.* (*C*), 1969, 411.
30. M. G. Barlow and K. W. Cheung, *Chem. Comm.*, 1969, 870.
31. G. G. Flaskerud and J. M. Shreeve, *Inorg. Chem.*, 1969, **8**, 2065.
32. C. G. Krespan, *J. Org. Chem.*, 1969, **34**, 42.
33. C. G. Krespan, *J. Org. Chem.*, 1969, **34**, 1278.
34. C. S. Rondestvedt, *J. Amer. Chem. Soc.*, 1969, **91**, 3054.
35a. P. B. Sargeant and C. G. Krespan, *J. Amer. Chem. Soc.*, 1969, **91**, 415.
35b. R. Cramer, J. B. Kline and J. D. Roberts, *J. Amer. Chem. Soc.*, 1969, **91**, 2519.
36. R. E. Banks, A. Braithwaite, R. N. Haszeldine and D. R. Taylor, *J. Chem. Soc.* (*C*), 1969, 996.
37. W. R. Cullen and M. C. Waldman, *Canad. J. Chem.*, 1969, **47**, 3093.
38. W. T. Miller, R. H. Snider and R. J. Hummel, *J. Amer. Chem. Soc.*, 1969, **91**, 6532.
39. K. C. Ramey and W. S. Brey, *J. Chem. Phys.*, 1964, **40**, 2349.
40. W. S. Brey and K. C. Ramey, *J. Chem. Phys.*, 1963, **39**, 844.
41. S. L. Manatt and M. T. Bowers, *J. Amer. Chem. Soc.*, 1969, **91**, 4381.
42. T. R. Oakes, H. G. David and F. J. Nagel, *J. Amer. Chem. Soc.*, 1969, **91**, 4761.
43. J. D. Park, R. O. Michael and R. A. Newmark, *J. Amer. Chem. Soc.*, 1969, **91**, 5933.
44. P. D. Bartlett and G. E. H. Wallbillich, *J. Amer. Chem. Soc.*, 1969, **91**, 409.
45. J. D. Park, R. O. Michael and R. A. Newmark, *J. Org. Chem.*, 1969, **34**, 2525.
46. R. K. Harris and V. J. Robinson, *J. Magn. Resonance*, 1969, **1**, 362.
47. D. Lomas and P. Tarrant, *J. Org. Chem.*, 1969, **34**, 323.
48. R. R. Ernst, *Mol. Phys.*, 1969, **16**, 241.
49. R. R. Ernst, *J. Chem. Phys.*, 1966, **45**, 3845.
50. A. B. Clayton, R. Stephens and J. C. Tatlow, *J. Chem. Soc.* (*C*), 1969, 2329.
51. P. B. Sargeant, *J. Amer. Chem. Soc.*, 1969, **91**, 3061.
52. J. D. Park, S. K. Choi and H. E. Romine, *J. Org. Chem.*, 1969, **34**, 2521.
53. R. A. Newmark, G. R. Apai and H. E. Romine, *J. Magn. Resonance*, 1969, **1**, 562.
54. N. N. Shapet'ko, N. M. Sergeev, E. M. Panov and R. S. Sorokina, *Zhur. strukt. Khim.*, 1965, **6**, 641.
55. D. D. Callander, P. L. Coe, M. F. S. Matough, E. F. Mooney, A. J. Uff and P. H. Winson, *Chem. Comm.*, 1966, 820.
55a. R. A. Newmark, G. R. Apai and R. O. Michael, *J. Magn. Resonance*, 1969, **1**, 418.
56. V. W. Gash and D. J. Baner, *J. Org. Chem.*, 1966, **31**, 3602.
57. E. F. Mooney and P. H. Winson, *Ann. Rev. NMR Spectroscopy*, 1968, **1**, 261.
58. P. L. Coe, R. G. Plevey and J. C. Tatlow, *J. Chem. Soc.* (*C*), 1969, 1060.
59. W. Regel and W. von Philipsborn, *Helv. Chim. Acta*, 1969, **52**, 1354.
60. C. W. Jefford, D. T. Hill, L. Ghosez, S. Toppet and K. C. Ramey, *J. Amer. Chem. Soc.*, 1969, **91**, 1532.
61. J. B. Dence and J. D. Roberts, *J. Amer. Chem. Soc.*, 1969, **91**, 1542.
62. G. L. Anderson and L. M. Stock, *J. Amer. Chem. Soc.*, 1969, **91**, 6804.
63. L. Cavalli and G. Rigatti, *J. Chem. Soc.* (*B*), 1969, 253.
64. R. Kaiser, *J. Magn. Resonance*, 1969, **1**, 534.
65. G. Camaggi and F. Gozzo, *J. Chem. Soc.* (*C*), 1969, 489.
66. M. G. Barlow, R. N. Haszeldine and W. D. Morton, *Chem. Comm.*, 1969, 931.

67. M. G. Barlow, R. N. Haszeldine and R. Hubbard, *Chem. Comm.*, 1969, 202
68. D. M. Lemal, J. V. Staros and V. Austel, *J. Amer. Chem. Soc.*, 1969, **91**, 3373.
69. R. S. H. Liu and C. G. Krespan, *J. Org. Chem.*, 1969, **34**, 1271.
70. L. P. Anderson, W. J. Feast and W. K. R. Musgrave, *J. Chem. Soc. (C)*, 1969, 211.
71. H. Röttele, P. Nikoloff, J. F. M. Oth and G. Schröder, *Chem. Ber.*, 1969, **102**, 3367.
72. R. J. Kostelnik, M. P. Williamson, D. E. Wisnosky and S. M. Castellano, *Canad. J. Chem.*, 1969, **47**, 3313.
73. J. L. Roark and W. B. Smith, *J. Phys. Chem.*, 1969, **73**, 1046.
74. W. R. Young and C. S. Yannoni, *J. Amer. Chem. Soc.*, 1969, **91**, 4581.
75. J. E. Loemker, K. M. Pryse, J. M. Read and J. H. Goldstein, *Canad. J. Chem.*, 1969, **47**, 209.
76. J. Hirst and S. J. Una, *J. Chem. Soc. (B)*, 1969, 646.
77. V. Grakauskas, *J. Org. Chem.*, 1969, **34**, 2835.
78. E. Lustig, E. A. Hansen, P. Diehl and H. Kellarhals, *J. Chem. Phys.*, 1969, **51**, 1839.
79. C. Tamborski and E. J. Soloski, *J. Organometallic Chem.*, 1969, **20**, 245.
80. F. A. M. Ayanbadejo, *Spectrochim. Acta*, 1969, **25A**, 1009.
81. F. A. M. Ayanbadejo, *Spectrochim. Acta*, 1968, **24A**, 1249.
82. M. A. Cooper, *Org. Magn. Resonance*, 1969, **1**, 363.
83. R. J. Abraham, D. B. MacDonald and E. S. Pepper, *J. Amer. Chem. Soc.*, 1968, **90**, 147.
84. F. I. Abezganz and S. V. Sokolov, *Zhur. obshchei Khim.*, 1968, **38**, 2502.
85. A. E. Jukes, E. F. Mooney and P. H. Winson, unpublished work.
86. E. A. Cohen, A. J. R. Bourn and S. L. Manatt, *J. Magn. Resonance*, 1969, **1**, 436.
87. M. I. Bruce, *J. Chem. Soc. (A)*, 1968, 1459.
88. R. R. Dean and W. McFarlane, *J. Chem. Soc. (B)*, 1969, 509.
89. E. Lustig, E. A. Hansen and E. P. Ragelis, *Org. Magn. Resonance*, 1969, **1**, 295.
90. W. B. Moniz, E. Lustig and E. A. Hansen, *J. Chem. Phys.*, 1969, **51**, 4666.
91. W. T. Flowers, R. N. Haszeldine and J. E. G. Kemp, *Chem. Comm.*, 1969, 203.
92. A. J. Oliver and W. A. G. Graham, *J. Organometallic Chem.*, 1969, **19**, 17.
93. R. D. Chambers and D. J. Spring, *Tetrahedron*, 1969, **25**, 565.
94. D. Price, H. Suschitsky and J. I. Hollies, *J. Chem. Soc. (C)*, 1969, 1967.
95. R. A. Fletton, R. D. Lapper and L. F. Thomas, *Chem. Comm.*, 1969, 1049.
96. P. Sartori and A. Golloch, *Chem. Ber.*, 1969, **102**, 1765.
97. A. G. Hudson, E. F. Mooney and A. E. Pedlar, unpublished work.
98. M. G. Hogben and W. A. G. Graham, *J. Amer. Chem. Soc.*, 1969, **91**, 283.
99. H. Spiesecke and W. G. Schneider, *J. Chem. Phys.*, 1961, **35**, 731.
100. E. F. Mooney and P. H. Winson, unpublished work.
101. G. W. Parshall, *J. Amer. Chem. Soc.*, 1966, **88**, 804.
102. M. G. Hogben, R. S. Gay, A. J. Oliver, J. A. J. Thompson and W. A. G. Graham, *J. Amer. Chem. Soc.*, 1969, **91**, 291.
103. D. Gurka and R. W. Taft, *J. Amer. Chem. Soc.*, 1969, **91**, 4794.
104. R. E. Uschold and R. W. Taft, *Org. Magn. Resonance*, 1969, **1**, 375.
105. D. Doddrell, E. Wenkert and P. V. Demarco, *J. Mol. Spectroscopy*, 1969, **32**, 162.
106. W. Prikoszovich and H. Schindlbauer, *Chem. Ber.*, 1969, **102**, 2922.

107. H. Schindlbauer and W. Prikoszovich, *Chem. Ber.*, 1969, **102**, 2914.

108. S. M. Roberts and H. Suschitzky, *J. Chem. Soc.* (*C*), 1969, 1485.

109. T. Schaefer, S. S. Danyluk and C. L. Bell, *Canad. J. Chem.*, 1969, **47**, 1507.

110. R. E. Banks, R. N. Haszeldine, D. R. Karsa, F. E. Rickett and I. M. Young, *J. Chem. Soc.* (*C*), 1969, 1660.

111. R. D. Chambers, J. A. Jackson, W. K. R. Musgrave, L. H. Sutcliffe and G. J. T. Tiddy, *Chem. Comm.*, 1969, 178.

112. J. W. Emsley and L. Phillips, *J. Chem. Soc.* (*B*), 1969, 434.

113. L. P. Anderson, W. J. Feast and W. K. R. Musgrave, *J. Chem. Soc.* (*C*), 1969, 2559.

114. 114. Y. K. Kim and O. R. Pierce, *J. Org. Chem.*, 1969, **34**, 602.

115. H. W. Roesky and H. H. Giere, *Chem. Ber.* 1969, **102**, 2330.

116. P. Ogden, *Chem. Comm.*, 1969, 1084.

117. J. Burdon, G. E. Chivers and J. C. Tatlow, *J. Chem. Soc.* (*C*), 1969, 2585.

118. J. Burdon, J. G. Campbell, I. W. Parsons and J. C. Tatlow, *Chem. Comm.*, 1969, 27.

119. W. J. Middleton, *J. Org. Chem.*, 1969, **34**, 3201.

120. R. A. Falk and J. D. Readio, *J. Org. Chem.*, 1969, **34**, 4088.

121. D. K. Hindermann and W. E. Falconer, *J. Chem. Phys.*, 1969, **50**, 1203.

122. M. Karplus, C. W. Kern and D. Lazdins, *J. Chem. Phys.*, 1964, **40**, 3738.

123. H. A. Levy and P. A. Agron, *Noble-Gas Compounds*, H. H. Hyman, Ed., University of Chicago Press, Chicago, Illinois, 1963, p. 221.

124. W. Derbyshire, J. P. Stuart and D. Warner, *Mol. Phys.*, 1969, **17**, 449.

125. M. Rhodes and D. W. Aksnes, *Mol. Phys.*, 1969, **17**, 261.

126. R. A. Bernheim, D. J. Hoy, T. R. Krugh and B. J. Lavery, *J. Chem. Phys.*, 1969, **50**, 1350.

127. T. R. Krugh and R. A. Bernheim, *J, Amer. Chem. Soc.*, 1969, **91**, 2385.

128. A. D. Buckingham, E. E. Burnell and C. A. de Lange, *Mol. Phys.*, 1969, **16**, 299.

129. C. T. Yim and D. F. R. Gilson, *J. Amer. Chem. Soc.*, 1969, **91**, 4360.

130. A. H. Cowley and W. D. White, *J. Amer. Chem. Soc.*, 1969, **91**, 1913.

131. A. H. Cowley and W. D. White, *J. Amer. Chem. Soc.*, 1969, **91**, 1917.

132. J. Homer and D. Callaghan, *J. Chem. Soc.* (*B*), 1969, 247.

133. L. G. Vaugham and W. A. Sheppard, *J. Amer. Chem. Soc.*, 1969, **91**, 6151.

134. Y. K. Kim and O. R. Pierce, *J. Organometallic Chem.*, 1969, **19**, P11.

135. E. F. Mooney, M. A. Qaseem and P. H. Winson, unpublished work.

136. W. Gerrard, M. F. Lappert, H. Pyszora and J. Wallis, *J. Chem. Soc.*, 1960, 2182.

137. E. W. Randall, J. J. Elner and J. J. Zuckerman, *J. Amer. Chem. Soc.*, 1966, **88**, 622.

138. E. A. V. Ebsworth, *Chem. Comm.*, 1966, 530.

139. C. Tamborski and E. J. Soloski, *J. Organometallic Chem.*, 1969, **17**, 185.

140. S. K. Gondal, A. G. MacDiarmid, F. E. Saalfeld and M. V. McDowell, *Inorg. Nuc. Chem. Letters*, 1969, **5**, 351.

141. T. Chivers, *J. Organometallic Chem.*, 1969, **19**, 75.

142. M. Akhtar and H. C. Clark, *Canad. J. Chem.*, 1969, **47**, 3753.

143. E. W. Abel, M. A. Cooper, R. J. Goodfellow and A. J. Rest, *Trans. Faraday Soc.*, 1969, **65**, 1697.

144. M. Elder, J. G. Evans and W. A. G. Graham, *J. Amer. Chem. Soc.*, 1969, **91**, 1245.

145. A. B. Burg and J. S. Basi, *J. Amer. Chem. Soc.*, 1969, **91**, 1937.
146. R. Fields, M. Green and A. Jones, *J. Chem. Soc. (A)*, 1969, 2740.
147. R. G. Cavell, T. L. Charlton and A. A. Pinkerton, *Chem. Comm.*, 1969, 424.
148. J. F. Nixon and M. D. Sexton, *J. Chem. Soc. (A)*, 1969, 1089.
149. A. H. Cowley and M. W. Taylor, *J. Amer. Chem. Soc.*, 1969, **91**, 1929.
150. A. H. Cowley and M. W. Taylor, *J. Amer. Chem. Soc.*, 1969, **91**, 1934.
151. G. R. Miller, A. W. Yankowsky and S. O. Grim, *J. Chem. Phys.*, 1969, **51**, 3185.
152. J. Jonas and H. S. Gutowsky, *J. Chem. Phys.*, 1965, **42**, 140.
153. J. Burdon, I. N. Rozhkov and G. M. Perry, *J. Chem. Soc. (C)*, 1969, 2615.
154. S. E. Ellzey, *Canad. J. Chem.*, 1969, **47**, 1251.
155. W. R. Cullen, D. A. Harbourne, B. V. Liengme and J. R. Sams, *Inorg. Chem.*, 1969, **8**, 95.
156. M. Field and R. Schmutzler, *J. Chem. Soc. (A)*, 1969, 840.
157. D. I. Nichols, *J. Chem. Soc. (A)*, 1969, 1471.
158. O. Glemser, E. Niecke and H. W. Roesky, *Chem. Comm.*, 1969, 282.
159. M. Green, A. Taunton-Rigby and F. G. A. Stone, *J. Chem. Soc. (A)*, 1969, 1875.
160. T. R. Johnson and J. F. Nixon, *J. Chem. Soc. (A)*, 1969, 2518.
161. M. L. H. Green and W. E. Lindsell, *J. Chem. Soc. (A)*, 1969, 2215.
162. J. Ashley-Smith, J. Clemens, M. Green and F. G. A. Stone, *J. Organometallic Chem.*, 1969, **17**, P23.
163. J. Cooke, W. R. Cullen, M. Green and F. G. A. Stone, *J. Chem. Soc. (A)*, 1969, 1872.
164. R. B. King and N. Weleman, *Inorg. Chem.*, 1969, **8**, 2540.
165. R. B. King, R. N. Kapoor and K. H. Pannell, *J. Organometallic Chem.*, 1969, **20**, 187.
166. M. Cooke and M. Green, *J. Chem. Soc. (A)*, 1969, 651.
167. J. Browning, C. S. Cundy, M. Green and F. G. A. Stone, *J. Chem. Soc. (A)*, 1969, 20.
168. A. J. Mukhedkar, M. Green and F. G. A. Stone, *J. Chem. Soc. (A)*, 1969, 3023.
169. J. Ashley-Smith, M. Green and F. G. A. Stone, *J. Chem. Soc. (A)*, 1969, 3019.
170. M. I. Bruce and C. H. Davies, *J. Chem. Soc. (A)*, 1969, 1077.
171. M. I. Bruce and M. J. Melvin, *J. Chem. Soc. (C)*, 1969, 2107,
172. C. G. Barlow, J. F. Nixon and J. R. Swain, *J. Chem. Soc. (A)*, 1969, 1082.
173. D. A. Clement, J. F. Nixon and M. D. Sexton, *Chem. Comm.*, 1969, 1509.
174. M. A. Bennett and D. J. Patmore, *Chem. Comm.*, 1969, 1510.
175. P. M. Borodin, R. Singkh and V. A. Shcherbakov, *Zhur. strukt. Khim.*, 1968, **9**, 1078.
176. P. M. Borodin and E. N. Sventitskii, *Nuclear Magnetic Resonance*, 2nd Edition, p. 54, 1968.
177. J. Soriano and J. Shamir, *Inorg. Nuclear Chem. Letters*, 1969, **5**, 209.
178. L. Elegant, M. Azzaro, R. Mankowski-Favelier and G. Mavel, *Org. Magn Resonance*, 1969, **1**, 471.
179. N. M. D. Brown and P. Bladon, *J. Chem. Soc. (A)*, 1969, 526.
180. S. A. Fieldhouse and I. R. Peat, *J. Phys. Chem.*, 1969, **73**, 275.
181. R. W. Kirk and P. L. Timms, *J. Amer. Chem. Soc.*, 1969, **91**, 6315.
182. W. Airey and G. M. Sheldrick, *J. Chem. Soc. (A)*, 1969, 2865.
183a. K. G. Sharp and J. L. Margrave, *Inorg. Chem.*, 1969, **8**, 2655.

183b. D. S. Dyer and R. O. Ragsdale, *Inorg. Chem.*, 1969, **8**, 1116.
184. L. M. Zaborowski, K. E. Pullen and J. M. Shreeve, *Inorg. Chem.*, 1969, **8**, 2005.
185. K. Baum, *J. Org. Chem.*, 1969, **34**, 3377.
186. T. E. Stevens, *J. Org. Chem.*, 1969, **34**, 2451.
187. K. Baum, *J. Org. Chem.*, 1969, **34**, 2046.
188. K. Baum, *J. Org. Chem.*, 1969, **34**, 2049.
189. S. F. Reed and M. Lustig, *J. Org. Chem.*, 1969, **34**, 1338.
190. J. Freear and A. E. Tipping, *J. Chem. Soc.* (*C*), 1969, 1963.
191. V. A. Ginsburg, L. L. Martgrova, N. F. Privezentseva and Z. A. Buchek, *Zhur. obshchei Khim.*, 1968, **38**, 2505.
192. K. O. Alt and C. D. Weis, *Helv. Chim. Acta*, 1969, **52**, 812.
193. H. J. Emeleus, J. M. Shreeve and P. M. Spaziante, *J. Chem. Soc.* (*A*), 1969, 431.
194. V. Grakauskas and K. Baum, *J. Amer. Chem. Soc.*, 1969, **81**, 1679.
195. S. K. Brauman and M. E. Hill, *J. Chem. Soc.* (*B*), 1969, 1091.
196. L. Cavalli and P. Piccardi, *Chem. Comm.*, 1969, 1132.
197. D. H. Brown, K. D. Crosbie, G. W. Fraser and D. W. A. Sharp, *J. Chem. Soc.* (*A*), 1969, 872.
198. W. E. Hill, D. W. A. Sharp and C. B. Colburn, *J. Chem. Phys.*, 1969, **50**, 612.
199. T. L. Charlton and R. G. Cavell, *Inorg. Chem.*, 1969, **8**, 2436.
200. D. D. DesMarteau, *J. Amer. Chem. Soc.*, 1969, **91**, 6211.
201. H. W. Roesky and L. F. Grimm, *Inorg. Nuclear Chem. Letters*, 1969, **5**, 13.
202. L. F. Centofanti, G. Kodama and R. W. Parry, *Inorg. Chem.*, 1969, **8**, 2072.
203. H. W. Roesky, *Inorg. Nuclear Chem. Letters*, 1969, **5**, 453.
204. H. W. Roesky and W. G. Bowing, *Inorg. Nuclear Chem. Letters*, 1969, **5**. 597.
205. H. W. Roesky, *Inorg. Nuclear Chem. Letters*, 1969, **5**, 891.
206. J. F. Nixon, *J. Chem. Soc.* (*A*), 1969, 1087.
207. V. V. Sheluchenko, S. S. Dubov, G. I. Drozd and S. Z. Ivin, *Zhur. strukt. Khim.*, 1968, **9**, 909.
208. M. Lustig, *Inorg. Chem.*, 1969, **8**, 443.
209. C. A. Udovich and R. J. Clark, *J. Amer. Chem. Soc.*, 1969, **91**, 526.
210. A. H. Cowley and M. W. Taylor, *J. Amer. Chem. Soc.*, 1969, **91**, 1026.
211. L. Lunazzi and S. Brownstein, *J. Magn. Resonance*, 1969, **1**, 119.
212. P. A. W. Dean and R. J. Gillespie, *J. Amer. Chem. Soc.*, 1969, **91**, 7260.
213. P. A. W. Dean and R. J. Gillespie, *J. Amer. Chem. Soc.*, 1969, **91**, 7264.
214. R. E. Banks, R. N. Haszeldine and W. D. Morton, *J. Chem. Soc.* (*C*), 1969, 1947.
215. M. G. Barlow, R. R. Dean and J. Lee, *Trans. Faraday Soc.*, 1969, **65**, 321.
216. J. Steward, L. Kegley, H. F. White and G. L. Gard, *J. Org. Chem.*, 1969, **34**, 760.
217. C. J. Schack, R. D. Wilson, J. S. Muirhead and S. N. Cohz, *J. Amer. Chem. Soc.*, 1969, **91**, 2907.
218. J. Mason, *J. Chem. Soc.* (*A*), 1969, 1587.
219. W. M. Johnson, H. A. Carter and F. Aubke, *Inorg. Nuclear Chem. Letters*, 1969, **5**, 719.
220. H. W. Roesky and D. P. Babb, *Inorg. Chem.*, 1969, **8**, 1733.
221. O. Glemser and S. P. von Halasz, *Chem. Ber.*, 1969, **102**, 3333.
222. O. Glemser, R. Mews and H. W. Roesky, *Chem. Ber.*, 1969, **102**, 1523.
223. R. Mews and O. Glemser, *Chem. Ber.*, 1969, **102**, 4188.

224. O. Glemser and S. P. von Halasz, *Inorg. Nuclear Chem. Letters*, 1969, **5**, 393.
225. O. Glemser, R. Mews and H. W. Roesky, *Chem. Comm.*, 1969, 914.
226. H. W. Roesky and H.-H. Giere, *Chem. Ber.*, 1969, **102**, 3707.
227. M. Azeem, M. Brownstein and R. J. Gillespie, *Canad. J. Chem.*, 1969, **47**, 4159.
228. H. A. Carter and F. Aubke, *Inorg. Nuclear Chem. Letters*, 1969, **5**, 99.
229. F. A. Hohorst and J. M. Shreeve, *Inorg. Chem.*, 1966, **5**, 2069.
230. R. J. Gillespie and W. A. Whitla, *Canad. J. Chem.*, 1969, **47**, 4153.
231. H. A. Carter, W. M. Johnson and F. Aubke, *Canad. J. Chem.*, 1969, **47**, 4619.
232. H. D. Frame, J. L. Huston and I. Sheft, *Inorg. Chem.*, 1969, **8**, 1459.
233. J. F. Nixon and J. R. Swain, *Inorg. Nuclear Chem. Letters*, 1969, **5**, 295.
234. S. Brownstein, *Canad. J. Chem.*, 1969, **47**, 605.
235. J. Bacon, P. A. W. Dean and R. J. Gillespie, *Canad. J. Chem.*, 1969, **47**, 1655.
236. R. J. Gillespie and K. C. Moss, *J. Chem. Soc.*, 1966, 1170.
237. N. A. Matwiyoff, L. B. Asprey, W. E. Wageman, M. J. Reisfeld and E. Fukushima, *Inorg. Chem.*, 1969, **8**, 750.

AUTHOR INDEX

Numbers in parentheses are reference numbers and are included to assist in locating references when author's names are not mentioned in the text. Numbers in *italics* refer to the page on which the reference is listed.

A

Abbolito, C., 34(240), *64*
Abbott, E. H., 57(421, 422), *69*
Abd El-Aziz, S., 289(145), *309*
Abel, E. W., 454, *492*
Abezganz, F. I., 427(84), 430(84), 441 (84), 449(84), *491*
Abragam, A., 86(28), *224*
Abraham, A., 204(353), *233*
Abraham, R. J., 14(91, 92), *60*, 352 (29), *362*, 393, 425(83), *489, 491*
Abrahamson, K. H., 104(68), 202(68), 203(68), *225*
Acheson, R. M., 213(394), *235*
Adams, C. H. M., 18(124), *64*
Adams, D. G., 185(301), *232*
Adams, R., 156(211), 198(330), *229, 233*
Adelman, R. B., 21(153), *62*
Agami, C., 38(283), *65*
Agron, P. A., 449(123), *492*
Ahmad, M., 111(79), 207(366), *225, 234*
Airey, W., 470, *493*
Akabori, S., 145(186), 147(191), *228*
Akahori, Y., 15(101), *61*
Akhtar, M., 454, *492*
Aksnes, D. W., 449(125), *492*
Al-Baldawi, S. A., 36(264), *65*
Albrand, J. P., 21(151), 22(154), *62*
Alder, B. J., 278(108), *308*
Alexakos, L. G., 16(114), *61*
Alexander, S., 87, 192(32), *224*
Alford, A. L., 30(219), *64*, 237(1), 238 (3), 241(3), 244, 245(3, 6), 246, 247 (20), 249, 252(49), 253, 258(49), 270(49), *305, 306*
Alger, T. D., 36(259), *65*, 102(63), 104 (63), 193(63), *225*
Allan, E. A., 268(76, 77, 78), *307*
Allen, G., 14(94), *60*
Allerhand, A., 81(15), 82(19), 84(15), 102(54, 55, 56, 57, 59), 103, 104 (54, 55, 56, 57, 59, 65), 111(56), 113(57, 83), 202, 203(54), 206(54), *223, 224, 225*
Allinger, N. L., 111(81), 115(81), 135 (81), *225*
Allred, E. L., 166(253), 170(253), 172 (253), *230*
Alt, K. O., 474(192), *494*
Altman, J., 45(325), *66*, 125(131), 126 (131), 127(134), *227*
Altona, C., 111(81), 115(81), 135(81), *225*
Altreuther, P., 270, *307*
Alves, A. C. P., 19(133), 20(133), *61*
Amdur, I., 107(70), *225*
Amis, E. S., 36(263), *65*
Anand, N. K., 140(174), *228*
Anderson, C. L., 166(253), 170(253), 172(253), *230*
Anderson, D. J., 39(294), *66*
Anderson, E. W., 111(80), 114(88), *225*, 371(13, 16), *387*
Anderson, G. L., 416, *490*
Anderson, J. E., 7(14), 42(313), 43 (319), 52(369), *59, 66, 67*, 72(4), 110(4), 118(106, 107, 108), 119 (120), 122(106,107,108), 136(161), 140(173), 161(241), 163(241, 248), 166(251, 252, 254), 167(254), 168 (120), 170(252, 265, 270), 172(265, 270), 173(265), 174(270), 175(270), *223, 226, 228, 230, 231*
Anderson, J. K., 90(34), *224*
Anderson, L. P., 421(70), 425(70), 428 (70), 429(113), 439(113), 440(113), *491, 492*
Anderson, L. R., 395(13), 483(13), *489*
Anderson, R. G., 35(257), *65*
Anderson, W. A., 84(25), 211(25), *224*, 352(29), *362*
Andreades, S., 177(279), 187(306), *231, 232*
Andrews, B. D., 34(251), *65*
Andrews, T. G., 15(102), *61*

497

SUBJECT INDEX

The numbers in **bold** indicate the pages on which the topic is discussed in detail.

B

^{10}B isotope shift, 469

B–N bond, barriers to rotation about, 184

Barban, 247

Barrier to internal rotation, estimation of, 14

Basic strengths, using ^{19}F shifts, 437

Bay-coupling, 16

Baytex, 280

Benzaldehydes, *p*-substituted, 15

Benzene-d_1, in nematic phase, 9

Benzenes, orientation study, 10
  solvent interaction, 246
  vicinal *J* and substituent electronegativity, 15

Benzocycloheptenes, conformation of, 128

Benzodithiepin, conformation of, 130

Benzofurans, long-range *J* in, 16

Benzo[*c*]phenanthrene, solvent effects, 38

Benzophenones, 12
  fluoro-, 430
  hindered rotation in, 199

Benzopyrazine, fluoro-, 441

3,4-Benzopyrene, 14

[2]1,4-Benzo[2](1,4)-triptycenophane, conformation of, 47

Benzoxazines, tetrafluro-, 449

Benzoxazole, long-range *J* in, 16

Benzvalene, hexakis(trifluoromethyl)-, 420

Benzyl halides, restricted rotation in, 196

Benzylic coupling, 15

Betaines, triphenylphosphonium, 458

Bianthrones, *cis-trans* isomers of, 222

Bicyclic systems, fluoro-, **415**

Bicyclo[2.2.1]heptene, perfluoro-, 450

Bicyclo[2.2.0]hexa-2,5-diene, fluoro-, 416

Bicyclo[2.2.2]octa-2,5-dienes, fluoro-, 421

Bicyclo[2.2.2]octanes, fluoro-, 416

Bicyclooctatrienes, fluoro-, 420

Bicyclo[1.1.1]pentane, 345

endo-Bicyclic[2.1.0]pentan-2-ol, conformation of, 39

Bidrin, 239
  rate of hydrolysis, 281

Bifluoride salts, 469

Biological studies, **286**

Biphenyl systems, hindered rotation in, 199

2,2′-Bipyridine, 272

Bipyridinium salts, **271**

3,3-Bis(chloromethyl)oxacyclobutane, 385

Bis(difluoramino) derivatives, 473

Bis(ethylthiophosphorylfluoride)trisulphide, 479

Bisfluorenylidenes, rotational barriers of, 221

7,7-Bistrifluoromethylcycloheptatriene, conformation of, 133

Bistrifluoromethylnitroxide derivatives, 474

Bixanthylenes, *cis-trans* isomerism in, 222

Bomyl, geometrical isomers of, 287

Bond angles, effect of on ^2J(H–P–H), 13
  variation of *J* with, 488

π-Bonding and J(^{11}B–^{19}F), 470

p_π–d_π Bonding, effect on inversion barriers, 183
  and rotational barriers, 157

Bond lengths, relative, 8

π-Bond order, correlation with *vicinal J*, 14

Bond rotational barriers, **156**

Bond-shift processes in annulenes, 150

Borane, pentafluorophenylamino-, 454

Boron compounds, isomerization in, 52
  fluoro-, **469**
  fluoro-alkyl and aryl, **452**

Boron phosphonites, 455

Boron trifluoride complexes, 469

Brain tissue, water bonding in, 58

Bridged diphenyls, conformation of, 130

Broad-line NMR, 298

Bromacil, metabolites of, 294

5-Bromo-3-*sec*-butyl-6-methyl uracil, metabolites of, 294

1-Bromo-2-chloroethane, 4

3-(Bromomercuri)perfluorobutanoic ester, 452

5-Bromo-6-methyl-3-isopropyl-uracil, 274

RETURN TO ➡ CHEMISTRY LIBRARY

100 Hildebrand Hall • 642-3753

LOAN PERIOD 1	2	3
4	5	6

1 MONTH

ALL BOOKS MAY BE RECALLED AFTER 7 DAYS
Renewable by telephone

DUE AS STAMPED BELOW

DEC 2 1 '00 -4 PM		

FORM NO. DD5

UNIVERSITY OF CALIFORNIA, BERKELEY
BERKELEY, CA 94720-6000